Origins

The Science of the Genesis Creation and Global Flood.
The Origin of Matter, Space, Time, and Life.

by

Dr. Troy E. Lawrence

Email address: Lawrence@creationministry.org
Website: creationministry.org

Edited by George Macias

Copyright © 2019 by Troy Lawrence
3rd Edition

Published by Lawrence Publishing
ISBN: 978-1943185047

Printed in the United States of America.

Table of Contents

Preface

This book will explain for the everyday person and scientist the origins of matter, space, time, and life. This book explores the difference between evolution and creation. You will learn how dinosaurs became so large and why they are not visible today. We will cover such topics as whether it is probable for humans to live 900+ years of age? How old is the earth?

One of the major components of this book, is an explanation of how changes to Earth's environment have adversely affected all life on the earth. The changes to gravity, oxygen concentration, temperature, and the canopy of ice and salt water have resulted in a severe reduction in the length of life, the size of life forms, and in the earth having four seasons, polar ice caps, deserts, and more.

Give this book a chance, whether you think evolution is truth, or creation over eons is truth. I guarantee that this book will challenge your preconceived notions of the origins of life on earth and equip you with knowledge regarding the origin of life and the beginning of all things.

Most legal contracts have a clause that says, "If any portion of this contract is found to be invalid or non-enforceable, that does not invalidate the rest of the contract." So too with this book.

Introduction:

What compelled me to write this book? The primary factor is that the evolution is at odds with the Bible. Both cannot be correct since they make polar opposite statements on the beginning of life. Also, too many people lack knowledge regarding the origins of life.

Origins is such an important topic because how people view the origins of life shapes their entire outlook on truth and the purpose for life. Two basic views exist regarding the origins of life:

(a) Everything began and evolved by explainable natural processes in nature. For example, the Big Bang initiated all processes and laws, and all life forms evolved from a single-celled organism that spontaneously began from a primordial complex chemical mixture into the complexities of life we see today. This is called evolution.

(b) God created everything by natural processes with His supernatural decrees.

All of public academia teaches evolution. Almost all media teaches evolution. This teaching is so ubiquitous that even 90% of seminary schools and most churches teach an old Earth timeline to coincide with the evolutionary model.

The serious implications of the origins of life are striking. If evolution is correct, the Bible is not from God, but from men and filled with errors. If the Bible's account of creation is correct, then evolution is error. No middle ground exist, since the two views are opposing.

An honest scientist would say that evolution and the Big Bang are accepted hypotheses, but invariably when professors lecture, they say evolution is fact. Additionally, the Bible's Genesis account of creation is not to be taken literally because it does not coincide with science.

The Bible declares that God wrote the Bible through mankind (II Timothy 3:16). Therefore, if one error exist in the Genesis account of creation, the whole Bible cannot be infallible and be written by God. But if the Genesis account of creation is the truth, then indeed the Bible is the Word of God, and evolution and the singularity of the Big Bang are wrong.

Ignorance amongst Christians on the subject of origins is disobedience to the Word of God and is sinful. Christians are at war spiritually for the truth, and the word of God is the sword (Ephesians 6:12–17). Imagine how ineffective a Christian becomes at witnessing when they tell others to believe in the Bible, yet they do not believe the Genesis creation and global flood accounts.

Let us journey together through the sciences, logic, and the Bible to determine what is fact or fiction, what is truth or error, and what is from God or from man or demon.

Origins
Section I
Chapter 1
Gravity

Was gravity on the earth the same 6 to 10 millenniums ago as it is today? No. A premise of *Origins* is that the gravity of the earth is stronger today than it was in Adam's day. This stronger gravity has altered life by reducing the length of life and the size of life on earth. But how?

Gravity is defined as the gravitational attraction of the mass of a planet for bodies near its surface.[1] Gravity is based on the mass of the planet. The greater the mass of a planet, the greater the gravitational force. Newtonian theory was that a force, called gravity, pulled on objects. Einstein further defined gravity as affecting the space and time around an object that then alters the natural path of the object. Here is a crude analogy: the drain in the tub does not pull on a floating object; instead, the drain alters the water, the space and time, around the floating object. Einstein's theory of relativity was demonstrated to be correct by how the gravity of the sun bends light passing near its influence.

Is the mass of the earth changing? According to meteor specialist Peter Brown, the University of Western Ontario, the earth's mass is increasing each year by 40,000 tons (80,000,000 lb./year) of **space dust**. This seems like a lot of weight, but compared to the large mass of the earth, this is small. The earth's mass is 5.9×10^{24} kg or 1.3×10^{25} pounds. Therefore, the average of 80,000,000 pounds per year added by space dust added to Earth over six millennia, equals 4.8×10^{11}. This represents too small of a percentage to consider. Thus, young Earth creationist (YEC) may not use space dust deposit as the means that God increased gravity.

When the earth was inundated by meteors and asteroids during the global flood, that would have increased the earth's mass. However, hydrological cycles, tectonic plates, forest growth, water, and erosion have covered up most historic impact craters on earth. Scientists have discovered that the earth was impacted by asteroids in past millennia. Given the moon's vast amount of crater history, it is conceivable that during the global flood, meteorites/asteroids/comets hitting the earth may have been numerous enough to increase earth's gravity by two means:

1. Direct accumulation, adding mass to the earth, which increases earth's gravity.

2. Indirectly by asteroid impacts slowing earth's rotational velocity, which decreases centripetal force, which increases earth's net gravity.

One asteroid could add as much mass to the earth as 2.5 years worth of today's average space dust accumulation. Now, imagine a series of thousands of large asteroids bombarding the earth as the earth passed through an asteroid belt. Both the direct method (mass) and indirect method (rotational velocity) of increasing Earth's gravity are based on cumulative and multiple impacts on earth over millennia, not by one asteroid. Since the moon was impacted so often, then so too was the earth inundated by meteors and asteroids in the distant past.

Two asteroid belts exist, one that fills the space between Mars and Jupiter and the Kuiper Belt that is just beyond Neptune. They are remnants that suggest what all of space was potentially like before the gravity of each planet, star, and galaxy absorbed those asteroids and meteors into their mass. The asteroid belts could be the last vestiges of what our solar system looked like when it was young.

Since the earth is larger than the moon, with more mass, the earth's gravity is larger than the moon's. This suggests that the earth would attract and be hit by more meteors and asteroids than the moon. But since the earth has an atmosphere, the deadly effect of the impact is significantly reduced. And earth is dynamic, so the scars of prior impacts have been covered up, but the mass was added to the earth none the less, having the net effect of increasing earth's gravitational force.

---

1 *Merriam-Webster's* online dictionary definition.

The mass of the asteroid, multiplied by its acceleration, determines how much force hits the earth and determines how much energy is taken out of the earth's rotational velocity to slow the spin down.

How could asteroids hit the earth without obliterating life? From a Biblical perspective, there were two past events with large impacts. The first and largest occurred on the first day of creation with the creation of formless matter that was rotating and coalesce, but no life existed. The image of matter coalescing is similar to a hurricane, but instead of moisture coalescing, it was hot matter. And instead of an empty hole at the core, it was matter. And instead of air encompassing a hurricane, it was water. The second event was a series of asteroids impacting the earth during the global flood. How did Noah and the ark survive? Imagine a series of large asteroids hitting the earth. The impacts would devastate life on earth globally, unless there was a means of reducing the severity of the aftermath of the impacts. Those asteroids would have to pass through a canopy of ice and water surrounding the earth's atmosphere. The asteroids would cause the canopy to succumb to Earth's gravity and come down upon the earth as rainfall (40 days and 40 nights of rain). This global rainfall would have quelled all fires and explosive effects. When asteroids hit the earth's crust, this would have fractured Pangaea, releasing 1,650 years of tectonic potential energy, and the moving tectonic plates would have squished massive amounts of water hidden in caverns under the crust of the earth and caused the water to burst out of the earth (Gen. 7:11), thereby reducing the devastating effect of the asteroid impact. *Image credit: NASA*

A series of asteroids impacting the earth would cause a bottleneck of all life. However, the canopy of ice and water would have been instrumental in quelling the devastating effect from asteroid impacts, yet the Flood would have killed all life on earth that was not protected in the Ark.

With the account of the Biblical Flood, many asteroids could of hit the earth, directly adding mass to the earth without destroying all life on earth. Thus, increasing the earth's gravity. But this is not the primary means that I imagine God used to increase gravity on earth. For there needs to be too many asteroids hitting the earth to increase its mass enough to change it. So this scenario of asteroids increasing earth's gravity by direct accumulation of mass is a viable option, given enough time, but not the primary explanation for young Earth creationists (YEC).

Let us focus on the indirect method of how asteroids can increase gravity. This is with each asteroid impact slowing earth's rotational velocity and subsequently decreasing the centripetal force that counteracts gravity and thereby increasing earth's net gravity. This is demonstrated when a basketball player spins a basketball on his or her finger. With an incorrect tap of a finger on the ball, the ball slows its rotational velocity, loses its centripetal force, gravity takes over, and the ball falls.

The rotational velocity produces a force called centripetal force, which uses up some of gravity's strength and acts against gravity and thereby reduces the effect of gravity. Cosmologists concur with this concept and point to the effects of asteroid impacts altering the spin of the planet Venus. Venus spins in an opposite direction to the planets in our solar system. Cosmologists attribute the cause of the reversal of spin to large asteroid impacts that slowed Venus' original spin to zero and then subsequent impacts that reversed the spin slightly.

The Bible mentions asteroid impacts on the earth during the end times (Revelation 6:13). "The stars[2] of the sky fell to the earth, as a fig tree casts its unripe figs when shaken by a great wind." And Isaiah 24:18–20 says:

> The windows above are opened, and the foundations of the earth shake. The earth is broken asunder, the earth is split through, the earth is shaken violently. <u>The earth reels to and fro like a</u>

---

2   Strong's Concordance # 792: Astor: a star (as strewn over the sky), literal or figurative. root of asteroid.

<u>drunkard and it totters</u> like a shack.

This is a future judgment and destruction brought upon the earth from asteroids. The asteroid impact alters the earth's rotational velocity, just like when a top has lost its spin, it starts to reel to and from and wobble. Revelation 16:17–21 gives more details about this same event that "every island fled away, and the mountains were not found."

    Review: <u>This concept of asteroids impacting the earth and reducing the spin of the earth and thus reducing the centripetal force that tends to counteract gravity and thereby increasing gravity was not the primary source of increasing gravity. There still is a greater method ahead in our discussion.</u>

    What else could have increased the net gravitational force after the Flood? The spin of the earth, coupled with gravity, creates **centripetal force**, which is center seeking. One way to describe how centripetal force tends to counter gravity is that some of gravity's energy is used up in the spin of the earth. The by-product of centripetal force that opposes gravity is **centrifugal force**, which is center fleeing.

    Today, the earth's rotation velocity is approximately 1,037 mph. It seems like a high speed, but the size of the earth considerably reduces the effect, and since we are traveling with the earth, we cannot feel the velocity. Only changes in velocity, called acceleration and deceleration, are perceived. But this spin velocity still affects the earth's gravity. How do we know the earth is spinning this fast?

$$\frac{\text{Earth's circumference}}{\text{One rotation}} = \frac{24{,}900 \text{ miles}}{{\sim}24 \text{ hours}} \approx \frac{1{,}037 \text{ miles}}{1 \text{ hour}}$$

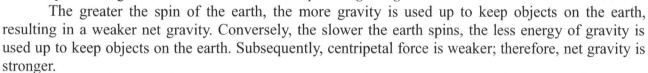

The centripetal force is used in physics because it is calculable; however, the centrifugal force is discussed by occupants at amusement park rides because that is the force that is felt and seen. The rotational velocity of the swinging chair merry-go-round creates the apparent centrifugal force that individuals feel pushing them away from the center of the ride, and they see the effect with hair standing up on end. While the centripetal force is also felt on the swinging chair merry-go-round, it is a real force, which the chair applies to the occupant sitting in the chair. *Photo credit: Wikipedia.org/swing ride.*

    The greater the spin of the earth, the more gravity is used up to keep objects on the earth, resulting in a weaker net gravity. Conversely, the slower the earth spins, the less energy of gravity is used up to keep objects on the earth. Subsequently, centripetal force is weaker; therefore, net gravity is stronger.

    Review: <u>The point is that the faster the spin of the earth, the weaker the gravity level. The slower the spin of the earth, the stronger the gravity level.</u>

    As a result of gravitational changes from centripetal force and the moon's gravity, the earth is not a sphere; it is ellipsoid (fatter at the equator than poles) in shape. An example of how spin can alter the strength of gravity: a 200-pound man will weigh slightly less at the equator (199 lb.) and slightly more at the poles (201 lb.) because a percentage of gravity's strength is lost due to the rotational velocity of the earth. Gravity at the equator is approximately (≈) 9.78 m/s/s (meters/second/second), while gravity at the poles is approximately 9.832 m/s/s. Therefore, gravity is ≈ 0.5% weaker at the equator than gravity at the poles.

    Another reason that gravity is weaker at the equator than the poles is because the moon's gravitational force is closest to the equator, and the surface at the equator is farther away from the iron core of the earth than the poles. To calculate the centripetal acceleration at the equator, we would use four multiplied by pi squared times the radius of the earth divided by the period of rotation squared:

$$\frac{4 \times 3.14^2 \times r}{T^2} = \frac{4 \times 3.14^2 \times 6{,}400 \text{ km}}{86{,}400 \text{ sec.}^2} = 0.034 \text{ m/s}^2.$$

Centripetal force at the North Pole is 0.0 m/s/s. Therefore, gravity is full strength at 9.832 m/s/s.
Centripetal force at the equator is 0.034 m/s/s, subtracting from mean gravity of 9.814 m/s/s = 9.78

m/s/s gravity at the equator.

Mathematics demonstrates the changes in gravity with spin. Let us speed up the rotation velocity of the earth and see what effect this has on gravity. Below are calculations of the earth's gravity with increasing spin velocities:

For a **24-hour day**:

$$\frac{4 \times 3.14^2 \times 6371 \text{ km}}{86,400 \text{ sec./sec.}} = 0.034 \text{ m/s/s Centripetal Force.}$$

~0.034 m/s/s – Polar Gravity ~9.832 m/s/s = **Equatorial Gravity = ~9.789 m/s/s.**
The difference between spin (equator) and no spin (poles) today is ~a 0.5% change in gravity.

For a **23-hour day**: Earth would become slightly more ellipsoid.

$$\frac{4 \times 3.14^2 \times 6,400 \text{ km}}{82,800 \text{ sec.}^2} = 0.037 \text{ m/s/s centripetal force.}$$

Hence, equatorial gravity 9.789 m/s/s – 0.037 m/s/s = **equatorial gravity = 9.752 m/s/s.**
This is a 4.2% increase in spin, which equals an 8.1% increase in centripetal force, which equals a 0.12% decrease in gravity.   Circumference = π x diameter.
Velocity = circumference/time, or π x 7948 m = 24,971 miles / 24hrs. = 1,086 mph.

For a **22-hour day**: Earth would become even more ellipsoid, so we'll add to the radius.

$$\frac{4 \times 3.14^2 \times 6,500 \text{ km}}{79,200 \text{ sec.}^2} = 0.041 \text{ m/s/s Centripetal Force.}$$

Hence, equatorial gravity 9.789 m/s/s – 0.041 m/s/s Cf = **equatorial gravity of 9.748 m/s/s.**
This is a 8.3% increase in spin from today and equals a 20.6% increase in centripetal force, which equals a 0.16% decrease in gravity.
Circumference = π x 8,073 miles = 25,362 miles / 22 hrs. = 1,153 mph.

For a **21-hour day**:

$$\frac{4 \times 3.14^2 \times 6,600 \text{ km}}{75,600 \text{ sec.}^2} = 0.046 \text{ m/s/s centripetal force.}$$

Therefore, equatorial gravity 9.789 m/s/s – 0.046 m/s/s = **equatorial gravity = 9.743 m/s/s.**
This is a 12.5% increase in spin from today and equals a 35% increase in centripetal force, which equals a 0.47% decrease in gravity.
Circumference = π x 8,197 miles = 25,752 miles / 21 = 1,226 mph.

For a **17-hour day**:

$$\frac{4 \times 3.14^2 \times 7,000 \text{ km}}{61,200 \text{ sec.}^2} = 0.074 \text{ m/s/s centripetal force.}$$

Hence, equatorial gravity 9.789 m/s/s – 0.074 m/s/s = **equatorial gravity @ 9.720 m/s/s.**
This is a 29% increase in spin from today, which equals a 117% increase in centripetal force, which **equals a 1.14% decrease in gravity**, thus,
Circumference = π x 8,694miles = 27,313 miles / 17 hrs. = 1,606 mph.

For a **15-hour day**:

$$\frac{4 \times 3.14^2 \times 8,000 \text{ km}}{54,000 \text{ sec.}^2} = 0.11 \text{ m/s/s centripetal force.}$$

Ergo, equatorial gravity 9.789 m/s/s – 0.11m/s/s = **equatorial gravity @ 9.680 m/s/s.**
This is a 37.5% increase in spin from today, which equals a 224% increase in centripetal force, which equals a 1.55% decrease in gravity, and
Circumference = π x 9,936 miles = 31,215 / 15 = 2,081 mph.

If the spin of the earth were fast enough such that one rotation were only 1.5 hours long, then gravity would be decreased by 100%. This is only for something connected with Earth's rotational velocity, such as standing on the earth's surface. Of course, if someone was floating in space and not connected with Earth's rotational velocity, the earth's spin would not affect them positively or negatively, they would have the same gravitational force affecting them whether one rotation was 2 hours or 24 hours.

Review: The spin of the earth effects net gravity. The faster the spin, the weaker the net force of gravity. Though the gross gravity would still remain the same, with the subtraction from centripetal force, the net force of gravity would be weaker.

The math reveals the fact that spin reduces the net effect of gravity, and a 17-hour day would reduce gravity by 1.14% from the equatorial gravity of today. Perhaps 1.14% does not seem like much, but it does have an effect because we are focusing on a cumulative effect. For example, if NASA engineers are off by 1%, they do not land on the moon, and so on.

It should be pointed out that the further back in time, the faster the earth spun. This evidence is destructive to the evolutionary model because they believe the first life occurred around 3.5 billion years ago. Well, we cannot go that far back in time, or else the earth will have zero net gravity and a spin velocity of one rotation in 1.5 hours, which is not sustainable for life. But before we get close to that velocity, the winds would be enormous, and way before that, the magnetic field would vaporize the earth's surface.

Review: Small increases in the spin of the earth are sufficient to reduce the net gravity enough to affect life on earth. It is a contributing factor to how gravity is greater today than when dinosaurs roamed the earth, but not the primary cause.

Another reason that an object is slightly lighter standing on the equator versus at the poles is the distance of the object from the core. This increased spin and increased centripetal force would result in a greater equatorial bulge. The earth is not a perfect sphere. It is ellipsoid (oval/oblong). Earth's radius (the distance from the core to the outer crust) at the equator is about 21,500 meters more than its polar radius. Radius at the equator: 6,371 km. Radius at the poles: 6,350 km.

The percentage difference between the equatorial radius and the polar radius is approximately 0.33% of the earth's total radius. When calculating centripetal force, the radius is in the numerator. Therefore, the faster the earth spins, the larger the radius becomes, and centripetal force increases too, and thereby net gravity decreases. When calculating centripetal force, the time is the denominator. So the faster the earth spins, the smaller the time becomes, and the centripetal force and radius increase, and thereby gravity decreases. Changing one component, such as the time it takes the earth to complete a rotation, effects the other components, such as the radius ("r"). For example, a faster spin equals a smaller "T" (the time it takes earth to complete one rotation) and thus a larger "r" and subsequently a larger centripetal force:

$$\frac{4 \times \pi^2 \times r}{T^2} = \text{centripetal force} = \frac{4 \times \pi^2 \times 6{,}371 \text{ km}}{86{,}400 \text{ sec.}^2} = 0.034 \text{ m/s}^2.$$

Consider the inverse square law: The greater the distance from the center of the earth, the less earth's gravity affects nearby objects. Therefore, the effects of gravity are fractionally weaker at the equator than the poles because of the difference in distance to the primary source of earth's gravity, the iron core. This is very slight and would not be felt by anyone comparing the two different locations. But the effects are real, and they have an accumulating effect on genomes over time.

Even a minor difference in gravity at the poles versus the equator affects earth's landscape. For example the earth is ellipsoid (slightly oblong). Therefore, if a minor change in gravity can cause the equator of the earth to be fatter than the pole-to-pole distance by 43,000 meters (approximately 24 miles), imagine what a greater change in gravity would do to life. Since a 0.5% change in gravity can alter the landscape of the earth and cause a human to weigh pound less at the equator than the mean, and a pound more at the poles than the mean, imagine what life would look like if the entire earth had 25% less gravitational force. Living beings (not just humans) would be able to live substantially longer (in age) and would be larger in size.

Review: Although the mass of the earth can remain relatively unchanged, the intensity of earth's gravitational force can be affected by rotational velocity. The rotational velocity of the earth affects the magnitude of gravity.

One of the contentions of this book is that dinosaurs lived in a weaker gravitational system. The first foundation of determining what the environment was like for dinosaurs and early man is that net effects of gravity can be weakened under certain conditions. Proving that gravity is not a constant and can be altered with several different conditions allows for the viable premise that gravity today is greater intensity than when dinosaurs and early mankind lived. Gravity can be altered by the spin of the earth, the radius of the earth, by the addition of space dust and asteroid mass to earth, and by the reduction of energy in the spin of the earth caused by asteroid impacts. Yet, those aren't the primary contributing factors to reducing earth's gravitational force before the Flood.

What is another cause of earth's rotational velocity slowing? The **moon**.

The moon's gravity causes our Earth to be ellipsoid and causes our ocean tides, and the tides take energy out of the earth's rotational velocity. Newton's first law of motion states that a body in motion will stay in motion until an outside force acts upon it. In this case, the body in motion is the earth spinning like a top, and the outside force is the moon's gravity, which slows it down.

The earth's rotational velocity and gravity produce **centripetal** force (center seeking), and earth's rotational velocity produces the apparent **centrifugal** force (center fleeing). These forces tend to counteract gravity. Every fractional slowing of the earth's rotational velocity caused by the moon's effect on earth's tides causes a net increase in earth's gravity because the centripetal force that subtracts from earth's gravity is becoming weaker. Although the earth's mass and gross gravity stay the same, the amount of centripetal force subtracted from the gravitational force results in a proportionate change to the net gravitational force. Look at the following flow schematic:

Moon's gravity → tides → ↓ Earth's rotational velocity → ↓ centripetal force → ↑ Earth's gravity.

<u>**Review:** The moon's gravity causes the ocean tides, which slow the spin of the earth by taking angular momentum (spin energy), which decrease Earth's rotational velocity, which causes reduced centripetal force and thereby increases net gravity. Therefore, the moon negatively affects the earth's centripetal force by slowing the earth's spin and positively affects the earth's net gravitational force by increasing gravity.</u>

What does the moon do with this energy that it takes from the earth? The energy propels the moon away from the earth. David Palmer, an astrophysicist, was asked, "At what rate is the earth's rotation slowing down?" He answered, "The interaction of the Moon and the tides is pumping **angular momentum** out of Earth's spin and into the Moon's orbit. Currently the day is lengthening by about 1.5–2 milliseconds per century."[3]

The moon is currently receding away from earth at 3.8 cm (1.5 inches) per year. Considering the inverse square law (the farther away a planet is from an object, the less effective its gravitational force is on an object), when the moon was closer to earth, it had a greater effect on ocean tides, which subsequently took more angular momentum out of the earth's spin velocity. This means that the earth's spin velocity is slowing at a slower rate today than in the past, which means that the further back in time we go, the faster the earth spun. Therefore, gravity was exponentially weaker in each prior millennium.

This works both ways; the earth's gravity affects the moon's tidal bulge as well. When the moon was active and hotter as a result of the earth's gravitational influence on the moon causing tidal friction, molten rock flowed onto the surface of the moon and formed the dark spots we see from Earth. The moon did not spin fast like the earth spins to cause the tidal frictions, but the moon orbits the earth in an elliptical pattern, and not in a perfect circle. We can visualize this elliptical pattern by observing the moon appearing larger in the sky at its **perigee** (362,600 km away from Earth) and smaller in the sky at its **apogee** (405,400 km away from Earth).[4] In the past, when the moon's elliptical perigee and apogee were closer to Earth, it caused greater internal tidal friction within the moon and generated enough heat

---

3   Ask an Astrophysicist (http://imagine.gsfc.nasa.gov/docs/ask_astro/answers/980421b.html).
4   Wikipedia, Orbit of the moon.

for lava to flow out onto the surface. But now that the distance from the moon and the earth has increased, the earth's influence that once caused tidal friction and subsequent lava to flow on the moon has ceased, and the moon is minimally active.

Review: Since the moon is getting farther away from earth, its gravity takes less angular momentum out of the earth's spin. Therefore, the earth is slowing at a slower rate today than in the past, which also means that earth spun exponentially faster in the past. Since centripetal force that counters against gravity was greater in the past. Therefore, gravity was exponentially weaker the further back in time we go.

The rate that the earth slows its spin is not constant; nor is it a linear line. It is gradually slowing at a slower pace. It is erroneous to state that the moon is currently moving away from the earth at the same rate today as in the past.

We know that the moon has had a parabolic rate of recession from the earth and that the effects that the moon has on the earth today are weaker than the effects the moon had on the earth around 5,000 years ago because the moon is farther away from earth today. When the moon was closer to earth, it caused greater tidal effects, and the greater tidal effects took more angular momentum (rotational velocity) out of earth's spin and translated that energy into the moon receding away from the earth. So the moon moved away from the earth faster in past millennia than it is moving away today. Well then, why isn't the moon traveling super fast away from the earth? Because the attraction of the two gravitational bodies keeps the moon's recession velocity low.

Why couldn't the earth-moon relationship be billions of years old? Since the moon is moving away from the earth at a parabolic rate of recession, then as we go backward in time, the moon gets closer to the earth. A point exist where the moon cannot be any closer to the earth, or the gravitational forces of the moon and earth would cause disintegration of one or both bodies. This distance is called the Roche limit.[5] But before reaching the Roche limit, tidal forces would be too large for life.

The rate at which the moon is receding away from the earth is gradually slowing. Physicist Donald DeYoung explains, "One cannot extrapolate the present 4cm/year separation rate back into history. It has the value today, but was more rapid in the past because of tidal effects. In fact, the separation rate . . . was perhaps 20 meters per year long ago, and the average is 1.2 meters per year."[6]

Below is an example of the parabolic rate of lunar recession and its relationship with gravity and the duration of the day.

Century	Change in a Day's duration/100yrs.	Rate of Moon's recession	Gravity	Length of Day
21st century	slowed 2 msec./100yrs.	3.8 cm/yr.	9.8m/s/s	~23 hrs, 56 min.
15th century	slowed 5 msec.100yrs.	7.5 cm/yr.		
10th century	slowed 25 msec./100yrs.	15 cm/yr.		
5th century	slowed 100 msec./100yrs.	35 cm/yr.		
1 BC	slowed 500 msec./100 yrs.	85 cm/1 yr.		
500 BC	slowed 3 sec./100yrs.	175 cm/yr.		
1,000 BC	slowed 12 sec./100yrs.	400cm/yr.		
2,000 BC	slowed 1 min./100yrs	1 meter/yr.		~23 hours
3,000 BC	slowed 7 min./100yrs.	5 meter/yr.		~22 hours
4,000 BC	slowed 30 min./100yrs.	20 m/yr.	~9.6m/s/s	~17 hours

Notice the length of a day around the time of Adam and Eve would have been about 17 hours long. It has been increasing ever since. This means that the earth would be spinning fast enough to weaken gravity by 1.14% for Adam and Eve. This by itself is not enough to appreciably alter life on earth. Yet, this adds to the cumulative effect on net gravity and the subsequent effect of life on Earth.

We have established that the moon was closer to earth in the past, and subsequently the earth was spinning faster in the past, and this caused net gravity to be weaker by about 1.14% before the global flood. However, this was not the primary cause of reducing net gravity before the Flood. But it

---

5 Roche limit: the distance at which the moon cannot be any closer to the earth without disintegrating, which is approximately 11,500 miles.

6 Physicist Donald DeYoung estimates that the moon has receded away from the earth 20 meters per year in the past.

leads us into the next phase of our discussion, which is to build on the premise that the moon was closer to the earth in past millennia.

With the moon closer to the earth, the moon's gravitational force would directly decrease the earth's gravitational force by "pulling" against it. This is different than the discussion above, where we discussed how the moon's gravitational force caused tidal shifting of the earth's oceans and how this took angular momentum out of the earth's spin velocity, which reduced the earth's spin and thereby reduced centripetal force and increased earth's net gravity. This discussion simply involves the moon's gravity pulling (changing the space and time within its gravitational field that changes the natural path of portion of earth nearest to the moon) in an opposite direction to earth's gravity, thereby decreasing earth's gravity directly via subtraction.

This is another cause of reducing earth's gravity in the past. As far as the shape of the earth being ellipsoid instead of spherical, the two primary causes are the moon's gravity, and the centripetal force generated from the earth's spin. The moon's gravity draws on the earth and creates the ellipsoidal shaped earth. Since the moon can effect the physical landscape of the earth, the moon can effect life on earth as well.

Gravity is not even uniformly constant on earth; it is not 9.8m/s/s all around the earth. In certain regions, gravity is greater due to changes in density beneath the crust of the earth, changes in elevation, and centripetal force. Therefore, since gravity is not even constant on earth, why would anyone think it is been constant throughout the millennia?

Since the earth's shape is ellipsoid, then utilizing how much distortion the shape of the earth has resulted from the moon's gravity, we can get an idea of the effect the moon's gravity has on countering Earth's gravity. The difference in the radii of the poles versus the equator is roughly 0.33%, so it is reasonable to hypothesize that at least some of the 0.33% reduction of the earth's gravitational force is due to the moon's gravitational force. Since the moon was closer in the past, the countering effect would be greater in the past.

When the moon was closer to the earth and had a greater effect on the earth's shape and the earth was spinning faster, the earth's size was larger.

Take for example a black hole. The gravitational forces are so high in a black hole that planets caught inside are squished down to the size of a dot. This is a negative example of the powerful effects of gravity and establishes the notion that gravity can reduce the size of a planet.

Now let us examine this from a positive perspective. Look at a dragster's (race car) rear tire, when the rotational velocity is increased, the actual circumference of the tire enlarges. Thus faster spin increases the circumference. Both the negative and positive views demonstrate that if earth's rotational velocity were altered, the size of the earth would be effected, and if the earth's gravity were altered, its size would be altered as well.

Donald Hamilton[7] suggests a 10% increase in the earth's equatorial bulge from a faster rotational velocity upon its axis. The fast spinning star Vega makes a full rotation about its axis once every 12.5 hours, which causes it to assume a 23% elliptical bulge at its equator, ergo, a 10% greater bulge for the faster spinning Earth is not out of the question. Essentially, this suggests that the faster the earth spun in past millennia, the fatter the earth was, perhaps with a 10% greater equatorial circumference.

Since the earth's rotational velocity is slowing down and the rate at which the earth is slowing down is decreasing, this proves that earth had a higher rotational velocity in the distant past, which is evidence that the earth was a slightly larger planet in past millennia than today. Why is this important? The inverse square law, suggests that the farther an object is from the source of gravity (the central iron core), the less gravity effects the space and time of an object. Therefore, an increased size of the earth means that the inhabitants are farther away from the iron core center of the earth, which is the primary source of its density and gravity. Below is a chart of earth's gravitational force at different altitudes:

---

7   Donald L. Hamilton is the author of *The MIND of Mankind.*

<u>The force of Gravity at Various Altitudes</u>

Altitudes(km)	Gravity(m/s/s)
0 km surface level	9.81
31 km = 20 miles	9.74* 1% weaker gravity
62.5 km	9.67
125 km = 77.5 miles	9.50* 3.2% weaker gravity

You can see that the farther away from the source of gravity, the weaker gravity becomes, and the primary source of gravity is the iron core. We have already established that the earth is larger at the equator than the poles because of the moon and spin and that the earth was larger in the distant past than today at the equator because of the moon's gravity and the faster spin of earth. So if the earth's surface were 31 km (20 miles) farther away from the iron core, then gravity would be an additional ~1% weaker at the equator. This is only an increase of 0.5% in the radius of earth. If the earth had an equatorial bulge of 125 km (77.5 miles), then gravity would be approximately 3.2% weaker. Even though are plausible scenarios of how gravity was weaker in the past, it is still not the primary reason for a reduced gravity that allowed dinosaurs to grow so tall. It is just a contributory factor, but all these contributory factors start to add up.

We know that the moon's gravitational force and earth's spin affect the shape of earth, but do they have an effect on living creatures? It does not matter whether gravity is large or small; the mass of an object remains the same. But with increases or decreases in gravity, the weight of an object will change, which is measured in newtons (N = mass x gravity) in physics, but on your bathroom scale, it is measured in pounds (lb.) or kilograms (kg). If the earth were to rotate faster, resulting in more centrifugal force and centripetal force using up more gravity to keep you on the surface while moving in a circle, your bathroom scale would read fewer pounds, since N = mass x gravity – Force$_{centripetal}$, which means that though you are the same mass, you would weigh less.

A 100-kg (220 lb.) person, standing at the North Pole would be attracted toward the center of the earth with a force of 983.4 newtons (about 220 lb.) and would be accelerating toward the center of the earth at (acceleration = F/m) 9.83 m/s/s (gravity). Now, if we move that 100-kg person to the equator, some of this acceleration (a = v^2/r = 0.034 m/s^2, where v = 463 m/s or 1037 mi./hr.) would be used up to keep the person in a circular orbit, and that person would weigh about 1.5 pounds less and would be accelerating toward the center of the earth at 9.79 m/s/s (gravity). [8]

Now, if we sped up the earth's rotation velocity so that a day were only 17 hours long, which is the estimated length of the day for Adam and Eve because of the moon, that same person would weigh 1.15% less, even though his or her mass had not changed at all.

Since earth's rotational velocity is fractionally slowing each year, that means the centripetal force countering gravity is fractionally getting weaker each year as well. Since the earth's mass is continually being added to by space dust each year, the earth's mass and subsequent gravity are fractionally getting higher each millennium. And since the moon is moving away from earth each year, and the moon's gravity counters earth's gravity, the earth's gravity is fractionally getting higher each millennium. Therefore, the net effect is that gravity has been increasing each millennium. But these changes are fractional and may only amount to a 2%–3% change in earth's gravity.

As a result of the moon taking angular momentum out of the earth's spin, the length of a day on earth is slowing by 2 milliseconds per 100 years at today's pace. But as we discussed earlier, the moon is receding away from the earth by 3.8 cm (1.5 in.) per year at an ever-decreasing rate, which is to say that the moon receded away from the earth around 20 meters away per year some 6,000 years ago. Since the moon causes our changes in tides, the farther away the moon is from the earth, the less the tidal changes occur. The changes in tides take angular momentum out of the rotational velocity of the earth (decreases the earth's spin), which means that the moon's effect on the earth's ocean tides is

---

8 Dick Plano, Professor of Physics emeritus, Rutgers University.

getting fractionally weaker each year. Therefore, the moon had a greater effect in slowing the earth in past millennia than today.

Below is a graph of the relationships between the moon's distance from the earth, the length of a day, and the earth's rotational velocity based on distance and time. The dashed (---------) line represents the incorrect view of thinking: for the moon's rate of recession from earth, for the change in the length of a day, and for the earth's spin velocity.

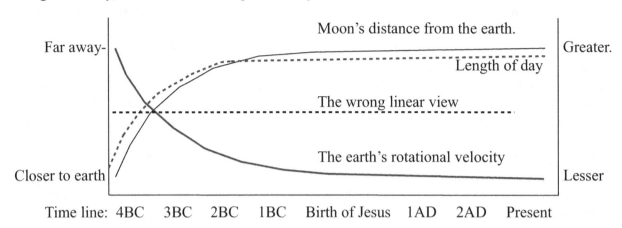

Far away-   Moon's distance from the earth.   Greater.
                                                          Length of day
                                        The wrong linear view
                                        The earth's rotational velocity
Closer to earth   Lesser

Time line: 4BC   3BC   2BC   1BC   Birth of Jesus   1AD   2AD   Present

Review: Whether it was by asteroids impacting the earth and adding mass or reducing spin, or whether it was the moon's gravitational force altering the space and time near the earth and changing the earth's gravity or the moon's gravity taking energy out of the spin of the earth, the bottom line is that earth's gravity has changed, and all the above are cumulative contributors.

Now that we have established that the earth's gravity can change and has changed from past millennia, now it is time for another piece of the gravitational puzzle. This is the final bit of evidence that the net gravity was weaker some 5,000 years ago. This final bit of evidence that changed gravity on earth is buoyancy—via the canopy of ice and salt water that hovered spherically around the atmosphere and caused the global flood.

How would a canopy of ice and salt water change gravity on earth? Is it because most of the oceans were formed from the 40 days and 40 nights of rain and the mass of water added to earth's mass and changed gravity? No. The global flood would have added a lot of mass to the earth. But even if we take the mass of the polar ice caps and 50% of the ocean water, which is a plausible estimate that came down upon the earth in 40 days and 40 nights, it amounts to 7.875×10^{17} tons. But since the earth's mass is 6.5×10^{21} tons (1.3×10^{25} lb.), that means the colossal global rain only added 0.012% to the earth's mass. Therefore, this is not significant enough to alter the earth's gravity. Could we bump up the estimate and say 100% of the oceans were formed from the canopy that rained down during the Flood? No—water also burst out of the deep caverns under the crust for 40 days and 40 nights (Gen. 7:11), and that mass was already part of earth's mass.

Is it that most of the ocean water—before being formed from the torrential rain—would be hovering above the atmosphere and thereby would increase atmospheric pressure, weight, and density of air? Yes.

How does an increased atmospheric pressure reduce gravity? Let us use water as an example to set the stage because the concept of buoyancy, which atmospheric pressure provides, is similar to the buoyancy that a pool of water provides, just at a significantly reduced level. This is based on **Archimedes'** principle of **buoyancy force**. When a body is submerged in water, either wholly or partially, it is buoyed up by a force equal to the weight of the liquid displaced by the body. When you get into water, a certain amount of volume of water is moved out of the way to make room for the volume of your body (not your weight). The mass of that amount of water displaced will create a force lifting you up. If your body weighs less than the weight of the volume of water displaced, then you'll float. If your body weighs more than the weight of the volume of water displaced, then you'll sink.

Therefore, if you ever wondered why one floats in water, it is because fat cells are less dense and weigh less than an equal volume of water displaced. The buoyancy force is greater because the volume of water displaced is denser and weighs more than a body filled with large amounts of fatty tissue that is less dense and weighs less. Subsequently, this buoyancy force is then greater than the force of gravity needed to pull an individual down to the bottom of the pool, so the individual floats.

Conversely, top athletes sink because muscle mass is denser and weighs more than the equal volume of water they are displacing. Therefore, the buoyancy force is weaker because the volume of water displaced weighs less than the muscular body, and thus buoyancy force is then weaker than gravity; thus, they sink. Here's the formula:

Buoyancy = weight of volume of liquid displaced – body weight.

If the sum is < 1, the body sinks. If the sum is > 1, the body floats. If the sum = 1, the body does not sink or float, but remains suspended.

Suppose a book suspended by a string weighs 10 newtons in a vacuum, with gravity acting on the book. Then imagine lowering the book into water, and in the volume of water, the book displaces 4 newtons of water. The net force exerted on the string holding up the book is represented by 10 newtons – 4 newtons buoyancy force = 6 newtons net. See how gravity was reduced by buoyancy force. This changed the net affect of gravity, and gravity was reduced by 40% in this fictitious scenario.

Can the amount of buoyancy force change? Yes, for example, a body of water with a very high saltwater content will have a greater buoyancy force than fresh water. Why? The salt water has more particulates per cubic volume of water, which means the salt water is denser. For example, in the Dead Sea in Israel, the water is so dense from the high salt concentration that one floats almost at mid-chest level in the water. That same person may sink in fresh water. Therefore, we see that buoyancy can change with changes in the density of water. Since Archimedes' principle equally applies to whatever medium an object is immersed into, including air, the buoyancy of our atmosphere (though less dense than water) can still change the amount of buoyancy force it applies against gravity depending on the density of air.

What is an example of how changes in atmosphere pressure affect buoyancy? Fishing. Why? High pressure or high barometric pressure (synonyms) means more atmospheric weight pressing down on the water. This means that the weight of the water that the volume of fish displaces will weigh more. This change in buoyancy force causes the fish to float. Hence, the fish will seek deep shelter to prevent them from rising and floating to the surface.

Another example is when someone has a painful joint and a storm is approaching. They are the first ones to tell everyone that their joints ache. Why? When a storm is approaching, the atmospheric pressure drops, and therefore less pressure. With less pressure, swollen tissue, scar tissue, and bone spurs expand and physically press on the nerves, sending pain signals to the brain. It is like their injured joint is a weather detector.

A really good example of the similarities of the buoyancy of air and water is the comparison of a jellyfish and a balloon. As starfish look up through an ocean of water to see jellyfish floating in the water, humans look up through an ocean of air to see balloons floating in the air. Both the jellyfish and the balloon are buoyed upward by a force equal to the weight of volume of fluid displaced by their volume.

The effect of a heavier atmosphere, creating higher atmospheric pressure, has the same application of Archimedes' principle of a larger buoyancy force, except that it is air being displaced by your body, rather than water being displaced. And just like water, the denser the air, the more buoyancy force is applied. The more air matter per cubic volume, the denser the air and the greater the atmospheric pressure, resulting in more matter being displaced by the body being in the atmosphere, which is a greater buoyancy force. Now, this is all fine and dandy up to a point. There comes a point where body tissue cannot handle too much pressure, or it starts to collapse on itself. Much like a submarine that sinks to the bottom of the ocean, when the pressure near the bottom of the ocean is too great, the submarine collapses like a tin can under a stomping shoe. Conversely, if not enough pressure exist, then our body tissue cannot hold itself together (we boil, not from heat, but from a change in pressure) and we explode. Just like when a balloon floats too high in the atmosphere and the pressure is too low, the balloon will expand and expand until the integrity of the walls explode. You may have seen the science fiction movie in which an astronaut loses pressure from being in space and explodes. Variations in pressure and density can have a profound effect.

Space → Zero pressure: humans explode.

High altitude → Very little pressure: balloons burst.

Surface → 1Atmosphere of pressure: today's normal.

→ Somewhere in here is the optimal pressure: Adam and Eve's normal.

Fresh water → Medium pressure: high buoyancy.

Salt water → Higher pressure: higher buoyancy.

Ocean floor →Extreme pressure: submarines are crushed.

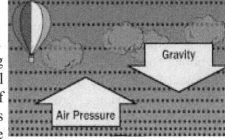

You can see that with different amounts of pressures, varying results occur. By looking at slight variations of pressure, beneficial results occur to buoyancy. Somewhere between one unit of atmospheric pressure (at the surface of the earth) and freshwater is a sweet spot of buoyancy force that existed in our atmosphere before the Flood and subsequently resulted in a reduction of net gravity.

Why is air a factor in terms of buoyancy, even though we cannot see it as we can with water? Air has mass just like water has mass, but air has a lesser amount per the same cubic volume. To test whether air has mass, just roll down your window while driving in a car at 55 mph. Then you will feel the mass of air, or the matter in it. *Image credit: Tom Harris, www.science.howstuffworks.com.*

What causes buoyancy in air? The pressure of the atmosphere is "pulled down" by gravity, and when the air reaches the surface of the earth, those air particles push up on the rest of the atmosphere and hold up 400 miles of air mass. This pushing up has a force, and that force is called buoyancy. Therefore, when a body is standing on the surface of the earth, that body is displacing a certain amount of volume of air, and that volume of air has mass and weight that creates a buoyancy force that lifts up.

The more volume of air per cubic meter displaced by an object, the more weight of air displaced and the greater buoyancy effect pushing upward in the opposite direction of gravity. Therefore, though gravity has not changed, its net force is subsequently reduced as a result of buoyancy force.

Here is how buoyancy works for air: All the air particles of the atmosphere are "pulled down" to the earth by gravity. This creates greater and greater pressure closer to the surface because more and more particles exist closer to the surface of the earth. This pressure creates an upward force working in opposition to the direction of gravity. More pressure exists near the surface of the earth because those air particles are holding up more atmosphere, than air particles 5 miles above Earth's surface.

Hence, the more weight that the particles of air have to hold up near the surface of the earth, the more pressure they exert on people on the surface of the earth and, subsequently, the more buoyancy force applied per volume of cubic air displaced. With greater buoyancy, the force of net gravity is weaker. All we need to do is determine if our atmosphere at one time had greater weight pushing down on earth; If so, the air particles nearer the surface would have to push up equally as hard, and this would increase the buoyancy force, which would reduce net gravity. Before the Flood, a canopy of water that hovered around the atmosphere, and it had a monumental amount of weight.

The canopy of water came down upon the earth in 40 days and 40 nights of rainfall. This means that before the Flood, this canopy water would have hovered above the atmosphere and would have added a great deal of atmospheric pressure, weight, and density, increasing the buoyancy force and subsequently reducing net gravity.

You may be surprised to hear that our atmosphere today weighs about 5.5 quadrillion tons[9] (one ton = 2,000 lb.). This is nothing new for the Bible, as it says in Job 28:25, "He imparted weight to the wind," which was written some 3,500 years ago.

What was the buoyant force before the Flood? Later on in the book you'll learn that no polar ice existed prior to the Flood. Therefore, we can take the entire weight of the polar ice caps, 32 quadrillion tons (3.2×10^{16} tons), and add that to the atmosphere's weight to help determine what the buoyancy force was before the Flood. Thus, putting the weight so far of the atmosphere plus the polar ice caps equals 3.75×10^{16} tons. The additional weight added to the atmosphere by the polar caps increases the buoyancy force by a factor of 6X. Now let us add a portion of the oceans as well. It is possible that a majority of our vast oceans were formed as a result of the canopy of water raining down onto earth. The oceans are estimated at 1.5×10^{18} tons. If we figure conservatively that only one-fourth of the ocean water came from the Genesis flood, that would add 37.5×10^{16} tons of ocean water, plus 3.2×10^{16} tons of polar ice caps to the weight of the atmosphere (0.55×10^{16} tons), totaling 41.25×10^{16} tons of atmospheric weight. That is 75 times greater than our current atmosphere's weight today.

Therefore, the estimated buoyancy force before the Flood and the environmental condition of early man and dinosaurs before the Global flood would have been 75X greater than today based on only **25% of the ocean** water stored up above the atmosphere in the canopy of water. This equals a buoyancy force great enough to reduce the net effect of gravity by almost 10%.

Weight of the atmosphere:	0.55×10^{16} tons
Weight of the polar ice caps:	3.2×10^{16} tons
Weight of **one-forth** the oceans:	37.5×10^{16} tons
Total:	41.25×10^{16} tons

This does not include the vast salt deposits that were formed from the Flood, which would increase the weight pushing down on the atmosphere and increase the weight of the atmosphere and thus increase the buoyancy force, which decreases net gravity. Below is a list of known values:

A cubic meter of air has a mass of 1.2 kg (12 newtons) today.
Space has a density of 0.0 kg/m^3.
Air has a density of 1.29 kg/m^3.
Fresh water has a density of 1,000 kg/m^3.
The ocean has a density of 1,027 kg/m^3 (2.7% heavier than fresh water).
Seawater has a density of 1,035 kg/m^3 (3.5% heavier than fresh water).[10]
The average human has a density of 1,000kg/m^3, and an average person weighs 70 kg,
The average volume of the human body = m/M = 70 kg/1,000 kg/m^3 = 0.07 m^3.

The weight of **ocean water** displaced by an average human being in ocean water is:
0.07 m^3 (volume of human) x 1,027 kg/m^3 (the density of salt water) = 71.9 kg of salt water displaced. Therefore, 70 kg (weight of the person) – the 71.9 kg of buoyancy force = a person weighing –1.9 kg in ocean water (net gravity is 102.7% reduced by ocean water, meaning that the person floats).

The weight of **fresh water** displaced by an average human being in fresh water is:
0.07 m^3 (volume of human) x 1,000 kg/m^3 (density) = 70 kg of fresh water displaced.
Therefore, 70 kg of buoyancy force – 70 kg (weight of the person) = zero (net gravity is 100% reduced by water).

The weight of **air (post-Flood)** displaced by an average human being in air is:
0.07 m^3 (volume) x 1.29 kg/m^3 (density of air) = 0.09 kg of air displaced.
Therefore, 70 kg weight – 0.09 kg of buoyancy force = a person weighing 69.9 kg (**net gravity is 0.12% reduced by air**).

9   *Encyclopedia Britannica.*
10 Hypertext.com/facts/2002/Edward LaValley *Density of Seawater.*

The weight of **air (pre-Flood w/ a canopy of water weight of 75X)** displaced by an average human being in air is 1.29 kg/m^3 (density of air) x 75 = 96.75 kg/m^3 (the density of air pre-Flood). And 0.07 m^3 (volume) x 96.75 kg/m^3 (density) = 6.77 kg of air displaced.

Therefore, 70 kg weight – 6.8 kg of buoyancy force = a person weighing 63.23 kg (**net gravity is 9.8% reduced by air pre-Flood that had 25% of ocean water**).

Now you can see how changes in the density of the volume of a fluid that a human body is submerged in determines the buoyancy force. If the canopy of water included only 25% of the ocean water, this increased air density by a factor of 75, which reduced net gravity by 9.8%. The rest of the ocean

> The above calculation is based on: 25% of ocean from the canopy of water,
> 25% of ocean from deep caverns below the crust, and
> 50% of ocean already in existence as seas.

If the amount of water that rained upon the earth from the canopy was **50% of the oceans**, and 25% of the ocean water came from the deep caverns within the earth that burst open for the Flood, and 25% of ocean water already existed in the form of seas before the Flood, then:

The weight of the atmosphere:	0.55×10^{16} tons
The weight of the polar ice caps:	3.2×10^{16} tons
The weight of **half** the oceans:	$\underline{75 \times 10^{16} \text{ tons}}$
Total:	78.75×10^{16} tons

Then 78.75×10^{16} tons divided by 0.55×10^{16} tons (current atmospheric weight) = 143 (factor of change). This means that the atmosphere before the Flood weighed 143X greater than it does today with 50% of the ocean water stored in the canopy before the Flood. The formula to estimate the buoyancy force of air prior to the Flood utilizing **50% of the ocean in the canopy** is:

> 0.07 m^3 (volume of a human) x 1.29 kg/m^3 (density of air) x 143 (factor of change) =
> 12.93 kg of air displaced.
> Therefore, 70 kg (weight of an average human) – 12.93 kg of buoyancy force = a person weighing 57.07 kg (**net gravity reduced by 18.5%**).

The question is, "How much water was stored up above the atmosphere as the canopy of salt water?" We cannot know the exact volume, but it has to be that a significant percentage of the oceans were formed from the rainfall coming down upon the earth from the canopy during the Flood because the air bubble samples in the glacial core samples, indicate that oxygen was 50% higher before the Flood. The primary way to increase oxygen is to increase the quantity of vegetation. The best way to increase vegetation is to reduce the size of the oceans that limit vegetation growth.

> **Review:** If 25% of the ocean was stored up in the canopy before the Flood, then gravity was reduced by 9.8% from buoyancy force. If 50% of the ocean was stored up in the canopy before Flood, then gravity was reduced by 18.1%. *Photo credit: www.sanandreasfault.org.*

This does not factor the weight of all the salt deposits, in a faster spinning earth, closer moon, larger earth radius, 50% higher concentration of oxygen before the Flood, asteroid impacts, mass being added to the earth, and so on.

We know God placed water under the surface of the earth because of Psalm 136:6: "To Him that stretched out the earth above the waters" and Gen. 7:11: "The fountains of the deep burst open." It is a safe bet that these fountains were water, and they burst out of the crust at the fault lines and volcanoes. Since most volcanoes erupt copious amounts of water as well in the form of steam and the most violent eruptions come from water contacting the hot magma and resulting in prodigious accelerated explosions, then quite possibly, the "fountains of the deep" that burst open could have been volcanoes around the globe. Especially since the discovery of ample amounts of water in the mantle. If this was the case, then an even greater portion of water was stored in the canopy, which increases the buoyant force and weakens gravity even greater. For example, if **75% of the ocean water was stored up in the canopy**, then 116.25 x 10^{16} tons of total weight divided by 0.55 x 10^{16} tons (current atmospheric weight) = 211.4 (factor of change). This means that the atmosphere before the Flood weighed 211X greater than it does today. The average human would have displaced 19.09 kg of air. Therefore, a 70 kg person would weigh 50.91 kg. This means **gravity is reduced by 27.3%**.

Even though there would be an increase in the weight of the atmosphere, the pressure would still be far below the pressure of being in water, and would be far below the density of water. Anyone who accepts that there was a flood has to put some percentage of the ocean formation from the rain that fell down upon the earth up into the canopy of salt water. Whether it is 25% or 75%, the force of gravity was reduced by the force of buoyancy by either 10% to 27%, or some percentage near or between them. Thus, a plausible explanation of how the net force of gravity was weaker before the Flood, some 4,400 years ago, has been established. Though the force of gravity resulting from the increased mass of the earth remained relatively stable from the time before the Flood to the time after the Flood, one can see that the net force of gravity is determined by many factors, and those factors have changed over time and have altered the net strength of gravity from the origins of life on earth before the Flood to today's current intensity. The bottom line is that the net force of gravity was weaker in the past.

Even if 100% of the ocean water was stored up above the atmosphere, thereby increasing the weight of the atmosphere, it would still only result in 37% of the density of freshwater. Therefore, life forms would not be crushed by the weight and pressure of the atmosphere, but would be more buoyant with a greater density, weight, and pressure of air.

Review: Buoyancy force is a real force that is felt, and the effects are observable, measurable, and calculable. It passes the scientific method of being observable and testable. Archimedes' principle of buoyancy force applies for both water and air. The denser the air, the greater the buoyancy force. The atmosphere is made denser by greater weight above it, which squishes the air molecules below closer together. Thus, before the Flood, the water being stored up above the atmosphere in the canopy of salt water created greater atmospheric pressure and greater air density, and the buoyancy force of air before the Flood was great enough to reduce the net effect of gravity by 10%–27%, depending on how much salt water was stored in the canopy of water.

Let us see how the laws in physics pertaining to the interaction between pressure, volume and temperature reduced gravity and affected life. **Boyle's Law** states when a gas is a constant temperature (which it was), its **pressure** exerted by a gas is <u>inversely proportional</u> to its **volume**. This means:

- If the pressure increases, the volume decreases.
- If the pressure decreases, the volume increases.

Before the Flood, the atmosphere was denser because the oxygen concentration was 50% higher and the canopy compressed it. Thus, the volume of the atmosphere was reduced, which increased the buoyancy force, which decreased gravity.

Applying this to the size of the atmosphere before the Flood, with the weight of the canopy hovering over the atmosphere, this increased pressure would have reduced the volume of the atmosphere. The formula is: $P1V1 = P2V2$. The atmosphere goes up to ~300 plus miles above the earth, but ~99% of the atmosphere is within the first ~60 miles, we'll utilize the volume of 60 miles for this formula, and estimate a 10% reduction in volume of the atmosphere from the weight of the canopy:

P1 = 1 atm   P2 = ?
V1 = 60 miles   V2 = 54 miles
1 atm X 60 miles = P2 (54 miles) = 1.1 atm = P2.

This illustrates how atmospheric pressure increased from the weight of the canopy compressing it. Since the temperature of the atmosphere was greater before the Flood than today, we will use:

Charles' Law: If pressure is held constant (as it was), the **Volume** of a gas is <u>directly</u>

<u>proportional</u> to its absolute **Temperature**, which means:

- If volume increases, the temperature increases.
- If volume decreases, the temperature decreases.

Applying this law, we gain some insight into the balance and subsequent homeostasis of the atmosphere before the Flood. The average global temperature today is ~14°C (57°F). The average global temperature before the Flood was roughly 23.8°C (75°F), then according to the formula: $V_1/T_1 = V_2/T_2$, the increased temperature of the atmosphere will increase its volume and thus limit the previous compressing of the atmosphere from the weight of the canopy—as discussed with Boyle's Law. If we suppose our atmosphere was squished down from 60 miles to 50 miles because of the canopy, which increased the atmospheric temperature, then calculating for volume pre-Flood would be:

V_1 = ? miles $\qquad\qquad\qquad\qquad$ V_2 = 50 miles

T_1= 23.8°C + 273 = 296.8 K $\qquad\qquad$ T_2 = 14°C + 273 = 287 K

V_1/296.8 K = 50 miles/287 K then V_1 = ~52 miles.

Applying this law demonstrates that the canopy would not squish the atmosphere too much for life. The warmer atmosphere before the Flood increased the volume, which counteracted the weight of the canopy, providing a homeostasis. For support of higher pre-Flood temperature, See chapter on Climate.

Gay-Lussac's Law: If volume is held constant (as it was), the **pressure** of a gas is <u>directly proportional</u> to the **temperature**, which means:

- If the pressure increases, temperature increases.
- If the pressure decreases, temperature decreases.

Applying Gay-Lussac's law with the values of today and the estimated increased temperature before Flood, then atmospheric pressure is proportionately increased. The formula is: $P_1/T_1 = P_2/T_2$

P_1 = ? $\qquad\qquad\qquad\qquad\qquad\qquad$ T_1 = 23.8°C + 273 K = 296.8 K

P_2 = 101 kPa (14.7 pounds per square inch) $\qquad$ T_2 = 14°C + 273 = 287 K

P_1/ 296.8 K = 101 kPa/287 K = $\qquad$ P_1 = 104.45 kPa (~15.2 pounds per square inch).

This demonstrates that life lived in an environment of increased atmospheric pressure before the Flood. This explains why some dinosaurs that had nostrils too small for their size, still thrived because there was a greater tidal volume of air that passed through their lungs with each breath. Also, since oxygen concentration before the Flood was 50% higher, then each breath brought in more oxygen, which caused all life thrive. All the above laws work together in harmony:

Combined gas law: It combines **Boyle's Law, Charles' Law**, and **Gay-Lussac's Law**:

$$\frac{P_1 V_1}{T_1} = \frac{P_2 V_2}{T_2}$$

Review: <u>The bottom line with the laws applied is that the atmosphere would have reached a natural homeostasis of equilibrium. The canopy above the atmosphere caused increased pressure that resulted in a force that squished the atmosphere, but an increased temperature caused an increased atmospheric pressure that pushed back. Although the volume of the atmosphere was smaller because of the increased weight and subsequent pressure applied to the atmosphere, there was an equilibrium that caused life to thrive. As someone is buoyant on an ocean of water, the canopy was also buoyant on the ocean of air and increased the buoyancy for everything on the surface of the earth.</u>

Today, oxygen concentration makes up roughly 21% of our atmosphere, and nitrogen makes up 78% (< 1% comprised of other elements). However, before the Flood, oxygen made up 31% (See Oxygen Concentration chapter) of our atmosphere, and nitrogen made up 68% (< 1% other elements). Since oxygen weighs more than nitrogen, this would have added to the atmospheric pressure, and oxygen atoms are slightly smaller, or denser, than nitrogen atoms, so this would have added to the density of the atmosphere. **Oxygen weighs 14.3% more than nitrogen** because it has more protons than nitrogen. This also results in a greater positive charge for oxygen, which pulls electrons closer to the nucleus, reducing its radius, thus making it denser.

Oxygen molecular weight = 32 g/mole.

Nitrogen molecular weight = 28 g/mole.

Considering that oxygen is 32 g/mole and nitrogen is 28 g/mole and oxygen had a 50% higher concentration before the Flood, this would increase the weight of the atmosphere by ~10.5%, thus increasing the buoyant force of the pre-Flood atmosphere by the following calculation:

The weight of air pre-Flood (not including the canopy) displaced by an average human being in air is 0.07 m^3 (body volume) x (1.29 kg/m^3 (density of air) x 1.105 (increased O2 concentration to 31%) = 0.1 kg of air displaced.

Therefore, 70 kg (average weight of a person) – 0.1 kg of buoyancy force = a person weighing 69.9 kg (**net gravity is reduced by 0.14%** from air having 31% of O2 concentration).

This is negligible, but it again shows that changes in the environment can have an effect on net gravity. We are only talking about an increase in oxygen concentration in the atmosphere from 21% (post-Flood) to 31% (pre-Flood), and net gravity is weakened by 0.14% from pre-Flood times versus post-Flood times just by changes in oxygen concentration.

Although dry air increases the density of the atmosphere and would have fractionally increased buoyant force, I do not accept that the climate had dry air before the fall or before the Flood. Why is moisture in the air less dense? Water vapor (a gas) weighs 18 g/mole, O2 weighs 32 g/mole, and N2 weighs 28g /mole. Therefore, with less water vapor (humidity) in the air, the air was denser. But it is important to note that although dry air increases the buoyancy force, it may be discarded because the evidence that tropical forests once dominated in the Arctic Circle and in the Sahara, and a mist rose from the ground to water the earth suggests that humidity was high.

Review: Before the global Flood, increased oxygen increased atmosphere mass and density, which increased the buoyancy effect and decreased net gravity, although it was by trace amounts. I use "net" gravity to draw your attention that the force of gravity from the mass of the earth would remain unchanged. It is the surrounding dynamic factors that affect the net effectiveness of the force of gravity.

Another element added to the weight of the atmosphere when a portion of the oceans was hovering above the atmosphere as the canopy, and that was salt. Before the celestial bodies were formed, the Spirit of God was hovering over the face of the waters (Genesis 1:2). Notice that *waters* is plural. It seems this represents abundance and that water existed in four forms: solid, liquid, gas, and plasma. For water to be in a liquid form while not having the sun (which was not finished coalescing matter until the fourth day), three principles of science need to be applied:

1. High pressure: reduces the freezing point and produces heat.
2. A high concentration of salt and alkaline elements: reduces the freezing point.
3. Coalescing matter generates heat.

These three principles allow water to remain in a liquid form without a sun. The Bible tells us that the universe was small at one time. For example, Isaiah 42:5: "The LORD, who created the heavens and stretched them out." Therefore, before God spread out the heavens, they were tightly compressed, which would exert an intense amount of pressure on the "waters" of Gen. 1, keeping a portion of the water in a liquid form. For details, see The First Day chapter.

Consider the expansive salt deposits on the planet: the Sifto Salt mine in Ontario, Canada, the Kewra Salt Mine in Pakistan, and the Wieliczka Salt Mine in Poland, as well as salt deposits under the Great Lakes and in Death Valley, the Dead Sea, and many others around the globe. All of these salt deposits were formed either during the formation of the hot Earth that was surrounded by water (the deeper salt basins), by the process of evaporation, and when the global flood occurred and freezing temperatures froze freshwater out of salty solution (shallower salt basins). Ocean water is 2.17X denser than freshwater, with water having a density of 1,000 kg/m^3 and salt having a density of 2,170 kg/m^3. When salt is diluted as a solute in water, the density of water increases to that of seawater, with a density of 1,035 kg/m^3 (3.5% heavier than fresh water). When the heavy rains came upon the earth in the Genesis flood, that highly salty rainwater saturated the waters below on the earth. After the 40 days and nights of rain, the waters prevailed for 150 days, this caused temperatures to plummet and freshwater began to freeze out of the salty flood waters. This process caused the saltwater near the fresh frozen ice to become saturated with salt. When the water reached a saturation point, which means no more salt could be diluted in the water, then as more water was frozen for the glacial age, the extra salt left behind in the salt water could not dilute into solution, and would sink to the bottom in solid form. This process formed the vast salt deposits.

What does salt have to do with buoyancy and gravity? It means the canopy was not freshwater, but heavier seawater. The salt added to the weight of the canopy hovering around the atmosphere prior to the Flood. Since seawater is 3.5% denser than freshwater, we may conclude that the presence of salt in the canopy added extra weight upon the atmosphere. This means that more pressure was exerted and resulted in a greater buoyancy force and reduced net gravity.

We have discussed how the spin of the earth creates centripetal and centrifugal forces, resulting in weaker net gravity. We have also noted that the moon takes angular momentum out of the spin of the earth, thus, net gravity was weaker in the past. This corresponds with a shorter day duration of ~17 hours for Adam and Eve. Also, that the moon was closer to the earth, reducing the earth's net gravity. We also discussed the notion that space dust adds to the earth's mass and increases gravity and that asteroid impacts affect gravity by adding mass and decreasing spin. Additionally, a faster spinning Earth would have a larger bulge at the equator, which would have reduced the net strength of gravity as one was farther away from the iron core. And lastly, we have described how the buoyancy force from the canopy of salt water hovering above the atmosphere also reduced net gravity. The exact percentage of how much each of those factors would have affected the intensity of gravity is estimated:

Conditional change:	Net change of Gravity:
Faster spin leading to 17 hours for one rotation	1%
Closer moon	1%
Larger Earth radius	1/2%
Asteroid impacts	1/2%
Space debris added to mass	1/10%
Increased O2 in the atmosphere	1/100%
Buoyancy force from the canopy with salt	12–30%
Total reduction of gravity before the Flood	~15.5%–33.5%

Chapter Summary: This chapter discussed the idea that the gravitational force can be reduced or increased depending on the environmental conditions. Also, it propounds that before the Flood of Gen. 7, net Gravity was 15.5% to 33.5% weaker than its strength today, which created an environment in which dinosaurs and humans could thrive. This leads us to the effects of a weaker gravitational system.

Chapter 2
__The Effects of Weaker Gravity on Life__

Now that we have established that gravity was ~15%—33% weaker before the Flood, the question is, "How does that affect life?" The human body is a dynamic system; that is, it is adaptable to various changes in the environment as long as those changes are not too large. We'll focus on specific adaptations of the body to changes in weight exerted on the body to mimic changes in gravity.

To illustrate how gravity affects the weight of a body, let us consider how a person is weighed. Two primary methods exist: pressure-based and mass-based scales. A person's weight is measured by a pressure-based weighing machine, such as the bathroom scales in most homes. With mass-based scales (such as at the doctor's office), a known counterweight is used. The weight is measured in pounds (lb.) or kilograms (kg), but in physics, the unit of measurement for weight is newtons (*force = mass x gravity = ma = m* (m/s^2). Whether we increase the *mass* or increase the *gravity*, the *force* increases proportionately. The force does not know whether it was an increase in *mass* or an increase in *gravity* that caused the force to increase.

Different planets have different densities and different mass, and this affects the intensity of their gravity. But whether someone stands on the sun, the moon, or Earth's equator, the mass of that person remains the same. However, newtons (or how much someone weighs) will vary greatly. Let us see some examples of someone's weight on different planets and see how they vary. For example:

A 100-kg man (220 lb.) weighs <u>16.5 kg</u> (36 lb.) on the **moon**. Mass equals 100 kg.

A 100-kg man (220 lb.) weighs <u>99.5 kg</u> (219 lb.) at the **equator**. Mass equals 100 kg.

A 100-kg man (220 lb.) weighs <u>100.5 kg</u> (221 lb.) at the north **pole**. Mass equals 100 kg.

A 100-kg man (220 lb.) weighs <u>2,804 kg</u> (6,169 lb.) on the **sun**. Mass equals 100 kg.

The following examples below will illustrate that extra axial loads, which mimics increased gravity, placed on the body will cause life to suffer.

When someone is overweight, that puts an extra strain on their knee joints, and they have an increased propensity of having **arthritis**. Arthritic joints are a result of increased wear, increased friction, and subsequent premature break down of the cartilage, synovial fluid, and meniscal material.

Let us say someone is weight lifting, and they are doing leg squats, which puts an increased load on the spine. The extra weight applied to their spine creates axial loads that increase the odds of compromising the integrity of the disc material and causing a **herniated disc**.

When someone is overweight, this usually increases blood pressure because it is harder to push blood longer distances to reach skin. This causes the heart to work harder, which causes it to increase in size (**cardiomegaly**), and can lead to death. This increased blood pressure can cause tiny tubules within the kidneys to spring leaks and rupture. These tiny see-through tubules are used for filtering the impurities out of the blood and discharging those impurities into the bladder for urination. The **diabetic** patient will need blood dialysis to clean out the impurities in the blood or a kidney transplant, or it may lead to premature death.

Another example of the effects of strong gravity on life relates to **height**. If someone is measured in the morning and measured the same day at night, they will be fractionally shorter at the end of the day. Why? Gravity squishes some of the fluid out of the vertebral disc, and each disc is then fractionally smaller. This even affects people in the long term. Older people start to shrink fractionally in size. You'll hear older people say, "I used to be 5 feet 11, but now I'm 5 feet 10."

With a stronger gravitational force, it is harder for a living being to grow to a great height and to live as long as in a weaker gravitational environment. Greater gravity restricts vertical growth and restricts longevity; the greater the gravitational force, the greater the strain on the body to survive. Increased gravity makes it harder for the heart to pump blood throughout the body and harder for the heart to pump blood up against gravity back to the heart. Increased gravity makes it harder for the body to pump interstitial fluid from the lower extremities up to the torso as well. This has a long-term adverse effect on subsequent generations because of mutations in the genome that are passed down to the offspring. For example, an obese person that subsequently suffers from kidney failure and mutates their gene as a result. Then their offspring are utilizing a genome with slight mutations in the DNA information that may impair their kidney function. This is not evolution, this is adaptation (See the Evolution Versus Science chapter). The ability to adapt to changes in the environment is based on the preexisting information in the DNA code. It is not that adaptation produces new information in the DNA that leads to new kinds of creatures, it is that preexisting DNA allows adaption and natural selection to occur. If the environment (mutations and/or natural selection) causes beneficial new information in the DNA that eventually leads to new functions and new kinds of life—then that is evolution.

An increased load on the skeletal system mimics stronger gravity and how that affects bone structure. If someone becomes grossly overweight, the body responds by increasing bone quantity (larger in girth, not length) and quality (denser and less porous) to compensate. Conversely, when people grow old, if they are too skinny, they increase their odds of suffering from osteoporosis (thinning of the bone) and their bones being more porous. With changes in gravity or axial loads acting upon the body, the body responds to changes in stimuli, with the skeletal system proportionately modifying its density and quality of bone structure to compensate for the changes in gravity or axial load. A thinner person simulates a weaker gravity, and the skeletal system will generally be more porous, less dense, and thinner. Conversely, a heavyset person simulates stronger gravity, the skeletal system will generally be denser and thicker.

To illustrate this point, astronaut's height will increase by 3% while in space. Although this is from an elongation of the disc soft tissue between the vertebrea, and not actual bone growth, the principle still holds true that a weaker gravitational force allows life to thrive, exemplified by the increased height.

Review: Increased gravity causes life to suffer, decreased gravity allows life to thrive. **Weaker gravity = more porous bones, and stronger gravity = denser bones.**

Evolutionary paleontologists believe that dinosaurs evolved into birds. Why? The primary reason is that both birds and dinosaurs have porous bone structures. Another one is that they both lay eggs. These notions are easy to dispute; dinosaur are reptiles, and they lay leathery eggs, while birds lay calcium-rich shells. They are different. Dinosaurs primarily have scales, and birds primarily have feathers. It is true that dinosaur bones are porous, and scientists have determined that if dinosaurs were alive today, their bone structure couldn't support their tonnage in today's stronger gravitational system. It is too porous to handle the axial loads.

The fact that **dinosaurs had porous bone** structures indicates that they lived in a weaker gravitational force on earth rather than because they evolved into birds. It is a mistake to think that dinosaurs evolved into birds because they both had porous bone structures when one considers how changes in gravity affect bone quality.

In a diagnostic class in graduate school, my professor said, "When you hear hooves, do not think of birds; think of horses." His point was that just because something is obvious does not make it wrong. Gravity affects our bone density, and dinosaurs had porous bones. Our gravity was weaker in past millennia, and a natural, obvious link exist. Dinosaurs had porous skeletal systems because gravity was weaker. This also explains why we do not see large dinosaurs today because gravity has increased over the millennia, not because dinosaurs evolved into birds.

Not too long ago, evolutionists were very excited to discover a fossil that linked dinosaurs evolving into birds. The archeologist who proclaimed the discovery of the missing link received a lot of accolades. However, it was later proven that the archeologist falsified his data. This infamous scientific hoax of the missing link is called "archaeoraptor."[11] No one will ever find a missing link that dinosaurs evolved into birds. Why? Because they are different kinds. The fertilization process does not cross

---

11 Http://en.wikipedia.org/wiki/Archaeoraptor: "The forgery was constructed from pieces of fossils from different species."

24

different kinds of animals. No fossil record exist of dinosaurs evolving into birds.

Review: Dinosaurs had porous bone structures in accordance with a weaker gravitational force, not because they evolved into birds.

Would the longevity of life increase with a weaker gravity? Let us look at the negative side to help determine the positive side. Increased gravity puts extra strain on the heart because the heart has to work harder to push oxygenated blood up to the upper extremities and the head, and the heart has to work harder to pull deoxygenated blood up from the lower extremities and torso to the heart. This extra load or strain that is because of gravity increases blood pressure. When someone has high blood pressure, this increases the risk of cardiovascular diseases, diabetes, stroke, aneurisms, varicose veins, and the like. Increased gravity causes life to suffer in terms of quality and quantity of years.

Since the negative aspect of increased gravity shortens life, the positive side of the argument should be valid as well. Everyone knows that a well-maintained blood pressure increases the odds of living a long life. A weaker gravity equals reduced blood pressure and less strain on the organs of the body. Therefore, **weaker gravity prolongs life**.

Even the integumentary system (dermis, or skin) is adversely affected by increased gravity. Skin benefits from a weaker gravitational force by less force stretching and pulling down on the skin. Skin that sags has the appearance of someone of old age. Skin can lose its elasticity and its ability to spring back with repeated years of pulling down on it. Well, under a weaker gravitational force, the skin is pulled on less and therefore sags less. This gives the appearance of youthfulness for a longer period of time. Therefore, weaker gravity aids in the quality of life.

Gen. 9:4–6 gives clarity to the significance of blood to life, "Only you shall not eat flesh with its life, that is, it is blood." Also, Leviticus 17:11, "For the life of the flesh is in the blood."

Life is in the blood. An increase in gravity makes it harder for the heart to pump blood throughout the body, and harder for the body to circulate interstitial fluid (fluid in between the cells) and causes such fluid to pool at the ankles. Patients with high blood pressure and circulatory problems, usually from being overweight (mimicking a stronger gravity), suffer from swelling of the ankles. Weaker gravity would alleviate this problem and make life easier to sustain.

When a **fighter jet pilot** pulls a large amount of "G" (Gravity) forces, their blood starts to pool around their lower extremities, and they pass out from a lack of oxygenated blood going to the brain. To combat this, they wear an anti-G suit to squish the lower extremities and abdominal region. This prevents blood from pooling in the legs and abdomen and helps keep the pilot conscious. Therefore, the effects of greater gravity make life harder to sustain.

Astronauts residing in space for a prolonged period of time lose a certain amount of bone mass. To determine the effects of zero gravity on the skeletal system, 13 astronauts stayed aboard the space station's orbiting laboratory for **six months duration**. When they came back down to the earth, they discovered that the average amount of bone mass lost was 14%. Three of the astronauts **lost up to 30% of their bone mass**. The brain perceives that the body does not require high amounts of bone density in a zero-gravity environment, and subsequently the brain signals to reduce the amount of calcium, phosphorus, and magnesium in the bone. The skeletal system adapts (based on existing DNA information) to the reduced gravity and adjusts bone quality, mass, or density to match the reduced loads (gravity), and the bone become more porous. After recovering back on Earth, the astronauts gained back all but 2% of the lost bone density, quality, or mass.[12]

The brain does not know if the changes in axial loads are from changes in gravity or from changes in body mass, it just adapts based on existing DNA and adds more bone mass or reduces bone mass to compensate. The same with the dinosaurs, they did not know they lived in a weaker net gravity, their brains, utilizing existing DNA, reduced the bone density to match the weaker gravity.

Does a change in gravity affect the height of living creatures on the earth? Logically, gravity affects height because growth in height is opposite to gravitational force. Therefore, weaker gravity

---

12 Space.com/6354-space-station-astronauts-lose-bone-strength-fast.html.

makes it easier to grow taller, and stronger gravity makes it harder to grow taller. But let us see if we can wrap our minds around the concept with some examples.

When building a sand castle, one quickly learns the height limitations because of gravity. Also, every sand hourglass demonstrates that the sand won't pile up to a steep angle greater than 34° because of gravity and the friction coefficient of sand. That is a simple way to illustrate that gravity affects the height of living creatures on earth. For if gravity was weaker, then sand would be able to pile up at a steeper angle. And if gravity were stronger, the sand would pile up at a lesser angle.

Another example involves looking at the fastest growing thing on the planet in terms of height. It is **bamboo**, and it can grow up to 3 feet in one day. One of the factors that gives bamboo an edge is that it has a thin-walled cortex and a hollow core. This reduces the amount of weight it has to push up against gravity, thereby reducing the amount of force needed to push it up. When determining force, one multiplies mass x gravity, and the "force" does not know if gravity is reduced or if mass is reduced.

The second fastest growing thing on the planet in terms of height is **kelp**. It can grow up to 1.5 feet per day. One of the factors that gives kelp an edge is buoyancy force. Gravity still remains at ~9.8 m/s/s, and kelp still has mass and can be quite heavy, but the amount of ocean water the kelp displaces weighs more; therefore, the kelp floats.

Take the earth itself as another example. It seems that since gravity can affect earth's terrain and the height of its landscape, then it would definitely affect the living creatures on the earth, as the earth seems less fragile than the life living on the earth. Since the earth is ellipsoid, this is positive evidence that gravity alters the height at which something can grow and the rate at which something grows because it is harder for gravity to affect rock and granite and frozen ice than it is to affect the height of a living organism.

Another example of the power of gravity in counteracting the height of objects is the movement of **glacial ice**. If gravity were super weak, the snow that falls on the North and South Poles would just pile up higher and higher. But because of gravity pulling on the glacial ice, the glaciers actually flow down the mountain through the valleys, just very slowly. Glacial ice can travel 20–30 meters/day.[13]

Since gravity can alter the earth, it can alter the height of something growing on the earth. Since we know gravity was weaker in past millennia, this explains a portion of how dinosaurs grew so large on a porous skeletal system in the past. This is because:

1. There was greater buoyancy force at creation.
2. Net gravity was weaker at creation.
3. Oxygen concentration was higher at creation.

Review: Weaker gravity equals greater height and accelerated vertical growth. But a weaker gravity is not the only cause of accelerated growth—gravity is just a contributory factor. A reduction of Buoyancy force and a reduction of oxygen concentration as a result of the Flood are the primary causes of a decrease in the vertical growth rate. The net effect before the Flood was a weaker downward force on the dinosaur's skeletal system from gravity. This allowed them to grow to great heights and size.

Since humans once lived 900+ years, and gravity was less intense, then why did not they grow 30 feet tall before the Flood? Humans and dinosaurs are not the same kinds of creature. **Dinosaurs are reptiles, and reptiles continue to grow as long as they are alive.**

Reptiles living in a weaker gravity with a greater buoyant force, and increased oxygen in the past, before the Flood, and living a long life span allowed those reptiles to continue to grow as long as they were alive until they became dinosaurs. But humans grow vertically for only a portion of their life. Vertical growth stops when the epiphyseal plates fuse. The epiphyseal plates are primary growth sites at the ends of long bones, and they contribute to the varying heights of humans. These growth plates fuse when the genetic predisposition for maximum height potential has been achieved. This point of cessation of vertical growth can be limited by sickness, disease, nutrition, and injury. Some humans produce a prolonged duration of growth hormones from the endocrine system (hormone production),

---

13 Wikipedia/glaciers.

and they grow slightly taller than other humans. The timing for when the fusion of these epiphyseal plates (cessation of vertical growth) takes place is hardwired in our DNA at around 17–21 years of age for boys and 15–17 years of age for girls. Therefore, this explains why humans never grew 30 feet tall before the Flood. However, because humans lived in a pre-Flood environment (with weaker gravity and an increased oxygen concentration) they did grow to ~10 feet tall (See Denisovan skull in Chapter 24, "Humans Lived 900+ Years and Adaptation from Origins.").

The Bible does talk about giants living at one time. These were men of renown that reached great heights. You may recall David slaying Goliath with a slingshot. Well, Goliath was 9 feet 9 inches tall (I Samuel 17:4): "a champion went out from the camp of the Philistines, named Goliath . . . whose height was six cubits and a span." A cubit is the length of an average forearm, or around 18 inches. And a span was half that at around 9 inches long. But this is not from a pre-Flood environment because this is long after the Flood. According to some Biblical scholars, Goliath comes as an offspring of the Nephilim that survived through the Flood, most likely as one of Noah's daughters-in-law. The Nephilim were children born from male demons that left their proper abode and took daughters of men and bore a half-human, half-demonic race shortly before the Flood (Gen. 6:1–8, Jude 6, and 2 Peter 2:4–5). The Nephilim, a Hebrew word meaning *giants,* went by several names, including Anak (Numbers 13:28 and 32–33). The passage reads, "We saw the giants." Besides Anak, the Nephilim were also called Rephaim, Zuzim, Emim, and Amorites in the Bible. Amos 2:9–10 describes "the Amorites . . . whose height was like the height of the cedars." Deuteronomy 2:10–11 explains that the Emim were as tall as the Anikim (Anak), and the Anikim were giants. Deut. 2:20–21 describes the Zuzim (Zamzummim) as giants, and Deut. 3:11, and 13 and 2 Samuel 21:16–20 describe the Rephaim (Raphah) as giants as well.

Taking the whole, the Nephilim, the giants were likely a combination of demonic DNA and buoyancy force, weak gravity, and increased oxygen concentration.

The Bible gives the ages of life of the genealogies from Adam to Joseph. A pattern is revealed when studying the ages. The average age of life from creation to the Flood is around 900+ years. Then the Flood comes, and the ages dramatically reduce. Look at the list of people who lived after the Flood:

Noah lived	950 years (Gen. 9:29).
Noah's son Shem lived	600 years (Gen. 11:10–11).
Shem's son Arpachshad lived	438 years (Gen. 11:12–13).
Arpachshad's son Shelah lived	433 years (Gen. 11:14–15).
Shelah's son Eber lived	464 years (Gen. 11:16–17).
Eber's son Peleg lived	239 years (Gen. 11:18–19).
Peleg's son Reu lived	239 years (Gen. 11:20–21).
Reu's son Serug lived	230 years (Gen. 11:22–23).
Serug's son Nahor lived	148 years (Gen. 11:24–25).
Nahor's son Terah lived	205 years (Gen. 11:32).
Terah's son Abram/Abraham lived	175 years (Gen. 25:7).
Abraham's son Isaac lived	180 years (Gen. 35:28–29).
Isaac's son Jacob lived	147 years (Gen. 47:28).
Jacob's son Joseph lived	110 years (Gen. 50:26).

The Bible does not directly say that the ages of mankind's life span dropped because of the decrease in buoyancy force, oxygen levels, or the increase in net gravity. We have to use deduction to put the pieces together. And here are the pieces: Before the Flood, a canopy surrounding the atmosphere, which resulted in global temperate temperatures, no deserts, no polar ice caps, smaller seas, and no oceans. This led to superabundant vegetation, which led to high oxygen production, increased atmosphere density and weight. This led to an increased buoyancy force, which led to a reduced net gravity. With net gravity weaker, this allowed living beings to live longer and grow larger.

Then a catastrophic event, the global flood, came roughly 4,500 years ago, resulting in the loss of the canopy. During the Flood, there were very high temperatures from asteroid impacts, which fractured Pangaea, which caused water to burst out of the crust from the fountains of the deep. This led to hundreds of volcanic eruptions and fast tectonic plate movements. The floodwater was mixed with sand, silt, rock, clay, dirt, soil, vegetation, and biomass, and this caused the formation of oceans and the formation of all fossils, petroleum, petrified rocks, coal, ice ages, and polar ice caps. Oceans limit vegetation growth, resulting in reduced O2 production. Losing the protection of the canopy of water meant the beginning of deserts, which also limit vegetation growth and reduce O2 production levels. The formation of polar ice and equatorial heat caused the initiation of trade wind, the hydrological cycle, rainbows, clouds, and rain. The loss of the canopy of water allowed solar energy, x-rays, cosmic rays, and gamma rays to penetrate Earth's surface, and increase harmful genetic mutations, that result in diseases, and a reduction of quantity and quality of life. All life had to adapt to the changes, and human beings lived shorter lives of around ~80 years (Psalm 90:10). The adaptation of life to these changes caused a reduction in life span and the size of living creatures.

With reduced life spans, creatures that continue to grow as long as they live, only have decades of growth instead of a millennium of growth. Therefore, creatures that share similarities with dinosaurs and pre-historic creatures, such as the crocodile, alligator, Komodo dragon, great white shark, and so on, are still living amongst us, but they are just much smaller than when their ancestors. All life will once again return to the same longevity, and it will be based on the DNA code that is already in us that allows life to adapt to a favorably new environment. Humans will live 900+ years again (Isaiah 65:20).

Review: The Bible is clear that humans lived 900+ years before the Flood, and their life spans gradually declined to around 80 years (Psalm 90:10). This is clearly a result of the Flood of Gen. 7 and the changes caused by reduced buoyancy force, increased gravity, and decreased oxygen concentrations.

The Bible explains that all of creation was physically adversely affected by sin so that creation groans and suffers and longs to be free from the physical bondage of sin (Romans 8:18–25). The whole of creation will be free from the physical bondage of sin again one day in the future, just like it was at creation. What will this look like? Ecclesiastes 1:9 tells us:

That which **has been** is that which **will be**, and that which **has been done** is that which **will be done**.

Let us take a detour and look at some examples: Humans once lived 900+ years and will return to living 900+ years (Isaiah 65:20), and at creation all creatures were herbivores (Genesis 1:29–30) and will be again (Isaiah 11:6–10). Gen. 1–3 discusses a new heaven and new earth, and Revelation 21–22 also mentions a new heaven and a new earth. In Gen. 2, the Garden of Eden had special trees in the midst of the garden that were unique and were called the trees of life. In Revelation 22, after sin has been completely resolved, a tree of life exists in the midst of Jerusalem again bearing 12 kinds of fruit and yielding its fruit every month, and the leaves of the tree are for the healing of nations. In the midst of the Garden of Eden (Gen. 2), there was a river that flowed out of the garden to water the land. During the reign of God over Jerusalem in Revelation 21–22, two rivers flow from the mount of God, one to the west (Zachariah 14:4) and one to the east (Ezekiel 47) to water and heal the land and restore it to pre-fallen conditions. Before the fall of Adam and Eve in Gen. 3, no curse existed; after the completion of the restoration in Revelation 22, no curse exist. After the fall of Adam and Eve, their son Cain killed Abel and God gave Cain a devastating mark; fast-forward to the end times, at the peak of evil, and mankind will take the mark of the beast. In the Garden of Eden of Gen. 6, Noah had 120 years of preparation before the judgment and deliverance and the promise land, and Israel had 120 years of Moses' life for judgment of the 10 plagues, deliverance from slavery, and the promise land. God dwelt with mankind before the fall, walking in the garden in Gen. 1–3, and God dwells on earth in Revelation 21–22. The first kingdom that fell (Gen. 10–11) was The Tower of Babel (the home of Babylon) with Queen Semiramus, who was titled the Queen of Heaven. It was said that she was the mother of all false religions. The last kingdom that falls (Revelation 18) is Babylon, the mother of all harlot false religions, the alleged Queen of Heaven. Joseph, in Gen. 37–50, parallels Jesus; both shepherded their father's sheep, and their fathers loved them dearly. They were hated by their brothers and plotted harm against them, and both were sold for the price of a slave (30 pieces of silver), tempted, and falsely accused. Both also started their ministry at the age of 30, Joseph as second only to Pharaoh, and Jesus second only to the Father, both as king of their people, and both saved people from death (physically from starvation in the case of Joseph and spiritually from hell in the case of Jesus). Jesus, before the start of His ministry, fasted for 40 days in the wilderness and was tempted, after His ministry, He was tempted at His crucifixion and remained 40 days after His resurrection. God created everything in six days for mankind and declared it was complete and rested on the seventh day (Gen. 1–2). God hung on the cross for six hours to save mankind and declared "it is finished" as He entered the seventh hour of rest (John 19:30). God sustains His creation for 6,000 years to reconcile mankind, and He declares "it is done" and reigns the 7000th year (Revelation 16:17 and 21:6). If we know how things will be, we'll know how things were and vice versa.

Does this mean that net gravity will be weaker again and buoyant force will be stronger? Yes. Will the canopy of ice and salt water surround the atmosphere again? Yes. How? A cataclysmic event is scheduled to occur soon, which we know from Revelation as seals, trumpets, and bowls, a series of judgments of catastrophic proportions that include asteroids crashing into the earth. The impact splits the earth asunder and it wobbles like a drunkard, like a slow spinning top (Isaiah 24:18–19). This should cause the ocean waters to pour into the super hot magma; this expels all the ocean water back up into space—where they were before the Flood, some of that water does not get high enough and comes back down as 100-pound hailstones. The water shooting up acts like a jet engine, and this results in the earth spinning faster. This restores the canopy and the environment back to creation days, with roughly 17 hour days. Revelation 16:17–21 adds some more details:

> There were flashes of lightning and sounds and peals of thunder; and there was a great earthquake, such as there had not been since man came to be upon the earth, so great an earthquake, so mighty. The great city was split into three parts . . . every island fled away, and the mountains were not found. And huge hailstones, about 100 pounds each, came down from heaven upon men.

That is the sound that asteroids make entering our atmosphere traveling at 30,000 mph. This would result in a new Earth, where there would be no ocean and a new heaven. Revelation 21:1: "Then I saw a new heaven and a new earth; for the first heaven and the first earth passed away, and there is no longer any sea (oceans)." There will be ample freshwater lakes, rivers, and seas, but no oceans. Just like at creation. As a result of the canopy being restored, this would also restore the buoyancy force and reduce net gravity, and with no oceans, then an increase of surface land exposed for vegetation, this would also increase oxygen levels back to pre-Flood conditions, thus causing life to thrive and humans to live 900+ years again and allowing reptiles to grow to dinosaurs again.

Chapter Summary: Human beings once lived 900+ years, and that day will return again when Jesus returns and the Revelation judgments are finished. Increased gravity adversely affects living creatures. The increased net downward pull of gravity has reduced the rate of growth, the height of living things, and life expectancy. Increased gravity even affects the terrain of the earth and the shape of the earth, changing it from spherical (like a ball) to ellipsoidal (a ball that is slightly fatter at the equator and squished at the poles). The Flood caused a reduction of buoyancy force, increased gravity, and decreased oxygen, which adversely affected life. Dinosaurs did not evolve into birds; they lived in weaker gravity and stronger buoyancy, which allowed the dinosaurs to have porous bone structures because skeletal structures become thicker with increased gravity and become more porous with a decrease in gravity.

Chapter 3
The Canopy

Before the global flood, the earth's environment was slightly different than today. For example, oxygen concentration was higher, the atmosphere was denser, a larger buoyant force, weaker net gravity, more usable land for vegetation, no oceans (only seas that were smaller in volume), no polar ice caps, no tornadoes, no hurricanes, no forest fires from lightning, no deserts, no four seasons, and no hydrological cycle to produce clouds or rain.

Only one thing that can cause all the above to exist; it is the canopy of water that surrounded earth's atmosphere. The canopy existed from the second day of creation until the global flood at ~2,348 BC. The two dimensional cross sections below, is to illustrate that the canopy was initially spherical around the atmosphere and morphed over time to a disk-like shape.

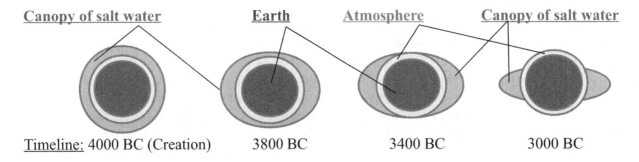

This is not a vapor canopy concept. Therefore, if anyone uses the arguments against a vapor canopy against a literal ice and salt water canopy, they are merely using a *straw man* argument.

Genesis 7 is the record of the canopy coming down upon the earth for 40 days and 40 nights that changed the environmental conditions on earth to our present environment. This resulted in increased gravity, decreased buoyancy force, decreased oxygen concentration, and a reduction in the longevity and size of life.

How do we know that a canopy existed? First, we must start from the beginning before the earth and galaxies were finished forming. In the beginning, God created (from His essence) all the matter and energy, in a confined space. At this moment, water and dirt were tightly packed. Though there was darkness, all the future stars, planets, and moons, were coalescing (gathering matter), and this caused heat. On the outside of the small universe, away from the hot coalescing future stars, there was an external shell of thick ice, this sealed in the pressure and allowed heat and charge to build. The combination of heat and pressure, allowed for water to exist in liquid form, and the earth was without its finished form. That is the first hours of the first day of creation. Let us focus on the water.

Where was the water located? The water was located throughout a small universe and in our even smaller solar system. At this point in Gen. 1:2, all celestial bodies looked like hurricanes gathering matter without their finished form, and the universe was squished to the size of many galaxies. Gen. 1:2 says, "The earth was formless and void, and darkness was over the surface of the <u>deep</u>, and the Spirit of God was moving over the surface of the <u>waters</u>." Why is *waters* plural? This probably refers to the four forms that water exists in: liquid, solid, gas, and plasma, and to the abundance of water. The word *deep* could refer to abundant waters. Gen. 7:11 cites the "fountains of the deep." Most theologians agree that the meaning is vast caverns of water. However, other words are included within the definition of *deep* that lend a broader view; for example, *deep* also implies: an abyss (as a surging mass of water), main sea or deep subterranean water supply, a deep place, and depth (Strong's Concordance #8415). Therefore, volcanoes fits the description of Genesis 7:11, and is an acceptable option.

Let us venture into some chemistry and physics to determine how water could exist in four forms (solid, liquid, gas, and plasma) before the formation of the sun, moon, and stars to warm it. A simple twofold solution exists to this problem. The first is salt and minerals. Water freezes at 0 degrees Celsius (32 degrees Fahrenheit) when it is pure H2O. But if we add NaCl (sodium chloride), this lowers the freezing point, and saturated salt water will freeze at -21°C / -5.8°F.

Before the fall of mankind, no death existed until sin enter the world (Romans 5:12). The Dead Sea could not have existed before the fall of mankind because nothing lives in it. It is an example of death. Therefore, the Dead Sea was formed after the fall of mankind and most likely from the Flood. My contention is that the Dead Sea and some of the saltiness of the oceans and the vast shallow salt deposits underground were created as a result of the Flood. The deeper salt deposits were formed from the formation of the hot Earth while it was surrounded by salt water. This environment caused evaporation, which separated freshwater away from the salt, this resulted in large deeper salt basins that are pure salt. This also resulted in freshwater being closest to the earth's surface (such as the fountains of the deep) and saltiest water being furthest away from the earth (such as the canopy of salt water) during the first two days of creation.

Imagine all the salt in the Dead Sea, the salt beds of Death Valley California, the salt deposits under the Great Lakes, all the salt mined by mankind, and some of the salt from the oceans stored up above the atmosphere in this canopy of salt water. Not only Na (sodium) but also other alkaline elements existed in the canopy, including Ca (calcium), Cl (chloride), SO4 (sulfate), Mg (magnesium), and K (potassium). With the combination of these alkaline elements in the canopy of salt water, this explains how water could remain in a liquid form without having the sun to warm it.

Review: A watery brine significantly lowered the freezing point down to -21°C.
I do not believe that freshwater rained down during the Flood, I contend it was salt water. This explains where the salt came from to form the Dead Sea, the salt beds of Death Valley, the salt deposits under the Great Lakes, and the salty oceans. This also explains how marine dinosaurs could have died off from a global flood. Why else would a marine or aquatic creature die because of more water? Marine life is sensitive to changes in the alkalinity, change too much and they will die. Potentially, the seas that were formed on the third day of creation were only 1% salt concentration, and some great sea creatures were not able to adapt to the change from 1% salty seas to the newly formed oceans (3.5% salt). During the Flood, so many volcanoes erupted and asteroids hit the earth that actual trauma or acid waters would have killed many creatures too.

How did the salt get collected together in some locations? Toward the end of the Flood saga, as temperatures dropped from intense heat to freezing because the globe was covered in water for 150 days, ice formed. When the ice formed, it was fresh water, thus leaving behind salt to saturate regions where the ice formed. With those areas saturated with salty waters, no more salt could be added to solution, thus it descended to the bottom in solid form and piled up where the ice was forming. The freezing of fresh water out of the salty floodwater, increased the oceans salt concentration to 3.5%, which killed off some water-dwelling creatures that couldn't handle the sudden increase in salt.

Review: Before the earth and atmosphere were formed, water and dirt existed; the dirt was formless. Formless means the earth was still coalescing matter together as it spun. The water existed in four forms (liquid, solid, gas, and plasma) and was very abundant. Some water remained in a liquid form partially because of the salt concentration in the very small universe before there were any stars, moons, and suns to provide heat, which also explains where all the salt came from on the earth.

What about before the sun and stars were finished forming, that is, on the first three days of creation? Space gets much colder than -21°C. The answer is pressure, friction, and heat. At this point in time (before the sun, moon, and stars had finished gathering matter), the universe was densely compact, and trillions of future stars were spinning, coalescing matter, and glowing hot from the middle of the first day until they ignited on the fourth day. The universe was much smaller in size than the vast spread-out size of our current universe. How do we know this?

For one thing, science has determined that the universe is still expanding and appears to be expanding at an accelerated rate away from a central location, potentially our Milky Way galaxy. The other way of knowing the universe is expanding is that the Bible explains that God spread out the universe (Isaiah 40:22), which means that it was densely packed at one time. Lots of pressure would have been required for water to have been in a liquid form in the coldness of space before the completed formation of the sun, moon, and stars. High pressure reduces the freezing point and generates heat.

Changes in pressure alter the freezing point, the boiling point, and the vapor point of water. With increased pressure exerted, the boiling point of water is higher and the freezing point is lower, and with lower pressure exerted, this raises the freezing point and lowers the boiling point of water. Since *waters* is plural in Gen. 1:2, then there was enough pressure and heat generated to not only keep water in liquid form, but also to turn water into gas and plasma. Both lead to expansion, but couldn't because the outside shell of this small, dense universe was solid frozen ice that was not near a heat source. This closed, sealed container called the universe, built up heat, pressure, and electrical charge as trillions of spinning balls of matter (eventual stars) coalesced into spinning plasma and magma (liquid matter) that each started to glow (at the middle of the first day of creation) from God saying, "Let there be light." Heat, pressure, and electrical charge grew to unsustainable proportions because of the solid ice outer shell, and this caused trillions of simultaneous Big Bangs (on the second day of creation); this sudden expansion caused cavitation (sudden release of pressure forms air bubbles) of the water surrounding every planet, leading them to form atmospheres. Physics explains that when a sudden release of pressure occurs in water, such as the second Big Bangs (the beginning of the second day of creation) would generate, then an instantaneous conversion of liquid to gas occurs; that would be our atmosphere (on the latter half of the second day of creation). This process is called cavitation, which is illustrated every time we open a new soda bottle. The release of the cap (Big Bang) violently converts liquid to gas because of a sudden reduction in pressure. This is also observed with the bends in scuba divers.

An example of how pressure alters the freezing point: an ice skater's blades are said to instantly liquify the ice when the blades touch the ice due to the high amount of pressure. To have lots of pressure in a small universe, it had to be densely packed. Maybe our entire universe was compressed into the size of a couple of hundred galaxies worth. It is not logical for all the universe to be have been compressed into the size of a dot, as Big Bang theorists hypothesize. It would require too much energy, intelligence, and design, to organize and compress all matter into an area the size of a dot as energy. Some cosmologists estimate that the temperature just prior to the Big Bang was 5.5×10^{28} °C. To put that in perspective, the sun is only 1.5×10^6 °C.[14]

Ice volcanoes exist on Saturn's moons Titan and Encelladus. Cosmologists have determined that as a result of their elliptical orbits around Saturn, the tidal and gravitational forces have built up friction and heat and melted water below the surface. Titan and Encelladus are too far away from the sun to be warmed, and they do not have atmospheres to contain warmth. Yet, because of tidal friction, they have liquid below its surface. This is similar to the principle of the canopy of water having a liquid internal reservoir, perhaps like the friction caused on Saturn's moons, but from the moon's gravity causing tides within the canopy itself, and from pressure generating heat. Also, thermal radiation from the sun would be absorbed by the canopy, which would keep the interior reservoir liquid. Tidal friction from elliptical orbits also explains why the earth is continuously warming. The cause is not man-made.

Review: Before God stretched out the universe, it was densely packed, and this resulted in high pressure. The high pressure reduced the freezing point of water and resulted in heat generation from friction. This kept water in a liquid state at the center of the compression and frozen on the outer shell. This correlates to the middle of the first day of creation.

When was the canopy of salt water formed, and how was it formed? The universe was expanded on the first half of the second day of creation (Genesis 1:6), which caused the atmosphere to expand on the second half of the second day (verses 7–10):

---

14 Cosmologist Ethan Siegel science blog "Starts with a Bang!" October 15, 2012.

6 Then God said, "Let there be an expanse in the midst of the waters, and let **it** separate the waters from the waters,"

This first expanse is the universe. Scientists have discovered that water was once every throughout the universe.[15] After all, hydrogen is the most abundant element in the universe. The stars, planets, and moons exist in this heaven. When the universe expanded, **it** separated the waters from the waters that surrounded every celestial body via the process called cavitation. This means gases formed between the waters that once surrounded every celestial body, which are atmospheres of varying types. When the universe expanded, this reduced the extreme pressure from a tightly compact universe to zero pressure. As a result, abundant amount of gas formed between the waters and this is how our atmosphere formed.

The first expanse, the universe (the Big Bangs), is what caused our atmosphere to form. Although the sun, moon, and stars are not fully formed (ignited) until the fourth day, God initiated the expansion of the universe that caused the expanse of the atmosphere. No reason exist to think that God would not have stretched-out the universe, galaxies, solar systems, and every celestial body's atmosphere in the same manner, by separating the waters above from the waters below. A tightly packed universe, with a shell of thick ice surrounding it, would increase internal pressure as coalescing stars vaporized water. As each coalescing future star rotated liquid metal, this caused electrons to flow and build up a charge. This unstable build up of electricity and electromagnetism, would have caused violent lightning discharge to spread throughout the densely packed universe. Thus, instantly vaporizing water and increasing the pressure. Another vital component in the violent expansion of the universe is the reaction of Alkali Metals (Lithium, Sodium, Potassium, Rubidium, Cesium, and Francium) with water. Tiny amounts of these metals cause a TNT like explosion with water. These metals are abundant enough to represent ~5% of earth's crust. With such low melting (180 °C to 28 °C) and boiling points (1342 °C to 944 °C), these metals would be separated from other sediment, leading to being in contact with water by the second day of creation and resulting in violent explosions that expanded the universe.[16] When the internal pressure exceeded the tensile strength of the exterior shell of ice, the universe violently expanded (trillions of Big Bangs), this sudden release of pressure in the expanding universe, caused the water surrounding the earth (includes every planet and moon that had water surrounding it) to instantly vaporize into gas. This process is called cavitation, and is seen every time a soda bottle is initially opened and pressure is released. Potentially, every planet in the universe may have had waters above and waters below its atmosphere at its origin. However, conditions were not favorable for retention of their atmosphere, or of their waters.

7 God made the expanse, and separated the waters which were below the expanse from the waters which were above the expanse; and it was so. 8 God called the expanse heaven. And there was evening and there was morning a second day. 9 Then God said, "Let the waters below the heavens be gathered into one place and let the dry land appear"; and it was so. 10 God called the dry land earth, and the gathering of the waters He called seas.

Later on, God places birds in this second expanse/heaven. Therefore, this expanse is our atmosphere, and the text is clear that water existed below and above the atmosphere. If this isn't clear enough to show that water existed around the atmosphere and around the universe, consider Psalm 148:4, which says, "Praise Him Highest heavens, and the waters, that are above the heavens!" And 2 Peter 3:5 says, "The earth was formed out of water and by water." By now, there should be no doubt that the Bible declares that a canopy of water existed around the atmosphere.

The creation of the atmosphere was a result of God utilizing natural and supernatural processes. For example, the matter that He supernaturally created at the beginning of the first day, He did so with

---

15 Www.blog.nationalgeographic.org/2010/03/22/in-space-theres-water-everywhere/.
16 www.wikipedia.com/alkali-metals.

rotational motion already established for each celestial body, and they immediately began coalescing matter. With enough mass coalesced, the spinning matter began to glow hot from magma at the middle of the first day. Pressure, heat, and electrical charge continued building until the frozen exterior shell of the small universe could not contain the immense internal forces, and trillions of Big Bangs occurred at the beginning of the second day of creation. This rapid expansion caused cavitation and the instantaneous release of pressure on the liquid that surrounded Earth, and this caused our liquid atmosphere to instantly turn to gas with water below and water above at the middle of the second day.

After God created the atmosphere and the canopy of salt water hovering around the atmosphere, what kept the water suspended in space and hovering around the atmosphere? Why did not the canopy come crashing down upon the earth immediately? There were five contributing factors: distance, buoyancy force, the arch/ice support, the spin of the earth, and covalent bonds.

Distance: The greater the distance from earth, the weaker gravity becomes by a factor of 4π squared because of the inverse square law. This means that the farther the distance from the source of gravity, the greater the area that gravity's energy is shared by or divided by, and thus, the weaker gravity's force would be. Therefore, the farther away the canopy of salt water was from the earth's iron core, the weaker gravity's force would be. Look at the acceleration due to gravity at various altitudes:

Altitude	Gravity (m/s/s)
0	9.81
31 km = 20 miles	9.74* 1% weaker gravity
62.5 km	9.67
125 km = 77.5 miles	9.50* 3.2% weaker
250 km = 155 miles	9.19
1,000 km= 621miles	7.33

This table above illustrates how gravity gets weaker the farther away something is from the surface of the earth. One of the ways of keeping the canopy hovering around the atmosphere is simply by placing it at a certain distance from the earth's gravitational force. *Image credit: World-builders.org. Charter College, Cal. St. Univ., Los Angeles.*

The **exosphere** extends 640 to 64,000 km or 400 to 40,000 miles above earth. This is too far away for the canopy to cause buoyancy force.

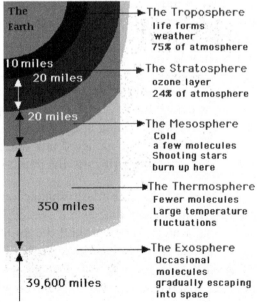

The **thermosphere** extends 80 to 640 km or 50 to 400 miles above earth; solar radiation absorption here = 230°C (440°F). Heat for the liquid inner reservoir.

The **mesosphere** extends 50 to 80 km (31 to 50 miles) above the earth; at -90°C (-130°F), space debris burns up and shooting stars blaze. A possible location of the canopy to compress the atmosphere down to this altitude, exert buoyancy force, and remain elevated until the global flood.

The **stratosphere** extends 16 to 50k m (10 to 31 miles) above the earth; this is a protective area where the ozone layer floats and 20% of the molecules in the atmosphere exist; here, the air gets warmer. Another possible altitude for the canopy, here it would exert greater buoyancy force, as the atmosphere would be denser.

The **troposphere extends** up to 16 km (10 miles) above the earth; it is where weather forms and storms grow. It contains 75% of the molecules in the atmosphere. The troposphere extends 8 km (5 miles) up from the North and South Poles and 16 km (10 miles) up at the equator. The different altitudes are from the spin of the earth and resultant centripetal force. It gets cold near the top.

The physical weight of the canopy of water uniformly pushing down on the atmosphere would have increased the buoyancy force and reduced the net gravitational effect. The canopy of water would not need to be 600 miles away from earth, but maybe in the mesosphere around 40–50 miles from earth's surface, which would only make gravity 1.5% weaker. This isn't much by itself, but it does contribute.

Buoyancy Force: The pressure exerted from the canopy of water pushed down upon the atmosphere, causing the atmosphere to be compressed. This increased the density of the atmosphere and increased pressure, which created a buoyancy force that counteracted gravity. A principle in physics can be applied to reveal a mystery of the suspended canopy. It suggests that for every action, there is an equal and opposite reaction. Therefore, as the canopy pushed down on the atmosphere, there came a point of homeostasis where the atmosphere pushed back up upon the canopy with the same force. Thus, an equilibrium occurred in which the weight of the canopy was equal to the pressure of the atmosphere's push upwards; thus, the atmosphere held the canopy in place by the buoyancy force. This principle alone is enough to account for the canopy hovering in the stratosphere.

As a result of the increased atmospheric pressure, this prevented clouds from forming,[17] which means no rain and no rainbows. When evaporation occurred, the moisture turned to gas, and in the cool of the night as the atmosphere contracted, dew (the mist of Genesis 2:6) was deposited on the ground.

Arch/Ice Support: During the first day of creation, the water around the earth would be all liquid from the heat and pressure, encompassing the earth with no air surrounding the earth. But after the violent expansions (Big Bangs), and sudden release of pressure, resulted in a rapid expansion to form the atmosphere—via the process of cavitation, the outer and inner portions of the canopy would be subject to freezing temperatures. Thus, the exterior portion of the canopy would be frozen almost instantly, except the interior portion of the canopy would still be liquid. Since the canopy of water was spherical on the second day of creation, with a frozen exterior and inner circumference (and an internal liquid reservoir), it would act as a support bridge holding itself up. An example of this is an igloo. Eskimos use an arch method and build a house completely out of ice with no other supports, and their igloos can withstand gravity and severe arctic blizzards. When a crack occurred in the canopy near the equator because of tidal expansion from the moon and sun, the liquid interior reservoir would fill the crack and be resealed via the cold. Thus the spherical canopy morphed toward a bulge at the equator with each rotation of the canopy with the earth and lunar tide.

Architects will tell you that the strongest structures have arches. Have you connected the link between the Hebrew word for firmament/expanse in Gen. 1:6 with the word *arch*? One of the definitions for firmament/expanse in Hebrew is "arch in the sky." Strong's Concordance #7549 defines *raqiya* as an expanse, that is, as the firmament or (apparently) <u>visible arch of the sky</u>. The continuous arch of water (ice) surrounding the atmosphere would be suspended in space by its own support system and other contributing factors countering the force of Earth's gravity.

Spin of the earth: The other means of keeping this canopy of salt water hovering around the atmosphere would be the spin of the earth.

At the beginning of creation on the first day, the waters that were to become the canopy and the atmosphere and the seas, and the matter that would form the earth, they were already set in motion and spinning. This is illustrated by the words "evening and morning first day," and by "x" day, which indicates that everything dealing with the earth was rotating before the earth was finished forming. Cosmologists accept that each celestial body was spinning as it accreted (gathered) matter, much like a hurricane. Therefore, when the atmosphere and canopy were created on the second day of creation, they too were rotating in harmony with the forming earth because of friction, gravity, covalent bonds. Like Saturn and its rings, they spin together. An example of this would be to take a cup of water and start rotating the cup. Eventually, the water in the cup will spin with the cup.

The earth is spinning 1,037 mph today (with a radius of 6,371 km), but back 6,000 years ago, the length of a day was ~ 17 hours, which means that the earth spun ~1,600 mph+ (incorporating a 10%

---

17 Science360/Formation of high pressure weather systems: High pressure prevents cloud formation.

increase in circumference due to a closer moon and faster spin, thus a radius of ~7,000 km). Currently, the entire depth of the atmosphere is estimated at 1,000 km, or 621 miles. It is unknown as to where our atmosphere actually stops because the higher up in altitude, the fewer the air molecules, and no defining edge exist. We'll have to play around with the numbers and give it our best estimate to determine the rotational velocity of the canopy.

With canopy hovering at an altitude of   1,000 km (**621 miles**)
+ the radius of the earth at creation with a faster spin and ~17 hr day: ~7,000 km (4,347 miles)
Total radius of the earth, atmosphere, and canopy   =   8,000 km (4,968 miles)
Total diameter of the earth, atmosphere, and canopy =   16,000 km (9,936 miles)

The formula for determining the circumference is $C = \pi \times$ diameter, where
$C = 3.14 \times 16,000$ km $= 50,265$ km (31,215 miles) the canopy at an altitude of 1,000 km, and
The formula for determining the rotational velocity of the canopy is $V = D/T$, where
$V = 50,265$ km (31,215 miles) / 17 hours = ~2,956 kmph (~1,836 mph).

At this altitude, there may not be a 1:1 rotation velocity that matches the earth's rotational velocity, but friction would keep it close. However, gravity at this altitude is very weak at only 0.13 m/s/s (roughly 1.3% of surface strength). And considering the spin produces centripetal force that tends to counteract gravity, and presuming a 17-hour day (length of a day around the time of creation), the earth spinning at 1,690 mph would produce the following centripetal force:

$$\frac{4 \times 3.14^2 \times 50,265 \text{ km}}{61,200 \text{ sec}^2} = 0.53 \text{ m/s/s centripetal force}$$

Gravity at that altitude is 0.13 m/s/s – 0.53 m/s/s centripetal force = the canopy flying off into space because the centripetal force is greater than gravity. **Therefore, the canopy of water could not be 621 miles away from the earth. Let us** try an altitude of 62 miles above the earth's surface:

With the canopy hovering at an altitude of   100 km (**62.1 miles**)
+ the radius of the earth at creation with a faster spin and ~17 hr day: ~7,000 km (4,347 miles)
Total radius of the earth, atmosphere, and canopy   =   7,100 km (4,409 miles)
Total diameter of the earth, atmosphere, and canopy =   14,200 km (8,818 miles)

The formula for determining the circumference is $C = \pi \times$ diameter, where
$C = 3.14 \times 14,200$ km $= 44,611$ km (27,703 miles) the canopy at an altitude of 100 km, and
The formula for determining the rotational velocity of the canopy is $V = D/T$, where
$V = 44,611$ km (27,703 miles) / 17 hours = ~2,624 kmph (~1,630 mph), and
The formula for determining centripetal force is $4 \times Pi \times$ circumference / time^2

$$\frac{4 \times 3.14^2 \times 44,611 \text{ km}}{61,200 \text{ sec}^2} = 0.47 \text{ m/s/s centripetal force, and}$$

The formula for the strength of gravity at 100 km altitude with spin is 9.55 m/s/s – 0.47 m/s/s centripetal force from spin = 9.08 m/s/s, which means that gravity is 7.5% reduced at a 100 km altitude with the earth and canopy spinning fast enough for 17- hour days. This is not enough by itself to prevent the canopy from raining down upon the earth, but it does contribute.

Since the Hebrew word for expanse/firmament means "a visible arch in the sky." This supports the hypothesis that as the earth spun, then so too did the canopy of waters. The combination of the moon's gravity and centripetal force resulted in moving water from the poles of the canopy toward the equator. This would cause the shape of the canopy to morph toward a disc shape. Initially, on the second day of creation, the canopy would be a perfect sphere, but as time passed, cracks would occur in the exterior shell of the canopy closest to the equator; the liquid interior water would fill those gaps, and the spherical canopy would gradually morph to an equatorial bulge. The more that water accumulated above the equator, the more visible an arch would be. During the life of Adam and Eve, most likely they observed a thickening of the equatorial bulge over time that eventually formed a visible arch in the sky from water accumulation. This process continued for each planet in the universe, until some formed rings like Saturn; some lost all that water, and one in particular (the earth) maintained an arch in the sky made of ice (with an internal liquid reservoir) just in time for the Flood.

Covalent Bonds: These are the bonds on a molecular level that bind the water molecule H_2O (hydrogen and oxygen) together. They are bonded and held together by mutual attraction and shared electrons in the same valence (the orbit of electrons from the nucleus). Covalent bonds is not the strongest force in the universe by any means, but its bond is strong enough that we can make water flow up against gravity by water's connective properties of bonding. Thus, with the instant formation of ice on the exterior of the canopy because of the cold of space, the interior liquid reservoir of the canopy would have an affinity to cling tightly to the solid support arch of the ice and thus suspend the entire canopy of salt water in space surrounding our atmosphere.

As the ocean tides are affected by the moon's gravity, so too would the canopy be affected. However, the canopy was floating on air. Therefore, as the canopy spun, the side that was closest to the moon would be drawn toward the moon and slightly slide away from the earth, and conversely, since the canopy moved as one unit, the opposite side would slide closer to earth.

Review: The canopy of salt water was held in place at its designated altitude by its distance from earth, its spin, a frozen arch support, the buoyancy force of the atmosphere, and the covalent bonds of water itself.

As the canopy thinned at the poles and thickened above the equator, there came a point when the atmosphere was able to escape through holes in the canopy at the polar regions. This would cause the atmospheric pressure to slowly decrease over centuries. Could this have initially occurred when Adam and Eve sinned, and the reduced pressure allowed plants and weeds to grow thorns? Perhaps.

Notwithstanding, eventually the canopy was no longer held up by the buoyancy of the atmosphere. Thus only the frozen structural arch support prevented the canopy from raining down on the earth. An arch of ice and liquid was suspended around the atmosphere until meteors and asteroids came crashing down through the icy arch of the canopy, breaking the entire support structure, allowing gravity to bring down all that water in 40 days and nights of rain upon the earth. The inundation of meteors and asteroids coming down upon the earth could have been the means that God used to initiate the rain that led to the Flood. And these asteroids crashing down upon the crust of the earth would have caused deep caverns of water hidden under the crust of the earth to burst violently into the atmosphere (Gen. 7:11) and crack the shell of Pangaea.

The Bible uses the word *expanse* to describe the location of where our atmosphere is and where the sun, moon, and stars are located. Why? The Hebrew word for expanse is *raqiya*, which means extended surface, expanse, firmament, or visible arch of the sky (Strong's Concordance #7549) (the vault of heaven supporting the waters above). The root word of *raqiya* is *raqa*, which means to expand (by hammering), to make broad, or to stretch. The idea behind the words *raqiya/expanse/firmament/heaven* is that God violently stretched out space much like a blacksmith would violently stretch out metal, not that metal exist in the sky, but it is how God did it with sparks flying from the violence of the rapid expansion.

Review: When God created the atmosphere, He created it in the "midst of the waters." This means that it was in a middle position, in the center, or having the condition of being surrounded or beset by something—here, beset by water. The physics behind God creating the atmosphere involves the understanding that when water is pressurized and then quickly released in pressure, the water instantly boils (not from heat). This is why divers are told to come up to the surface of the water slowly, so their blood does not literally boil, not from being hot, but from a change in pressure. Therefore, when God violently and quickly stretched out the universe (the second Big Bang) on the second day of creation, the waters that surrounded the forming Earth instantly boiled from the change in pressure and caused an opening in the midst of the water—atmosphere.

Since the *expanse* or *firmament* (they are synonyms for *raqiya*) is called heaven, God said, "Let the waters below the heavens be gathered into one place and let the dry land appear." Then God said,

"Let there be lights in the expanse of the heavens to separate the day from the night." Thus, there were two expanses created on the second day of creation. This explains why *expanse* is called *heaven* in verse 8 but pluralized when referring to the heavens one verse later in verse 9. We would only pluralize something that includes more than one. For example, "I created an Italian pie. I called the Italian pie pizza. Let the pizzas be served to the team." See how the singularity of pizza was used as the name of the Italian pie, but the plural of pizzas denoted more than one.

Review: The atmosphere was created in the midst (middle) of waters, which is equal to a spherical canopy of salt water around the atmosphere on the second day of creation. Three heavens exist: the atmosphere, the sun/moon/stars, and the Throne of God.

This expanse in Gen. 1:6 is not the heaven where the Throne of God is. The word *heaven* is plural because of the three heavens. The first heaven is our atmosphere (referenced in Gen. 1:7–8), the second heaven is where the sun, moon, and stars dwell (referenced in Gen. 1:6, 14–19), and the third heaven is God's throne (2 Corinthians 12:2–4), which is either physically beyond the edges of our universe or everywhere but beyond our dimension. Since God is omnipresent, I accept the later.

An important concept to consider is the buoyancy effect. For example, whales get to experience this concept that land dwellers do not get to experience as often. A canopy of salt water above our atmosphere would create higher pressure on all objects on the surface of the earth. This is a fraction of what whales in the ocean experience. The water puts pressure uniformly around the whale, creating a buoyancy effect. The higher atmospheric pressure would have uniformly put higher pressure on all objects on earth, and subsequently all those objects would have been more buoyant. Higher atmospheric pressure does not make someone heavier. Quite the contrary, the higher the density of the air, the more buoyant force one experiences. Thus, a higher pressure makes you lighter, not heavier, though your mass remains the same. For example, whales have the atmosphere pressing on them, plus they have water pressing on them, which means more pressure, but this creates a buoyancy effect; consequently, objects feel lighter in water.

Review: The watery canopy would have increased atmospheric pressure, which would have uniformly pressed on all objects, creating a buoyancy effect—similar to the experience of whales in the ocean but at a fraction of the buoyancy.

A benefit to life on earth from the existence of the canopy of water would have been shielding from harmful high energy from space. Light or energy comes in many forms, but higher frequency ultraviolet rays, X-rays, cosmic rays, and gamma rays are not visible to us and are harmful to life. We apply lotions with various degrees of SPF (sun protection factor) to protect us from ultraviolet rays, and we put lead on X-ray technicians to protect them from X-Rays. We do this because high-frequency energy damages life by causing mutations to DNA that adversely affect genes and destroy cells. Ultraviolet light breaks down collagen that connects tissue together and causes wrinkling. Additionally, X-rays, cosmic rays, and gamma rays can cause cancer. The canopy protected life on earth from the harmful affects of high-energy light penetrating down to the surface and from DNA mutations that lead to cancer or cell damage.

Before the Flood, each successive generation after Adam and Eve was a genetically closer copy than each successive generation after the Flood. The canopy of water shielded earth and significantly reduced the number of mutated genes from those harmful rays.

Some mutations occur in genes as a result of harmful radiation from the sun. The information in a DNA strand has a built-in mechanism of repair that acts by deleting the mutated portion of a gene or by fixing the mutated portion via protein markers to produce an accurate-as-possible copy of the genetic information. However, mutated DNA still occurs and may result in impaired function, cell death, or death of the host via cancer, but it never results in new information that creates a new function that does not already exist in the DNA code. It also will not result in a new kind of creature. This is the difference between adaptation and evolution. Evolutionists sometimes suggest that high energy can cause mutations in the genetic code spanning generations, and the mutated DNA can result in a new code with enough random, unguided errors that eventually produces a new function that was never before encoded in the DNA code. This has never been observed or tested to be valid.

Evolutionists believe that all living things are genetically related through one common ancestor and through a process of descent through modification. The central mechanism of evolution occurs in three steps:

1. Mutation of DNA by external stimuli that enhance the code to eventually produce a new DNA code for a new function or new species, which eventually leads to a new kind of creature.

2. Altered embryological development.

3. An environmental scenario that causes the natural selection of a new type of creature.

However, mutated DNA or mutated cells or mutated genes from high energy or even chemical stimuli resulting in mutations always has an adverse outcome. Most of the time the adverse effect is so minuscule that it goes undetected and is considered neutral. But never does a mutation have a beneficial affect on the DNA code for the offspring or parent. On the other hand, adaptation is the ability to modify features that better fit the environment from information already existing in the DNA code. Therefore, when a gene is mutated from high-energy rays, then based on information already existing in the DNA code, protein markers are dispatched to try and repair the mutated genetic code, not rewrite the code to try to evolve to the situation. Thus, adaptation is based on a preexisting DNA code, not a new DNA code. Therefore, evolutionists are in error to use adaptation as evidence for evolution. In addition, natural selection is also based on a preexisting DNA code, so a mutated DNA code gets eliminated, not passed on. Arguing that natural selection supports evolution is getting the cart before the horse because the information to select must be created first.

The problem for evolution is that when mutation of the DNA code occurs from catalysts such as high-energy radiation, the host is weaker, has a distorted external appearance, becomes sterile, is stillborn, dies prematurely from predators or climate, or has impaired function, though it is still the same kind of creature. But in every situation, the opposite sex has DNA information that forces them to only select individuals who are the strongest and the most genetically accurate copies of their kind. Different kinds of creatures cannot mate outside of their kind (e.g., all cats stay within the cat family), and secondly, their DNA is preprogrammed to avoid the mutated and the weak.

In the case of asexual reproduction, when a gene code gets mutated from the sun's radiation, there is usually impaired function or a loss of function and sometimes the death of cells before the code gets anywhere near forming a wholly new meaningful alternate genetic code for a new function. For example, let us take a simple single-celled organism and say a simple genetic code for one protein is represented by "All cows eat grass." Now mind you, this is ultra simple because a genetic code that forms just one single protein is 1,500 nucleotides long. For this example, each character is a nucleotide. A single cell has around 250–500 proteins, with each having its own associated gene, so this is ultra simple. Now let us add some harmful radiation that alters the code with a series of mutations: "All cows eat grass" becomes "All *jows* eat grass," then "All *jows xat* grass," then "All *jows xat frass*." Now it is to the point where the function of the message is lost, yet we are far from another functional phrase. Thus, with a loss of function, the cell dies way before a meaningful new function comes along. And this is where the evolutionary hypothesis needs too great of a miracle to be believable. Evolution not only needs a miracle once for this one genetic code to alter the function of one protein, but it needs trillions upon trillions upon trillions of successful miracles to evolve one single cell into the diversity and complexities of life that we see today. And no amount of time can solve this problem because once the single cell loses the function of the protein, the cell may die, and then the process of continually degrading the genetic information—hoping beyond hope to reach a different level of useful genetic information for a new protein function—is stopped.

The canopy of water blocked solar ultraviolet light, X-rays, cosmic rays, and gamma rays from penetrating to the surface of the earth and thereby protected the DNA code of all life from mutation errors that adversely affect life on earth. Thirteen feet-eight inches of water reduces gamma rays by a

39

factor of a billion.[18] This allowed life to function on a cellular and genetic level at optimal design, free from the impairment or loss of function associated with a mutated DNA code, which prolonged the longevity of life. In fact, scientists who are planning for humans to travel vast distances in space and without the protection of the earth's magnetic field have had to come up with a solution to protect astronauts from cosmic rays, gamma rays, and X-rays. Their solution is that the water needed for space travel and for life to be sustained will be stored around the ship's hull to block high energy from penetrating into the ship and to protect the passengers. It is the same principle and the same outcome as the canopy of water.

If you want a simple explanation of waters' ability to shield an object from the higher energy of a star, just spend the summer in a pool: the parts of your body below the water line will have less tan the farther away they are from the surface.

Review: The canopy of salt water shielded life on earth from harmful high-energy rays. This protected the DNA code from mutated errors and allowed life to thrive on a genetic level, with accurate copies of DNA information being passed on to offspring.

You may be wondering: would a canopy of ice and salt water block the sunlight for photosynthesis? Neither ice or salt water blocks sunlight. Therefore, the canopy would allow the sun's light to penetrate through, but the harmful rays would be shielded from passing through—just like light penetrates water and lights up the sea floor or a pool, so too would light penetrate this canopy and light up the earth. The sunlight penetrates more freely with less of a reduction in strength from the depth of water than higher energy rays (ultraviolet). Ultraviolet rays can penetrate to a depth of 40 meters (120), but visible light can penetrate to a depth of 150 meters (450 feet). This is illustrated in the drawing by:

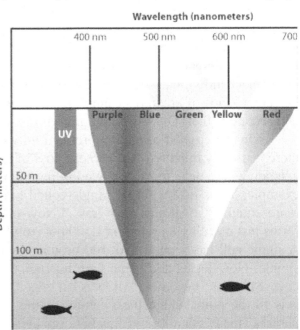

www.manoa.hawaii.edu.[19] The canopy of water would shield life on earth from UV rays, and the UV rays would be reflected back into space. The remainder of the UV rays would be scattered and filtered as they passed through the water. This is why C-14 dating is flawed. The canopy caused all life to live in an environment of trace C-14; they did not half-life down to trace from a full compliment, they only had a trace amount of C-14 in them when they died because the canopy shielded the harmful radiation from penetrating to the atmosphere and converting nitrogen to radioactive carbon.

Light penetrates through water and ice, but it is refracted or bent, which means that the angle at which the light enters water and ice is different than the angle that light exits water and ice. For example, if you were a spear fisherman, and you wanted to hit a fish near the head, you would aim for the tail of the fish because the view is changed from the water refracting/bending the light. Therefore, light does not pass straight through water and ice. This refraction aspect of water means that the sun's light and warmth would also be scattered abroad the earth, hence illustrating the daily temperate temperatures across the globe, which means no winters or summers. The poles would receive enough light and warmth to prevent freezing, and the equator would have enough light and heat refracted to prevent deserts. Without ice at the poles and deserts at the equator, there would not be a global wind (jet stream). Without a global trade wind, then no tornadoes or hurricanes.

The ice of the canopy would be colorless, and not have soil or sediment to impede the light

18 Www.nuclearconnect.org/know-nuclear/science/protecting.
19 https://manoa.hawaii.edu/exploringourfluidearth/physical/ocean-depths/light-ocean

passing through. Only alkaline elements would be diluted in a clear brine, as in the South Pacific, so the ice and water would be clear. Snow is white because it reflects all the colors, and ice is clear because it transmits all the colors. They are different, so the canopy would not be white like snow, but clear.

Review: The shape of this canopy of water was spherical at its formation on the second day of creation, but with the earth's spin and subsequent canopy's spin, centripetal force morphed the canopy toward a more disk-like shape. Shortly after the formation of the canopy, as temperatures in space began to cool after the Big Bangs, then a frozen external structure formed, probably by the end of the second day of creation. This prevented Earth's gravity from pulling the canopy down to the planet surface. With the moon's gravity causing two daily tides, the canopy would bulge nearest the moon, and the liquid from within the canopy would fill any cracks. The process of centripetal force from the spin of the canopy and the two daily tides that affected the canopy would have caused the spherical canopy to steadily morph to a bulge at the equator over decades, and then a disk-like band would have been around the earth for centuries. This disk-like band would be visible and look like an arch in the sky (*raqiya*). As the canopy thinned near the poles and thickened near the equator, there would be openings in the thinning canopy that would allow the atmosphere to escape to higher altitudes, thus losing a component helping to hold up the canopy, and that was the buoyancy of the atmosphere pushing up against the canopy. With the fullness of a thick disk-like formation of the canopy, the only thing holding up the canopy was its frozen arch support. Potentially, a shadow could have been cast upon the surface of Earth, but by this time, Noah was building the ark in preparation for the Flood.

Scientists have discovered that Saturn is not the only planet in our solar system that has ice rings. Uranus, Neptune, and Jupiter also have rings, albeit not as prominent. This means that 50% of the planets in our Solar System have rings from when they once had a canopy. The premise of the canopy is observable and testable. As much as atheist and theistic evolutionists make fun of YECs for coming to the logical conclusion of the canopy hovering around the atmosphere, a preponderance of evidence exists from the Bible, observation, and science. *Image Credit: http://www.britannica.com/topic/solar-system.*

Review: Even considering the depth of the water and structural ice in the canopy, light would still pass through to the earth, but harmful UV rays and C-14 would be trace.

Prior to the Flood, all the water that rained on the earth for 40 days and 40 nights came from two locations: The canopy of salt water and ice, and freshwater burst out of the earth from deep caverns just below the surface of the earth (Gen. 7:11). With the canopy spinning with the earth in a geosynchronous (same distance) orbit, something changed to cause this canopy to be pulled down to earth. The earth has the scars to prove it, and so does the moon. Multiple asteroids hit the frozen arch support structure of the canopy and caused the canopy to slowly come down upon the earth in the form of rain. A few large chunks of the frozen canopy may have been charged enough and near enough in proximity to the electromagnetic field generated by the earth, to effect its descent trajectory, and plummeted toward the polar regions as chucks of ice. This would explain how woolly mammoths froze in the upright position with undigested tropical food in their digestive tract. A series of asteroids hitting earth would cause profuse fires and fracture Pangaea, which would set in motion the tectonic plates. A "dinosaur killing" impact at the Yucatan Peninsula is the likely culprit. *Image credit: www.NaturalMagnetism.com*

The Yucatan Peninsula crater is called Chicxulub. It is one of many larger impact craters on the earth, but Chicxulub was potentially the major occurrence that initiated the Flood. This is because it landed near the equator, which means that it passed through the space that the canopy occupied. Within the layers of the crust exists a layer of ash from asteroid impacts and subsequent fires that reveal how devastating this global flood was. We know that asteroids have hit the earth by the craters they have left behind. We also know that layers of ash are caused by asteroid impacts because of the amount of iridium present in a thin layer of ash. Iridium is not naturally found on earth. The moon also shows the same scars from the same time in history, when both the moon and the earth were bombarded by asteroids and meteors.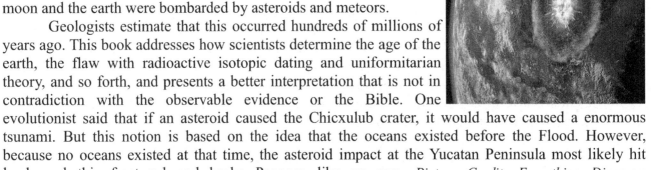

Geologists estimate that this occurred hundreds of millions of years ago. This book addresses how scientists determine the age of the earth, the flaw with radioactive isotopic dating and uniformitarian theory, and so forth, and presents a better interpretation that is not in contradiction with the observable evidence or the Bible. One evolutionist said that if an asteroid caused the Chicxulub crater, it would have caused a enormous tsunami. But this notion is based on the idea that the oceans existed before the Flood. However, because no oceans existed at that time, the asteroid impact at the Yucatan Peninsula most likely hit land, and this fractured and broke Pangaea like an egg. *Picture Credit: Everything Dinosaur.* http://blog.everythingdinosaur.co.uk/.

After the Flood, the waters receded because of the glacial age, and the mountains rose and the valleys sank (Psalm 104:8), and oceans came into existence. But the ocean surface level was a couple of hundred feet below their current level for a couple of hundred years. This allowed animals to migrate to what are now islands and continents, and to eventually allow humans to be scattered across the globe because of the Tower of Babel. As the glacial age continued melting, the ocean levels rose until all life was cut off from each other. This began to change in 1492 when Columbus sailed the ocean blue.

If you want to get an idea of what life felt like when the dinosaurs roamed, get in water. When you get in water, the water and the atmosphere combine to increase pressure on you to push you upwards, and that creates the buoyancy effect. The buoyant force from the canopy was about 20% to 30% of the buoyancy effect that water has on a swimmer. As you feel gravity getting weaker and your body relax in the water, think how much easier it becomes to sustain life with a weaker gravity.

One question that was posed to me in a debate was if dinosaurs roamed the earth with mankind, why did not the dinosaurs kill off mankind? This answer is found in Gen. 9:2: "The fear of you and the terror of you will be on every beast of the earth and on every bird of the sky; with everything that creeps on the ground, and all the fish of the sea, into your hand they are given." Today, animals, fish, and birds would rather avoid human contact, and in the same way, prehistoric creatures avoided human contact. Also, Gen. 1:30–31 reveals that all creatures were herbivores. No death existed (thus no fossils, coal, or oil) on earth before the fall of mankind. After the fall of mankind, when some creatures became carnivores and began killing other species, then mankind had to avoid some dinosaurs, just like we avoid crocodiles today.

Another hypothesis regarding the canopy could solve how God caused thorns and thistle to form after the fall of Adam and Eve. Since the canopy provided weight or downward pressure on all the vegetation, it could be that this pressure prevented thorns and thistles from growing. And when Adam and Eve sinned, that was the exact time that the canopy morphed enough from spherical to disk-like, that some of the atmosphere leaked out and around the canopy near the poles, relieving just enough pressure to allow thorns and thistles, but not enough to reduce buoyancy force, or reduce pressure enough to allow cloud formations. This hypothesis would still maintain the mist system that supplied water around the globe. This hypothesis accepts the premise that Adam and Eve lived awhile (decades) before sinning, and had many children as well, before sinning.

Chapter Summary: The canopy of salt water above the atmosphere increased buoyancy, countering earth's gravity and weakening gravity's strength by ~20% and allowed life to thrive. Initially, the canopy spherically surrounded the atmosphere; it morphed toward a disc shape because of tidal forces and centripetal force over time and was suspended above the earth by:

1. **Its physical distance from the earth's full gravitational force.**
2. **The earth's rotational spin, which created centripetal force countering gravity's pull.**
3. **The atmosphere's buoyancy force equally pushing up on the canopy.**
4. **A frozen structure, which created a suspension arch in the sky.**
5. **Covalent bonds, which held it together.**

Chapter 4
Climate

What would a canopy do to Earth's climate? This would create a greenhouse effect scenario, not in the negative sense, as in too much CO_2, but in a positive sense, as in stable temperate global temperatures with high O_2 concentrations. Temperate temperatures on the surface of the earth would mean no polar ice caps, no deserts, and abundant lush green tropical vegetation uniformly growing around the globe.

Before the Flood, extensive amounts of water was stored above the atmosphere in the canopy and stored below the crust of the earth in deep caverns (the source of the 40 days and nights of rain); oceans would not exist, only smaller seas.

Does the Bible support temperate temperatures before the Flood? Yes. Gen. 3:7: "Then the eyes of both of them (Adam and Eve) were opened, and they knew that they were naked; and they sewed fig leaves together and made themselves loin coverings." Adam and Eve lived in such a temperate climate that they were always naked. Notice that they did not put on jackets for winter or clothes after they sinned. They merely covered their reproductive organs. Therefore, the climate did not change. Their eyes were spiritually open to the knowledge of good and evil. Also, after and during God's creation, He kept saying, "It was good." Deserts and polar ice caps are bad for the growth of vegetation and for living beings to thrive. Also, the change of seasons from cool springs to hot summers and from hot summer months to cooler autumn months would have brought destructive and harmful tornadoes, which did not occur before the Flood because of the relatively constant temperate global temperatures. One cannot argue that tornadoes, hurricanes, and other natural disasters occurred on the globe before the fall of Adam and Eve because those conditions result in death and destruction. This is clarified in Romans 5:12 and I Corinthians 15:21, that death did not enter creation until Adam sinned.

Do evolutionary scientists support the notion that at some point, there were temperate global temperatures? Yes, allegedly during the Cambrian explosion of life, oxygen levels were high enough and temperatures stable enough for life to thrive and eventually lead to dinosaurs and a great variety and complexity of creatures. Though we differ on when those optimal conditions were, we both accept a time of optimal conditions caused life to thrive.

Think about the benefits for living beings; there would be no wasted energy to warm a cold body, no shivers and goose bumps, and no need to cool an overheated body with perspiration.

Review: From the origins of life till the Flood, there were mild, temperate global temperatures, and this helped life to thrive.

Does the Bible support the scenario of no polar ice caps and no deserts before the Flood? Yes. The existence of polar ice caps and deserts creates global changes in temperature from one region to another on the earth. These differences in temperature from different regions on the earth cause a global wind called the jet stream. When did the wind first occur? Immediately after the Flood of Gen. 8:1: "God caused a wind to pass over the earth."

With the loss of the canopy of water resulting in the Flood, this would have significantly reduced atmosphere pressure and ended the mist rising from the ground globally. A reduction of atmospheric pressure allowed the evaporation to form into clouds, which led to rainfall and rainbows. This is the hydrological cycle as we know it today. With a canopy of water hovering around the atmosphere, this would have increased atmospheric pressure significantly enough that evaporation of water from the earth would not have formed clouds, but when the cool of the day occurred, the moisture in the air would rest on the soil as dew. Thus, a mist rising from the earth to water the whole earth. Gen. 2:5–6 "For the Lord God had not sent rain upon the earth, and there was no man to cultivate the ground. But a mist used to rise from the earth and water the whole surface of the ground." *Mist* can also be translated to "flow." With a mist rising from the ground to water the earth, there were no tornadoes, no hurricanes, no floods, no droughts, no lightning, and no hail. With the loss of the canopy of water and the subsequent reduction in atmospheric pressure, this allowed for cloud formation as the means for watering the ground, which subsequently led to hurricanes, tornadoes, hail, lightning, floods, droughts, and so forth. These weather events are a reminder of the curse of sin placed upon all creation. "Mist is tiny droplets of water hanging in the air. These droplets form when warmer water in the air is cooled, causing it to change from invisible gas to tiny visible water droplets."[20] We still see a remnant of this pre–flood mist written of in Genesis 2:6, we call it dew.

With no clouds and no rain prior to the Flood, then there would have been no rainbows. This is why rainbows did not exist until after the Flood. Gen. 9 says that God set his rainbow in the sky as a covenant not to destroy life with flood waters again. With the loss of the canopy of water hovering around the atmosphere, this significantly reduced atmospheric pressure, allowing the formation of clouds and subsequently rain and light refraction from the raindrops to form rainbows in the sky.

The first mention of winter and summer, and cold and hot is not until after the Flood in Gen. 8:22. This is evidence that before the Flood, there were no winters, no summer, no cold, and no hot days of summer. In Gen. 1:14, when God finishes forming the sun, moon, and stars and says, "Let them be for signs and for seasons," He uses the Hebrew word "moed," (Strong's Concordance # 4150) for seasons, which does not mean spring, summer, fall, and winter. No—it means appointed sign for congregation, feasts and festivals, and appointments of assembly.

Review: From the origins of life until after the Flood, there were no ice caps, no deserts, and no global jet stream, only mild breezes. The hydrological cycle bypassed clouds and rain and converted evaporation into a mist because of atmospheric pressure, and this is why there were no rainbows until after the Flood.

Romans 8:18–23 sheds more light on the climate at the time of Adam and Eve and the dinosaurs. Verse 20 reads, "The creation was subjected to futility, not willingly, but because of Him who subjected it." This means that as a result of Adam's sin, all of creation was subjected to the fall and cursed. All of creation needs a savior to save it from the physical curse of sin, which is death. Currently, our climate goes through a symbolic manifestation of the effect of sin, the four seasons: death (fall), burial (winter), resurrection (spring), and life (summer). Romans 8:21:

In hope that the creation itself also will be set free from its slavery to corruption into the freedom of the glory of the children of God. For we know that the whole creation groans and suffers the pains of childbirth together until now.

This means that as the children of God will receive an immortal body free from death, so too will all of creation return to a "pre-sin" state and no longer suffer death (fall), burial (winter), resurrection (spring), and life (summer). Therefore, before the fall of Adam and Eve, creation was not subjected to futility and was not "groaning to be reborn," and therefore, there were no four seasons. That is why Adam and Eve were naked; they lived in perfect temperatures every day and every night because the canopy created perfect global temperatures. The four seasons commenced after the global flood.

Prior to the sin of Adam and Eve, no natural disasters existed. Such as, no active volcanoes, no earthquakes, no droughts, no tsunamis, and so on because there was no "groaning and suffering" of creation to be set free from the corruption of sin, which leads to death, physically and spiritually.

Scientists discovered that the earth once had a supercontinent called Pangaea. This is in accord with the Bible because when most of the ocean waters were stored in the canopy and in the deep caverns, the surface of the earth was potentially 70% usable land for vegetation—a supercontinent if you will. Thus, before Pangaea broke up into the continents we see today, there were far fewer earthquakes. From a Biblical perspective, there were no earthquakes before sin, and most likely none until the Flood. While Pangaea remained as one land mass, then tectonic potential energy built up until the Flood when Pangaea broke apart from tectonic movements. Earthquakes represent an unstable Earth adjusting itself to release tension and pressure. This movement and release indicates a fallen

20 *National Geographic*, Education/encyclopedic/mist.

state, a state of unease, and an attempt to relieve tension. This does not sound like the perfect creation that God describes in Gen. 1. I could see God causing a mild tremor with the first sin, but Pangaea did not break apart until the Flood. Therefore, a hypothesis of this book is that potential energy was building up from the first sin until the Flood, which is when Pangaea broke apart, and all that potential energy was released as fast moving kinetic energy.

Tectonic plate movements often allow cracks in the crust of the earth for lava to pour through, so one of the hypotheses of this book is that before tectonic plate movements and before the Flood, there were no volcanoes. Tectonic plate movements cause tsunamis as well, so to be consistent, there were no tsunamis before the Flood either.

Review: From creation until after the Flood, there were no four seasons, just spring. Before sin entered the world, and most likely before the Flood, there were no natural disasters, such as earthquakes, volcanoes, tsunamis, floods, droughts, tornadoes, hurricanes, and so forth.

Let me illustrate the benefit of a canopy and the atmosphere on the temperature of the surface by discussing what happens when no atmosphere exist. The moon has substantial temperature swings from the light side versus the dark side. It has a daylight high of 130°C (265°F). The dark side has a low of -110°C (-170°F). Why? It is because the atmosphere no longer exists. An atmosphere creates an environment of moderately stable temperatures. An atmosphere with a canopy around it would create an environment of even more stable temperatures. For Adam and Eve to be comfortably naked, the nighttime lows were probably around ~72°F, and the daytime highs were probably around ~85°F.

Does the Bible support lush vegetation globally? Yes. With no wind prior to the Flood, there were no polar ice caps, no deserts to drive the jet stream, and no oceans, only seas (smaller bodies of water). Gen. 1:10: "God called . . . the gathering of the waters He called seas." Where was all the ocean water? Since the global flood caused the oceans, then potentially before the global flood, 50% was stored in the canopy, 25% was stored in the deep caverns under the crust, and 25% was the seas, which leaves 75% of the earth's surface for vegetation growth. That dry land was covered in lush vegetation, and a mist/flow (evaporation into gas, that settles as a mist in the cool of the night. We see a remnant of this in the morning—dew) of water rose from the ground to water the whole earth. Not much grows in deserts or at the polar caps; it is just not good for life. When God made all the plants/trees/grass on the third day, "God saw that it was good" (Gen. 1:12)—not barren (as represented by deserts and polar ice caps), but good as in lush, abundant, and thriving. This is why remnant tropical forest are found below the ice of the polar regions and the Saharan desert.

Review: Today the oceans and polar ice caps and deserts limit or prevent vegetation growth that produces oxygen for life to thrive. Before the Flood, there were no oceans, no ice caps, and no deserts, allowing expansive amounts of vegetation to grow and an increased production of oxygen, which allowed life to thrive.

During the Flood, large asteroids and meteors bombarded the earth, breaking the frozen support arch of the canopy that held it in place. With the earth's gravity pulling down on the frozen canopy of water and the support arch structure broken, the ice and water fell upon the earth, causing rain for 40 days and 40 nights. The impacts of the asteroids fractured Pangaea, released 1,650 years of built up tectonic plate potential energy, and resulted in earthquakes and the breaking apart of Pangaea. The weight of the tectonic plates that were resting on the super heated deep caverns, forced the water out of the fractured crust (Fault lines) and they burst violently open. Volcanoes erupted as well, followed by rain for 40 days and nights, which quenched the fires. After the 40 days of extreme heat, the globe was covered by water for 150 days. This caused the temperature to drop, plunging the earth into an ice age, creating polar ice caps that stretched down from the North Pole to North America, Europe, and Asia and from the South Pole to South America, Africa and Australia.

After the waters receded, there was no canopy to protect the equator from the sun's heat, which led to the eventual death of the Saharan landscape and subsequently produced the Sahara, Mohave, and Gobi deserts over the following one to five years after the Flood (without moisture, it does not take long to kill an entire area).

Prior to the Flood, the lush vegetation on a global scale would have produced an atmosphere rich in oxygen concentration. That is exactly what scientist find in **amber** (petrified tree sap), and deep air bubbles in the polar ice caps, indicating higher oxygen concentration levels in the past.

Scientists have discovered that the oxygen concentration of the atmosphere in the distant past was 50% higher than today's levels. Today, our atmosphere has a 21% oxygen concentration. The oxygen concentration was 31% prior to the Flood. What caused an environment for higher oxygen? The answer is the canopy. Since the canopy formed the oceans, then prior to the Flood only seas existed. And since the canopy prevented polar ice and deserts, then prior to the Flood about 75% of the earth was covered in vegetation. This vast amount of vegetation would have yielded very high levels of oxygen concentrations because vegetation produces oxygen. More vegetation equals more oxygen. Less vegetation equals less oxygen.

Review: From the origin of life until the Flood, oxygen levels were 50% higher in concentration than today's value.

With freshwater stored in the fountains of the deep and the higher atmospheric pressure before the Flood, the earth had a high water table for streams and rivers to flow out of the ground. The high buoyant force, and high atmosphere pressure aided the "mist to rise from the earth and water the whole surface of the ground" (Genesis 2:6).

When did the mist rising from the ground watering the earth stop and the hydrological cycle, as we know it, begin? This was after the global flood saga. The loss of the canopy reduced atmospheric pressure and allowed clouds to form, and the loss of the underground water reduced the high water table, which limited the mist rising from the ground. Then the hydrological cycle included clouds, rain, rainbows, snow, hail, tornadoes, hurricanes, and so forth. Gen. 8:1: "God caused a wind to pass over the earth, and the water subsided." For global wind to occur, there needed to be large changes in global temperatures. There needs to be a low-pressure atmosphere to allow cloud formation and rain. Water vapor is less dense than oxygen and nitrogen gas, so there needs to be less atmospheric pressure. Therefore, with the loss of the protective canopy, equatorial heat grew and the polar regions became covered in ice; this combination generated global wind, and a reduction in atmospheric pressure allowed the hydrological cycle to include cloud formation and rain, with resultant rainbows.

It is noteworthy that as a result of the hydrological cycle, erosion occurs because of the rain, yet no erosion marks exist between each of the layers of soil of the crust. Why? The flood water was not clear, but filled with prodigious amounts of soil, sand, silt, clay, rock, and so on. This resulted from the asteroids hitting the earth and the deep caverns of water bursting out from the earth (fault lines), volcanoes, and the breaking apart of Pangaea. When all the sediments mixed in the flood water settled, they settled according to density and formed the layers of the crust we see today. Those layers are uniformly laid, with no evidence of erosion, and subsequent intermingling of the sediment. Just look at the walls of the Grand Canyon for an example.

Although dry air increases the density of the atmosphere and would have fractionally increased buoyant force, I do not accept that the climate had dry air before the fall or before the Flood because the evidence that tropical forests once dominated in the Arctic Circle and in the Sahara, and a mist rose from the ground to water the earth suggests that humidity was high. Humidity is great for the skin.

The process of rain falling under direct sunlight also led to a new phenomenon of light refraction from water droplets, creating rainbows. Gen. 9:12–14:

47

This is the sign of the covenant which I am making between Me and you and every living creature that is with you, for all successive generations; I set My bow in the cloud, and it shall be far a sign of a covenant between Me and the earth. It shall come about, when I bring a cloud over the earth, that the bow will be seen in the cloud.

Review: Before the Flood, there were no rainbows, no rain, and no clouds. The atmosphere was denser, humidity was higher, and a mist rose from the ground to water the earth—Dew. Picture gentle global breezes because of nighttime temperature drops and daytime temperature increases, but not global trade wind (i.e., no jet stream) and no gusts or gales or strong winds because no large temperature changes existed to cause that.

With no oceans, deserts, or polar ice before the Flood, dense tropical vegetation covered the globe with smaller seas, lakes, rivers, and such. This caused our atmosphere to have 50% greater oxygen concentration than today. The increased oxygen concentration existed from creation until the Flood. The current oxygen concentration in our atmosphere is 21%, and when dinosaurs roamed the earth, the O2 concentration was more than 31%. Scientists have discovered this in amber (petrified tree sap) bubbles.

Tiny air bubbles in amber (petrified tree sap) and glacial core samples, have shown that oxygen concentration was higher in the earth's atmosphere before the global flood. That oxygen-rich environment would have caused life to thrive, with accelerated growth and larger life forms. This explains how some dinosaurs lived with such small nostrils and small lungs compared to body mass. Brachiosaurus had nostrils the size of a horse. Their survival and thriving in life was only possible because they could get enough oxygen to their large bodies due to the high oxygen concentrations and higher pressure before the Flood. If brachiosaurus lived today, their nostrils and lungs would be too small to allow enough oxygen in to support their size, and they would physically suffer and potentially die off just from a lack of O2. Also, an oxygen-enriched atmosphere allows us to understand how humans lived so long in the past—because oxygen causes life to thrive. Given that our atmosphere has less oxygen now than before the Flood, this sheds light on subsequent genetic adaptations to changes in oxygen concentration and gravity intensity. The Bible gives us the record of what caused the change in O2 concentration: the Flood. This flood was global, and every mountain was covered (Gen. 7:19–21). It rained for 40 days and 40 nights, and that water stayed and covered the earth for 150 days (Gen. 7:24). This would have resulted in expansive polar ice caps and created an ice age.

How did dinosaurs and humans coexist in the Book of Job (Chapters 40–41), yet not coexist today? The reduction in oxygen concentration in the atmosphere because the oceans, polar ice, and deserts limit vegetation and increased gravity because the buoyant force was reduced. These changes have altered the living conditions on earth, and life adapted because of the information embedded in the DNA code from creation, and natural selection—based on those DNA codes—has allowed certain species to dominate populations in certain regions of the globe (this is not evolution). This means that living beings do not grow as tall or live as long as they once did before the Flood. Dinosaurs could still be living amongst us, but they are just too small for us to recognize them as dinosaurs, so we call them by other reptilian names.

Chapter Summary: The climate before the Flood had temperate global temperatures, no oceans but seas, more land exposed that was covered with vegetation, no polar ice caps, no deserts, higher oxygen concentration, higher buoyancy force, weaker gravity, no global jet stream, no hydrological cycle, and no rainbows. Potentially, an arch formed from the frozen canopy of water and was visible to those on Earth. Additionally, living beings inhaled more oxygen with each breath, all vegetation was larger, dinosaurs roamed the earth, mankind lived 900+ years, nights were not as cold, and days were not as hot—a perfect Utopia for optimal growth and life.

Chapter 5
Oxygen Concentration

Oxygen concentration in our atmosphere is vital to life. Currently, the oxygen concentration in our atmosphere is ~21%, and 78% of the molecules in our atmosphere are nitrogen and <1% other.

Since a lack of oxygen kills life, would an increase in oxygen make life thrive? What would happen to life on earth, if the oxygen concentration in the atmosphere was 50% higher than today? This would mean that oxygen in the atmosphere would make up ~31% of the atmosphere. A research team at Arizona State University[21] did a study of insects in an atmosphere at 31% oxygen concentration (a hyperoxia environment), which is a 50% increase in our current oxygen concentration in the atmosphere. The researchers also studied

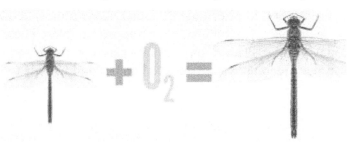

insects in an atmosphere at 12% oxygen concentration (a hypoxia environment).

The results were staggering; most of the insects raised in hyperoxia conditions were larger in size than normal, which clearly demonstrates a thriving life. Only the cockroach remained the same size. However, the cockroach's internal tracheae (tubes that carry oxygen throughout the body) were smaller than normal as a result of living in a 31% oxygen environment, which allowed other organs and tissues to grow larger. Other tissues that grew larger were muscles, blood vessels, tendons, ligaments, nerves, and more, which means those cockroaches would be faster, stronger, and quicker and have improved endurance and a faster response time. It was a superior cockroach.

In a hyperoxia (31% O2) environment, insects grow larger. And the ones that do not seem to grow larger (because of an exoskeleton restricts growth) would eventually grow larger in time as they adapted to the increased oxygen concentrations because of the ability to adapt already exists in the DNA. This is called adaptation or "speciation" (this is not evolution because they are still the same kind of creature). *Photo credit: www.asunow.asu.edu/big-insects-provide-big-answers-about-oxygen.*

Conversely, the research showed that the insects grown in hypoxia (12% oxygen concentration) were smaller in size. And even though the cockroach remained the same size, its internal tracheae (tubes that carry oxygen throughout the body) grew larger to compensate, which forced other organs and tissues to be smaller. Having smaller tissues, such as those related to muscles, tendons, blood vessels, and nerves, means that those cockroaches would be less active and weaker, slower, and less endurance. Life suffers with a lack of oxygen.

<u>**Review:**</u> <u>The higher the oxygen concentration, the smaller the tracheal tubes are required to transfer low volumes of air into the body to thrive. The lower the oxygen concentration, the larger the tracheal tubes are required to transfer high volumes of air into the body to live. Experiments show that higher oxygen concentration causes life to thrive. Life will grow larger, faster, and with greater longevity in an environment with higher oxygen concentrations.</u>

Today, we have cockroaches that are about 2.75 inches long, but the fossil record shows cockroaches that grew to 18 inches long. That is 6.5 times larger. Today, we have dragonflies with a wing span of 6 inches, but the fossil record shows dragonflies with wingspans up to 50 inches. That is 8.3 times larger.

---

21 The Geological Society of America, "Raising Giant insects to unravel Ancient Oxygen."

Today, the chambered nautilus (it looks like a squid in a shell) grows to about 10 inches in diameter, but the fossil record shows that they once grew to 8 feet in diameter. That is 9.6 times larger. *Image credit: www.askabiologist.asu.edu/explore/prehistoric-insects.*

Why did the research team use the value of 31% oxygen to represent the hyperoxia portion of their study? Why not choose 25% or 40% or another arbitrary number? Because other scientists doing other explorations and studies in other parts of the world have found that the oxygen concentration in our atmosphere was 31% in prehistoric times.

How did the scientists determine that the earth's atmosphere had a 50% higher oxygen concentration in prior times versus today's atmosphere? They bored into amber bubbles and tested the oxygen concentration inside the trapped bubbles. They found oxygen levels that were 50% higher than today's value. Prior to the Flood, when tree sap oozed out of a tree, the sap trapped air in bubbles. The sap petrified and was then called amber and had air trapped inside from prehistoric times. The trapped air bubbles stayed inside the amber until researchers found it and tested it.

It should be noted that sap will only petrify because of a <u>sudden</u> covering of a lot of sediment, moisture, pressure, and heat. Nothing petrifies or fossilizes with a slow covering of sediment and moisture. This is important later in the book for discerning timelines and aging the earth. But in a nutshell, the only event in the history of earth that provides all the ingredients for petrification, coal formation, oil reserves, salt deposits, the glacial age, and fossilization is the global flood.

Another way that mankind has determined that oxygen concentration was higher in past millennia is through deep glacier drilling and testing of the air bubbles trapped inside those deep glacier core samples. When core samples were examined, researchers noticed that there were pockets of air bubbles. They tested the captured air pockets and determined that oxygen levels were 50% higher in the distant past.

<u>**Review:** Scientists have discovered that the earth's atmosphere had 50% higher oxygen concentration than today. This was discerned via air bubbles trapped in amber and glacial ice caps.</u>

A low oxygen concentration can reduce life's size, decrease longevity, and kill life. A host of diseases and ailments are associated with a lack of oxygen to the tissue, organs, or body, from paleness, lethargy, ischemic necrosis, avascular necrosis, anemia, gangrene, sickle cell anemia, brain damage, heart attack, and death. Why are there so many conditions and diseases resulting from a lack of oxygen? Because God breathed life into all creatures and humans.[22] Take away the blood that carries the oxygen or take away the oxygen, and you take away the life. Therefore, when someone's blood is lost, they will die, or when someone's breath is taken away, they will die. Therefore, life is in the blood, which carries oxygen.[23]

No one disputes the importance of oxygen. Research clearly proves that life thrives with higher oxygen concentrations and suffers with a lower oxygen concentrations. But what does this have to do with origins? Well, one of the major tenants of this book is that the higher oxygen concentration in the past allowed animals and plants to grow to enormous height and weight and to live a long life. Dinosaurs/reptiles once stood 100 feet tall and weighed 100 tons, and probably lived ~800+ years. Also, humans once lived 900+ years and probably stood 10–15 feet tall. How can this be? Oxygen and buoyant force.

<u>**Review:** Many diseases and ailments occur due to a lack of oxygen to a particular body part or to the entire body in general. Simply put, a lack of oxygen kills or decreases life's potential. Also, God teaches that life is in the breath and in the blood. Both directly and indirectly get oxygen to the body.</u>

If we could discern how and when the oxygen concentration dropped from 31% to 21%, that

---

22 Gen. 2:7: "Then the LORD God formed man of dust from the ground, and breathed into his nostrils the breath of <u>life</u>; and man became a <u>living</u> being." Gen. 1:29–30: "Then God said, '. . . and to every beast of the earth and to every bird of the sky and to every thing, that moves on the earth which has <u>life</u>."

23 Lev. 17:10–14: "Any man . . . who eats any blood, I will set My face against that person who eats blood and will cut him off from among his people. For the life of the flesh is in the blood . . . For as for the life of all flesh, its blood is identified with its life . . . You are not to eat the blood of any flesh, for the life of all flesh is its blood.'"

would tell us approximately when dinosaurs stopped growing so large and when humans stopped living 900+ years. If we look at what is preventing oxygen from being at a higher concentrations today in the atmosphere, maybe we can work backward to determine what caused oxygen levels to decline and why, how, and when.

To have oxygen in the atmosphere, we need vegetation. Plants, grass, and trees produce oxygen. To determine what is preventing oxygen in our atmosphere from being at 31% concentration as in prehistoric times and keeping oxygen at 21% concentration today, we need to determine what is preventing vegetation growth. If we determine what is preventing vegetation growth, we will find a major clue as to what happened to reduce oxygen concentration from 31% to 21%.

The primary limiting factor that physically limits vegetation growth is the ocean. The oceans cover ~71% of land and thereby prevent oxygen-producing vegetation on the land from growing. The interaction between photosynthesis and the ocean depth is divided up into three zones: the euphotic, disphotic, and aphotic. Vegetation only grows in the euphotic zone. No photosynthesis and no vegetation exists in the Disphotic or Aphotic zones because too little light penetrates to those zones. This is 90% of the ocean floor. *Image credit: enchantedlearning.com.*

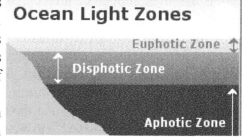

The second limiting factor that has reduced the oxygen concentration in our atmosphere and has prevented oxygen concentration from rising is the lack of uniform temperatures around the globe. The variance of global temperatures around the globe, from hot at the equator to cold at the poles, has created two results: hot deserts and cold polar ice caps. These two regions physically prevent oxygen-producing vegetation from growing on 10% of the earth's surface. The arid, dry deserts are too hot and lack enough water to allow vegetation to grow. And the arid polar ice caps are too cold to allow vegetation to grow. That leaves only 20% of earth's surface for vegetation growth to produce oxygen.

Therefore, since the oceans, polar ice caps, and deserts prevent higher oxygen concentrations in our atmosphere, and since oxygen concentration was indeed higher in the distant past, we need to determine when there were no polar ice caps, deserts, and oceans. Then we can determine when oxygen concentrations in our atmosphere were higher. And by doing that, we'll find the cause.

Geologist Peter deMenocal of The Earth Institute, Columbia University, studied Atlantic core samples just off the coast of the Sahara Desert. He discovered that the Sahara is a recent phenomenon in geological terms and is roughly 5,000 years old. He discerned that the easterly winds tend to blow arid sand into the Atlantic ocean, and by taking core samples and counting seasons like rings of a tree, he was able to come up with an estimated age of the Sahara Desert. His research also revealed that the Sahara had lush vegetation just prior to desertification.[24]

This fits nicely with the Bible, as deMenocal's research has a timeline of when the lush tropics of North Africa became deserts. This is near enough to when the Flood occurred, which resulted in too much heat and loss of moisture in the Sahara region, changing it from a tropical area to a desert. With the loss of lush vegetation producing O2 in the Sahara region after the Flood, O2 levels decreased.

The deserts are caused by being too close in proximity to the sun's harmful heat and lack of precipitation, and the polar ice caps are caused by being too distant from the sun's beneficial heat. Both conditions are remedied by uniform global temperatures. This means that before the formation of polar ice caps and deserts, the earth had temperate temperatures globally. The question is when did the oceans form to cover 71%s of land and reduce O2 production? We need to find an event that formed the oceans and subsequently converted lush vegetation into deserts and polar ice caps. The vast volumes of water in the oceans need to be stored somewhere before this catastrophic global event.

Therefore, the key in unlocking this mystery of "when" and "what" caused the reduction of our oxygen concentration from 31% to the present day 21% is to find a global catastrophic event that not

24 algeria.com/The Green Sahara Desert.

only formed the polar ice caps and the deserts but also formed the vast oceans and changed global temperatures from uniform to regions that are very cold and other regions that are very hot. How to get rid of 352 quintillion (that is a billion x billion) of gallons of water? Only two choices exist: either the water came from beyond our atmosphere, and/or it came from deep caverns within the earth.

A record of a catastrophic flood in the earth's history was captured by mankind and nature. This event occurred in the not-too-distant past. The first clue is that the Sahara desert is rich with marine fossils that are found in sand layers above buried remnant fossils of a once lush forest. This is irrefutable evidence that an ocean once covered and destroyed the lush vegetation of the Sahara region and deposited the sand filled with marine fossils.

The global flood recorded by the Bible and by approximately 25 cultures around the globe are in harmony with the evidence that lush vegetation existed, then a global flood destroyed everything. The Bible gives enough details regarding this earth-changing global flood to discern that this event fits perfectly as a cause for our oceans to form, for temperatures to change, and for subsequent polar ice caps and deserts to form, resulting in the reduction of O2 production.

Before we get to the recording of the global flood, we need to determine where the water came from to cover the entire earth. Did the water come from space and/or from deep caverns within the earth? The answer is both. We turn to Gen. 1:2: "The earth was formless and void, and darkness was over the surface of the deep, and the Spirit of God was moving over the surface of the waters." Okay, before the earth was formed into a sphere, it was formless and void of life. But notice that water is everywhere. Gen. 1:6:

> Then God said, 'Let there be an expanse in the midst of the waters, and let it separate the waters from the waters.' God made the expanse, and separated the waters which were below the expanse from the waters which were above the expanse.

God made the universe expand, and this reduced the weight and pressure on the waters surrounding the earth, which caused them to separate (expand) to form our atmosphere with water above and water below. The waters below the atmosphere became seas, and the waters above the atmosphere became the canopy of ice and salt water. While this canopy remained above the earth's atmosphere, it provided temperate temperatures globally. This means relatively uniform temperatures existed from the equator to the poles, such that no global wind (jet stream) existed. This canopy then came down to the earth's surface in a deluge of 40 days and 40 nights of constant rain. Look at Genesis 1:9:

> Then God said, 'Let the waters below the heavens [the plural form representing the throne of God, the universe, and our atmosphere] be gathered into one place, and let the dry land appear; God called the dry land earth and the gathering of the waters He called seas.

No oceans were formed, only smaller seas. The Bible does not mention the word *ocean*, instead the Bible uses the word *deep* to refer to oceans, and thus distinguishes between the smaller *seas* and the larger oceans (the deep). For example, in Job 28:14 both the deep and the sea are mentioned in the same verse. This draws the reader's attention that they are different bodies of water. Since the deep is mentioned in Gen. 1:2 while the earth was formless and void of life, and since the earth was made out of water (2 Peter 3:5), and in Gen. 1:9 the seas are the only water mentioned, then a fair conclusion is that on the third day of creation God formed seas and not oceans on the surface. The final evidence of this is in Genesis 7:11, "All the fountains of the great *deep* burst open, and the floodgates of the sky were opened." Since the *deep* means oceans, and since the canopy stored the water for the oceans as well, the only conclusion is that smaller seas existed on the surface of the earth prior to the Flood.

There we have it: before the Flood of Gen. 7, from Adam to Noah's time, there was a canopy surrounding our atmosphere. This canopy of ice and salt water would have created a tropical greenhouse effect, thereby resulting in temperate temperatures around the globe. The temperate temperatures resulted in no deserts and no polar ice caps, and since the Flood had not occurred yet, the vast oceans were stored in that canopy and in deep caverns within the earth. With temperate temperatures and no oceans, there would be approx. 4 times more useful land covered in thick, lush vegetation on earth than what we see today. This massive amount of vegetation would produce 50% more oxygen than our current vegetation and phytoplankton does today. Now, we have a record of when the earth had 50% higher oxygen concentration. That record is in the Bible and is evidence of how and why our atmosphere had much higher oxygen concentrations.

Today, 71% of the globe is covered by oceans, which results in phytoplankton having the major role in regulating carbon dioxide and oxygen concentrations. Phytoplankton are marine and aquatic based microscopic plant-like organisms that absorb CO_2 and produce O_2. However, before the Flood, only 20% of the earth was covered by water, the remaining 80% was covered by dense, lush tropical forests, and they had the major role of regulating CO_2 and O_2 concentrations.

In addition, before the Flood of Gen. 7, because the canopy added weight and pressure to the atmosphere, it created higher atmospheric pressure. Combining that with the 50% higher oxygen concentration, allowed a greater tidal volume of oxygen to enter the body with each inhalation. This means that more oxygen entered the body with each breath. This caused life to thrive and made life easier. In the sports world, an illegal technique of enhancing performance is by blood doping. Blood doping is the practice of removing blood from the body a week prior to an event; the body will produce additional blood, and then the day of the sporting event, the blood that was withdrawn is put back into the body. This means that the body has extra red blood cells (RBCs, erythrocyte) to carry extra oxygen to the muscles, which gives an unfair advantage to the athlete with the extra RBCs. That athlete will not get tired as quickly and will have greater endurance. Hence, it is illegal. Hence, extra oxygen to the body causes life to thrive.

The only logical conclusion for what caused earth's atmosphere to have 50% higher oxygen concentration levels in the past versus today's value. That is the earth's landscape did not have oceans and the land had more vegetation. The land available for vegetation was quadrupled versus today, and the density of vegetation was greater, and the height of the vegetation was higher because the buoyant force was greater, which reduced net gravity. This combination produced 50% increase in O_2. This caused life to thrive.

What event in the history of earth could have caused a decrease in vegetation, increased oceans, expansive polar ice caps, deserts, uniform layers of the crust, petroleum reserves, petrification, and coalification? Only one event does all that, and it is the global flood. That much water coming upon the earth from above and deep caverns below the crust would have covered the globe, initiated an ice age and formed vast oceans. Only the Flood of Gen. 7, where it rained for 40 days and 40 nights and the water covered the globe for 150 days could have reduced the high heat from the asteroid impacts, volcanoes, and violent tectonic plate movements of the Flood, and blocked the sun to produce expansive polar ice caps that reached down from the North Pole to central North America and Central Europe (called the Ice Age or Glacial Age). Only the Flood, with the loss of the protective layer of water above the atmosphere, would then cause the deserts to form some 4,300 years ago as they baked near the equators. Only the global flood of highly salty water could have killed massive aquatic dinosaurs that lived in water. Potentially, they were unable to adapt to the increased salty oceans and the violence during the Flood saga. Only the Gen. 7 flood, where water burst violently out of the earth, could have sent enough soil mixed in the Flood waters (called high turbidity) to then settle in uniform layers of the earth's crust as we have today without the earmark of millions of years of erosion commingling the layers. Only the Flood of Gen. 7 could put seashells on the tops of all mountains. Only the Flood of Gen. 7 could have killed every creature not on Noah's ark, and then with bacteria causing bloating weeks after death, it caused the dead creatures and the soil to settle according to density. Combine this with a global tide, since the continents and mountains could not stop a global roaming tide. This global roaming tide caused liquefaction, and this disturbed and broke free the static friction of the soil to settle according to density, thereby forming the so-called geological column. Only the Flood gives an explanation of how dinosaurs grew so tall before the Flood, as only the pre-Flood canopy could create a buoyancy effect great enough to counteract gravity so that the reptiles could grow so large. Only the Flood explains how humans lived 900+ years before the Flood, as only the pre-Flood canopy could create temperate global temperatures for vegetation to grow massively dense and produce such high concentrations of oxygen in the atmosphere, which caused life forms to grow larger and faster and to live longer. Only the Flood answers all these questions. The pre-Flood conditions allowed the earth to have a weaker gravity and higher oxygen concentrations for dinosaurs to be so massive.

Review: Prior to the Flood, vegetation was times more plentiful and produced 50% higher O2 levels than today. As a result of the Flood, polar ice caps, deserts, and oceans were created. All three of them physically limit oxygen-producing vegetation. Prior to ~2,350 BC, the earth did not have oceans. The earth had only seas. The earth did not have polar ice caps or deserts. The earth had temperate global temperatures. All this combined resulted in vast amounts of vegetation, which produced massive volumes of oxygen. And the result was that earth's atmosphere had 50% higher oxygen concentrations before the Flood of Gen. 7.

Higher oxygen concentrations in the past allowed animals and vegetation to grow to enormous height and weight and to live almost a millennia. Dinosaurs stood 100 feet tall and weighed 100 tons. The Bible records that most humans lived 900+ years before the Flood. Gen. 5:5: "So all the days that Adam lived were nine hundred and thirty years and he died." The first man, Adam, lived 930 years. His son Seth lived 912 years (Gen. 5:8). Seth's son Enosh lived 905 years (Gen. 5:11). Enosh's son Kenan lived 910 years (Gen. 5:12). Kenan's son Mahalalel lived 895 years. Mahalalel's son Jared lived 962 years (Gen. 5:20). Jared's son Enoch lived 365 years, and then he walked with God and went to heaven without dying (Gen. 5:24). Then Enoch's son Methuselah lived 969 years (Gen. 5:27). Methuselah's son Lamech, lived 777 years (Gen. 5:31). Lamech's son Noah lived 950 years (Gen. 9:28). You can see that people from all the generations before the Flood all lived long lives averaging 900+ years. The Bible gives the age of the fathers when they had their son. This is how Archbishop James Ussher came up with 4004 BC as the date when Adam was formed.

Then, with the advent of the global flood, along came massive oceans, polar ice caps, and deserts. They decreased the amount of vegetation, which reduced production of oxygen. And as populations of all life increased, this reduced the oxygen concentration in the atmosphere and made life harder to sustain. After the Flood, in the recordings in the Bible of the genealogy of Noah, you can see that life expectancy decreased with each passing generation as oxygen levels gradually reduced. Based on the DNA code, they adapted to less and less oxygen until we reached a homeostasis of life expectancy with oxygen concentration. Noah's son Shem lived 600 years (Gen. 11:10–11). Shem's son Arpachshad lived 438 years (Gen. 11:12–13). Arpachshad's son Shelah lived 433 years (Gen. 11:14–15). Shelah's son Eber lived 464 years (Gen. 11:16–17). Eber's son Peleg lived 239 years (Gen. 11:18–19). Peleg's son Reu lived 239 years (Gen. 11:20–21). Reu's son Serug lived 230 years (Gen. 11:22–23). Serug's son Nahor lived 148 years (Gen. 11:24–25). Nahor's son Terah lived 205 years (Gen. 11:32). Terah's son Abram, who became Abraham (the father of the Jews and Muslims), lived 175 years (Gen. 25:7). Abraham's son Isaac lived 180 years (Gen. 35:28–29). Isaac's son Jacob lived 147 years (Gen. 47:28). Jacob's son Joseph lived 110 years (Gen. 50:26). You can see that with each passing generation, the effect of oxygen reduction is proportionately affecting the longevity of life. Within 13 generations, the average life expectancy declined from 900+ years of life to 110 years.

Following timelines of genealogies in the Bible, scholars have determined: The date of the Genesis Flood was ~2348 BC; Abraham lived from 2166–1991 BC (The 10th generation from Noah to Abraham). The time span from the global flood to the death of Abraham was only 357 years. Therefore, in 357 years, life expectancy was reduced from 900+ years to 175 years.

Review: Before the Flood, humans lived 900+ years. After the Flood, life expectancy dropped dramatically. In 357 years (10 generations), life expectancy dropped from 900+ to 175 years.

Why is this significant? For one major reason: it is easy to see that life expectancy declined with each passing generation after the Flood. All the while, this reduction in life expectancy was paralleling the gradual decline of oxygen concentration in the atmosphere. While oxygen levels were decreasing in production, human life and animal life was increasing their consumption of oxygen as they increased in population.

With the research revealing a connection between the quality and quantity of life and oxygen concentration, it is easy to see that the reduction in the longevity of life and the post-Flood environment are inextricably linked.

Review: The reduction in life expectancy is directly linked to the post-Flood environment of reduced oxygen concentration.

The second major important consideration in terms of the connection of quality and quantity of life with oxygen concentration, is the book of Job. In the book of Job, Chapter 42:16 reads, "After this, Job lived 140 years, and saw his sons and his grandsons, four generations." Since Job was a fully mature adult at the beginning of the book that bares his name and Job lived long enough to father 10 children and to accumulate massive wealth,[25] then Job was probably 65+ years of age when the book starts. This means Job lived around 200+ years in total. Because "After this" is referring to "after all the troubles written in the book of Job," he lived an additional 145 years. This puts the timeline of when Job lived and had all his trials between the seventh and ninth generation after the Flood. Why is this noteworthy? Because the book of Job describes dinosaurs in Job 40:15–41:10 and 41:15–34. God illustrates His awesome power, and the most impressive creature He has created when He says to Job, "You cannot even conquer what I've created, so who are you to question me?" Here are a few references to dinosaurs: "Behold now, Behemoth [Behemoth means gigantic or colossal beast], which I made as well as you; He eats grass like an ox. Behold now, his strength in his loins and his power in the muscles of his belly. He bends his tail like a cedar." Cedar trees in the Mesopotamian area at Job's time were massive trees that were 100–120 feet tall. This creature that God describes to Job (and Job is aware of the creature) is so large that this Behemoth's tail is likened to a cedar tree that was 100–120 feet tall. What animals have tails 100 feet long? That would be none other than dinosaurs, such as the argentinosaurus. "The sinews of his thighs are knit together. His bones are tubes of bronze; His limbs are like bars of iron. He is the first of the ways of God; Let his maker bring near his sword." God is being sarcastic to Job, telling him to bring his sword against God's Behemoth and telling him he would lose. "If a river rages, he is not alarmed; He is confident, though the Jordan rushes to his mouth. Can anyone capture him when he is on watch, With barbs can

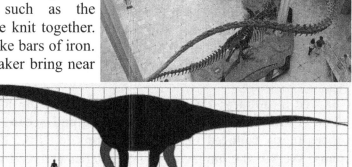

DIMENSIONS IN METERS   © www.prehistoric-wildlife.com

anyone pierce his nose?" This cannot describe a hippopotamus for they have small tails, and they do not exist in the Jordan River. And obviously men can and have captured hippos. In chapter 41, God describes an even more impressive fire breathing dinosaur in the oceans. *Image credit: Prehistoric-Wildlife.com.*

Since the book of Job describes dinosaurs in Chapters 40–41 and Job lived in the sixth to ninth

---

25 Job 1:3: "His possessions also were 7 ,000 sheep, 3,000 camels, 500 yoke of oxen, 500 female donkeys, and very many servants; and that man was the greatest of all the men of the east."

generation after the Flood, and since we do not see dinosaurs today, then (a) dinosaurs gradually all became extinct after the book of Job, or (b) dinosaurs are still living amongst us but too small to be called dinosaurs. Their life spans are too short (because of a lack of oxygen and the strength of gravity) now for them to grow to the same large sizes as before. Therefore, some may still live amongst us but are too small to be recognized as dinosaurs and are seen as just reptiles.

The first option suggests that mankind coexisted with dinosaurs before and after the Flood until dinosaurs were all extinct. There were no catastrophic events after the Flood, and since dinosaurs survived the Flood and were alive for God to use them in His illustration for Job, in that case, they are most likely still living amongst us, but their life span is too short because of a lack of oxygen and because of a strong force of gravity for them to grow large again. Remember that dinosaurs had to adapt to the changes in the post-Flood environment as well as other creatures, including humans. Since humans survived the change, then so too did dinosaurs. Since dinosaurs were adapting to the post-Flood environment, they would gradually have a reduced longevity of life as humans did. Additionally, since all dinosaurs are reptiles, we know that reptiles continue to grow as long as they are alive. In pre-Flood conditions with high oxygen concentrations, weaker net gravity, and higher buoyancy, the dinosaurs could live 900+ years, constantly growing larger and taller, which explains how their porous bone structures could support such massive size. But in post-Flood conditions, with lower oxygen concentrations and higher net gravity and a weaker buoyancy force, the dinosaurs would have gradually adapted to the conditions as all life forms did. Their life expectancy would have decreased proportionately in the same way. Imagine a dinosaur that in prior generations lived 900+ years and had all those years to grow. Now imagine a dinosaur in post-Food conditions only living 200 years at the time of the book of Job, and then imagine a dinosaur only living 15–25 years today. We would call them lizards, tuataras, Komodo dragons, crocodiles, and so forth.

Review: The Bible describes dinosaurs about six to nine generations after the Flood in the book of Job. Dinosaurs could still be living amongst us, but would just be much smaller than their ancestors. We would not call them dinosaurs, but reptiles.

How do we prove that there was a global flood and that this flood changed the landscape of the earth from a place with abundant vegetation to a world with sweeping polar ice caps, multiple large deserts, and vast volumes of oceans? We will take this in stages. First, we'll use the Bible as the foundation, and then we'll use science and finally logic. We could rely exclusively on the Bible through faith alone, but we won't have to rely on one piece of evidence to stand on its own. The totality of the evidence will lead to an overwhelming logical conclusion after ruling out the impossible. A wise author once wrote: "Once you eliminate the impossible, whatever remains, however improbable, must be the truth" (Sir Conan Doyle, the creator of Sherlock Holmes).

Chapter Summary: Oxygen concentration in the atmosphere was 31% before the Flood. The Flood resulted in polar ice caps, deserts, and oceans that physically limit vegetation growth and subsequently reduced O2 concentrations to 21%. This caused life to suffer and shortened life spans. We see the longevity of genealogies reduced with the Biblical record, and thus, animals' longevity also suffered the same reduction in life span. This significantly reduced the quality and quantity of life. Atlantic ocean core samples reveal that the desertification of the Sahara occurred around the time of the Flood.

Chapter 6
Land Was More Plentiful in the Past

The premise of this book is that the earth's net gravity was approximately ~15.5% to 33.5% weaker in some past millennium and oxygen concentrations were 50% higher than today. Those two changes caused life forms to be enormous in size and to live a long time. What did earth look like when net gravity was weaker and oxygen levels were higher?

In order for the above premise to occur, with ~15.5% to 33.5% weaker gravity and 50% higher oxygen concentrations, there needs to be more land and less ocean water covering that land. The more land that is accessible for vegetation growth, the more oxygen is produced by vegetation. The ocean water needs to be stored in a place that somehow reduces gravity and blocks the sun's harmful rays. Therefore, this book's premise needs fewer oceans to expose more land. The oceans limit the amount of vegetation that can grow and thereby directly reduce the oxygen concentration in the atmosphere. Also, there cannot be any deserts or polar ice caps because both of them limit vegetation growth as well and thereby directly limit the oxygen concentration.

For dinosaurs to live long and grow to enormous sizes, gravity needs to be weaker than today. This means that either the earth's mass needs to be less to support weaker gravity, or Earth needs to have spun much faster, or buoyant force needs to be much larger, or some combination of that. For dinosaurs and humans to live almost 1,000 years, oxygen concentrations needs to be around 50% higher than today's current value, which means more land needs to be exposed to grow more vegetation and produce more oxygen.

The solution that solves the above problem and fulfills both requirements of this book's premise of weaker gravity and higher oxygen, is removing the earth's oceans and placing some of that water around the atmosphere and some in deep caverns under the crust (surface) of the earth, leaving only smaller seas.

Review: Removing the ocean waters and placing that water in two locations—outside and around our atmosphere and in deep caverns under the crust of the earth—would weaken the earth's gravity because of the buoyant force and increase the earth's oxygen concentration by increasing the exposed land for vegetation growth.

In addition, a solution that aids the premise in reducing gravity is a faster spinning earth. The faster the earth spins, the less effect gravity has on objects. The moon slows down the earth's rotational velocity by taking angular momentum out of the earth's spin with each tide. The moon uses up that angular momentum that it takes from the earth's spin to move farther away from the earth. This means that the further back in time, the faster the earth spun on its axis and the closer the moon was to the earth, compounding how much angular momentum the moon could take out of the earth's spin.

Also, with some of the water stored in deep caverns under the crust of the earth, the water table would be at ground level, and there would be no need of rain for watering the ground. This is a good thing, because in this scenario of water surrounding our atmosphere, this would create too much atmospheric pressure for clouds to form and create a greenhouse effect and subsequent temperate temperatures on a global scale. This would convert deserts and polar ice caps into lush vegetation. And since plants produce oxygen, that would subsequently increase oxygen concentrations in the atmosphere by the necessary 50%. In this scenario, since large global changes in temperatures are required for the jet stream, there would not be a jet stream and subsequently no hurricanes or tornadoes. As a result of the high atmospheric pressure, evaporation would condense into a mist in the cool of the night—dew—bypassing cloud formation, and therefore there would be no rain or rainbows.

Review: Removing the oceans and placing ~50% of that water surrounding our atmosphere and the other 25% in deep caverns under the surface of the earth would result in a weaker gravity and a 50% increase in oxygen concentrations in the atmosphere.

Is this fantasy? No, even scientists hypothesize that some of the water on Earth possibly came from outer space. They suggest that several comets possibly impacted Earth to deliver the water. The Bible records a similar premise that "the earth was formed out of water and by water" (2 Peter 3:6).

In the beginning, God made seas on the earth, not oceans. What is the difference? An ocean is about 20 times larger than a sea. Consider Gen. 1:9–10 as it describes the third day of creation "gathering of the waters He called **seas**." Job 28:14 illustrates they are different: "The deep says, 'It is not in me'; And the sea says, 'It is not in me.'" The deep is the ocean, and the sea is the sea. Genesis 7:11 reveals the two sources that formed the oceans: "All the fountains of the great deep burst open, and the floodgates of the sky were opened. The rain fell upon the earth for 40 days and 40 nights." Notice that the rain fell upon the earth, not fell on a particular city or region or continent. Also notice that it rained 40 days straight on the entire globe. All that water came from the canopy that was surrounding the atmosphere from when God created the atmosphere "between the waters" on the second day of creation. Furthermore, the deep burst open and poured its water onto the top soil to form the deep oceans mentioned in Job 28:14.

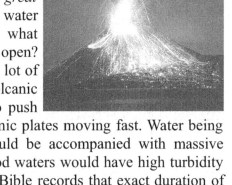

The global flood explains how reptiles are no longer dinosaurs, where the oceans came from, how the polar ice caps formed, when deserts were created. why mankind no longer lives 900+ years, why we have rainbows, and why petrified trees and fossils transcend many sedimentary layers that are supposed to take millions of years to form. It also accounts for all the layers of the earth's crust, sea fossils at the tops of mountains, wind, the hydrological cycle, and layers of the earth's sediment, and possibly, it could explain what happened to the missing city of Atlantis. *Photo credit: www.sanandreasfault.org.*

When the Bible uses the words of *all the fountains of the great deep burst open*, it is referring to either massive volumes of water violently erupting through the fault lines or volcanoes. Now, what happens when deep caverns inside the earth violently burst open? Earthquakes occur, volcanoes erupt, and tectonic plates shift, and a lot of dirt gets mixed into the water. Earthquakes are a result of volcanic activity and tectonic plate movement. The source of the force to push massive volumes of water out of great deep caverns was the tectonic plates moving fast. Water being forced out as fountains and bursting from within the earth would be accompanied with massive amounts of dirt, sediment, silt, clay, rock, mud and so on. The flood waters would have high turbidity (not clear water). It takes time for soil in the water to settle—the Bible records that exact duration of the entire flood saga as almost one year.

It is important to note that the amount of mass divided by the volume of an item determines its density. The greater the density of sediment, the faster it sinks in a medium such as water. The lesser the density of sediment, the slower it sinks in a medium such as water. Thus, the degree of mass compaction of the matter mixed in the flood waters determined the rate of descent from floating to settling on the ocean floor. This degree of mass compaction is called density.[26] Therefore, density determines the rate of descent while matter is floating in a medium such as water. All things will settle according to their density, based on the laws of physics. All that dirt, rock, soil, sediment, clay, and the like mixed in the turbulent and violent Flood settled according to density and formed layers, which is exactly what we have today. Aiding the segregated settling of the different soil—based on their densities—was a twice daily global tide (this process is called liquefaction).

A strong thunderstorms may release 3 to 4 inches for every 30 minutes of rainfall. Some extreme cases have been reported with 6 inches for every half hour of rainfall. Since the global flood was a judgment from God and since this was not from cloud formations, it is safe to say that the rate of the rainfall was beyond what clouds can deliver. Perhaps it could have been 20–30 inches of rain per

---

26 http://physics.about.com/od/fluidmechanics/f/density.htm.

half hour. We'll use 25 inches of rainfall per half hour for 40 days and nights. This does not account for the likely impact of a frozen comet impacting Earth near the Arctic Circle, which would have been able to freeze woolly mammoths in an upright position with undigested food in their stomach (several such specimens have been discovered in Siberia). Frozen comet impact(s) would have brought massive amounts of water, and evolutionists contend that at some time in the past, frozen comets of water have impacted earth. Let us work through the math to determine how much rain per hour is needed from the canopy of water to form 50% of the oceans and polar ice caps.

$$\frac{\sim 50 \text{ in. rain}}{\text{hr}} \times \frac{24 \text{ hrs.}}{1 \text{ day}} \times 40 \text{ Days} = 48{,}000 \text{ inches of global rainfall or } 4{,}000 \text{ feet of water.}$$

This is not enough water to cover the tops of mountains today, but remember that the mountains rose and valleys sank after the Flood. Look at Psalm 104:6–8:

> You covered it [earth] with the deep as with a garment, the waters were standing above the mountains. At your rebuke they fled, at the sound of Your thunder they hurried away. The mountains rose, the valleys sank down to the place which You established for them.

Thus, we do not need water to cover the existing height of mountains, but the lower height of mountains back in Gen. 7 time period.

Today, if all the mountains and valleys were smoothed out on the spherical earth, the water would be ~1.5 miles deep, which is ~7,900 feet. Then if we estimate that 20% of the oceans existed as the seas, that accounts for 1,580 feet of the water, and 50% of the oceans came from the canopy, that accounts for 3,950 feet of the water, and 30% of the oceans came from the fountains of the great deep, that accounts for 2,370 feet of the water (not including a comet). This accounts for where all the water on the earth may have come from. With an estimated 4,000 feet of water globally from rainfall, plus the water bursting out of the fountains of the deep, plus 20% of the ocean water from the existing seas before the Flood, we account for more than enough volume of water to form the oceans. This would be a complete deluge, and no thunderstorm would come close to the Biblical judgment of the Gen. 7 flood as far as the amount of rain per hour.

How do we know this was a global flood and not a local regional flood? It is because every piece of land on earth has indicators that it was once covered by an ocean. Every Park Ranger working as a tour guide in underground caverns, with stalactites and stalagmites, will tell you an ocean was once above the cave, and archeologists have found seashells and marine fossils at the tops of all mountains, and paleontologist have found countless marine fossils in the desert. Or we can go to Genesis 7:19–23:

> The water prevailed more and more upon the earth, so that ALL the high mountains EVERYWHERE under the heavens were covered. The water prevailed 15 cubits, and the mountains were covered. ALL flesh that moved on the earth perished, birds and cattle and beasts and every swarming thing that swarms upon the earth, and ALL mankind; of ALL that was on the dry land, ALL in whose nostrils was the breath of the spirit of life, died. Thus He blotted out EVERY living thing that was upon the face of the land, from man to animals to creeping things and to birds of the sky, and they were blotted out from the earth; and ONLY Noah was left, together with those that were with him in the ark.

Use logic with Gen. 8:3: "The water receded steadily from the earth, [not regionally] and at the end of one hundred and fifty days the water decreased. [A local flood does not take 150 days to decrease, but this global flood took almost a year to recede.] In the seventh month, on the seventeenth day of the month, the ark rested upon the mountains of Ararat." (A local flood would not put a ship the size of a football field on top of the mountains of Ararat. Those mountains are high, and Noah's Ark has been found in those mountains.)

The picture is in Turkey up in the mountains of Ararat. The image shows the fossil remains of a wooden vessel with a collapsed roof and with exact proportions and material recorded in the Bible for Noah's Ark. *The water decreased steadily until the tenth month, the **<u>tops of the mountains became</u>** visible*. The flood started on the second month, and in the 10th month, the mountain tops were visible!

It seems like a crazy notion that after nine months, the mountain tops would be visible. For example, the average absorption rates of lake water at the peak of summer in hot Texas weather is 4 to 6 inches per day. But with the global flood and darkness covering all the earth for 40 days, global temperatures would have plunged to subfreezing at the poles and potentially in the 50s at the equator. So this would have been a slow process of a global flood being absorbed by earth. *Photo credit: Ron Wyatt.*

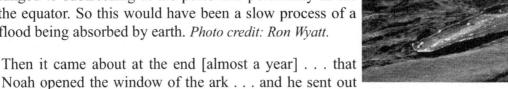

> Then it came about at the end [almost a year] . . . that Noah opened the window of the ark . . . and he sent out a . . . dove from him, to see if the water was abated from the face of the land; but the dove found no resting place for the sole of her foot, so she returned to him into the ark, for the water was on the surface of **<u>all the earth</u>** (Gen. 8:6–9a).

There it is—the water was on the surface of all the earth. At this point, if you still refuse to believe this was a global flood, then you must question your faith in God because God declared it in His testimony. You can take it at face value and look like a fool before mankind, or you can reject it and interpret it as allegorical to pacify nonbelievers, but do not think the Bible does not clearly record a global flood.

For so much rain to come down and fountains of water to burst open, this indeed would have formed the oceans as we know it. This means that before the Flood came, the earth had a lot more land available for vegetation growth that produced massive amounts of oxygen, 50% more than today. Considering Ecclesiastes 1:9 "<u>That which has been is that which will be</u>," and Rev. 21:1 "A new earth . . . <u>there is no longer any sea</u>." The concept of more usable land before the Flood is also supported by future prophesy.

Chapter Summary: The Flood brought so much water upon the earth that it created the world's oceans. There were no oceans before the global flood. Before the Great Flood, only seas existed. Prior to the Flood, there would have been extra land that would have had extra vegetation, and that extra vegetation would have produced extra oxygen—50% more than after the Flood.

Chapter 7
<u>Meteors, Asteroids, and Comets</u>

In the burgeoning first day of the universe, the space between forming planets, stars, solar systems, and galaxies were filled with matter in the form of water and soil. After the rapid expansion of the universe, galaxies, and solar systems on the second day of creation, the space between the galaxies and solar systems were filled with asteroids, meteors, and comets, much more than we observe today. Most of those floating objects were drawn into the nearest planet's, moon's or star's gravitational force. On planets that are active, such as Earth, the impact craters have been covered up from erosion, tectonic plate shifts, forest, oceans, and so forth. But those planets and moons that are not active show a vast array of impact craters, indicating that there was heavy activity in past millennia of impacting meteors and asteroids. Most of the asteroids and meteors that were circling the sun between the planets have been drawn in by those planet's gravity and have been absorbed by now. But still two belts of asteroids and meteor clusters remain within our solar system, called the Kuiper Belt and Main Asteroid Belt.

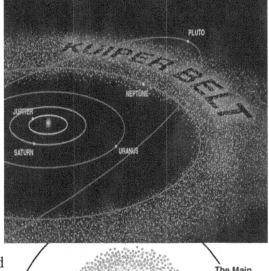

The Kuiper Belt is located between Neptune and Pluto and consists of millions of asteroids that encircles our solar system and may be the last remnants of how our solar system existed with free floating molten masses before they coalesced into planets. The remaining cooled asteroids are what is left over of what floated all throughout our solar system, not just encircling outside of it. One would imagine that there were many more asteroids floating around just like the Kuiper Belt at the beginning of the solar system. After the asteroids had impacted planets over millennia, almost all had been absorbed into the planets that they impacted, except those remnants encircling our solar system in the Kuiper Belt. *Image credit: NASA and – I believe – G. Bacon (STScI).*

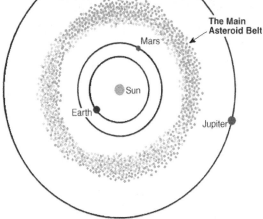

The Main Asteroid Belt lies between Mars and Jupiter and is a cluster of asteroids and meteors. This belt could represent what our solar system looked like before God finished forming all the planets of our solar system and the sun, moon, and stars on the fourth day of creation. Some cosmologists have suggested that there should have been a planet between Mars and Jupiter, and that planet would have absorbed all the asteroids and meteors that currently exist in this Main Asteroid Belt, which is plausible. Who knows, maybe the iron core that exists in the center of our earth exists in the center of each planet, and these iron cores were the basis for the early molten masses floating and coalescing and being drawn toward each planet's center. A plausible reason that no planet exist between Mars and Jupiter and only the remnants of molten mass remains as cooled asteroids and meteors is that the iron core that was supposed to form the planet between Mars and Jupiter got caught in the gravitational force of Jupiter and was absorbed into Jupiter's mass. Could this be the cause of the permanent scar (in the form of a red dot) on Jupiter? Iron oxidizes when it comes into contact with gases and turns red. However, cosmologists agree that Jupiter is a gas giant, so it likely does not have an iron core, and they say the planet has no detectable surface. But it is plausible that the red dot on Jupiter is where the rusted iron core of the missing planet entered Jupiter. Scientists suggest that the red dot is a giant storm caused by high winds that draw reddish material from deeper within Jupiter, which tenuously corroborates the hypothesis. *Image credit: NASA/Goddard Space Flight Center.*

Review: More asteroids, comets, and meteors existed in past millennia than today. Two asteroid belts remain, the Main Asteroid Belts between Mars and Jupiter and one farther away called the Kuiper Belt, which is beyond Neptune.

Why have a chapter about asteroids, meteors, and comets? Because they played a significant part in the formation of the celestial bodies of our solar system, may have initiated the global flood, and will be used by God to fulfill the end time prophecies. Both creationists and evolutionary cosmologists, accept that in the beginning hot molten matter coalesced into the nearest celestial body, to form either planets, stars, or moons, and that the two asteroid belts are the remnants of that period. They just differ on when this process occurred, and how long this process took.

Also, both creationists and evolutionary cosmologists, accept that after life began on Earth, there was another period of asteroid, meteors, and comets bombarding the earth. The difference is that the evolutionists' view suggests a major event occurred 65 million years ago, and in the creationist view, the event occurred at the initiation of the Gen. 7 catastrophic flood. When I read an evolutionist explain how some massive asteroids hit the earth 65 million years ago that caused a mass extinction, I say, well the same scenario played out at the beginning of the global flood. Evolutionists contend that the impact would have sent debris 400 miles wide and a shock wave 1,000 miles wide. A creationist agrees with the synopsis. Evolutionists further say that the terrain burned and left a layer of carbon-based ash and soot. Agreed. The heat from the blast would have increased global temperatures to more than 100°F and would have killed off what the blast zone did not. Also, there would have been acid rain in the blast zone. All these suppositions are in agreement with the creationist view of what was going on in the initial stages of the global flood. Evolutionists further say that this asteroid impact event plunged the globe into an ice age. That's agreed to as well. With so much agreement, why do we differ on when it occurred? That is based on the layers of the crust of the earth. For that discussion, see the chapter regarding the layers of the crust.

Each time a comet orbits about the sun, it loses matter. Water and debris is ejected off the comet until the ice is gone. This is demonstrated by its tail that points away from the sun. Also, the ice on comets is constantly reducing because it evaporates into space, this process is called sublimation. Since no evidence exists of comets being formed, or existing comets having frozen water added to them, we may conclude that each time we observe a comet with its tail, it is strong evidence of a young solar system and galaxy. If the universe was millions of years old, the comets would have lost all their water. Evolutionary cosmologists counter this theory with a hypothetical Oort cloud that icy material to each comet. However, this has never been observed, thus it leaves the reality of science and enters faith based religion. *Image credit: Wikipedia.org/comets.*

Let us work through some concepts about asteroid impacts and determine how their impacts have shaped life on earth. Each of the comets and asteroids that impacted Earth would have adversely affected the planet's spin velocity and added to Earth's mass and increased gravity and quit possibly caused the 23.5° tilt. For the most part, the effect of adding mass to increase gravity was so small that it is not noticeable and only determined through calculations. But there were large impacts that did have a noticeable change on life on earth. However, a concept of this book is that asteroids impacting the earth initiated the Flood by colliding into the frozen arch support structure that was instrumental in holding up the canopy that surrounded the atmosphere, and fractured Pangaea, which released 1,650 years of built up potential energy in the tectonic plates.

As the asteroids passed through the canopy of water and impacted the earth, this could have slightly disrupted the spin velocity and direction of the earth. How? Imagine a basketball player spinning a ball on his finger. To keep that ball spinning, the basketball player must tap the ball at a precise location, in a precise direction, with a precise angle and with a precise force to keep the spin of the ball going fast enough to maintain the angular momentum. (The angular momentum generates a gyroscope effect, which keeps the ball balanced on the finger.) If the basketball players taps the ball in the wrong location or wrong direction or at the wrong angle or with improper force, the ball will lose its gyroscope effect, lose its axis spin, and fall off the finger. The same principal applies when comets and asteroids impact the earth. If enough asteroids hit the earth in a precise location, with a precise angle, in a precise direction and with enough force, that would fractionally increase the spin of the earth. But probably the odds are ~99.999% of the asteroids hitting the earth do not have the precise location, angle, and direction. Subsequently, their impacts take angular momentum out of the earth's spin, resulting in a reduction in speed of the earth's spin. How much is taken out of the earth's rotational velocity is determined by the force of the impact, and the angle, this is called the vector of force. The force is determined by the mass of the object multiplied by acceleration. Over the last 4,500 years, this has been negligible; otherwise, life would have been adversely affected. But there was a time in the recent past when large asteroids impacted the earth. These impacts changed the environmental conditions of life on earth.

When the earth was formed, there were many more asteroids, meteors, and comets. How do we know this? Well, every time a comet, asteroid, or meteor collides into a celestial body, it is gone forever. We do not see any factories producing asteroids or comets. Our moon, though it is very small compared to Earth and has a weaker gravitational force to attract asteroids, has thousand of impact craters; thus, we may infer the earth has been hit more than the moon. The more mass a planet/moon/star has, the greater the gravitational force to attract asteroids and comets. Usually, more mass means a larger planet/moon/star, but not always. For example, four moons can fit inside the earth, but the planet has 45 times more mass than the moon (www.wikipedia.org/earth.) and therefore a significantly greater gravitational force. The moon is no longer active, so its impact craters are not covered up by erosion, earthquakes, wind, oceans, snow, forest, vegetation, and so on. (Also, our atmosphere disintegrates most meteorites before they impact the earth). Therefore, the earth has been hit more than the moon, but the impacts are not as obvious. In addition, Jupiter is so much larger than our planet that 1,321 Earth's can fit inside of Jupiter. With Jupiter being that much larger and its mass being so much greater than Earth, it would attract many more asteroids. We can safely say that Earth has been hit far fewer times than Jupiter. Likewise, the sun is so massive that 1.3 million Earths could fit inside the sun. With such a large sun and with such a great gravitational force, the sun has been hit proportionately more by asteroids than the earth. Put all this together and it means that there were potentially hundreds of millions more asteroids and comets many millennia ago as compared to today.

What is the point? Well, the frozen external portion of the canopy would have provided the necessary support to maintain the set altitude, but it is nice to discover there was additional assistance to maintain the canopy up above the atmosphere. Such as support from centripetal force. A threshold is a principal in physics, that is a point exceeded to begin producing a given effect. For example, when water is 33°F, it is just cold and not freezing. When water crosses the threshold to 32°F, water freezes. It is the same with hot water; at 211°F, it is just hot water, but when it gets to 212°F, a threshold is crossed and the water boils. Potentially, the threshold of geosynchronous orbit for the canopy was a tug of war between the spin of the earth versus the gravity of the earth. This tenuous balancing act could have been decided by the frozen external arch support of the canopy. As the moon slowed the spin of the earth from creation till just before the start of the global flood, the threshold was being crossed and gravity was starting to overcome the countering affect of centripetal force, with only the frozen external arch support now standing in the way of gravity winning out and pulling the canopy down to Earth. Potentially, asteroids crashed into the canopy, breaking the frozen external support arch and initiated the Flood. The threshold of gravity causing the canopy to come down upon the earth. If the canopy did not come down as rain from gravity, it would have formed rings like Saturn's rings.

Several craters exist on the earth, but the largest impact crater is located at the Yucatan Peninsula. It could have been the asteroid impact that broke the ice arch support of the canopy and commenced the global flood, fractured Pangaea, altered the axis of the earth, and been the so-called "dinosaur killing asteroid(s)."

Is there physical evidence supporting the theory of an asteroid impact large enough to corroborate my theory? Yes, ample evidence exists of large enough impacts to be the legendary "dinosaur killer." One of the most telling pieces of evidence is a thin layer of iridium that is found around the globe. *Photo credit: sciencebuzz.org.*

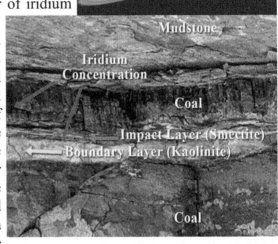

What does the picture show? For one, when trees and vegetation get blown over by asteroid impact zones and covered up by the subsequent ash from the fires and other layers, the trees, they turn to coal from the heart and pressure. This is in harmony with the Bible. The layer of iridium concentration came from asteroids. Asteroids have an abundance of iridium, but the earth does not have iridium unless it is brought from an outside source. A layer of iridium like this in several locations around the globe indicates that at one time, many large asteroids impacted the earth around the same time frame. How do we get a second layer of coal above the asteroid impact layer? Tree bark gets separated from the trees during impact trauma, and trees rubbing together knock the bark off while in the water, which sinks after being dislodged from the trees. The bark combines with other vegetation and trees and eventually forms the additional layer of coal. The higher second layer of coal could have come from trees and vegetation that floated for a week because they were less dense and sank on top of the impact layers, thus causing the second layer of coal. Then the muddy waters from the Flood would have settled on top of the vegetation over the next months. The different sediment would have settled by density according to the laws of physics, hence creating the mudstone layer on top. This could explain the reason for these similar layers around the world.

Review: Coal is created from plants and trees compressed by soil, moisture, heat, and pressure. The layers of the earth reveal the record of the Flood: lush vegetation killed by asteroid impacts and a muddy flood. The initial coal deposits are from the trees, bark, and vegetation covered by the impact soil that would have been lifted up by the asteroid impact and asteroid debris. The higher coal deposits are from trees and plants that floated until they sank and were covered up by the muddy flood waters.

Coal is created from botanical life covered with pressure, heat, and moisture. A global flood is a perfect scenario to convert botanical life to coal. It has the pressure, heat, and moisture necessary to accomplish coalification. At the beginning of the 40 days of rain, there was a massive amount of heat generated on the planet from several major events, such as asteroid impacts, which fractured Pangaea like an egg and released 1,650 years of stored-up tectonic plate potential energy, causing the tectonic plates of Pangaea to break apart at fast speeds of ~0.5 mph.[27] The Bible mentions a book called Jasher several times. Jasher is mentioned in Joshua 10:13 and 2 Samuel 1:18, but since the only copies of Jasher are in a fragmented incomplete form, the early patriarchs elected not to include the book in the Bible. But potentially, the book of Jasher may give a clue as to what caused Pangaea to crack into the different continents we see today. Jasher 6:11: "And on that day the Lord caused the whole earth to shake, and the sun darkened, and the foundations of the world raged, and the whole earth was moved violently, and the lightning flashed, and the thunder roared, and all the foundations in the earth were broken up." Food for thought, this indicates the violence associated with the Genesis flood as Pangaea was broken.

---

27 Today tectonic plates speed of travel is between the rate of hair growth to fingernail growth rates.

The force from the shifting of tectonic plates caused water from deep caverns to burst out (through faults and volcanoes) from under the crust of the earth, sending tons of sediment into the air and eventually into the floodwater. While the massive tectonic plates were moving, they caused fountains of lava to erupt from hundreds of volcanoes around the globe from multiple eruptions during the Flood event. Remember that the floodwater of Gen. 7 would have been filled with massive amounts of dirt/soil because the deep caverns burst open. What caused the deep caverns of the earth to burst open? Asteroid impacts and tectonic plate movements. When the sediment in the water finally settled,

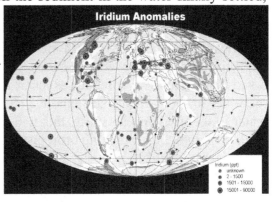

the soil settled in layers. That is exactly what we find on top of the iridium layer, layers of sediment. *Image credit: www.sites.google.com/site/thatdinothing.* The picture shows the locations of iridium. Iridium deposits are evidence of asteroid impacts.

All the planets in our solar system conserved the counterclockwise spin of the sun when they spun off of the sun on the second day of creation with God commanding the universe to expand. As each celestial body was coalescing matter on the first and second days of creation, the earth should have mirrored the sun's counterclockwise spin on a 0° axis. However, the earth has a tilt of 23.5 degree. Cosmologists accept that the earth was hit by asteroids, particularly the "dinosaur killer" asteroid, that tilted the earth's axis. This causes our four seasons as the earth orbits the sun. I contend this notion has merit, and that before the global flood, the earth did not have a tilt, and it was as a result of asteroid impact(s), that commenced the Flood, that caused the earth's tilt. Asteroid impacts on Venus is said to have caused that planet to reverse its original spin. Also, asteroid impacts is said to be the cause of Uranus' horizontal axis spin that is perpendicular to the sun. Saturn and Neptune both have a 30 degree tilt, also as a result of asteroid impacts. It appears that nearly every planet was bombarded by asteroids to alter each one's initial zero degree, counterclockwise spin from the sun. Physics demands the conservation of motion, and since each planet spun off from the sun, they would have conserved the sun's zero degree axis and counterclockwise spin until a force (asteroid impact) altered them.

Do evolutionary geologists support my hypothesis? Yes and No. No: they do not believe these impacts happened 4,500 years ago during the Genesis Flood. Yes: They believe there were asteroid impacts but that they occurred hundreds of millions of years ago when they wiped out the dinosaurs.

Does the Bible support asteroids hitting the earth? Yes, it supports an asteroid event in Joshua 10:10–11. God launched meteors and asteroids at the enemies of Israel. More on this later. The Bible also supports asteroid events in the near future in Revelation 6:13. "The stars [Greek word is "aster."] of the sky fell to the earth, as a fig tree casts its unripe figs when shaken by a great wind." If a large enough asteroid hit the earth, this would slow the spin and cause the earth to wobble off its 23° axis, much like when a gyroscope slows and starts to wobble. This notion is corroborated in Isaiah 24:18b: "For the windows above are opened, and the foundations of the earth shake. The earth is broken asunder, the earth is split through, the earth is shaken violently. The earth reels to and fro like a drunkard and it totters like a shack." When does this happen? Revelation 16:17–20:

Then the seventh angel poured out his bowl upon the air, and a loud voice came out of the temple from the throne, saying, 'It is done.' And there were flashes of lightning and sounds and peals of thunder; and there was a great earthquake, such as there had not been since man came to be upon the earth, so great an earthquake was it, and so mighty, the great city was split into three parts, and the cities of the nations fell . . . And every island fled away, and the mountains were not found. And huge hailstones about one hundred pounds each, came down from heaven upon men.

The Scriptures indicate that a large asteroid hits the earth so hard that it splits the earth through and causes the largest earthquake ever. The earth currently has a likely point that is ideal for splitting asunder. Note that *asunder* indicates the splitting of one part into two parts. This is used, for example, in the vow, "What God has joined together, let no man split asunder." In marriage, two becomes one, and in divorce, one becomes two. In this case, we're talking about splitting asunder the earth. A likely location is at the Mid-Atlantic Ridge. The Mid-Atlantic Ridge stretches from the North Pole region to the South Pole region and is literally a place where the earth is splitting in two halves through a process called divergence. At this Mid-Atlantic Ridge, the earth is pushing up and away from itself, which causes the African and European tectonic plates to push into Asia, and the North American and South American tectonic plates to push into the Pacific plate. This causes the ring of fire. The ring of fire is a hot active zone of plate tectonic subduction where one plate goes underneath another plate. It should be noted that when the earth splits asunder, all the oceans will pour into the hot mantle and core, causing the water to shoot up and surround the atmosphere, reconstituting the canopy of water again. While the water is shooting up into space, this will create a jet engine of force on a global scale that will put the earth back into a fast spinning orbit just like before the Flood. This could explain why in Revelation 22, "there is no ocean."

Review: Asteroids have hit the earth, and the Bible pronounces that they will hit the earth again. Could an asteroid hit the earth and increase the length of the day? Yes. If a large asteroid hit the earth in the opposite direction of the earth's spin, the earth could slow its rotation and subsequently lengthen the day. If the impact landed on an isolated tectonic plate, it could dislodged that plate and have the plate slide in the direction of the vector of force. If that direction is toward the west with the sun's apparent setting, that plate would slide on the surface of earth parallel with the sun's trajectory, causing the occupants standing on the surface of that plate to view the sun as though it is standing still. But since all the oceans, seas, and all dirt on the planet are still spinning at the same speed as the earth, the energy (called inertia) of all that matter would force that momentarily moving tectonic plate to continue rotating with the earth. Has this ever happened to earth? The day was prolonged in Joshua 10:12–14:

> Joshua spoke to the LORD, 'O sun, stand still at Gideon, and O moon in the valley of Aijalon.' So the sun stood still, and the moon stopped, until the nation avenged themselves of their enemies. Is it not written in the book of Jashar? And the sun stopped in the middle of the sky and did not hasten to go down for about a whole day. There was no day like that before it or after it.

This is from the perspective of the viewer on earth, so the sun did not stand still. Consider the following hypothesis: the tectonic plate that they were standing on moved parallel with the sun's normal trajectory of setting in the west. We do this every morning and evening when we say, "Oh what a lovely sunset/sunrise." The sun did not rise, and the sun did not set; the earth rotated. We do not say, "Oh what a lovely Earth rotation." That is the same concept here. Since they did not have stopwatches back in Joshua's day, they used sun dials. They did not know exactly how long the earth slowed its rotation. That's why the text reads "about a whole day," which could have been six to eight hours of daylight. They say, "time flies when you are having fun." Well, it is not fun to be in a battle for your life. Each moment of combat could seem like a long period of time, so when the fighter on the battlefield reports the length of time that the earth has slowed its rotation, it is from the perspective of someone who is fighting for his life. Maybe it seemed like a whole day. But this is a terrible argument if one holds that the Bible is the infallible Word of God. It is best to just accept the rendering in the Bible as it is and believe that the day was prolonged from a tectonic plate was moved from an asteroid impact and this movement seemed to appear as the sun stood still for about a whole day for potentially ~7 hours, as we are still limited by the endurance of a human at a stressful point in time. Going for prolonged periods of time in continuous fighting would cause exhaustion and would definitely takes its toll. Even a highly trained soldier in top shape—after spending hours engaged in hand-to-hand combat and pursuing an enemy on foot—would get fatigued and tire long before the day was lengthened by six hours.

How did God cause the sun and moon to seemingly stand still? Perhaps it was by momentarily causing a tectonic plate to slide along the path of the sun from the earth spinning. I contend it was from asteroid impacts. Just prior to Joshua recording that the sun stood still in Joshua 10:12–14, he describes God striking and killing the wicked people in verses 10–11 with:

> The LORD confounded them before Israel, and He slew them with a great slaughter at Gibeon and pursued them . . As they fled . . . the LORD threw large stones from heaven on them as far as Azekah, and they died; more died from the stones than those whom the sons of Israel killed with the sword.

This is exactly what we would expect to read if an asteroid caused a tectonic plate to slide along the path the sun moves. It indicate that the "large stones from heaven" were asteroids and meteors, which were from heaven (space). Those asteroids killed more people than Joshua and his armies did by sword. This fits perfectly with asteroid and meteors hitting the earth, killing a bunch of people. The force from the impacts caused a section of the surface crust of earth to slide and mirror the rotational spin of the sun to seemingly prolong the day, potentially by sliding the entire tectonic plate on top of magma until the inertia of all the matter on earth and the spin of the iron core and inner mantle caused the earth's crust or that particular set of tectonic plates to resume its movements.

Geologists estimate that an iron core inside earth is spinning faster than the surface, with the surface crust of earth resting on liquid magma. A plausible scientific explanation is of the surface being hit by a large asteroid and the surface alone moving, with the inside iron core still rotating at the same velocity. The liquid magma in between the two would allow for the surface to move for a moment and for the iron core to continue spinning. Then, eventually friction would win out, and the spin of the iron core would cause the surface crust to spin along with it. Therefore, scientific evidence exist to support a literal reading of the text that the day stood still from the viewer's perspective on earth. The best and safest approach for the correct interpretation of Joshua 10 is a literal rendering.

Chapter Summary: Asteroids have hit the earth, and the Bible pronounces that they will hit the earth again. Both God and geologists agree that asteroids have impacted the earth, but they disagree as to when those asteroids impacted the earth. It is possible for asteroids to hit the earth and reduce the spin of the earth, or cause a tectonic plate to slide. It is probable that the "dinosaur killing asteroid(s)" such as the one that hit the earth at the Yucatan Peninsula could have initiated the Flood.

Chapter 8
Earth's Spin at Origins

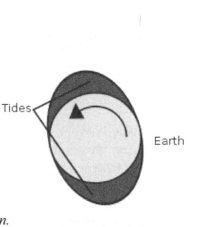

In the beginning, on the first day of creation, when God started rotating the formless mass of water and dirt that was to be Earth, that rotational speed was faster than the current rotational speed of the earth. This means that the evening and morning of the first day occurred slightly faster and in shorter time than the current 23 hours, 56 minutes, and 4.1 seconds it takes for one rotation of the earth today.

How do we know this? The moon is one reason we know this for certain. The moon's gravity takes angular momentum away from the earth's rotational velocity, and the moon uses the captured energy to move away from the earth. Each ocean tide, twice a day, is caused by the moon's gravity, and they take angular momentum out of the earth's rotational velocity. This is to say that the moon is slowing the earth down by means of gravity. *Image credit: wikipedia.org/wiki/tidal_acceleration.*

Since the moon is moving away from the earth, the moon was closer to the earth in past millennia. When the moon was closer to the earth, the moon's gravitational force caused greater ocean tides, which took more angular momentum out of the earth's spin, which caused a greater the reduction in the earth's spin velocity.

Therefore, when the moon was closer to earth, the moon slowed the spin of the earth to a greater degree. Thus, the earth spun faster in past millennia. With a faster spinning earth, the length of one day was shorter. This begs the question: "How long was a day when dinosaurs roamed the earth?"

Currently, the earth is slowing 2 milliseconds per 100 years. But this rate of reduction of speed is not constant. In prior centuries, the rate of reduction would be larger. Why? Because the moon would have been closer and its gravitational force would have caused greater ocean tides, which would have taken more speed out of the spinning earth. The further back in time we go, the greater the reduction of spin exponentially. In addition, large asteroid impacts would have reduced the earth's spin velocity. Also, when large asteroids hit the earth to initiate the Flood and the breakup of Pangaea, the large tectonic plate movements would have also taken away angular momentum from earth's spin. Putting these pieces of the puzzle together, an estimate of the length of day at the time of Adam and Eve, some 6,000 years ago, would be approximately ~17 hours long.

The velocity of the earth's spin when Adam and Eve and the dinosaurs roamed the earth would have been around 1,606 mph,[28] which is ~60% greater than the current rotational velocity of 1,037 mph. This would also have reduced the gravitational effect from centripetal force. It should be noted that there have been several Yellowstone eruptions and hundreds of volcanic eruptions around the globe. With the catastrophic flood and most of those volcanoes erupting during the global flood saga, the force of the hundreds of eruptions would have taken angular momentum out of the spin of earth as well. The net result is that the eruptions would have fractionally contributed to slowing the spin of the earth. Each earthquake and dam built to hold back water fractionally slows the spin of the earth.

Therefore, the Bible does not mention "24 hours" for good reason. Since the duration of the day is about 4 minutes short of 24 hours today, and the day is progressively getting longer, it is impossible for the day to be 24 hours during Adam's lifetime. The best conclusion is a ~17 hour day during Adam's life. Creationists should never use "24 hours" to describe the days of creation. Instead, they should say, "the days of creation were literal rotations of the earth."

Chapter Summary: The earth spun faster in past millennia and subsequently had shorter days and weaker gravity as a result of the faster spinning earth because of centripetal force.

---

28 Factors in an enlarged equatorial bulge from faster spin.

Chapter 9
The Flood

The Flood deserves an entire book dedicated to the subject. This event is so instrumental in changing the conditions on the planet and life on Earth that it needs some attention. Discerning what the Flood caused and changed will reveal what the conditions and life on Earth looked like from creation till the Flood. One can interpret the Bible's flood record and use the Bible's record to interpret observable evidence to understand from coal deposits, shallower salt deposits (the deeper salt deposits were formed during creation), oil deposits, petrified wood, dinosaur fossils, layers of soil in the crust, deserts, polar ice caps, the continental shelf, seashells on top of mountains, ancient cultures with flood stories, large asteroid impact craters, tectonic drifts, mountains, and valleys. All that we see today can be explained in the context of the Flood, either directly or indirectly, including the notion that mankind once lived 900+ years while dinosaurs roamed the earth.

We'll go through a description of the Flood based on the Bible, including hypotheses based on deduction from observable evidence and science and then attempt to break down the major points throughout this book, hoping that by covering the major points, the fine details associated with the Flood will also be exposed. The overall goal is to use the Flood to shed more light on what the environment and life were like on the planet before the Flood.

The Bible records that God stored water in three locations at the time of creation to allow optimal living conditions on Earth. Two of those locations were later used for judgment with the Flood. One location of water storage was in the deep caverns just below the surface, which housed a great deal of water (Gen. 7:11). The second location of water storage was in the canopy of ice and salt water, which held a great deal of water hovering above the atmosphere (Gen. 1:6–8). The third location of water was the seas (including fresh water lakes per Gen. 1:9–10). The potential percentages of water in these three locations that currently make up our oceans and seas, range from ~50% in the canopy, ~30% the deep caverns, and ~20% as seas. This utopian setup that God created was called Eden, from the time of creation until the Flood. There were no oceans, but there were small seas, and the exposed land, a supercontinent called Pangaea (Gen. 1:9 and 10:25), that covered ~80% of Earth's surface, was covered in lush vegetation, which produced more oxygen. With no polar ice caps and no hot deserts, there was no jet stream (Gen. 8:1). There were no four seasons, just spring. There was too much atmospheric pressure from the canopy to form clouds, and therefore there were no rain and no rainbows (Gen. 9:13–16). Resulting from evaporation and high atmosphere pressure, the hydrological cycle skipped clouds and rain and went straight to a mist that rose from the ground and watered the whole earth in the cool of the night (Gen. 2:5–6). The moon was closer, which caused sea tides to be greater. The earth spun faster, which shortened the day to ~17 hours. As a result of this canopy (and other factors) hovering above the atmosphere, a large increase in the buoyancy effect reduced net gravity by around ~25%. The result of weaker gravity and greater oxygen allowed reptiles to grow to massive heights and sizes (Job 40 and 41 Leviathan) despite having porous bones and allowed humans to live to 900+ years of age (Gen. 5). Life thrived.

But then mankind sinned and set in motion an environment in which all of creation would groan and suffer (Rom 8:22) until the Messiah returns as a conquering lion to restore all of creation back to its pre-fallen state (Isa. 11:6–10). At the moment of the first sin in the Garden of Eden, the movements of judgment began with the inner earth churning to set up future earthquakes and future volcanic activity and future tectonic plate movements. Though connected as Pangaea until the Flood, the potential energy began building up for the judgment at the global flood. Asteroids were colliding in distant space to set off chains of events for future collisions with Earth, yet the result of these movements and activities would not be seen until the earth passed through the path of these asteroids and comets. The canopy is morphing from a spherical shape to a disc-like shape from its spin with the earth. With a more abundance of water pooling along the central portion that is closest to the pull of the moon's influence. So that occupants on the surface of the planet could see a visible arch in the sky.

As time passed on, Adam and Eve had many children from nine months after the sixth day of creation until the birth of Seth, when Adam and Eve were 130 years of age. They were obedient to God's command on the sixth day to multiply. It is estimated that the population from Adam to Noah, with people living 900+ years and having many more children, that the population was 7 billion.

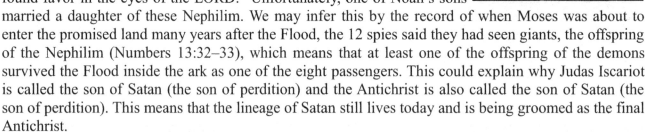

Mankind from the first sin till the commencement of the Flood became so wicked that the Bible records that some demons left their natural abode and bore a half-demon, half-human race with the daughters of men and produced offspring called the Nephilim, who were mighty giants and men of renown. (Gen. 6:1-8) says "that every intent of the thought of his heart was only evil continually. The LORD was sorry He had made man on the earth, and He was grieved in His heart. . . But Noah found favor in the eyes of the LORD." Unfortunately, one of Noah's sons married a daughter of these Nephilim. We may infer this by the record of when Moses was about to enter the promised land many years after the Flood, the 12 spies said they had seen giants, the offspring of the Nephilim (Numbers 13:32–33), which means that at least one of the offspring of the demons survived the Flood inside the ark as one of the eight passengers. This could explain why Judas Iscariot is called the son of Satan (the son of perdition) and the Antichrist is also called the son of Satan (the son of perdition). This means that the lineage of Satan still lives today and is being groomed as the final Antichrist.

120 years pre-Flood:

When God saw the wickedness of mankind, He said you have 120 years until judgment (Gen. 6:3). Noah and his three sons built an ark that was 300 cubits, 50 cubits wide, and 30 cubits tall, with lower, second, and third decks (Gen. 6:15–16). This provided ~17 feet for each deck, made out of gopher wood and covered inside and out with pitch (a petroleum resin) (Gen. 6:14). The total volume was 1.4 million cubic feet. Imagine the faithfulness of Noah and his family to build an ark when it had never rained. A cubit is the distance from the elbow to the finger tip. Today that is 18 inches, but before the Flood, closer to 20.6 inches. All life was taller before the Flood—just look at the fossil record—which means that 300 cubits was closer to 515 feet (172 yards), and not 450 feet as believed.[29]

Seven days pre-Flood:

Two of every kind of land and air creature entered the ark, one male, one female. This includes dinosaurs and other very large creatures, but excluded aquatic life. Utilizing young animals, especially when it came to reptiles, would have solved the logistical problems, and would solve predatory problems. With seven days before the commencement of the Flood, Noah entered the ark, sealed by God (Gen. 7:4 and 7:11).

The first day of the Flood:

As asteroids neared the earth ~1,600 years after creation (~4,400 years ago around 2,400 BC), some collided with the moon and many collided with the canopy on their way to Earth. As a result of the multiple collisions with the canopy, the asteroids broke the frozen arch support structure of the canopy and gravity gradually "pulled" it down. This would have been a slow descent that spanned 40 days from start to finish because the canopy had zero descent speed and had centripetal force from spinning ~1,600 mph, and since the canopy's bulge was at the equator, it would have spanned tens of miles of altitude at its apex central portion, and by this point after 1,600+ years of spinning, there may not be any water hovering over the atmosphere at the polar regions. With rain drops having a maximum terminal velocity of ~10 mph at Earth's surface,[30] and having a large equatorial bulge from its spin, the water would have come down over a duration of 40 days and nights, and not all at the same time. The

29 http://wyattmuseum.com/noahs-ark-the-early-years/2011-697#. Ron Wyatt discovered the Noah's Ark—petrified.
30 Raindrops falling to earth has a velocity range from 4 mph to 20 mph.

asteroids, however, were traveling potentially ~30,000 mph, and they reached the earth's surface in seconds after contacting the canopy of water.

With Noah and family and the creatures safe in the ark, they would have heard the peals of thunder as the asteroids whizzed by, and they would have heard the asteroids impact the earth off in the distance and felt tremors. Surrounding those asteroid impact zones, life was devastated with collateral damage, debris, and fire. The shock waves of the multiple large asteroid impacts and thousands of meteors knocked down trees and caused fires and sent debris into the atmosphere. The initial layer of debris covered much of the vegetation and biomass, which would eventually form large coal deposits and oil reserves. *Image credit: Imperial College London.*

The hot freshwater stored in the deep caverns and canopy salt waters were released for the Flood. Potentially huge chunks of the frozen canopy headed toward the north pole because of colliding with the asteroid and its electrical charge interacting with the electromagnetic field of the earth. The asteroid impacts fractured the crust of the earth into tectonic plates. The similarity of coal deposits in South America and Africa indicate that vegetation was covered with a layer of debris in those regions before those tectonic plates started separating. With 1,600 years of tectonic plate tension built up, the tectonic plates that made up Pangaea split in many regions, allowing the release of all that stored potential energy as kinetic energy. The tectonic plates accelerated apart by hydroplaning (theory by Walter Brown) on the deep caverns at high rates of speed (~0.5 mph, See chapter Tectonic Plates), which forced the fountains of the deep to burst open.

The first week:

As Pangaea broke apart, this caused countless volcanic activity. The Yellowstone's super volcano erupted its first of several eruptions, and the beginning formation of the Emperor Ridge, a series of cooled magma, erupted their first of many eruptions as the Pacific plate moved over a hot spot. This sent global temperatures rising and caused rock to liquefy under the friction of tectonic plate movements. At the same time that the volcanic activity was occurring from the break up of Pangaea, the energy from the massive tectonic plates moving forced vast amounts of water stored in deep caverns under the surface to burst open (Gen. 7:11), spewing tons of super heated water and soil into the atmosphere. The deep caverns of water that the plates rested upon was the source of the reduction in friction that allowed the tectonic plates to freely slide apart and, in a sense, hydroplane[31]. With the mixture of water bursting out of the ground, volcanoes erupting massive amounts of debris in the air, pockets of acid rain, and asteroids colliding on the earth, it was one hot chaotic planet—not suitable for life outside a protective ark.

The African tectonic plate separated from the South American tectonic plate, and the North American plate separated from the European tectonic plate from a central divergent zone called the Mid-Atlantic Ridge. While the planet was on the verge of too much heat that would kill all life, the canopy of water started raining upon the entire surface of earth. It eventually quelled the fires, blocked the sunlight, and cooled the environment. The rain (without clouds) saved eight humans and two of every kind of animal on an ark larger than the size of a football field from dying from too much heat. But not all was calm, as that was just the first week of chaos.

Second week:

31 Author Dr. Walt Brown, In The Beginning. Part II of his book discusses his hydroplane theory.

With this much chaos, the waters would be very turbulent, and a boat that was not stabilized would capsize. This potentially explains why archeologist have found many 9-foot-tall, 2-ton anchor stones with attachment holes for ropes near the region of the ark.[32] These anchor stones would have reduced the boat's lateral pitch and yaw and sway with the waves.

With so many volcanoes erupting sulfuric particulates in the air, they caused sulfuric rain, which caused some ash, bone, teeth, coral, and shell fragments to break down to calcium carbonate and form the first layer of limestone.

As time passed, the tectonic plates picked up speed (~1 mph), moving land off old volcanic hot spots, off the pluming vent of magma, and moving new land over the magma vent. New eruptions occurred, and new islands formed, eventually forming a chain of ridges on the Pacific floor. The old Yellowstone eruption remnants drifted west-by-southwest, and new land moved over the Yellowstone vent, and another eruption occurred with new debris, sending massive amounts of sediment and water into the atmosphere. All the while, the water was still bursting out of the many deep caverns just like Yellowstone, and rain was still falling from the canopy to cool the planet. The movements of the tectonic plates created large vortexes of swirling debris of sediment, vegetation, and biomass. *Photo credit: Ron Wyatt, www.arkdiscovery.com.*

Within the Pacific plate, there were multiple smaller volcanic eruptions daily, as the plate moved north by northwest, creating a chain of tiny islands along the way from Hawaii toward the northwest. From all the magma displacement and asteroid impacts, the earth would have been too hot, yet the sun's light was blocked by the rain and debris in the atmosphere, and the rains would have continuously quelled the flames and heat. The planet did not overheat, but things buried near the heat started the accelerated decay process of forming coal deposits or oil reserves. By this time, the floor of the Pacific plate had seen nearly a 100 volcanic eruptions over the entire plate, with water levels rising and new ridges forming by the day. The Pacific tectonic plate continuously moved north by northwest as the subducted Pacific plate dove under the Asian plate. Noah's Ark was built in the Mesopotamian fertile crescent valley, and since there were no sails, no oars to row, no motor for mobility, and since there were potentially several two-ton anchor weights that stabilized the boat's movement, the ark remained relatively stationary.

One month:

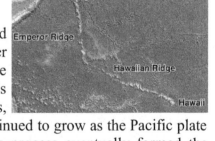

The rains still persisted, volcanoes continued to erupt, and super heated water continued spewing out of deep caverns, allowing for freer movements of the tectonic plates. Somewhere around this time, the Pacific plate took a turn and started heading west-by-northwest. This change of direction caused a temporary pause of volcanic eruptions, but only for a couple of days. The chain of newly formed islands continued to grow as the Pacific plate continued to move fresh land over vents of pluming magma. This process eventually formed the Hawaiian Islands and remnant chain of ridges. A third Yellowstone eruption occurred through new fresh land that moved over the magma vent, blocking the vent only temporarily for this large eruption of super heated water, soil, ash, and flowing magma. The Indian tectonic plate slammed into the southern border of Asia and began the process of forming the Himalaya mountain range.

Although the volcanic activity was still ongoing, the global rains and sun blockage prevented this catastrophic period from plunging the earth into a superheated inferno. The temperatures came off their highs for the first time and cooled to an average global temperature of ~90°F on the surface, but below the water, the soil was hot, as liquid magma continued melting rocks. The ark, however, being partially submerged in water, got the benefit of cooler temperatures because the flood waters were

32 Ark discovery.com/Noah's Ark stones.

cooler than the soil. However, at the poles, snow may have been falling at an accelerated rate, with woolly mammoths freezing in an upright position with undigested tropical food still in their stomach, indicating that the snow came down so fast that they couldn't even fall over. Could it be that a frozen comet impacted near the poles or chunks of the frozen canopy hit the poles? Yes.

The tectonic plates were traveling at around ~0.5 mph, and water was still bursting through fault lines from the deep caverns as the tectonic plates forced the water out. The oceans were rising chaotically, and they were filled with massive amounts of sediment, a mixture of soil, debris, vegetation, and biomass. The floodwater was filled with so much sediment that the turbidity of the water was very high and the translucency was zero. This was about the fifth week of the chaos.

The ark that Noah and his sons had built over the preceding 120 years was built for survival, like a barge; it was not meant to travel, but just to float.

The last week of the chaotic flood was much calmer than the preceding weeks. Volcanic activity had declined significantly. Every island that was formed from volcanic activity and every mountain was covered all across the globe, and the highest mountain was covered by 15 cubits of water (Gen. 7:19–20). The fountains of the deep caverns were almost exhausted. The tectonic plate movements that once hydroplaned on the water of the deep caverns below them were now encountering bedrock below, and friction was slowing the movements of the tectonic plates. However, inertia would continue to drive the plates to eventually form deep valleys and high mountains (Psalm 104:5–9). The global temperature was steadily dropping so that the first emergence of ice had formed at both poles. The Hawaiian islands were still being formed under the ocean. The rains from the canopy was almost exhausted as well. The entire surface of earth was covered by water. The creatures that once had the breath of life in them were all dead, except for those on the ark (Gen. 7:21–22). Much of the biomass and vegetation that had once covered the surface of the earth was covered by the initial asteroid impact and debris. The mixture of debris, biomass, and vegetation would then begin the processes of coalification, fossil fuels, fossilization, and petrification.

The 40th day:

The fountains of the deep caverns and the rains had ceased. The Indian tectonic plate had crashed into the Asian plate, and the Himalayas had started to rise. The Andes mountains and all the other mountain ranges formed by tectonic plate movement had started to rise, yet they had a ways to go. All the mountains were still covered by water 15 cubits deep (Gen. 7:19). The tectonic plates that once hydroplaned slowed their velocity, yet their inertia would eventually cause the great mountain ranges we see today. The waters prevailed upon the earth for the next 150 days. The rains from the canopy of water had finished descending upon the earth and was gone. Global temperatures continued to drop with the entire planet surface covered in water. The ice at the poles continued to expand, leaving piles of salt at the bottom of the water below. The volcanic activity had stopped, and the massive amounts of soil and water that cover the volcanoes acted like a cap to cork and cover the magma vents. All seemed calm for the first time in 40 days, except for a large global tide that swept across the waters twice daily. The massive tide reduced static friction of the sediments and made it easier for soil to settle according to density, forming layers according to their kind based on the laws of physics. The only living creatures (except insects on floating debris, aquatic life, micro-organisms, and so forth) on Earth were the survivors on Noah's Ark.

The Floodwater prevailed (covered) over all mountains on the earth for 150 days (Gen. 7:24, 8:3). Then the waters receded as the polar caps continued to grow in ice and the valleys sank down, and the mountains rose from the tectonic plates colliding, and the inertia buckled the crust of Earth (Psalm 104:5–9). A global wind began for the first time as a result of the polar ice cap formations and the heat from the sun at the equator (Gen. 8:1). After the waters prevailed for 150 days, the mountaintops were still not visible below the flood waters. The soil, vegetation, and biomass that was mixed in the waters was still settling according to density and forming layers of sediment. Due to the product being ejected from the deep caverns, and livestock population in an area, and vortices of the waters from the catastrophic activity, there were areas around the globe that had more bones, teeth, coral and shell fragments pooled together and areas around the globe that had sand predominately pooled together. This caused some areas to have more limestone formations and other areas to have more sandstone formations, though both areas were still layered. The waters continued to recede steadily.

<u>Fifth month from the start of flood:</u>
On the fifth month from the start of flood (which was the seventh month of the calendar year, on the seventeenth day), the ark, with its deep berth, rested upon the mountains of Ararat (Gen. 8:4), but the tops of the mountains were still not visible because of the waters.

<u>Seven and half months from start of flood:</u>
It was not until three months later that the mountaintops became visible for the first time since the Flood had covered the entire earth (Gen. 8:5). Noah waited 40 days after the mountaintops were visible to open the window of the ark to send out a raven, but the raven flew to and fro and returned to Noah empty-handed (Gen. 8:6–7). The water steadily receded as the glacial age continued to grow, and the valleys sank down and the mountains continued rising (Psalm 104:5–9). The mighty Himalaya mountain range had formed. Then Noah sent out a dove, but she also returned to him as there was no resting place for her feet. Noah waited another week and sent out the dove again. This time the dove returned with a freshly picked olive leaf in her beak (Gen 8:11). Noah waited another seven days and sent out a dove again, but this time she did not return.

<u>10.5 months from the start of the Flood (Gen. 8:12–13):</u>
The ground was dry, and the glacial age had begun. Ocean levels were 200 feet below today because the extensive polar ice caps had absorbed vast amounts of freshwater out of the salty oceans (leaving behind vast salt deposits) and extended from the poles to the middle of the Southern and Northern Hemispheres. This exposed the continental shelf, the coastline. Thus, England was connected to the mainland, and Australia was connected to Asia via the shelf, allowing the less aggressive animals to flee away from predators. Some migrated all the way from the mountains of Ararat (Turkey) to Australia via the exposed continental shelf. At the one year and 10 day mark, God instructed Noah to leave the ark and take every creature out of the ark so that they could breed and abundantly fill the earth (Gen. 7:11–8:14).

The picture is of a petrified wooden vessel that meets all the standards described in Genesis for the ark, and matches the location of the resting place, thus we may infer that this is Noah's Ark. Points A,B,C, and D, outline the vessel with a collapsed roof. The second image shows the petrified wood of the hull's side. *Photo credits: Ron Wyatt, www.arkdiscovery.com.*

Shortly after leaving the ark, Noah saw clouds for the first time and heard the voice of God speak to him; he saw rainfall off in the distance that was refracting sunlight. Noah saw his first rainbow (Gen. 9:11–16) as God declared the rainbow to be a covenant not to destroy the earth by water again. Animals freely roamed about and were able to travel from continent to continent along particular travel routes called the continental shelf and/or ice. All the continents remained connected because the floodwater receded and allowed life to venture from the mountains of Ararat to places around the globe. With much of the water stored in the ice caps, the ocean levels would remain below the continental shelf level until shortly after the Tower of Babel, during the life of a man named Peleg (he was born 101 years after the Flood)(Gen. 10:25). His name means "in his days the land was divided." The Tower of Babel existed at a time when all the people had one language and one purpose to become like God. God confused their languages and scattered them around the world (Gen. 10:25–11:9). They traveled to distant continents via the exposed continental shelves and the frozen landscape. After arriving to their new locations, the oceans continued rising as a result of the melted glaciers, and this caused the oceans to rise above the continental shelf. This made Australia an island, and protected such animals as kangaroos from the predators of Asia and cut off traveling to different continents until the Vikings and then Christopher Columbus in 1492.

Review: The catastrophic global flood was not gently falling rain from heaven. Asteroids impacted the earth, Pangaea broke apart, and the tectonic plates hydroplaned across the surface of deep caverns, forcing water to burst out with soil and multiple volcanic activity on a daily basis. The waters were filled with soil, vegetation, and biomass. The waters were turbulent, causing swirls and pools. The planet was on the verge of being overly heated, and then plunged into the ice age.

Today, we cannot perceive the abundance of animal life that was on the earth before the Flood. But to give you an image of how abundant and dense the population was, consider that 15-foot-tall camels have been found in the Arctic Circle along with the remains of 150 million frozen woolly mammoths.[33] Imagine a herd of 150 million woolly mammoths roaming. Think of the abundant vegetation to feed them. I think humans can scarcely take it in, the creative abundance of what God established as far as vegetation and animals. Not only have researchers found woolly mammoths with tropical vegetation in their mouths, but also frozen in the upright position. This indicates an almost instant freeze, with the animals freezing within four to five hours, suggesting that a frozen comet or a chunk of the frozen canopy may have struck the area and sent it into a deep freeze. Also, they have found frozen bobcats, camels, and bison along with the mammoths in the Arctic Circle. This means there were lush green grasslands in the Arctic Circle before the Flood, and it got really cold really fast. Comets are estimated to have temperatures that are 300°F to 400°F below zero. That could be the culprit that caused a quick freeze and to freeze the mammoths with food undigested in their stomachs.

The the mountains we see today are much higher than the mountains before the Flood, and the valleys we see today are much deeper (Psalm 104:5–9). The mountains around the globe have seashells and petrified giant clams (in the closed position) on their peaks, because they were once smaller.

How did the aquatic dinosaurs die from the Flood? Potentially, some perished by the rain upon the earth; it had high salt and mineral content, and this increased the salinity of water that marine life forms were used to. Some adapted and survived, and some did not and died. Some perished by trauma from asteroids and volcanoes, also includes increased water temperature or acidity of water near volcanoes. Many that survived the flood, became stranded in inland seas that were destined to evaporate to dry land, and thus, they died in a massive confined grave as they pooled together to an ever tighter and tighter population as the water receded. But some survived the flood, such as the Leviathan that God references in Job 41. The Bible records that there were seas from the beginning, so potentially the seas had the same alkalinity, and thus many sea creatures survived the Flood.

God promises a redemptive plan for all of His creation, that the earth and life will return to Utopia, to Eden. This is found at the end of the book of Revelation and throughout the Old Testament.

Chapter Summary: The Flood destroyed life on earth (but two of every kind survived on the ark) and changed the conditions. Knowing what the Flood did and knowing where the source of the waters came from tells us what life was like before the Flood and what the conditions of the environment were like. Those conditions allowed life to thrive. Dinosaurs grew large and humans lived 900+ years. The flood took away the buoyant force of the canopy of water, decreased atmosphere pressure, decreased oxygen concentration, and increased gravity. Consequently, living beings no longer thrive as they used to before the Flood.

---

33 *New York Times*, "Trade in Mammoth Ivory, Helped by Global Thaw, Flourishes in Russia." March 25, 2008.

Chapter 10
<u>No Deserts before the Flood</u>

The title of this chapter seems to be pretty bold. Were there really no deserts from the origin of life until the Flood? Correct. Let us look at some evidence to lay a foundation, and then we'll go to the Scriptures to confirm it. [A satellite image of sand being blown from the Sahara Desert into the Atlantic Ocean.]

Winds blow the tan sand from the Sahara Desert into the Atlantic Ocean. Scientists observing the sand from the Sahara Desert blowing into the Atlantic Ocean got the bright idea to look into the soil of the ocean floor to determine if there was any evidence that would suggest when the Sahara Desert formed. How? The desert sand of the Sahara is different than tropical soil. The Sahara Desert sand has distinct reddish-tan granules. Tropical forest soil blown into the ocean has a distinct brownish-green color. Since the wind is blowing sand into the Atlantic Ocean and that sand has a particular color, then by viewing ocean core samples, scientists can detect the color changes to determine when the sand began being blown into the ocean and covering the prior brownish-green tropical deposits. Then they can discern how long the Sahara region has been a desert. *Photo credit: Space, Science, and Engineering Center, Madison Wisconsin University.*

When geologists viewed the core samples in their lab, they saw tan sand sediment with striations. Each horizontal striation indicated durations of time or years in the past. With deeper Atlantic floor samples, they saw a distinct color change from reddish-tan sand to darker brownish-green soil. This color change tells the story of when the Sahara region stopped blowing darker brownish-green colored soil into the Atlantic Ocean and began blowing light-colored reddish-tan sand into it. This shift in color is unmistakable and reveals the history of when the Sahara region stopped being a tropical forest and began being a desert.

Review: <u>Atlantic ocean floor soil samples have revealed that the Sahara Desert blows reddish-tan sand into the ocean floor and that the desert was formed in the recent past. Beneath the desert sand, exists a layer of greenish-brown sediment that was deposited when the Sahara region was tropical.</u>

When Geologist Peter deMenocal of The Earth Institute at Columbia University studied the Atlantic core samples,[34] he estimated that approximately every one-fourth inch of soil represented approximately 200 years. Therefore, 1 inch down would be approximately 800 years in the past at today's current rate of deposit. He discovered that below the reddish tan dust from the Sahara Desert, there was brownish-greenish soil. This brownish-greenish soil comes from clay minerals from tropical deposits.

Would not you know that the Atlantic Ocean core samples revealed that the Sahara Desert has been in existence for an estimated ~5,000 years. This coincides right around the time of the global flood—and not millions of years.

How did deMenocal come up with this approximate date? He observed horizontal lines in the core sample and viewed them as rings, as on a tree, and combined them with an estimate of the current rate of soil deposit per year. He then measured the depth of the layer and divided the current rate of soil deposit by distance. This came out to an average of one-fourth inch per ~200 years. If the rate of

---

34 news.columbia.edu/africaclimate.

deposit has been consistent over the past five millennia, this dating method is accurate. If there were periods of change in the rate of deposition, the dates would change accordingly. This method of dating is similar to how evolutionary geologists determine the age of the layers of earth. However, it is difficult to account for periods of accelerated deposits from catastrophic global floods that resulted in high soil deposits, which is exactly what the Biblical flood wrought. This is different from radioactive isotopic dating, which measures the age of items based on the number of stabler elements, such as lead, versus unstable elements, such as polonium. The problem with radioactive dating is that the "constant rate of decay" is not constant now, nor has it been constant in the past.

Review: The Sahara Desert began shortly after the Flood. The core samples reveal that prior to the lighter reddish tan dust blowing in from the Sahara desert, there was brownish-green soil blown into the Atlantic ocean. This brownish-green-colored soil represents that the Sahara region was once dense in tropical vegetation. This empirical data is in harmony with the Bible.

Peter deMonecal further states that the change from lush vegetation to desert would have taken about 100 to 200 years. Anyone living in the region would have noticed the continued changes and would have been aware that the region was becoming uninhabitable. He clarified that each generation living in the region would have seen a change from what their parents saw. This parallels nicely with the Bible. After the Flood, each generation would have noticed that life on earth was changing. They would have noticed that life expectancy was significantly dropping and that deserts were forming right in front of their eyes. However, it seems the change from the Sahara being covered with tropical vegetation before the Flood and then becoming desert after the Flood, may have taken less time than one would think. Vegetation needs water, so to go from an abundant and consistent water supply from the mist rising from the ground to severe drought as it is today would not take long. I contend that Peter deMonecal's numbers could be high and that the transformation was within one to five years after the Flood. Before the Flood, there was tropical forest, with dense lush vegetation. Then comes the Flood with 40 days and nights of rain that kills all the vegetation and then covers it with soil and water for 150 days (Gen. 7:24). Then the floodwater started to recede, and it took almost six months (almost one year for the entire flood saga) to drain the floodwater and have the polar ice caps absorb most of the water. While the floodwater receded, what was left behind was soil void of vegetation, void of any plant life that was alive, with only seeds remaining. Those seeds sprouted when the water drained off and when sunlight was able to provide the energy for photosynthesis. The sprouts leaped forth from the ground, yet there was no water to sustain them, the ground becoming ever more dry. The new sprouts died off quickly in weeks, and what was left was the sedimentary sand that we still see today.

The duration for desertification could have been one year after the Flood to the seeds germinating, growth, drought, and death.

Review: Geologists estimate that the transformation of the Sahara from tropical lush forest to desert may have taken 100–200 years. Let us remember that this is an estimate. It is plausible that the desertification of the Sahara region occurred much faster, around one year.

The first mention of heat, cold, summer, and winter is not until after the Flood in Gen. 8:22. Therefore, before the Flood, optimal temperatures existed globally. Why did the Sarah region die?

In Gen. 2:5–6, the Bible tells us that before the Flood, "The LORD God had not sent rain upon the earth . . . But a mist used to rise from the earth and water the whole surface of the ground." Well, this system of watering the whole earth was gone after the Flood. The flood changed the conditions on Earth. The new method of delivering water to the parched soil was now via rain clouds. Combine this information with Gen. 9:8–17: "God said, 'This is the sign of the covenant . . . I set My bow in the cloud." This is the first mention of a rainbow and a cloud in the Bible. The canopy prevented clouds by the pressure it exerted on the atmosphere. Clouds cannot form in high pressure. All evaporation was in gas form until the cool of the night condensed the gas to a mist (dew) that watered the ground.

Lastly, the Bible indicates in Gen. 8:1 when the Sahara desert first started having its sand blown into the Atlantic ocean with: "God caused a wind to pass over the earth." This reveals for the first time that there was enough heat at the equator and cold at the poles to create enough change in global temperatures to cause wind. As hot air rose from being less dense around the equator and cold air sank from being denser (high pressure) around the poles, wind, in the form of the jet stream, began for the first time. It is that wind that blows Sahara sand into the Atlantic ocean.

How does a mist rise up from the earth? It is simple. At night when the temperature drops, the air molecules contract and get smaller with the cooler temperature, and therefore, the air is unable to hold as much moisture. Thus, the moisture in the air—as a result of evaporation—settles to the ground. We see a semblance of what used to be when we see the dew in the morning that settles on the grass. Also, Moses described the mist rising up from the ground, which is scientifically accurate because evaporation is from water on the surface.

Even today with high pressure systems, no cloud formations occur. On the plus side, this very high atmosphere pressure caused a buoyant force that made life thrive as net gravity was ~20% weaker than today.

Review: Before the Flood came and destroyed all life (animal and most botanical life), the Sahara region was watered by a mist that rose from the ground. Super-high atmospheric pressure resulting from the canopy prevented cloud formation. Therefore, it prevented rain and rainbows before the Flood. After the Flood, the highly pressurized atmosphere was reduced to its current condition, which allows cloud formations and rain, which resulted in light refraction and rainbows.

Samples taken from air bubbles trapped deep within glaciers cores and air bubbles trapped in amber (petrified tree sap) indicate that the earth had no deserts and no polar ice caps and that the world was covered in vegetation because the oxygen concentration in the atmosphere was 31%, which is 50% higher than today. Before the numerous phytoplankton in the oceans, it was the vegetation that produced the high oxygen concentration. Therefore, one could conclude that the earth's vegetation was abundant all around the earth prior to the Flood, and this includes the desert regions and the polar regions. After the Flood, with the equator now exposed to the harsh sun, then vegetation declined and finally gave way to deserts that were not hospitable to vegetation growth.

Review: Glacial core samples of oxygen and air trapped in amber indicate that oxygen was 50% higher in the past, which corroborates what the Atlantic Ocean floor samples confirm, which is that the Sahara Desert was once covered with lush vegetation and only recently became a desert about 5,000 years ago.

High oxygen concentration allows for accelerated growth and the longevity of life. This explains why human beings lived 900+ years before the Flood. And after the global flood, the number of years lived by Noah's heirs kept declining by almost 100 years each generation. As the oxygen concentration continuously dropped, all living creatures—based on existing DNA code—adapted to the progressively lower oxygen concentrations, which correlated to reduced life expectancy.

Likewise, all dinosaur babies and all other creatures (one male and one female of each kind) that Noah brought onto the Ark had to adapt to the reduced oxygen concentration as well. Since all dinosaurs are reptiles, and reptiles grow as long as they are alive, it is easy to see the connection of reducing oxygen concentration with reduced life expectancy. The shorter the life expectancy of a dinosaur, the smaller maximum size it can grow to.

How do deserts play a role in reducing oxygen? With the intense heat and lack of water, vegetation does not grow well, especially in places like the Sahara Desert. Therefore, the deserts play a role in keeping oxygen levels below the pre-Flood 31% level, a level at which life thrives by growing faster, stronger, and bigger.

Review: Deserts play a role in preventing vegetation growth and thereby are involved in the reduction of oxygen production. Since oxygen causes life to thrive, deserts indirectly hinder the quality and longevity of life.

The Sahara Desert has remnants of bygone freshwater lakes, with fossilized freshwater aquatic life and residual freshwater deep bottom algae deposits. This reveals that before the desert came, there were freshwater lakes in the Sahara region that were teeming with life alongside the lush tropical vegetation. NASA has photographs of where the freshwater lakes were and estimates of their size.[35]

In addition, fossils of saltwater marine life and saltwater seashells have been found on top of the freshwater fossil layers. Therefore, the ocean covered freshwater lakes teeming with life, lush vegetation, and an abundant of life. This is in perfect harmony with the global flood of Genesis.

Review: The Sahara Desert has remnant fossilized vegetation under the marine life. Therefore, prior to the ocean water and prior to the marine fossils and seashells, evidence exist of vegetation that once thrived in Africa. Therefore, Africa once thrived as a tropical forest, then it was covered in salt water, and then it became the desert we see today.

Scientists have discerned that the Sahara became a desert some ~5,000 years ago. Other scientists doing other research, have found saltwater marine life in the Sahara Desert, and then they have dug a little deeper to find freshwater fossils and remnants of tropical forests. This is consistent with Biblical events. But then it is mind-boggling to read that evolutionists say that Africa was covered by an ocean some 250 million years ago. Well, wait a minute, that is impossible because the Atlantic Ocean floor is not lying when its core samples reveal that the Sahara was lush tropical vegetation just ~5,000 years ago—and above the tropical sediment on land, existed saltwater marine fossils in the desert sand. You cannot have the ocean existing 250 million years ago on top of the tropical forest remnants that existed ~5,000 years ago. The observable evidence on the floor of the Atlantic Ocean suggests that if the ocean existed and its oceanic marine life was deposited on top and covered up the tropical forest, the ocean covering Africa by default came after the tropical forests existed.

Some evidence is more compelling than other bits of evidence. The fact that evidence from the Atlantic Ocean shows that the Sahara Desert changed from a tropical environment to a desert some 5,000 years ago is compelling evidence that authenticates the Bible and disproves a billion-year-old earth. This is so simple that it is profound. The Atlantic Ocean floor proves that the Sahara was a tropical forest ~5,000 years ago. Thus, the evolutionary estimates that an ocean that covered the desert 250 million years ago is absurdly wrong.

Review: Soil samples in North Africa confirm Peter deMonocal's research that suggests that Africa was once covered with lush tropical forests and with freshwater lakes and freshwater aquatic life ~5,000 years ago. Then, ocean water covered everything and left saltwater seashells and sedimentary layers on top of the lush vegetation and freshwater aquatic life. The evolutionary estimates that an ocean that covered the desert 250 million years ago is absurdly wrong.

The reddish-tan dust on the Atlantic Ocean floor just off the coast of northwestern Africa is from sand blowing into the ocean from the Sahara Desert, and this started about 5,000 years ago. Peter deMenocal gave his best estimate based on analyzing how much dust is blown into the Atlantic each year and based on the average amount of sand being blown into the ocean being somewhat constant for 5,000 years. We do not have certainty that it was exactly 5,000 years ago when the Sahara started. It could be that the amount of dust blowing each year varied in some years, The variations could put the date of the Sahara desertification around 2,500 BC. Even if Peter deMenocal's findings are off by 500 years, it still puts us near the time of the Bible's global flood.

Since no one is able to give exact dates and guarantee that their date is 100% accurate, then all that we need is for the dates to be close. And they are very close.

How close are the dates? Well, some Biblical scholars say that the Flood occurred around 4,400 years ago. The data suggests that the Sahara Desert started around 5,000–5,500 years ago. Meanwhile, the evolutionary community proclaims that the ocean covered the Sahara region 250 million years ago. Then a difference of creationists being off by 600 to 1,100 years as compared to evolutionists being off by 250 million years is a painful reality of how ridiculous the evolutionary timelines are.

Considering that the Sahara desert is the largest desert on Earth, and growing, this suggests that it was the first desert on the planet, which supports the notion that a canopy protected the earth at the

---

35 dailygalaxy.com/ Lakes of the Sahara desert from the International Space Station. March 2010.

equator from the sun's harmful rays. Consider that the oldest tree on Earth is roughly ~4,300 to 6,000 years old (some trees have produced a double ring for some years, making them appear older), and some have claimed to have found a tree that is a couple of thousand years older (perhaps trees that existed from the time of creation). Gen. 7 does not record that all trees died (just all that had the breath of life), so it is possible that a tree as old as creation still survives. Notwithstanding, it still supports a young earth perspective, with the point being that no tree exists that is 100,000 years old or greater. Scientists estimate that the Great Barrier Reef is only 4,200 years old; this also supports a young earth and indicates that ocean water may be a relatively new phenomenon.

    Review: Two separate interest groups (creationists and geologists) arrive at a close estimate of when the Sahara Desert began. Secular scholars say it is ~5,000 old, and creationist say it is about ~4,300 old; both are around the same time frame.

    We have scientific evidence that the Sahara Desert formed recently and that prior to being a desert, northern Africa was a tropical forest with freshwater lakes. This perfectly coincides with the Bible's description of what God created. The Bible describes that after God had created everything, He looked over all that He had created and declared it was very good (Gen. 1:31). Then on the seventh day of creation, after God had spent six days creating the universe, He rested and declared, "Thus the Heavens and the earth were completed, and all their hosts. By the seventh day God completed His work which He had done" (Genesis 2:1–2). This is to say that God's work was complete, lacking nothing, and very good.

    Taking in a bird's-eye view of the Bible, we get even more clarity of what "very good" and "complete" means regarding God's work of creation. Death did not enter creation until the fall of Adam and Eve (Romans 5:12). Therefore, before the sin of Adam and Eve, there was no death anywhere. Since the desert is a symbol of death and represents the suffering of creation groaning for freedom from sin and death (Romans 8:20–22), then before sin entered the world, there was no deserts.

    Utilizing a literal interpretation of the Biblical genealogies, Adam and Eve lived on the earth roughly 6,000 years ago. This fits perfectly with findings that the Sahara Desert did not begin until some 4,500 years ago at a time shortly after the Flood. Imagine the problem if someone discovered that the Sahara Desert began 100,000 years ago.

    Review: Before the fall of man, there was no death. Deserts represent this death; by default, before there was sin in the world, there was no death and subsequently no deserts. The canopy surrounding the atmosphere, by protecting the Sahara region from the harmful heat of the sun, allowed the Sahara region to flourish in a lush vegetative state. The canopy coming down upon the earth resulted in the global flood. Without the canopy's ability to protect the earth from the sun's harmful rays led to the formation of the Sahara Desert. As the deserts were being formed from their inability to adapt, all creatures on Earth were having to adapt to the changing climate, increased gravity, and decreased oxygen. Animals could move to new locations, and even botanical life could travel, with the winds lifting their seeds in the air or with the current of the oceans, but the Sahara couldn't move, and it died.

    After God created the vegetation He said, "It was good." This implies that there were no deserts in His creation at this time. When God looks over all that He created, He does not see the death of the desert, He does not see the bareness of the desert, He does not see the futility of the desert, and He does not see the suffering in the desert. No, quite to the contrary, He sees the lush vegetation teeming with life. All deserts are an indication of death resulting from sin. As a result of sin, all of creation suffers futility and is in bondage to the corruption of sin (Romans 8:18–22).

    God had created a physical boundary to block and prevent the death of the desert and to block and prevent the death of the polar regions with ice. What was the physical boundary? The canopy. This canopy hovered above the atmosphere and created temperate global temperatures that prevented both deserts and polar ice caps from forming.

Theologically, it must be pointed out that God did not react to Adam and Eve's sin and say after they sinned, "Oh well, let me see how to judge them and save them." No, quite to the contrary, God had predetermined that the global flood was going to occur on a precise date before creation began. God the Father predetermined before creation began, with foreknowledge of future events, that He was going to send His Son, God in the Flesh—Jesus—to die on a cross for the sins of mankind (Acts 2:23–24). When was the plan established? Ephesians 1:4 says that it was "just as He chose us in Him before the foundation of the world." Thus, it was before the foundation of the earth.

Therefore, God, who never increases in knowledge for He knows all things (Psalm 139:4), already knew that Lucifer and his demons would fall, that Adam and Eve would sin shortly after that, that His Son would die on the cross to save all creation from the cost of sin, and that Judgment will come to eradicate the effects of sin on all creation. All of His plans were predetermined before creation. All believers were preselected on the first day of creation. God did not react to Lucifer's fall; Lucifer was fulfilling predetermined Scripture. God did not react to Adam and Eve's fall; they were fulfilling predetermined Scripture before it was even written. God did not react to Jesus' crucifixion; this was fulfilling Scripture. Every major event has occurred spot on, according to God's predetermined plan.

This is not to say that we are robots; nor does it mean that God cannot seemingly change His mind from our point of view regarding minor events. For God does change His mind with minor events that do not conflict with the overall plan (Jeremiah 18:6–10).

Review: God predetermined that the canopy would rain upon the earth and subsequently result in deserts near the equator.

Deserts serve a spiritual purpose to remind us that sin is death. As a result of sin, what was a completely lush planet became flawed. Deserts remind us of the fulfillment of Romans 8:19–22: "The whole creation groans and suffers the pains."

Deserts, however, are not how the planet will be after Christ returns. Deserts will become a thing of the past. The whole of creation will be reborn, created anew. This topic deserve a whole book, but to give you an overview, I refer to Isaiah 24:18b–23: "The windows above are opened, and the foundations of the earth shake. The earth is broken asunder, the earth is split through, the earth is shaken violently, the earth reels to and fro like a drunkard and it totters like a shack." This is in parallel with Revelation 6:12–17, as it says that "a great earthquake . . . and the stars of the sky fell to the earth." This is saying that asteroids will impact the earth in the future, and "every mountain and island were moved out of their places." Asteroids will hit and split the earth.

When the earth splits asunder, all the earth's oceans will pour deeply into the superheated mantle and even into the core. This would cause water to explode up and shoot outside our atmosphere like a massive Yellowstone geyser. As all the ocean water hits the superheated core and shoots up into space, this will act like a huge jet engine and cause the earth to begin spinning faster again. This will stop the earth from wobbling like a drunkard or a slow spinning top from the multiple asteroid impacts, and the oceans will shoot up into space and cause the earth to spin smoothly like a top again. The increased spin will mean that the days will be about 17 hours long, as they were at the origin of creation. This will reconstitute the canopy of ice and salt water back around our atmosphere. This also will increase atmospheric pressure, which will recreate the buoyancy effect, which will reduce the effects of gravity. The recreation of the canopy and the buoyancy effect will be a restoration of the Garden of Eden environment. The canopy will create temperate global temperatures. No polar ice caps and no deserts will exist. Those barren regions will be lush plant life. With the loss of oceans, lush vegetation will grow where the oceans once were (Revelation 21:1). This will increase oxygen concentrations back to pre-Flood conditions.

This explains how humans again will live to 900+ years again. Isaiah 65:17–26:

> For behold, I create new heavens and new earth . . . No longer will there be in it an infant who lives but a few days, or an old man who does not live out his days; the youth will die at the age of one hundred and the one who does not reach the age of one hundred will be thought accursed . . . as the lifetime of a tree, so will be the days of My people . . . the wolf and the lamb will graze together.

This is just how life was in Gen. 1:30–31: "To every beast of the earth and to every bird of the sky and to every thing that moves on the earth which has life, I have given every green plant for food . . . God saw all that He had made, and behold, it was very good." The result of the earth splitting asunder from God's wrath is that conditions on the earth will return to the pre-fallen state, which means no deserts.

One thing that I've always wondered about is what life would be like with no thorns; imagine a rose bush with no thorns. I haven't heard of anyone growing rose bushes in increased oxygen and increased atmospheric pressure—which are pre-Flood and post end-times judgment earth conditions—but I hypothesis that the thorns would disappear with increased pressure and increased oxygen concentration over time. The deserts we see today will be gone one day soon, when Christ returns and destroys all evil. There will be a new heaven and a new earth.

Chapter summary: Before the Flood, there were no deserts. There were tropical forests, lush vegetation, and freshwater lakes. Those tropical forests left sediment deposits on the Atlantic Ocean floor and on the land of the Sahara region. The remnants of tropical forests and freshwater aquatic fossils were covered up by oceanic fossils and sediment from the Flood. The desertification process probably took one year from the first rains of the Flood till the waters receded. After the Flood, there was no longer any canopy of water to shield the equator from the destructive sun, no deep caverns of water, and no mist that rose from the ground and watered the whole earth. This caused the deserts. The deserts limited vegetation growth, which limited oxygen concentration, which limits life from thriving.

Chapter 11
<u>When and What Caused the Polar Ice Caps and the Ice Age?</u>

If the glacial age formed slowly over thousands of years to hundreds of years, there would never be hundreds of millions of woolly mammoths frozen (and other creatures) in the Arctic Circle,[36,37] some in the standing position with undigested tropical flora in their mouths, stomachs, and digestive tracts. They would have migrated south for food as the cold crept in and killed off the vegetation. Elephants are descendants of woolly mammoths, and they require ~200 liters of water each day and tons of food, which means that no elephant could live in the current icy Arctic Circle. The evidence that millions of mammoths have been found in the Arctic Circle means that the area was once lush with vegetation. Digested food moves from the mouth to defecation in about 8 hours. Since some mammoths were found frozen in the standing position with tropical flora undigested in their stomachs and digestive tracts,[38] suggests that the glacial age began quickly. Such as with the global flood that could have caused the mammoths to swim to stay alive. Then the waters froze, and the mammoths froze as they tried to swim to safety. And/Or a few chunks of the frozen canopy may have been charged enough because of tidal friction and the electromagnetic field generated by the earth, to effect its descent trajectory, and plummeted toward the polar regions as chucks of ice. Or the asteroid that broke the frozen arch support of the canopy could have knocked a large chuck of canopy ice toward the north pole. This would explain how woolly mammoths froze instantly in the upright position with undigested tropical food in their digestive tract.

The current evolutionary glaciologists' hypothesis of a slow buildup to the glacial age has a major hole in it when one considers the frozen creatures found frozen in the standing position in the Arctic Circle with undigested tropical flora in their digestive tracts. This information gives us a clear picture of what life was like before the Flood. There were billions of animals around the globe roaming the lush green earth. They roamed from around the equator to the poles because there were no polar ice caps, and there was lush vegetation worldwide to support a population of 150 million woolly mammoths roaming around in the Arctic Circle, which is considered inhospitable. This information is in perfect harmony with the Bible.

Deep beneath Antarctica, Russian researchers have discovered petrified and frozen remnants of entire tropical and subtropical forests along with freshwater lakes. In Alaska, drillers found trees that were 300 feet tall and frozen vertically at the base of the ice. Alaskan temperatures in the area where these trees were discovered was vastly different before the Flood. A quick freeze occurred in both polar regions during the Genesis flood saga. *Image credit: Museum of Zoology, St. Petersburg.*

<u>**Review:** Woolly mammoths that were found in an upright position with undigested tropical flora in their digestive tracts indicate that there were no polar ice caps before the global flood, but there were lush tropical forests. Also, that the polar ice came suddenly, not over thousands of years or hundreds of years. The observable evidence is in harmony with the Bible, but not with a slow build-up</u>

---

36 www.creation.com/the-extinction-of-the-woolly-mammoth-was-it-a-quick-freeze.
37 *New York Times*, "Trade in Mammoth Ivory, Helped by Global Thaw, Flourishes in Russia." March 25, 2008.
38 kgov.com, Real science radio: frozen mammoths. *Photo image credit of baby mammoth and girl.*

as evolutionary timelines preach.

Evolutionary scientists' tendency to fit billions of years to the age of the earth has forced several conclusions from observations to fit their preconceived paradigms. For example, mankind sees the rate of snow accumulation on the polar ice caps today and surmises that the rate of snow buildup has always been at this rate—the Uniformitarian theory—because this fits their predetermined belief of an old earth. But, if the snow and soil rate of accumulation today is much slower than the buildup say, 4,300 years ago because of the Flood, the assumptive old age of the ice pack and layers of the crust would be wildly off and much younger than speculated. The **Uniformitarian theory** is the belief that the processes observed today acted in the same manner, intensity, and frequency as they did in the past. Thus, they believe that this constant uniformity is sufficient to account for all geological change and is the basis for all dating methods involving soil and ice accumulation and radioactive isotopes. Therefore, no Biblical global flood.

For example, determining the age of an item is to utilize the rate at which items decay on a molecular level. This is done by measuring the loss of electrons circling the nucleus and the atomic mass reduction of a radioactive element, this is the radioactive isotopic dating technique. Radioactive elements (such as uranium, plutonium, etc.) are unstable due to so many electrons circling their nuclei. To become stable, they lose an electron at a known rate until the elements become stable. This known rate of losing an election is called the constant rate of decay. The first stable element on the periodic table after the radioactive elements lose enough electrons to become stable is lead (Pb). The quantity is measured with an ion mass spectrometer. A mathematical formula is implemented involving the number of stable lead ions, divided by the number of unstable radioactive polonium ions, and multiplied by a constant rate of decay to determine the age of an item. Mankind takes a tremendous leap of faith by suggesting that the rate of decay that we measure today has always been constant—the Uniformitarian theory. This is a huge leap of faith, as no one alive today lived thousands or millions years ago to observe the rates of decay back then. Scientists have discovered compelling evidence that the rate of decay can accelerate and has accelerated from time to time with certain traumas on the earth. This means that the age of the earth is not nearly as old as we are being told.

The basis for this seemingly accurate dating system is radioactive isotopic dating, which uses the multiplier "constant rate of decay (CRD)." Here is an example:

lead (Pb) ions / # polonium (Po) ions X CRD = age of the item tested.

I'm not saying that the calculations are wrong. I'm saying that the multiplier for the formula, the CRD, is not constant and therefore the formula is flawed. This means all their conclusions based on that multiplier being constant are wrong.

If the rate of decay has always been constant, then their formula would be correct, and the age of the earth would be billions of years old. But the CRD is not constant. Let us go over some terms. An atom has a nucleus that contains protons (positive charge) and neutrons (neutral charge); surrounding the nucleus are electrons (negative charge). The number of electrons, protons, and neutrons determines the element on the periodic table. An isotope is when an element has a different number of neutrons than protons. Let us look at some examples to illustrate that the CRD is not constant. In nature, several examples exist where the rate of decay has accelerated with trauma. In fact, the examples will show evidence that the age of the earth is very young and that traumas to the earth have accelerated the aging process drastically.

Nuclear physicists are likely screaming right now saying, "Do you know how many kilojoules of energy are required to ionize uranium 238 to accelerate the decay process?" It would take three to five lightning bolts for each uranium molecule. Well, currently 100 **lightning bolts** occur every second on the planet. That is 3.15 billion lightning bolts every year.[39] The global flood was so catastrophic, with asteroids, volcanoes, and fast-moving tectonic plates, all of which produced electric discharge for lightning. In fact, volcanoes have been registered to produce 7,000 lightning bolts per hour. Now

39 Www.learn.weatherstem.com/modules/learn/lesssons/36/02.html#.

imagine hundreds of volcanoes erupting daily for the 40 days of the Flood. Additionally, multiply that number by billions more to equal the electric charge generated from all the tectonic plates sliding across the surface of the earth. The amount of electrical discharge that occurred during the Genesis global flood accelerated the aging process. Several ways exist to accelerate the decay of elements. Such as alpha particle emissions, beta particle emissions by electron ejection, nuclei capture of an electron, positron ejection, and nuclei fragmentation into two smaller elements.

In addition, evidence exists that (a) there was a global flood, and (b) the Flood accelerated the decay rate. This evidence is found in microscopic crystals called **zircon**. Zircon is often found in black mica (a biotite that is a black, dark brown mineral occurring in many igneous and metamorphic rocks). When Uranium238 decays and loses alpha particles to form Thorium234, the byproduct is helium, and the helium often gets stored in crystals called zircon. Within zircon are helium concentrations that exceed the normal rates of decay under natural conditions to the tune of 1.5 billion years worth of accelerated decay. The problem is that helium dissipates from the zircon crystals at a known rate, and uranium loses alpha particles to form helium at a known rate, Therefore, since the concentration of helium in zircon exceeds this rate of equilibrium by 1.5 billion years, whereas it should be zero, then there was a catastrophic event that caused a massive acceleration of uranium 238 decay to have that much helium stored in zircon crystals in igneous rocks. Since the zircon crystals still have this exceedingly high abundance of helium, then this event occurred recently, within 4,000–8,000 years ago.[40] Otherwise, if this accelerated aging event occurred millions of years ago, the helium in the zircon crystals would have dissipated by now to an equilibrium state.

Review: Mankind has invented a method of determining the age of things that fits their preconceived notion that the universe is billions of years old. They did not have a blank canvas; their beliefs determined their interpretations and guided their formulas. Zircon crystals indicate that something traumatic occurred on the planet recently, and it accelerated the aging process. Do not be fooled when you hear that the earth is billions of years old and that the glacial age began millions of years ago.

The destruction of the Flood was so powerful, with so much energy released, that it solves how rates of decay were accelerated. My hypothesis is that asteroids kicked off the event by colliding into the frozen arch of the canopy of water and then slamming into the crust of the earth. The impact of the asteroids fractured the crust of the earth and initiated the breaking apart of Pangaea. Proof of the asteroids' impacts is a layer of iridium beneath the layer of the soil. The breaking apart of Pangaea caused massive and multiple volcanoes to erupt simultaneously around the globe. When volcanoes erupt, they usually have lightning accompanying them. With the tectonic plate movements, this would have been accompanied by massive amounts of static discharge (lightning) in the soil as well. The breaking apart of Pangaea caused the fountains of the deep to burst open (such as Yellowstone, Ring of Fire, etc.), and massive numbers of lightning strikes were the result. Altogether, there was so much energy released that there was plenty of energy to ionize enough U238 to accelerate the aging process. When mankind does radioactive studies today using today's rate of decay, there appears to be billions of years of existence. But it was the destructive global flood and the second day's violent expansion of the universe and the first day's creation of matter that caused billions of years worth of accelerated decay. The evidence of this is in the amount of helium stored in zircon crystals in igneous rocks, revealing that there were 1.5 billion years of acceleration from around the global flood.

The following are some examples of how the rate of decay is accelerated by processes we can observe and test today.

Petrified trees: We are told that petrification takes 500,000 to millions[41] of years with a slow process of decay, yet Washington's Mount Saint Helens erupted in 1980 and has produced petrified trees in only

---

40 Encyclopedia of Creation Science, "Accelerated decay."
41 Live Science/ How Long Does it Take to Petrify Wood?

30 years time. These petrified trees are indistinguishable from other petrified trees that are said to have taken 500,000 years to petrify. That's an acceleration of 499,970 years from the believed CRD. That's an acceleration of going from wood to stone in 1/16,700th of the time that the CRD determines for petrifying wood. Petrification does not take a long time. Many WWII materials have petrified, and that's only 70 years. Petrification has been known to occur in less than a year. It does not take 500,000 years. Of course, it should be said that those sages that tell us it takes 500,000 years to produce petrified wood were not there to observe this long process; they make an educated guess based on the rate of decay seen today. But somehow their guesses become fact to the populous. Others argue that the 1980 eruption caused erosion that unearthed petrified trees from previous eruptions, such as from 1842, but the concept is the same; trauma accelerated the aging process. Even if an atheist argues that the petrified wood was from 1482, 1,200 BC, or 2,500 BC,[42] the concept is the same; trauma accelerated the aging process from 500,000 years and reduced it to 4,000 years or 30 years. *Photo credit: Carl Baugh, 1936, a hammer in the alleged cretaceous rock (145-65 million years ago), which debunks the old earth theory.*

Coalification: We are told that the formation of coal primarily took place 300 million years ago with a slow process of decay. Yet, in a lab, we can mimic the Flood conditions (of a buried piece of wood near a volcano) by taking a piece of wood, adding trace elements of clay, adding trace amount of H_2O, sealing the wood in a vacuum (no air), and adding heat (150°C) and time (eight months) and create 100% coal that is indistinguishable[43] from the coal formed naturally by all the techniques so far applied to it.[44] Dr. Robert Gentry confirms this. He has repeatedly observed lead-uranium ratios in coal that demonstrate that "both the initial uranium infiltration and coalification could possibly have occurred recently within the past several thousand years."[45] His findings contradict the current hypothesis that coal formed in either the Tertiary period (60 million years ago), or the Cretaceous period, or the Jurassic period (160 million years ago), or the Triassic (220 million years ago), but recently in geological terms, such as thousands of years ago, and the layers were formed simultaneously. The evidence indicates a severe acceleration of hundreds of millions of years from what evolutionary geologists believe took place long ago. Since the CRD is used as the basis for calculating the age of coal to be hundreds of millions of years old, this illustrates the flaw in believing the CRD has remained constant. When formulas are contrived to back a theory, the formulas sometimes come with a variable. For example, a calculation may have a ±10% error ratio. Well, the ±% error ratio for the CRD is off the charts. Again, no evolutionary scientist was there 300 million years ago to observe their hypothesized large time frame for forming coal. Yet, it is taken as the Gospel truth. No fossil has a date stamped on it. Scientific fact comes from repeated experiments in a laboratory; therefore, the CRD is just an arithmetic calculation and not evidence for an old earth. Considering we can make coal in eight months that is indistinguishable from coal formed naturally, this is a serious red flag in this old age hypothesis and means radiometric dating is merely radiometric fiction.

Petroleum: We are told that oil generation was a very slow process that began hundreds of millions of years ago. Yet, algae with water cooked at high temperatures and pressure converts the algae to petroleum in minutes,[46] and chicken byproducts that are not sold to the public, such as adipose (fat), veins, ligaments, tendons, cartilage, and the like, are heated up to 150°C and 100% petroleum can be produced through distillation techniques in 30 minutes. Since we can produce oil in a brief amount of

42 Mt. Saint Helen, Wikipedia.
43 Nature, page 316, March 28, 1985.
44 tgm.org/Creation_coal. "Coal: Evidence for a Young Earth."
45 Science, Dr. Robert Gentry, October issue, 1976.
46 gizmag.com/aldae-crude-oil-process, Science, algae to crude oil: Million year natural process takes minutes in the lab.

time that is indistinguishable from oil that allegedly is hundreds of millions of years old, the CRD that forms the basis for determining the age of oil, is radiometric fiction. This illustrates how the CRD is just an aspect of a formula to support an old earth that subsequently adds the necessary time element for evolution, rather than scientific fact.

<u>Fossils:</u> We are told that fossils turn to stone through a slow process. However, no fossil ever forms naturally as sediment is slowly deposited over 100,000 to a million years because vegetation or biomass decays into dust long before a millimeter of sediment is covering it. Thus, nothing left to fossilize. Only with a quick deposit of soil, moisture, and pressure will the organic material change to stone before decaying into its base elements and being converted to nutrients for soil. Just the fact that we have fossils is observable and testable evidence that there was an acceleration of soil deposited quickly as in weeks to months, such as with the global flood. Another aspect that indicates how fast things occurred during the catastrophic Genesis flood: many dinosaur bones did not even have time to turn to dust because a deep freeze came over them in the Arctic Circle and froze them. *Image credit: American Museum of Nat. His. shows the quickness of fossil formation*

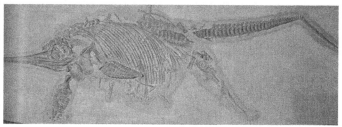

with a birth captured in the process. Only the Flood accounts for a healthy female being covered quickly, unless you want to believe that there were mudslides all over the globe that covered every single fossil for every single layer of the crust.

Therefore, considering the preponderance of the evidence, the CRD never been constant. In fact, petrifaction occurs in 1/16,700 of the time necessary, coalification occurs in 1/30 millionth of the time necessary, and petrolification occurs in 1/877 billionth of the time necessary with trauma. A German lab released decay-rate data after a 15-year study, confirming that uranium-226 has seasonal and monthly variations.[47] This is observable and testable evidence that the CRD is not constant. Also, lightning strikes 100 times every second around the globe, ionizing elements and accelerating the decay process. The helium stored in zircon crystals is the final nail in the coffin. Not only is the CRD not constant, but it never has been constant. Thus, the purported evolutionary timeline of the age of the earth and life on earth is also seriously flawed. Since evolutionists declare that the earth is 4.6 billion years old, one would suspect that if they are wrong and the earth is young, the evolutionary calculations that support their view would be off by huge numbers. That is exactly what we find. The evidence is that the calculations supporting the 4.6 billion years is off so much that it supports the young earth view. It is not like the evolutionary timeline is off by hundreds of thousands of years or millions of years; no, they are off by billions of years. YECs who take a literal view of the Genesis creation account, do not have a problem with trauma accelerating the process of aging because it fits perfectly with the Bible.

Some evolutionists argue that since there was an ice age and things age slower during an ice age, the age of the earth is possibly older than their calculations suggest. This is flawed thinking because it misses the point that their calculations are wildly off. In addition, even an evolutionist has to admit that the ice age would slow the evolutionary process, and is just a tiny blip of time on their huge time scale, and even if the so called ice age lasted millions of years and nothing aged one day during that time period, then their numbers would only be off by a tiny fraction of the total 4.6 billion-year-old earth. But that is a moot point because their calculations are based on a flawed CRD, and we have established that evolutionary aging numbers are off by multiples of billions of years.

Review: With extreme trauma to the earth, such as earthquakes, asteroid/comet impacts,

47 Power Spectrum Analysis of Physikalisch-Technishe-Bundesanstalt, Decay-Rate Data: Evidence for Solar Rotational Modulation/ Published online: November 17, 2010.

volcanoes, tectonic plate movements and subsequent electrical discharge, ultraviolet light, cosmic rays, gamma rays, a global flood, and so on, the rate of decay (aging process) was accelerated, and the CRD is an error that is used as a foundational bedrock for evolution.

What does this have to do with the polar ice caps and the ice age? Well, since nature and mankind can accelerate the rate of decay (aging process), and we know the CRD is not constant, then when evolutionary glaciologists use false timelines as foundational to date the ice age, you know their purported dates are in error. The ice age did not occur 2.4 million years ago, and the glacial age did not occur 1.8 million years ago, the glacial/ice age occurred ~4,400 years ago from the severe cold resulting from the aftermath of the global flood.

Furthermore, when evolutionary glaciologists tell you that the polar ice caps and ice age are hundreds of thousands of years old, you now know that they are using dating techniques that are flawed, and their primary agenda is to establish an age that supports billions of years of life to allow evolution enough time and to promote theories that are contrary to the Bible's timeline. Remember, (a) they were never there, and (b) the CRD on which the dating process is built upon is systematically flawed.

Just because the model of dating the age of the earth is flawed and filled with errors does not mean that the Bible is true by default. But it is ironic that the size of error in the radioactive isotopic dating system utilizing the CRD coincides with the Bible's timeline more so than not. Does the Bible have anything to say about the ice age? Let us look at some texts that give us some clues about a recent ice age and the recent formation of the polar ice caps.

How did the polar ice caps form, when did the polar ice caps form, and when was this ice age? The Bible gives us clues to this mystery. In the chapter "The Canopy," we discussed the source of the 40 days and nights of rain, which was the canopy of salt water and the deep caverns of water.

How do we know that there were no polar ice caps during the time of Adam and Eve? The canopy would have provided temperate global temperatures and shielded the earth from harmful cosmic energy and extreme variances of hot and cold temperatures globally. After all, Adam and Eve were naked all the time, and after sinning, they only covered their private parts. At the time just prior to the global flood, the global temperate temperatures would have been probably around 75°F at night and 85°F during the day at the equator—and potentially 50°F at night to 70°F during the day at the poles. This is not cold enough to cause ice formation and does not provide enough change in temperatures to create a jet stream. Gentle breezes would be the forecast.

Review: Before the Flood, the canopy of water created global temperate temperatures, preventing the polar regions from getting cold enough for ice to form. This is why Gen. 8 reveals the beginning of the jet stream at the first formation of the polar ice caps.

Well, could this mean they lived near the equator? Yes. So let us go further. Prior to the Gen. 7 flood, there could not be polar ice caps or deserts because there was not enough global change of temperature from the equator to the poles to cause a global wind. We learn that after the Flood in Gen. 8:1 that God causes a wind to pass over all the earth; this is our jet stream, and this is caused by changes in global temperature. Also, from a creation point of view, as was pointed out in the chapter on deserts, God created everything complete, and everything was very good, lacking nothing, and there was no death. The polar ice caps are a symbol of a planet suffering the pains of sin and death. Antarctica is considered to be the largest desert on the planet, a vast waste land of arid cold death, the perfect symbol of the absence of God, who represents light, energy, warmth, and life. Therefore, when God looked over all His creation and inspired Moses to write, "God saw all that He had made, and behold, it was very good" (Gen. 1:31), there was no death (Romans 5:12), and since deserts and polar ice caps are representatives of death, they were not existing at that time. Romans 8:20–22 reveals that all of creation suffers as a result of sin. One of the judgments of sin came about at the global flood, which initiated the four seasons, the hydrological cycle, and death represented by the polar ice caps and deserts. The four seasons represent the death (fall), burial (winter), resurrection (spring), and life (summer). The four seasons were not created on the fourth day of creation. The word *seasons* in Genesis 1:14, was not used to indicate weather, but to indicate festivals (e.g., the Sabbath, the feast of the Tabernacle, Passover, etc).[48] Either God created the earth with a tilt and the canopy of water prevented the four seasons, or the global flood and large asteroids impacting the earth caused the earth's tilt of 23 degrees on its axis and caused the four seasons.

When God created the universe, He did it completely, lacking nothing, and without deserts and polar ice caps because they represent the near absence of life. No other earth-shattering event occurred to alter the perfect climate God created until the Flood.

The Bible implicitly declares that there were no polar ice caps until after the Flood and explicitly declares there was no death prior to the fall of mankind to sin. Therefore, we can infer that prior to the fall of mankind, there were no polar ice caps and no deserts. The polar ice caps and the deserts (including Antarctica) do not come close to what God declared after creating everything. He said, "It was very good."

Also, remember that woolly mammoths were living in the Arctic regions and feeding on tropical vegetation and fruit. The temperature was cold enough for woolly mammoths to live comfortably with their fur, but not too cold as to prevent vegetation to flourish and other animals to thrive, such as camels. Since there were vast areas of tropical vegetation to support 150 million woolly mammoths and an array of other animals in the Arctic Circle, this means no polar ice caps. You cannot have polar ice and tropical vegetation next to it.

Review: There could not be polar ice caps and deserts prior to sin entering the world because all that God made was very good and complete. No other earth-shattering event exists until the Flood to change what God had made. Also, the deserts and polar ice caps are representatives of what sin has brought, which is that All creation suffers and groans for freedom from the bondage of sin and death.

When did the ice age (or the glacial age) occur? The massive ice age that scientists refer to, which allegedly occurred 2.6 million years ago, occurred as a result of the global flood. How is this possible? Scientists look at glacial cores and observe layer upon layer, and knowing the rate that each layer builds up today (the Uniformitarian theory), they count backwards and hypothesize that the first of five glacial ages started 800 million years ago, and the most recent ice age started 2.6 million years ago. This is hokum. They are interpreting the data to fit their already conceived time paradigm that attempts to provide enough time for evolution.

The global flood was caused by massive amounts of asteroids and volcanoes and tectonic plate movements and heat and water and dirt bursting out of deep caverns and rain for 40 days and nights globally. The temperatures would have been very high in the initial period of the Flood, so high that if there was not rain and water bursting out of the deep caverns to calm things down, the earth would have baked to super-high temperatures, killing everything, even Noah and those inside the Ark. With the rains preventing a global inferno, the temperatures stabilized, though it was very warm. Toward the end of the 40 days of rain and end of 150 of the waters covering the globe, the temperature would no longer be stabilizing and would succumb to supercool temperatures, as the asteroid impacts would have stopped within the first couple of days, and the volcanoes subsided, and then the temperatures started to plummet quickly as a result of the sun being blocked and a globe covered in water. Potentially, this record-setting cold freeze, with such a prolonged period without sunlight, may have plunged the planet from a comfortable 66°F high at the poles before the Flood to a low of 0°F at both poles toward the middle of the Flood, freezing woolly mammoths in there place while they still had tropical food in there belly and

---

48 Strong's Concordance: #4150: *mowed*: an appointment, i.e., a fixed time or season specifically a festival; conventionally a year of assembly; technically the congregation place of meeting; also a signal, feast.

plummeting the poles to -50°F by the end of the Flood. Then plunged the globe into a massive ice age toward the end of the Flood. This would be so severe and extensive that the ice from the North Pole would have reached as far down as central North America, all of Europe, and most of Asia. From the South Pole, it would have reached as far up as southern South America, South Africa, and the southern portion of Australia. At this time during the glacial age, the ocean levels would be below the continental shelves because the ice absorbed a lot of the water out of the oceans and left behind massive salt deposits. *Image credit: www.theresilientearth.com. by Doug L. Hoffman.*

The entire flood saga took almost one year; there was 40 days and 40 nights of rain, 150 days of water prevailing over everything, and then about 6 months of water absorption. Combining this information with the mammoths being frozen alive, indicates that the poles froze quicker than anticipated. This caused the ocean levels to drop lower and lower as more ice formed until the ocean levels were at the level of the continental shelves. The ocean levels stayed below the continental shelves until immediately following the time of the Tower of Babel, in the days of Peleg (Gen. 10:25). From the peak of the glacial age (almost one year after the Flood), the glaciers started to recede.

Review: Through deductive reasoning, one can see that the records in the Bible implicitly indicate that the glacial age began within the first year from the start of the Flood. Key indicators include the woolly mammoths that fed on tropical fruit in the Arctic Circle and were frozen alive, 150 days of water prevailing over the entire earth, the global wind that started after the Flood while the waters were receding, and the statement, "Everything God created was complete and very good."

The extent of the glacial age is observed through the directions of rock scourings and scratches and patterns that are unique to glaciers. Many valleys around the globe that have the typical horizontal cutting and scraping formations associated with glacier movements. Rock deposits the size of cars have been carried by the massive force of the glacial movements and deposited in regions 1,000 miles away from their origin. This is called **moraines**.

Several regions are still rising from once being compressed by the massive weight of ice. This process is called a **post-glacial rebound/glacial isostasy**.[49] Since the land is still rebounding from the huge amount of weight of ice being removed, this suggests a recent removal—as in thousands of years as creationists believe, and not millions of years as evolutionists believe. Does the Bible give additional clues about when the Glacial age occurred? Yes. Gen. 10 and 11, the narrative picks up 3 generations from Noah (King Nimrod was Noah's grandson), all of mankind spoke one language, and they wanted to make a name for themselves, so they built a tower to reach the heavens, and God in the flesh (Jesus) came down and confused their language and scattered them around the globe. After the language was changed to the multiple languages that we hear today, the people migrated away from each other and from the central location of Babel (later known as Babylon, and now Turkey). Since this is shortly after the Genesis flood, we may infer that the people migrated away from each other to different continents along the continental shelves or ice, both allowed each continent to be accessible at that time. to have

the continental shelves exposed as dry land, massive amounts of water had to be frozen as glacial ice to reduce the water level below the continental shelves. That is what the Bible records, that the waters receded. Therefore, we may conclude that as the Glacial ice grew toward the end of the year long flood saga, the more the ocean level dropped. Thus, the formation of the glacial age was instrumental in causing the Genesis flood to recede. *Image credit: www.colonial.net/Plate.*

The image illustrates a **continental shelf** (extensions of continents) adjacent to the coast-line, currently the shelves are hundreds of feet below the ocean level because

Continental Shelf connects Asia to North America

49 www.wikipedia.org/wiki/Post-glacial_rebound.

the ice age has melted, but during the ice age, the water level was much lower. During this lower ocean level, and at the time of the Tower of Babel, a boy named Peleg was born (Noah begot Shem, Shem begot Arpachshad 2 years after the Flood, Arpachshad begot Shelah at age 35, Shelah begot Eber at age 30, and Eber begot Peleg at age 34, 5th generation from Noah). His name means "in his days the earth was divided" (Gen. 10:25). This indicates that mankind was able to travel to different continents via exposed continental shelves and ice that connected continents. After successfully walking to other continents, it was at this time that enough ice melted that the waters of the oceans rose above the continental shelves and cut off each cultural tribe with vast oceans.

This is further Biblical evidence that the glacial age existed during the days of Peleg, who was born 101 years after the Flood, 2250 BC, some 4,265 years ago.

Review: Pangaea broke apart during the 40-day flood, the glacial age began as the polar ice grew, and the floodwater receded into ice until the water level was below the continental shelves, marking the peak of the glacial age. Peleg was born 101 years after the Flood; during his time is when enough ice had melted to cause the ocean waters to cover the continental shelves that connected each continent and island and cut off cultures from each other until modern times. This occurred after the scattering of the people from the Tower of Babel event (Gen. 11).

How does the Bible's global flood account for glacial core samples that determine oxygen concentrations were 50% higher in the distant past than today? Higher oxygen concentrations before the Flood is in perfect harmony with the Bible. We know that there was abundantly more vegetation on the surface of the earth producing oxygen and that life thrived in the higher oxygen concentration environment and that human beings lived 900+ years before the Flood. So we are in accord with oxygen being 50% higher before the Flood and being reduced after the Flood with the onset of deserts, polar ice caps, and vast oceans that physically limit vegetation from growing to produce oxygen.

How does the Biblical account of the global flood deal with all the layers of snowpack at the poles? With each day of rain during the Flood, there would be changes of temperatures from the highs of the day to the lows of the night. This change in the apex of warmth and the low of the cold would allow for changes in the type of precipitation deposited. During the beginning of the Flood, there were only raindrops globally because of the high global temperatures from the fires, asteroid impacts, volcanoes, and tectonic plate friction, but toward the end of the 40-day flood, the global temperatures would gradually decrease and decrease. At some point during the 40 days of rain, water raining down from the canopy at the polar regions would have been falling as snow, hail, and sleet at the poles. The temperatures started dropping drastically in the polar regions, and the snow would have fallen most of the day. Presuming one to two hours of sleet and rain, this change of precipitation intermingled with rain and sleet, and freezing floodwater would have caused new layers of ice on a daily basis. Spanning the year-long Flood saga, temperature variations throughout the day of warm and cold would have caused layers of ice deposited on the North Pole and South Pole; combining this with a twice-daily global tide created the layers of ice we see today. *Photo Image: Peter Prokosch, www.grida.no.*

Evolutionists claim that the Egyptian dynasties occurred around the estimated time of the Biblical flood, and therefore, this debunks the Flood. The estimates that are given for the dates of Egyptian history are just that, estimates. Biblical theologians, combining the records of Genesis and Exodus with observable evidence of the pyramids, estimate that the Egyptian dynasties began after the Flood, when one of Noah's sons (Ham) settled near the region and begot a son named Egypt (Gen 10:6). Then, the Tower of Babel occurred (Gen 11). Then, the Egyptian era began after the Tower of Babel, and the empire was already established when Joseph was sold into slavery in Gen 37. The peak of the dominance of the dynasties of Ancient Egyptian is explained in Gen. 41 and Exodus 2. This was aided by the mass arrival of the Jewish people. The building of the pyramids were probably best performed by the Jews and accelerated by Jewish slaves during their 430 years of captivity (Ex 12:40). Jews are famous for providing high-quality work because of the blessing of God. But the Egyptian dynasties came to an abrupt end with Moses leading an estimated two million people (Ex 12:37) out of Egypt, and Egyptians were compelled by God to give the Jews their silver and gold, crippling the Egyptian economy (Ex 12:35–36), and this led to the immediate downfall of the Egyptian reign.

Do not get caught up in evolutionary geologists and archeologists saying that the Egyptian era debunks the timing of the Flood. Evolutionists are always willing to suggest a date that is incongruous with the Bible. The Bible implicitly explains how the pyramids were built—on the backs of skilled Jewish laborers (Exodus 1–2). Plenty of time exists for Egyptian monuments to have been built and dynasties to have reigned from 2300 BC till the induction of Joseph and the arrival of the original 70 Jews in 1875 BC to the great pyramids being built by the slave labor of the Jewish people, to the mass Exodus with Moses around 1445 BC.

<u>Review:</u> <u>Many layers of ice formed from the global flood, and then the vast glacial age began. Theologians studying Bible records discern from the genealogical records that the Flood occurred around ~2,350 BC–~2,400 BC.</u>

Fast-forward to today, and a scientist observes and measures the current rate of deposit of snowfall in the Arctic Circle, and then using today's rate, works backward to determine the age of the glaciers. The scientist then misinterprets the data and sees layers in the glacial cores in terms of yearly layers instead of layers formed in hours or days or weeks. Well, an odd situation that throws a monkey wrench in evolutionary glaciologists' timeline: glacier core samples have layers, and evolutionists count 135,000 annual layers with 10,000 feet of ice built up. But how do they know those are yearly layers and not a more frequent layer formation pattern?

A WW2 airplane was buried 263 feet down below the ice, and there was only 48 years of snowfall between the estimated origin date (1942–1948) to the discovery of the plane. That comes out to (263 feet/48 years) an annual deposit rate of 5.5 feet per year. Therefore, dividing the estimated 10,000 feet of ice by 5.5 feet per year equals 1,824 years of glacial core sampling, not 135,000 years as evolutionary geologists contend.[50] The conclusion is that the layers that evolutionists proclaim to represent yearly deposits are not annual layers. No, they are temperature swing layers from warm to cold, warm to cold, and so on, not annual layers. The image of the layers is

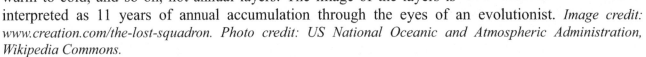

interpreted as 11 years of annual accumulation through the eyes of an evolutionist. *Image credit: www.creation.com/the-lost-squadron. Photo credit: US National Oceanic and Atmospheric Administration, Wikipedia Commons.*

What is the motivating factor for evolutionists to interpret the layers in years versus temperature swings? Two reasons exist to why they deviate from the Bible:

1. Evolutionary glaciologists use rates of deposit that are seen today and extrapolate the rate of deposition as if they have been relatively constant. This is a voluntary choice to choose dates and interpret data that support an evolutionary timeline and that by default conflict with the Bible. Some rely on man's wisdom as the standard for discerning what is truth, instead of relying on the wisdom of God and what His Word reveals as the standard (Proverbs 3:5–6).
2. The unsaved person is unable to discern the truths in the Bible because their spirit is hostile and alien to God's Spirit. This is an involuntary choice because the Truths in the Bible are spiritually discerned,

---

50 Sepetjian.worldpress.com/ Age indicating factors, ice cores, the poles, the lost squadron, July 07, 2012.

thus without the Holy Spirit revealing the truths of creation and the global flood, they can only be fairy tales to the unsaved (I Corinthians 2:14–16).

A saved person bound for heaven can fall into category 1, but their effectiveness in furthering the kingdom of God is reduced because it is harder to logically share the Gospel to someone and tell them to believe in an all-powerful God that has errors in His Word. Both categories fulfill two end-time prophecies regarding evolution and creation. Romans 1:18–32:

> That which is known about God is evident within them . . . For since the creation of the world His invisible attributes have been clearly seen, being understood through what has been made, so that they are without excuse. For even though they knew God, they did not honor Him as God or give thanks, but they became futile in their speculations, and their foolish heart was darkened. Professing to be wise, they became fools.

And 2 Timothy 4:3–4 says:

> The time will come when they will not endure sound doctrine; but wanting to have their ears tickled, they will accumulate for themselves teachers in accordance to their own desires, and will turn away their ears from the truth and will turn aside to myths.

Review: Evolutionary glaciologists postulate that there were 5 glacial ages, with one allegedly occurring 800 million of years ago to coincide with the massive number of years required for evolution, whereas a believer in God's word matches up their interpretations to coincide with the Bible. Either God's Word is correct, or man's wisdom is correct.

The pieces of the jigsaw puzzle are slowly falling into place. What caused the global flood—the canopy of salt water—is the very same source that kept the planet in temperate temperatures for maximum vegetation growth and prevented polar ice caps from forming. The extra abundant vegetation produced a greater percentage of oxygen, which allowed life to thrive. Hence, human beings and other creatures lived 900+ years before the Flood. This canopy also increased atmospheric pressure on the inhabitants of the earth, which created a large buoyant force that reduced the net effect of gravity, and it allowed dinosaurs to grow extremely large (despite porous bones structures) and to live extremely long lives because of increased oxygen. But the canopy was lost to the global flood.

Chapter Summary: The polar ice caps and the glacial age (ice age) formed as a result of 40 days and nights of rain and no sunlight (Gen. 7), with the waters being absorbed by the polar regions over the following 12 months. Before the global flood, the canopy of salt water hovered around the atmosphere and created temperate global temperatures, preventing polar ice caps and deserts from forming. The glacial age began around 2,400 BC.

Tectonic Plates and River Deltas

Scientists have determined that at one point in time, the earth's continents were all connected together and they hypothesize that the seas/oceans were in one place surrounding the land. The seas that were gathered in one place they call them Panthalassa and Tethys, and the land that was gathered in one place was called **Pangaea**. <u>The only problem with the drawing is that there were no oceans until the global flood–only seas, freshwater lakes, and rivers.</u>

Pangaea is Greek; *pan* means "entire," and *gaea* comes from *gaia*, meaning "Mother Earth."

The continental shelf is ~200 feet below the surface of the oceans. It extends around the continents and was the shoreline during the ice age. When one takes a look at the continents and the continental shelves, one can see that the continents fit even better together with the continental shelves than with the actual coastlines. It becomes very clear that the continents were all together at one time.

Since Pangaea is an accepted premise, does the Bible discuss anything about the land of the earth being in one place and the water/seas/oceans being in the other place surrounding the land? Let us take a look. On the first day of creation, God creates matter, space, motion, time, and energy. The burgeoning Earth was already rotating on an axis, hence the phrase of evening and morning and one day. On the second day of creation, God stretches out the universe (celestial bodies are still forming at this point) and this causes the atmosphere to form between the waters that surrounded the earth (Gen. 1:6). At this point in creation, the earth was surrounded by an atmosphere and a canopy of water, but the land was not in its finished form, as the waters were covering the dirt. Look at Gen. 1:9:

> Then God said, 'Let the waters below the heavens be gathered into one place, and let the dry land appear', and it was so. God called the dry land earth, and the gathering of the waters He called seas; and God saw that it was good.

The word *gathered* means "gathered." The words *one place* is derived from two words. The word *place* is *maqom* in Hebrew (Strong's Concordance # 4725), and it means country, home, open, place, room, space, and whithersoever. In other words, let the waters be gathered according to their natural home or place. The word *one* is *echad* in Hebrew (Strong's Concordance # 259), and it means alike, alone, altogether, anything, apiece, and a certain. *Echad* is derived from "achad," which has the same meanings but includes the numeral "one" in its definition; this is where interpreters get the numeral one from. Therefore, we are not forced to use the number one in the verse, and we may use the preferred meaning of "<u>like kinds.</u>" As in, "Let the waters below the heavens be gathered into like kinds." For example, saltwater gathered to form seas, and freshwater gathered together to form deep freshwater reservoirs under the crust, which then bubbled up to form rivers and lakes once the dry land rose. Since God said He spoke to Moses clearly, not in veiled visions or nor dreams, but face to face as a friend does to a friend (Numbers 12:6–8), then the words of Moses are straightforward, and can be read on face value. Therefore, when God said, "Let the waters below, the heavens be gathered into like kinds . . . and the waters He called seas," this indicates that the land was technically gathered together by default because there were no oceans yet. The Hebrew word for *seas* is "yam" (Strong's Concordance # 3220), it means a sea or the Mediterranean Sea. Since the *seas* are vastly smaller bodies of water than oceans, and a completely different word than the ocean (which is the "deep"), then by default the majority of the earth's surface was exposed land, which forces the conclusion that the land was together. After all, under the water the land is still together today. While moving saltwater around together to form seas, at the same time God said, "And let the dry land appear."

The Bible explicitly declared that the waters were gathered together and the dry land appeared, which means that the Bible implicitly declared that the land was gathered in the other one place, hence Pangaea.

Review: <u>A mutual consensus is that the continents were at one time connected together in a supercontinent called Pangaea.</u>

When did Pangaea break apart? We need to lay a foundation. First, the continents are sitting on **tectonic plates**, which move, causing the continents to move. There are **divergent zones** where the crust of earth is splitting apart pushing the large continents away from a central origin. The **Mid-Atlantic Ridge** pushes the North American and South American plates into the Pacific Plate, which forces the Pacific Plate under the Asian plate. This is called a **subduction zone**, and it results in the "**ring of fire**," the source of many earthquakes and volcanic activity.

Based on the Uniformitarian theory, evolutionary scientists believe that Pangaea broke apart some 120–220 million years ago. How do they come to this conclusion? They use the average current rate of tectonic plate speed, estimated at 2.5 cm/yr, and they divide the speed into the distance traveled, which is ~1,770 miles (2848 km) (The distance between South America and Africa), that equals ~115 million years ago when Pangaea broke apart. But wait a minute. We do not need to know the distance from South America to Africa; we need to know the distances from South America to the Mid-Atlantic Ridge (sight of origin) and from Africa to the Mid-Atlantic Ridge. That distance is half the amount, or 885 miles (1424km). We need to convert 2.5 centimeters per year to kilometers:

2.5 cm/year x 1 m/100 cm x 1 km/1,000 m = 0.000025 km and

1,424 km / 2.5 x 10^{-5} km/year = ~57 million years when Pangaea broke apart.

How do YEC handle the ~57 million year date?

Sometimes the tectonic plates move quickly, allowing for a hypothesis that it is possible for tectonic plates to move quicker than 2.5 centimeters per year, which opens the door for a younger Pangaea breakup. In 2011, Japan had an earthquake that moved the main island 8 feet closer to Alaska in only two minutes.[51] This equates to a velocity of 10 million centimeters per year as compared to the current projected velocity of 2.5 centimeters per year. This is evidence that tectonic plates can and have moved faster at times.

With a fast moving tectonic plate hypothesis during the Genesis flood, we would expect to find a direct correlation between the build up of potential energy with a proportionately larger kinetic energy, and that tectonic plates are capable of storing and have stored immense quantity of potential energy, and we would expect to find some evidence that the friction which slows tectonic plate movement was substantially reduced during this fast tectonic plate event. That is exactly what we observe and measure. Remnant deep reservoirs of water exist, that did not get squished out by the weight and movement of the tectonic plates during the Flood. Several places around the world scientist have found freshwater reservoirs, such as underneath Israel, which opens the door to a hydroplaning hypothesis (by Dr. Walter Brown). In addition, geologist affirm that tectonic plates are capable of storing potential energy, and suddenly releasing the stored up energy as fast kinetic energy, which allows the hypothesis that potential energy stored up from creation to the Flood. If there were no tectonic plate movements from creation till the Flood, there would be ~1,650 years of potential energy stored up, which is a sufficient amount of potential energy to match the fast moving kinetic energy

---

51 Www.cnn.com/2011/world/aslapcf/03/12/japan.earthquake.tsunami.earth/index.html.

hypothesized with a quick plate movement during the Flood. Since the term fast tectonic plate movement is relative, we are only talking about 2.5–5 kmph (1–2 mph) during the yearlong Flood saga. To put that in perspective, humans walk at 2.5 mph. This is certainly plausible. One earthquake in 2011 caused one tectonic plate (that Japan is on) to slide 164 feet against another plate in minutes, and the 2004 Sumatra earthquake shifted a tectonic plate ~80 feet.[52] But what is different about the plate movements during the Flood is that they were hydroplaning on the fountains of the deep to reduce the drag/friction coefficient. Whether the hydroplaning of the tectonic plates were on water or on low viscous lava (flows like oil) is immaterial because scientists have discovered that volcanic eruptions emit a large quantity of water. When volcanoes erupt, they do appear as fountains from the deep. It seems the "fountains of the deep" are both, water and volcanoes.

Since the tectonic plates are currently moving at an average rate of 2.5 cm/yr (1 inch/yr), and since the rate of movement is slow enough to allow river deltas to form, then there should be at least one trail of sediment on the ocean floor from where the rivers once laid sediment to the current mouths of rivers. Like the trail of volcanic islands left behind as the Pacific tectonic plate moved to form the Emperor Ridge and Hawaiian chain and Hawaiian islands, so too should river sediment leave evidence of continuous deposits of its prior location on the ocean floor. One may argue that this is impossible because the mouth of the rivers are traveling with the tectonic plate and therefore, there cannot be a trail. But this is only a half truth because several locations around the globe exist where fault-lines intersect rivers and their deltas, and thus there should be indicators of prior deltas that establish an existence greater than 4,500 years. For example, on the northern California coastline, several rivers empty into the Pacific ocean, and their sediment deposits cross over the San Andreas fault. But guess what? No detectable trails of sedimentary deposit exist from any river, and more importantly, no river delta's sediment represents greater than 5,000 years of existence. The implication is that the tectonic plates once moved too quickly for rivers to deposit a sediment trail on the ocean floor as the continents have drifted and that the date of Pangaea breaking apart is relatively recent.

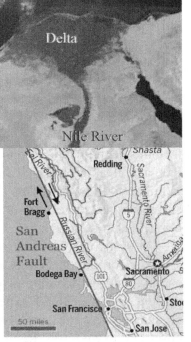

Psalm 104:5–9 provides a summary of Earth's history; this is what it says, *He established the earth upon its foundations, So that it will not totter forever and ever.* That is the third day of creation, at the foundation of the world. Then it says, *You covered it with the deep as with a garment; The waters were standing above the mountains.* This is the catastrophic global flood: *At your rebuke they fled, at the sound of Your thunder they hurried away.* God rebuked the floodwater, and no mention or association of God rebuking any portion of the water during the creation moment of Gen. 1–2 because all that God made was very good (Gen. 1:31), so this is after the rain stopped on the 40th day and after the water had remained above the mountains for 150 days. Psalm 104:8: *The mountains rose; the valleys sank down to the place which You established for them.* This verse aids in the clarity that the tectonic plates were still moving from the breakup of Pangaea at the start of the Flood. They had drifted quickly across the surface of the earth and had now reached contact with other tectonic plates. The fast-moving tectonic plates were traveling at ~1–2 mph as they impacted with other plates, causing collisions that buckled the crust of the earth and sent mountains higher and valleys lower. The tectonic plates buckled either up or down to alleviate the force, just like the buckling of a car in a crash. This set the boundaries to prevent another global flood. Psalm 104:9: *You set a boundary that they may not pass over, So that they will not return to cover the earth.* The brevity in terms of how quickly the tectonic plates moved to achieve this explains why the Himalayas are so tall yet have

---

52 *National Geographic, Daily News,* "The 2011 Japan Tsunami was caused by largest fault slip ever recorded."

seashells on them. It explains where the waters went, and for this discussion, it explains why no trails of sediment deposits from river deltas exist on the ocean floor.

The Pacific tectonic plate is moving west-by-northwest, and it moves over a hot spot where magma pours out of the crust of the pacific ocean floor to form islands. Specifically the Hawaiian Island chain. Now, because the tectonic plate is moving slowly today this allows for islands. However, hundreds of tiny mountains under the water are too small to appear above the surface of the waters, why? Because the Pacific tectonic plate was moving too fast to allow enough time for lava to pour out of the hot spot and form islands. This evidence authenticates Psalm 104:8.

As a side note, evolutionists are quick to say, "There is not enough water on earth to cover the high Himalayas, so the Bible legend of the Flood was regional or did not happen." Well, the mountains we see today are much taller than when the Flood occurred, and the valleys we see today are much deeper than when the Flood occurred, as explained in Psalm 104:5–9. In fact, if the spherical Earth were smoothed out with no mountains and no valleys then the entire planet would be covered ~1.5 miles deep with water. And Gen. 7:19–20 says every mountain was covered 15 cubits (cubit: the length from the elbow to finger tip) by water, not a mile, so the earth was not void of mountains and valleys, but they weren't as tall as we see today. This suggests that the tallest mountains during the Flood era was ~5,280 feet high (one mile). A global flood explains why giant petrified clams with closed shells exist on top of the Andes mountains. Clams lose motor control with death and cannot keep their shells closed; therefore, their shells open up when they die. Thus, the closed shells suggest that they were quickly covered with soil, moisture, and pressure as the Genesis flood provides.

Additionally, before the Flood, there was a canopy of water that hovered around the atmosphere. This canopy significantly raised the atmospheric pressure and prevented air moisture to form into clouds for raindrops. The Bible helps with this information by explaining that a mist rose from the ground to water the whole earth (Gen. 2:6), and the first cloud and the first rainbow came after the Flood, when atmospheric pressure was reduced to current levels. What does this have to do with having enough water to flood the earth? Well, before the Flood, the atmospheric pressure was too high to have moisture in the form of clouds. But Today, "the atmosphere contains 37.5 million billion gallons of water, in the invisible vapor phase. That is enough water to cover the entire surface of the earth (land and ocean) with one inch of rain."[53] *Photo credit: Arturo Vildozola.*

At some point, when one sees that evolutionary hypotheses are false and that each record in the Bible is supported with science and evidence, then one must accept the Bible and reject evolution. If they do not, then evolution is their religion. If they accept a little of both, they are fooling themselves because both tenets are mutually exclusive. A time is coming when every island and every mountain will be removed (Rev 16:20), and an asteroid will hit the earth so hard that it will split the earth asunder, and it will wobble like a drunkard (Isaiah 24:18–20) and lead to the removal of the oceans (Rev 21:1). Therefore, if one struggles with the verses that recorded the past and then changes the Scriptures to fit man's hypotheses, then one might as well throw the whole Bible out because greater things are coming soon.

Review: Tectonic plates move at an average rate of ~2.5 cm/yr (1 in./yr), and this is slow enough for river deltas to form, but no trail exist by any river delta along the ocean floor. The

---

53 Google search, "How much water is in the atmosphere."

implication is that the tectonic plates moved too quickly for sediment to form deltas along the way.

Evolutionists may argue that since oceans are not static bodies of water, maybe the ocean currents picked up the sediment and moved it away. Oceans are dynamic and have currents, but ocean currents are not at the same velocity at different depths. The currents at the ocean floor are 1/100 the speed of the surface currents. Therefore, the argument that the sedimentary delta trails along the Pacific Ocean floor (where the San Andreas fault intersects many river deltas) disappeared because of turbulent currents, are simply false because they utilized the surface speed of ocean current, which is 100X greater than the speed of the currents on the ocean floor. The current at the bottom of the ocean is 0.044 mph (0.02 m/s).[54] That is 1/25th of 1 mile per hour. To put that in perspective, the average human walking at a gingerly pace has a velocity 56 times faster than ocean currents near the ocean floor.

Review: Currents on the ocean floor move too slow to have wiped away all remnants of sedimentary deposits left by the rivers as Pangaea broke apart. The reason no trails of deposits exist on the ocean floor from delta formations is because the tectonic plates have moved too quickly for trails to form.

A **river delta** is a fan-like shape of soil deposits at the mouth/opening of a river. Each river has a delta with deposits of sedimentation. But since Pangaea allegedly broke apart 120–220 million years ago, there should be some rivers with enough sediment deposits to confirm that date.

Evolutionists may not be aware or unwilling to accept this, but no river on the face of earth exist that has enough sediment deposit to establish that Pangaea broke apart 120 million years ago. In fact, no river on earth has enough sediment deposit at the mouth of the river to establish that Pangaea broke apart 10,000 years ago. Well, given the rate of sediment deposit and the amount of sediment deposited, then what age is supported? It is roughly 4,500 years worth of sediment deposit. That's right, no river on earth has enough sediment deposit to establish that Pangaea broke apart greater than 4,500 years ago. *Image credit: UniverserToday.com. Mississippi River Delta.*

The Mississippi River deposits ~500 million tons of sediment annually, and this causes the delta to grow by ~15 to 50 miles every 5,000 years.[55] This is enough sediment deposited to impede boat traffic, so that dredging sediment from the river delta is an ongoing project. Although, in recent years, the delta has been receding because of man-made walls controlling the river. We still can determine a rough age of the river based on the delta's pattern of advance in the past. Since the Gulf of Mexico is 800 miles from northern edge to southern edge, we divide that distance by the rate of delta advance per 5,000 years, to determine how long it would take to fill the gulf. The range is ~15 to 50 miles/5000 yrs:

800 miles / 50 mi/5000 yr = ~80,000 years until the Gulf of Mexico is filled with sediment. If the rate of advance was 15 miles per 5000 years, then:
800 miles / 15 mi/5000 yr = ~267,000 years until the Gulf of Mexico is filled with sediment.

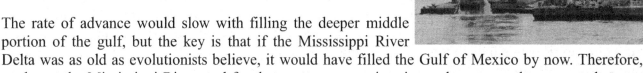

The rate of advance would slow with filling the deeper middle portion of the gulf, but the key is that if the Mississippi River Delta was as old as evolutionists believe, it would have filled the Gulf of Mexico by now. Therefore, we know the Mississippi River, and for that matter, every river is much younger than reported. *Image*

54 http://hypertextbook.com/facts/2002/Eug...ikov.shtml.
55 Https:/lacoast.gov/new/about/ba.

Review: Evolutionists believe that Pangaea broke apart 220 million years ago, yet no river exist that has enough sediment deposit to establish that Pangaea broke apart prior to 4,500 years ago and no trails of sediment are visible on the ocean floor. Combining the information together leads to one conclusion: Pangaea broke apart around 4,500 years ago during the global flood. During that chaotic event, all previous deposits from river deltas were disrupted and destroyed, and the tectonic plates moved too quickly for a trail of river sediment to form on the ocean floor as the continents drifted apart from Pangaea. After the Flood saga ended, the continental tectonic plates have been moving 1.5 inches per year (2.5 cm/yr.).

As we discussed earlier, the concept of Pangaea is in harmony with the Bible. The Bible explains that God created everything in six days about 6,000 years ago. This can be determined by taking a plain reading of the Genesis account and utilizing its genealogies. Then a major catastrophic event occurs around 4,350 years ago, just 1,650 years after creation. But many people miss the importance of one excerpt from Gen. 7:11: "The fountains of the great deep burst open." The Bible gives us an indication that something powerful forced water to burst violently out of deep caverns from under the crust of the earth, which indicates that the tectonic plates may have been hydroplaning on a bed of water. This would make the tectonic plate movement easier and quicker and would have forced water and soil to burst out of the deep caverns. Science gives us some help in identifying the possible kick–starter of this global catastrophe—asteroids.

Seismologist Tom Jordan of the University of Southern California explains that adding fluid to the crust of the earth "decreases the strength of the rock, and therefore they break,"[56] causing earthquakes and faults. Adding water to the crust of the earth is exactly what the Flood accomplished to weaken Pangaea's fault lines.

Imagine large asteroids passing through the canopy that once hovered above the atmosphere. The asteroids would have broken up the external frozen arch support of the canopy, causing the water to start to come down upon the earth as rainfall. The asteroids impacted Pangaea, fracturing the crust and setting in motion the events that split Pangaea into multiple large fragments that we call continents. The fragments moved away from what was Pangaea, causing openings to the great fountains of the deep, with the weight of the fractured crust squishing down upon the deep caverns, causing water to burst violently out of the great fountains of the deep. The asteroid impacts sent tons of iridium ash and soil into the air, which settled upon the seven new continents.

One thing to remember is that fossils, petrification, coalification, and petrolification do not need millions of years to form as we have been told. They need botanical or biological specimens to be covered quickly with soil, moisture, heat, and pressure, within a brief amount of time. The Bible teaches that there was no death prior to Adam and Eve sinning (Romans 5:12 and I Cor 15:21). Since no other catastrophic event occurred prior to or after the Flood, this means no fossils, petrified wood, coal deposits, or oil reservoirs existed prior to the Flood. All the fossils and petrified wood were formed as a result of the Flood because they all represent something that was covered quickly before decaying to dust. All things decay to dust in a brief amount of time. For leaves, they decay to dust within months. For creatures, they decay to dust within years. Thus, every fossil is testimony against a slow deposit hypothesis from evolutionists, and is positive testimony for the Bible's catastrophic flood record.

Review: The Bible records the global flood event with water bursting violently out of deep caverns below the surface. We surmise this was from fast moving of tectonic plates around 4,400 years ago. The lack of sedimentary deposit trails on the ocean floor is in harmony with fast-moving tectonic plates during the Flood. No river delta has enough sediment deposits to represent being older than 4,500 years, which is also in accord with a recent breakup of Pangaea and with the Bible.

The Bible gives us some clues regarding when Pangaea broke apart, but we get additional information when the broken Pangaea and the subsequent seven continents were no longer

---

56 Secrets of The Earth, Man-Made Earthquakes, 2014.

connected/accessible by traversing along the continental shelf or ice pack. This information is in the genealogies of the Bible. The scene is immediately after the Flood, when one of Noah's sons named Shem had a son named Arpachshad two years after the Flood (Gen. 11:10–18), Arpachshad lived 35 years and became the father of Shelah. Shelah lived 30 years and became the father of Eber. Eber lived 34 years and became the father of Peleg (note that for each father, the Bible records that they had other sons and daughters). At this time, we are (2 + 35 + 30 + 34) 101 years after the Flood, the continents are separated, and the only way to move to different continents was by traveling along the continental shelves or ice. The name **Peleg** means "divided, to split, earthquake (Strong's Concordance #6385 to #6389), and son of Shem" (Great Grandfather of Peleg). Therefore, Peleg's father named him Peleg "for **in his days** the earth was divided" (Gen. 10:25). Peleg was born in the fourth generation after Noah, 101 years after the Flood, and King Nimrod was born in the fourth generation after Noah. This puts Peleg's life during the time of King Nimrod's fatal decision to build the Tower of Babel, which led to the scattering of the people around the globe. Thus, the moment of when the Tower of Babel occurred was during the days of Peleg, not at his birth 101 years after the Flood.

Many scholars have debated the date when the Tower of Babel occurred, and some interpret that since Peleg was born during the time of the "Tower of Babel," when the people were scattered around the world—his name points to that event. What was the **Tower of Babel**? Noah's great grandson, King Nimrod, wanted to make a name for himself, so all the people with one language and one accord built a tower to reach the heavens to become like God. Well, God came down and confused their languages and scattered them abroad over the face of the whole earth.

When looking at the Hebrew definition for **Peleg** (#6389) in the Strong's Concordance, I noticed that there was an alternate definition right above *Peleg*. #6388 *peleg*: a rill (i.e., a small channel of water, as in irrigation), river, or stream.

The alternate definition sheds some light on the second century after the Flood, the ice would be melting gradually each day, month, and year, and the ocean levels would be rising from small channels of water, rivers, and streams from the melting ice. My contention is that Peleg's name provides more information regarding the time of the Tower of Babel, when God confused their languages and how God scattered them abroad over the face of the earth. That people literally walked along the continental shelves and the ice to the different continents as God motivated them to do so. In other words, God used natural means to carry out His supernatural miracle of scattering the people across the globe. When the waters rose above the continental shelves, the people were no longer connected because enough of the polar ice caps had melted to raise the ocean levels to cut off the routes of passage between the continents.

During the time of the Tower of Babel, God changed people's languages, and then they literally walked to their new locations, establishing different cultures with different languages. The people adapted to climate change, new diets, and diseases.

This would have been a sad event for mankind. Only four generations after the Flood, there weren't that many people living on the planet. They all would have known each other and would have been a relatively tight-knit kingdom. Seeing friends and family having to leave each other and venture off to another land would have been heart wrenching and confusing. Even Noah, the father of all the people, lived 300+ years after the Flood, thus he witnessed seeing his family moving away from each other to distant lands. No wonder God influenced Eber (father of Peleg) to name his son prophetically of the coming future event of the earth being divided.

To be fair, I have read that some pastors interpret the dividing of the people and the earth at Peleg's birth differently. This alternate view of the day when Peleg was born is accompanied with the concept that a great earthquake ripped Pangaea apart. It is not a well supported interpretation because then that weakens the argument in terms of the destructive power of the global flood, and then the mechanism that forced water out of the deep caverns is gone for Gen 7:11. And Psalm 104 declares that when the Flood covered the earth, then God rebuked the waters and caused the mountains to rise and the valleys to sink. That's why I like the melted ice theory, in which enough ice had to form to start the glacial age, which caused ocean levels to decline, and then as ice melted, this caused ocean levels to rise above the continental shelf during the days of Peleg, thus dividing the lands.

Names back in the patriarchal times were prophetically given based on the influence of the Holy Spirit, and based on events that would occur or the nature of that person's life. Today, we may not fully fathom the influence of the Holy Spirit guiding parents to name their children. To understand the importance of names, consider the meaning of the names of the people in the Bible in order:

Name (Strong's Concordance), Definition.

Adam (# 120)	Mankind, man, Adam
Seth (# 8352)	Appointed (to), substituted, corresponding to.
Enosh (# 583)	Mortal.
Kenan (# 7015–7018)	Sorrow, lamentations.
Mahalalel (# 4111)	The Blessed God.
Jared (# 3382)	Shall come down, a descent, descendant, an heir.
Enoch (# 2585, 2596)	Discipline, dedicate, train up, teaching.
Methuselah (# 4967)	His death shall bring [Methuselah died the year the Flood started].
Lamech (# 3925, 3928)	Disciple, instructed, learned the Despairing.[57]
Noah (# 5146)	Rest/comfort.
Shem (# 8034-5)	Prosperity, a memorial of individually by honor, authority, character.
Arpakshad (# 775)	of for.
Shelah (# 7974-5, 7999-8004)	Fountain of peace, peace, Jerusalem, make amends, make restitution.
Eber (# 5676-7)	A region across, on the opposite side (of water), passage, other side.
Peleg (# 6388)	A rill (i.e., a small channel of water, as in irrigation), river, or stream. "for in his days the earth was divided."

Putting the meanings of the names together forms a prophetic message for all of creation: "Mankind, appointed to mortality, and sorrow. The Blessed God shall send an heir teaching. His death shall bring the despairing disciples rest and prosperity of Peace across the regions that are divided by water."

The point of the names for this discussion, besides the Gospel message, is that the names of the people seem to be for future events, not past events. Thus Peleg, though his name means divided, does not equate to "at his birth the earth was divided," but to "in his days the earth was divided." Therefore, the time when enough ice melted to raise the ocean levels above the continental shelf occurred during Peleg's days, sometime after the Tower of Babel. This means that the people of the Tower of Babel were able to travel to distant continents and gradually adapt to the new environment and become all the different cultures and races we see today.

Chapter Summary: The glacial age was still receding four generations after the Flood, during the days of Peleg's life (not at his birth), and people were scattered around the globe because of the sin of that occurred at the time of the Tower of Babel. Shortly after the people had traveled to distant continents, enough ice had melted to raise the ocean levels above the continental shelves. Their travels were cut off when the ocean levels rose, until technology would connect mankind again. The evidence suggests that the tectonic plates moved quickly during the Flood, and that explains why no sedimentary delta trails exist. If the tectonic plates are moving slow enough to allow river deltas now, then there should be a single trail on the ocean floor somewhere on the earth. But because no prior trails of deltas exist, this indicates that the tectonic plates were moving too fast for sediment to form a delta fan trail. In addition, and a better bit of evidence, is that no river on Earth has enough sediment at its delta to establish an age greater than 4,500 years. This too indicates that Pangaea broke apart recently, around 4,500 years ago, rather than 200 million years ago as we have been told.

---

57 abarim-publications.com/Meaning of Lamech.

Chapter 13
Radioactive Isotopic Dating

We are told the earth is 4.5 billion years old. This is taught from elementary school to graduate level education. All secular television shows teach an old-earth belief paradigm and mock YEC. All government-supported institutions teach an old-earth belief system as well and have fired "rogue" YEC professors for speaking up. Even 90% of all seminary schools teach an old earth as well. Are all of them correct? Let us find out.

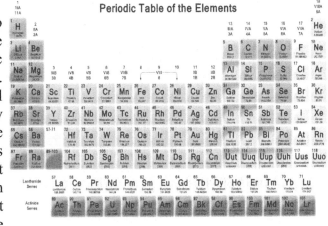
Periodic Table of the Elements

The best and most accurate method to determine the age of the earth is radioactive isotopic dating. This is a simple algorithmic (math) formula based off of the periodic table. Radioactive elements are unstable in their natural state, and they want to become stable. The way they become stable is that they lose electrons. The first stable element on the periodic chart is hydrogen (H), and the last is lead (Pb). The rate at which an unstable radioactive element loses an electron is measurable. Therefore, we can look at the number of stable lead ions compared to the number of unstable polonium (Po) ions and determine how long the unstable element has been in existence and losing ions to become lead.

The simple math of taking the number of Pb ions divided by the number of Po ions (a radioactive element) multiplied by the **CRD "Constant Rate of Decay,"** (the time it takes for a radioactive element to lose an alpha particle in an attempt to become more stable). The more alpha particles of electrons that have left the radioactive element, the older the object is that is being tested. *Image credit: Wikipedia/Periodic Table of the Elements.*

Where is the problem? Two problems exist. One is that in granite rock, on each continent, they contain polonium halos in a primordial (first developed/original condition) state with no parental halos. Meaning that no evidence exist that the polonium descended from heavier elements. More on this later. The other problem is the special multiplier, the CRD. Of course, the formula is only accurate if the CRD has always been constant. This is a fact that no scientist can verify because the ion mass spectrometer is a modern invention and no scientist today lived 1,000 years ago to test the rate of decay back then. Scientists can only determine that since they have been able to quantitatively measure the rate of decay, it seems to be a constant in our limited observation.

What a leap of faith it is to say that the primary way of determining the age of the earth is by multiplying by a rate of decay that we perceive to be constant today, when we really have no assurance that it has always been constant. Should we just rely on faith in what evolutionary scientists are telling us? That sure sounds familiar to the criticism that atheists have of religious believers. If the rate of decay has not been constant, the entire algorithm formula is wrong, and the age of the earth is wildly inaccurate and younger than we have been told by orders of billions of years.

This rate of decay is also the foundation of evolution. Since evolution needs billions of years for life to start and evolve, and radioactive dating tells scientists that the earth is billions of years old, evolutionists need the rate of decay to be constant. If the rate of decay has moments of acceleration, the foundation of evolution is gone because the foundation of evolution is that life evolved over billions of years. Evolutionists would be in a pickle if life on earth was only 6,000 to 10,000 years old.

Evolutionists may want to validate their point by saying that the rate of decay may have had moments of deceleration, thus giving evidence that the earth and life on earth is much older than anticipated. For example, a deep freeze; however, freezing things slows the decay process. But deep freezes also slow growth, and by definition, would slow evolutionary changes. If an evolutionist wants to employ the deep freeze theory as evidence to counter the argument of accelerated rates of decay, they are using an argument that weakens their own belief system. In a deep freeze, their Darwinian evolutionary systems grind to a halt. Therefore, any deep freeze on the planet to explain a theory of an older earth hinders the evolutionary process and thereby gains no ground for the argument. Also, when an evolutionist says that there were moments of decelerated rates of decay, they validate the argument that the CRD is not constant, and there were/are moments of accelerated rates of decay.

Review: Evolutionists need a CRD to support a time frame of billions of years of existence. But if the CRD had moments of acceleration, then not only is radioactive isotopic dating wrong, but the age of the earth and life on the earth is billions of years younger.

Are there any examples of acceleration in the rate of decay? Yes. Imagine twins born and at birth that were separated for this aging experiment. One lives in the Sahara Desert, with its dry air, more of the sun's harmful radiation, and hot temperatures depleting moisture from the skin with each passing day. Now let us add some vices to this twin. Let us add smoking cigarettes, abuses alcohol, outburst of anger, worry, anxiety, which causes stress and loss of sleep.

The other twin lives in a mild climate with high humidity and protects his or her skin from the sun's radiation. This twin's godly lifestyle consists of healthy eating, exercise, and sleep. On the twins' 60th year birthday party, they are reunited. Though the twins are the same age, with the same genetic makeup, the rate of decay was not constant for both of them. The twin that lived in the desert would look older than the twin who lived in the mild climate. Why? The aging process was accelerated.

But we are talking about the earth, not a life form. Are there examples of the rate of decay not being constant for the earth or objects on the earth? Yes. Dr. Robert Gentry has done great work on this. He has taken a piece of wood and subjected the wood to trauma. He sealed wood in a vacuum (no air) with trace elements of clay and water, and baked it for eight months at 150°C (mimicking a buried earth scenario next to a volcano to represent the "trauma"). The piece of wood changed to one hundred percent coal. What is interesting about this experiment is that scientists have purported that coal forms after 20 million years from decaying wood. However, laboratory created coal is indistinguishable[58] from the coal formed naturally.[59] Scientists at Argonne National Laboratory have produced coal from natural materials in less than one year, that is indistinguishable from naturally formed coal by all the techniques so far applied to it.[60]

What does this mean? It means that in a controlled environment, such as a lab, trauma (from heat and pressure) accelerated the aging process of wood to coal. A process that allegedly takes 20 million years to occur, took only eight months. This is another example that the "constant" part of CRD is not constant. This is evidence that the age the earth, as scientists tell us, could be off by billions of years.

What about in the real world outside the lab? Are there examples in nature of trauma accelerating the aging process? Yes. Mount St. Helens, Washington, had a violent volcanic eruption in 1980. The massive trauma resulted in the petrification of trees in only three decades. Petrification is the process of a tree turning into stone. Scientists tell us that this process takes 500,000 years. Petrification needs four basic requirements to occur: (1) trees quickly covered with soil (this must be accomplished before the tree decays to dust—within decades), (2) moisture, (3) pressure, and (4) heat and a source of silica. Why did some trees petrify in 30 years, when scientists tell us it is a process that takes 500,000 years to occur? It was because the violent trauma from the volcanic eruption accelerated the aging process. Scientists base the rate of decay on what we see today and extrapolate that the rate of decay today was also the same rate of decay forever in the past. This is a leap of faith. Some argue that the Mount St. Helens eruption in 1980 only uncovered petrified wood from prior eruptions that converted

---

58 Nature, page 316, March 28, 1985.
59 Dr. Robert Gentry, Halos.com/videos, "Finger Prints of Creation." and "The Young Age of the Earth."
60 Chemical & Engineering News. November 21, 1983. Page 42.

wood to stone. Well, then how far back do they want to speculate as to which prior eruption caused the wood to turn to stone? Therein lies the crux of the matter, for if they speculate that the 1980 eruption did not produce petrified wood but only uncovered the eruption of 1847[61] or 1800 or 1500s or 1400s, this still validates the point that trauma accelerates the aging process. For any of those dates does not come close to the 500,000 year mark that evolutionary geologists purport that it takes for petrification to occur.

Another example of the rate of decay being accelerated is in the conversion of carbon-based organisms into petroleum. In today's society, not much goes to waste. Even parts of a chicken that are not socially accepted as edible are not wasted. Chicken byproducts, such as adipose, ligaments, tendons, veins, arteries, cartilage, and others, are converted to usable products, such as oil.[62] The chicken byproducts are heated, and through a process of distillation, a highly valuable fluid is created: petroleum oil. The length of time to go from chicken byproducts to petroleum oil is only 30 minutes.

We are told that over a very slow decay process, organic material, such as algae and animals, decayed for millions of years to form petroleum some 50 to 300 million years ago. Yet, no scientist was ever there to confirm this huge length of time. Evolutionists either do not know or will not tell you that chemists have figured out how to convert organic material to oil in 30 minutes. In fact, distillation factories are popping up near large chicken farms across North America to produce oil.

You may be a little disappointed that evolutionists tell us petrification takes 500,000 years, coalification takes 20 million years, and petrolification takes millions of years, but they won't tell us that nature produces petrified trees in 30 years and mankind can produce coal from wood in eight months and petroleum oil from organic material in 30 minutes. Our property tax money goes to fund this unproven hypothesis of earth's age of billions of years, and our unsuspecting children hear this one-sided hypothesis. Whether we are discussing radioactive decay rates, cellular decay rates, molecular decay rates, and so forth, trauma accelerates the decay process. Trauma, whether mechanical, chemical, or radioactive energy, accelerates the rate of entropy. Thus when radioactive isotopic dating determines something to be hundreds of millions of years old, that is based on a leap of faith that the decay rate has always been constant, as nature and mankind have proven that decay rates are not constant. A German lab, Physikalisch-Technishe-Bundesanstalt, confirmed that uranium-226 has seasonal and monthly variations based on solar activity.[63] Thus, proving the CRD is mathematical trickery. Considering that lightning can ionize elements, then as Pangaea was breaking apart, and tectonic plates were sliding across the surface of the globe during the Flood saga, massive amounts of electrical energy accelerated the decay rates of radioactive elements. The violence by which God created all the matter on the first day, and then expanded the universe on the second day with Big Bangs, those two days were so extremely violent that they both trump the energy released during the Genesis catastrophic flood. Since trauma accelerates the rate of decay, it is no wonder that the age of things appear older than their chronological age.

The reality is that when trauma occurs, the rate of decay is accelerated. Therefore, the alleged best and most accurate means of testing the age of the earth and the things on the earth is wrong. Radioactive dating tell us that things are far older than they really are. Comparing the notion that Mount St. Helens' volcanic eruption produced petrified trees in 30 years to the notion of radioactive dating telling us it takes 500,000 years to produce petrified trees, suggests that radioactive dating could be off by 99.99%.

What are some traumas that accelerate the aging process of the planet and life on the earth? They include asteroid impacts, fires, earthquakes, land slides, volcanoes, pyroclastic flows, floods, comet impacts, lava flows, tsunamis, tectonic plate activities, and extreme heat, all of which occurred

61 History of Mount St. Helens, mountsthelens.com/history.

62 Alternet.org, chickens into oil.

63 Power Spectrum Analysis of Physikalisch-Technishe-Bundesanstalt, Decay-Rate Data: Evidence for Solar Rotational Modulation/ Published online: November 17, 2010.

during the Flood. Other things to include are hurricanes, tornadoes, solar flares, coronal mass ejections (from the sun), ultraviolet light, infrared, visible light, gamma rays, x-rays, and droughts, all of which occur on Earth because of the loss of the canopy of water that caused the Flood.

Review: Trauma accelerates the aging process. Natural catastrophic events, such as the creation of all matter on the first day of creation (a Big Bang), the violent expansion of the universe on the second day of creation (Big Bangs), the violent global flood, and today's natural disasters accelerate the aging process. Mankind is able to quickly make coal and oil. This is strong evidence to show that one should not take the leap of faith and believe that the rate of decay has always been constant. The CRD multiplier is not constant and thereby renders the best dating technique inaccurate. The age of the earth is extremely younger than we are being told.

The second problem with radioisotope dating is the premise that elements always start from the heaviest radioactive element (elements range from the lightest element, hydrogen, to the heaviest natural element, uranium), and as they emit radioactive particles over time to become more stable, they eventually become lead. Well not so fast—the theory is partially correct; it is true that unstable radioactive elements decay by losing electrons to become more stable. But the problem is that elements do not always start with the heaviest element on the period table. When granite rock (the foundation rock of the crust) is cracked open and rock samples are analyzed under a microscope, one can see halo rings that are remnants of primordial (original condition) polonium.[64] These halos only form when rock cools from a liquid state to a solid state. During this solidification process (which geological evolutionists theorize took millions of years as the planet cooled), radioactive elements emit particles as effervescent bubbles similar to Alka-Seltzer in water. The problem with that is polonium halos are found in granite rock around the globe that do not have rings from a heavier parental element, implying that they began as polonium rather than coming from other elements, such as let us say, uranium to radon to plutonium to polonium. Each halo represents when alpha particles are emitted off, and each one leaves a ring. These emitted radioactive particles are fleeting, lasting one to three seconds; therefore, the fact that granite rock has captured these fleeting effervescent rings is irrefutable evidence that the granite rock cooled almost instantaneously. This evidence supports a literal interpretation of the Genesis creation account. If granite rock cooled over millions of years, or even over one year, no polonium halos would have been captured. Dr.

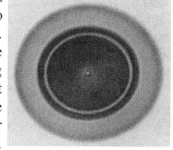

Robert Gentry likens this to showing someone a 1,000 years from now the effervescent bubbles of Alka-Seltzer in water; you would have to instantly freeze the water to show the bubbles. The same principle applies with the spherical halos (they are bubble-like) from the emitted particles.[65] The image is of primordial polonium halo in granite rock. *Photo credit: www.Halos.com, by Dr. Robert Gentry.*

In addition, the observable evidence that halos of polonium exist in their primordial state means that without the tell-tale rings of heavier elements, polonium was created as polonium and did not evolve into polonium from uranium. Therefore, since the granite bedrock instantaneously froze to capture polonium halos, this begs the question, "How?"

The six day creation model has granite formed by the end of the first day of creation, albeit in liquid form because of the densely packed universe is applying massive amounts of weight and pressure, and this is generating a lot of heat. But once the universe expands on the second day of creation, the weight and pressure of the universe is completely removed and subsequently the temperature is reduced as a byproduct, this is when granite solidified as solid rock. The granite cooled almost instantly from a creation model and captured polonium halos, corroborating Dr. Gentry's findings. Pressure alters the freezing and boiling points of matter. For example, an ice skater's blade technically never touches ice because the immense amount of weight and pressure causes the ice to

---

64 Halos.com by Dr. Robert Gentry.
65 Youtube.com, Finger prints of God, Dr. Robert Gentry.

instantly liquify. Conversely, the intense reduction of weight and pressure caused the molten granite to instantly freeze. This is how granite solidified quick enough to capture polonium halos.

Since polonium halos exist without heavier parental halos, the radioisotope dating system is flawed. That particular dating system presupposes that the rate of decay has always been constant. During creation, the rate of decay process that we perceive today was altered. Similarly to Adam and Eve being created as fully mature adults without an umbilical cord, the natural aging process and the normal means of offspring were altered during creation.

The evolutionary community has vehement attacked Dr. Robert Gentry. For example, he was fired from his job. Secondly critics say that he is a physicists and not a geologist, so he should not be commenting outside of his field. Thirdly, the preponderance of opinions from the scientific community agrees with an old earth model. Fourthly, the courts heard Dr. Gentry's evidence and ruled in favor of evolution to be taught in schools.[66] First, all who desire to live godly will be persecuted (II Timothy 3:12). Secondly, truth is truth, whether from a five year old or an old sage. One does not have to be from a specific field to talk about that field. Look at Bill Nye, a comedian, he always speaks outside of his field. Thirdly, the majority does not equal truth. Fourthly, the courts do not use absolute morality, or absolute truth. The courts utilize relative morality and relative truth, which means, what seems most moral and most truthful today is what determines the law. This is why many court rulings are overturned. So the court ruling does not mean that Dr. Gentry is wrong, it means the law today does not agree with his findings. Dr. Robert Gentry addressed each critique leveled against him, and his evidence is irrefutable.

Review: The existence of polonium halos in granite rock and in their primordial (first developed/original condition) state without parental halos are evidence that some polonium did not descend from a heavier parental element in a slow evolutionary process. Also, this shows that the matter was created quickly, as in the first day of creation rather. Granite rock solidified quickly, as on the second day of creation rather than slowly over millions of years. The existence of primordial polonium halos shows that the rate of decay was not constant in the past. If it was constant, there would be ancestral halos surrounding all polonium halos.

Are there catastrophic events in the history of the universe that fulfills the requirements to accelerate the aging process of the entire earth? Yes. The first and second days of creation. Those two days were the most violent days in the history of the universe. The first day violently brought about all the matter and the second day violently expanded the universe. Also, the global flood. The advent of multiple large asteroids passing through the canopy of salt water to get to the earth would have resulted in the canopy coming down (via gravity and covalent bonding of water molecules) upon the earth. And the asteroids impacting the earth would have fractured the crust of the earth, freeing tectonic plates to hydroplane on deep caverns and causing the water hidden under the crust of the earth to burst out, fulfilling Gen. 7, which explains that the deep caverns of the earth burst open during the forty days and forty nights. In addition, there would have been many volcanoes that erupted multiple times around the globe, causing massive heat and fires. The beginning portions of the Flood were met with high heat, which is a necessary requirement for the conversion of wood to coal and animals and algae to oil. The fires were put out by the rains, and the high heat was reduced by rain and sun blockage for forty days, which turned the tide of high heat to an eventual glacial age.

The earth has many large impact craters, scars that tell us of a time when multiple large asteroids impacted the earth. So too does our moon tell the same story. It all fits together like one giant puzzle to reveal that the catastrophic event during Noah's day caused all the oil reserves, coal deposits, fossils, the seven continents, the glacial age, deserts, continental shelves, decreased oxygen concentrations, increase gravity, and some of the salt deposits.

Why would God create the earth and everything in it so that it would appear old? Why would God create an environment so that traumas, such as volcanoes, asteroid impacts, a global flood, and the

---

66 talkorigins.org/faqs/po-halos/gentry.

like, would accelerate the aging process and give the indication that the earth is billions of years old? Why would He then indicate that life has existed for hundreds of millions of years by association? These presumptions would indicate to humanity that the Bible has errors in it regarding timelines and draw into question the Genesis' creation account of how God created everything. By default, they draw into question the existence of God. Why would God do this since He knows all things even before all things occur? Two ways exist to approach this answer:

1. God wants mankind to believe in Him by faith alone. God wants to know that we love Him for who He is and give Him glory through faith alone.
2. God did not create Earth and everything in it to appear old with a fake history, but He did create everything fully developed; that is, tall trees and Adam and Eve, were fully developed. Therefore, it is people's desire to disprove God by interpreting what they observe to be in contradiction with the Bible.

Let us address the first answer. Before you snicker at the simplicity of the answer, ask the question, "Are we so different?" We were created in His (God the Son's) physical image. But we were also created in His likeness, with His characteristics, thoughts, mind, emotions, and so on (Gen. 1:27). For example, take a man who is super wealthy and is seeking a bride. If that man shows up on the first date with a gold crown, furs, an expensive car, an entourage of servants, and so forth, that guy will never know if the prospective bride loves him for who he is or whether she loves him for what she can get out of him.

How did Jesus, the King of Kings and Lord of Lords, show up to court humanity—as a wealthy God with processions, pageantry, trumpets, feasts, and a who's who list of guest and attendees? No. He was born in a manger (feeding trough) inside a barn. Later, Jesus said He did not even have a place to lay His head. He was dirt poor. What about His beauty? Did Jesus come with blemish-free skin. Did he glow or sparkle and have beautiful eyes and strong muscles? Was He taller than others? Was He faster, stronger, or more handsome? The answer is NO, according to Isaiah 53:2: "**He has no stately form or majesty that we should look upon Him, Nor appearance that we should be attracted to Him.**" The point is that Jesus wanted us to love Him for who He is, Not for what He looked like or How wealthy He is (He owns everything. He is lending to us on a temporary basis).

This similar point is seen in many locations in the Bible. Take for example when John the Baptist, who was filled with the spirit of Elijah, was asked by the Pharisees, "Are you Elijah, the one who prepares the way for the Messiah?" John the Baptist said, "NO." But then he performs and verbalizes all the necessary prophesies to affirm that he was indeed the coming Elijah. John was physically himself, but he came in the spirit of Elijah to fulfill the prophesy of preparing the way for the Messiah. Even Jesus said, regarding John the Baptist, "Truly I say to you, among those born of women there has not arisen anyone greater than John the Baptist! . . . and if you are willing to accept it, John himself is Elijah who was to come" (Matthew 11:11–15). Why did not John the Baptist tell the Pharisees that he came in the spirit of Elijah to fulfill the prophesies? It is because God wants all humanity to accept Him through faith.

Jesus, though born of a virgin, was asked by the Pharisees, "Aren't you Jesus, son of Joseph?" Jesus knew that the Pharisees were looking for a descendant of King David born of a virgin and fathered by God. He replied, "Yes." Why did not He say, "Joseph is my legal father, but I am born of a virgin from God"? He did not want to prove facts to get love from the Pharisees.

When the Pharisees asked Jesus, "Aren't you Jesus of Nazareth?" Knowing that the Pharisees were looking for a Messiah born in Bethlehem, Jesus answered them with "yes." Why did not Jesus say, "I was born in Bethlehem, but raised in Nazareth"? A bird's-eye view of why He answered "yes" is because God in the flesh, Jesus, came to earth born of a virgin for two purposes: (1) to fulfill Scriptures (Matt 5:17), and (2) because all need to come to God the Father through faith in God the Son (Ephesians 2:8). As for the worm's-eye view of why Jesus answered "yes" to there inquiry: He was referring to the place where He was raised, not born.

The human view of why Jesus answered "yes" to their questions: He wanted to be loved for who He was/is through faith just like how we want to be loved. He did not want to prove it to get love, He wanted to be loved for who He was/is through faith.

Through all the amazing miracles that Jesus performed, each human still has to confess Him as Lord through faith alone. This is the foundation of the Bible: Jesus is the only way to the Father (John 14:6). There has never been a change in the method of salvation from Adam and Eve to all the Old Testament saints to those who saw Jesus alive and to us today. Salvation has always and will always be through Jesus to the Father and no other name.

Every single saved person in the Old Testament worshiped and were saved through Jesus. They just did not know Him by the name Jesus. They knew Him by other names, such as Yahweh, Elohiym, I AM, Lord, King of Israel, and others. How did the Old Testament saints worship Jesus? No one has seen God the Father at anytime–correct? Yes. Exodus 33:20: "You cannot see My face, for no man can see Me and live!" John 1:18 and I John 4:12: "No one has seen God at any time." Then all the Old Testament physical appearances of God were not God the Father, but God the Son, Jesus. Of all the many physical appearances of God, none of them are the Father. Why? For one, God the Father is invisible (Colossians 1:15). Secondly, God became flesh and dwelt among us as Immanuel (Jesus) (John 1:1–14 and Matthew 1:23). Thirdly, Jesus is the Word (John 1:1), and Moses wrote about Jesus (John 5:46), and all the prophets wrote about Jesus (John 5:39). Fourthly, passages from the first verse (Gen. 1:1) ("Elohiym" is the plural form of God, meaning Father, Son, and Holy Spirit) to the last verse (Malachi 4:5–6) of the Old Testament refer to Jesus. Also, passages from the first verse (Matt 1:1) to the last verse (Rev. 22:21) of the New Testament refer to Jesus. This is why Jesus is called the Alpha and the Omega, the Beginning and the End, the I AM, and the Almighty (Rev. 1:8). Fifthly, Jesus' own testimony was that He claimed to walk and talk with Abraham, and before Abraham was born, Jesus was the I AM (John 8:49–59).

The second approach to answering why God seemingly created everything to appear old is based on empirical evidence. God did not create anything to appear billions of years old. It is only mankind's interpretation of the observable evidence that is purposefully directed away from the Bible and away from God. For example, the layers of earth couldn't be from billions of years of soil deposits because erosion would have commingled the layers; therefore, the layers of the crust formed quickly via the Flood. Earlier, we showed how the processes of making oil and coal and petrified wood do not take millions of years, but days to decades. And all life forms on earth having similar DNA represents one maker utilizing the same dirt and elements to create life from and through Himself (Col 1:16), not one original prokaryote as the ancestor. The similarity of the DNA of creatures does not mean that we all descended from one ancestor; it equally means that life came from a common designer.

Review: From Adam and Eve to Abraham, Isaac, Jacob, King David, King Nebuchadnezzar, Mary and Joseph, and to you, salvation has always been through faith alone and through Jesus alone. God created earth and everything in it for us to accept Him by faith alone. God did not create the earth to appear billions of years old; it is man's interpretation that spins the empirical evidence to say it is old.

God spoke twice and wrote twice (in stone to Moses), "I am the LORD your God, you will honor the Sabbath Day, six days you shall work and the seventh day you shall rest, For I created everything in six days and rested the seventh day" (paraphrased from Exodus 20:8–11 and 31:17). A rogue few scientists will attempt, consciously or subconsciously, to get away from the Bible at any cost. The vast majority want the truth and are honorable, but when they view such a seemingly sophisticated reliable age-testing device, as the radioactive dating, and the numbers come out millions or billions of years of age, what is the honorable scientist supposed to do? Their eyes are not lying to them; therefore, by default, the Bible's timeline is in error, and they accept what the measuring device is telling them. The problem is not science or the honorable evolutionary scientist, but it is with the belief that the rate of decay is constant for those measuring devices that determine age and with those who push an agenda at the cost of truth (this is found in everything a human touches, even religion). You know what God says about those who deceive with a faulty scale?

Proverbs 11:1: "A false balance is an abomination to the LORD, But a just weight is His delight." Proverbs 20:10: "Differing weights and differing measures, Both of them are abominable to the LORD." Proverbs 20:23: "Differing weights are an abomination to the LORD, And a false scale is not good." The faulty radioisotopic dating technique utilizes an inaccurate CRD and is a faulty scale to judge time.

What does this mean? It means that if someone knowingly uses a faulty measuring device to steal, even if the theft is truth, they are committing acts of abomination against God, and severe judgment is coming upon them. God will visit their iniquities to the third and fourth generation of their heirs (Exodus 20:5–6). Those that unknowingly use a faulty measuring device, such as this faulty CRD, are stealing the truth from the masses, and they are unwittingly persecuting Jesus and being used by Satan to further his agenda. The radioisotopic dating, with its CRD, is the false balance, the differing weights, and the differing balance. Do not utilize this faulty measuring device.

Chapter Summary: Radioactive isotopic dating calculates the age of the earth to be billions of years old because of a flawed multiplier, the CRD. Also, radioactive isotopic dating assumes that each element descended down in an orderly time pattern over millions of years, yet the existence of primordial polonium with no spherical halos from a parental element proves a creative process and not a slow uniformitarian (a tenant for evolutionary) process. We have proven that the CRD, though it appears constant, is not and has not remained constant. The fact that granite rock has captured polonium halos proves that the rock solidified quickly, as in a creative process, rather than from a slow cool over millions of years. Therefore, the ages of all items tested are vastly younger, and the Bible's Genesis account of creation is still time tested and stands firm as the pillar of truth.

Chapter 14
Carbon-14 Dating

Carbon dating is not an accurate tool for determining the age of an item, and scientists acknowledge that carbon dating becomes increasingly more inaccurate the older the item is that is being tested. The primary reason is that our atmosphere is constantly adding radioactive carbon via the sun's energy, and our atmosphere has more carbon14 in it today than it did decades ago, and the further back in time, the less carbon14 there was in the atmosphere. When a creature dies, it contains in its tissue the same radioactive carbon concentration of the atmosphere. As time passes, the C14 in the dead creature decreases, and the amount of C14 lost to decay is divided by the rate of decay, and that tells us the age of the item being tested. Well, since carbon dating is comparing the number of radioactive carbon molecules in the decedent being tested to the number of radioactive carbon molecules in the atmosphere, as C14 increases in the atmosphere from the sun's energy, it gives a further inaccurate reading of the decedent's age; the item will seem much older than it is.

One of the flaws with carbon dating is that the atmosphere adds 20 pounds of C14 per year as a result of ultraviolet energy from the sun converting nitrogen in the atmosphere into carbon14. That may not seem like a lot, but it is when the whole point of carbon dating is to compare the number of C14 molecules in a dead organic item to the number of C14 (radioactive carbon) molecules in the atmosphere today. For each day that goes by from the death of an organism being tested to the day the sample is taken, the atmosphere is constantly adding C14. Therefore, the process makes the dead organic organism appear older than it really is. The process involves counting how many C14 molecules have left the dead organism, compared with carbon14 in the atmosphere. That tells you how long the organism has been dead. The half-life of C14 is 5,730 years, which means that the quantity of C14 is cut in half every 5,730 years. Do you see the problem? Since the atmosphere is constantly adding C14, the dead organism will by default have less C14 than the atmosphere and appear older than it actually is. The best way to test is to compare the amount of C14 in the organism with the amount of C14 in the atmosphere at the time of death, not millennia after the organism has been dead. No scientist knows the C14 concentration of the atmosphere 4,500 years ago. But creationist have an understanding of the amount of C14 in the atmosphere at the origin of life. The answer resides in the canopy of water that surrounded the atmosphere. Water blocks high energy from the sun, the more water—the more it blocks. Similar to someone standing in a pool all summer, the body parts that are the deepest have the least tan. Why? ultraviolet rays are reduced proportionately by the amount of water the rays have to pass through. Therefore, since there was a canopy of water that surrounded the atmosphere spherically at creation that morphed into a disk-like formation until the Flood, this blocked the cosmic energy from penetrating to the atmosphere to convert nitrogen into carbon14. Thus, the further back in time we go, the less C14, but when going back further in time during the existence of the canopy, the exceedingly less C14 exists in the atmosphere. Therefore, testing anything that existed when the canopy limited cosmic energy from penetrating to the atmosphere, that entity will appear much older than reality.

The atmosphere adds 20 pounds of C14 per year at the current rate. But we do not know the exact amount the sun's high energy converted N14 into C14 to the atmosphere in past millennia. For example, if an animal had died 5,000 years ago and the sun's ultraviolet and higher solar emissions were blocked from penetrating to earth's surface by a canopy of water surrounding the atmosphere from creation till the Flood (creation estimated at ~4,000 BC till the Flood at ~2,400 BC), so that close to zero C14 would have been added to the atmosphere per year, instead of the current 20 pounds per year, then carbon14 dating of any life form near that time period would be off by a massive amount. Potentially, the dating of the dead organism would indicate that it was 40,000 years older than it really is. It is a fact that water blocks high energy rays. Thus, C14 dating is inaccurate because there was a watery canopy surrounding the atmosphere, that protected life on the earth. Therefore, the description in the Bible of how God created the atmosphere on the second day of creation with water above and water below, is the primary reason C14 dating is inaccurate.

The importance of water in limiting the amount of harmful cosmic energy has not escaped the notice of NASA either. When they plan for long human space travel, the water needed for life will not be stored inside the hull, but around the perimeter of the hull to protect the astronauts from cosmic energy. That is exactly what the canopy did to all life and the atmosphere, the canopy limited the quantity of harmful cosmic energy from penetrating to the atmosphere and converting N2 to C14. And prevented that harmful cosmic energy from penetrating to the surface and mutating DNA in all life.

Review: A creature that died antediluvian (before the Flood), died with trace C14. Therefore, it did not naturally decay C14 by the half-life every 5,730 years to get to trace. No, it started with trace, which means that when an evolutionist test the creature for radioactive carbon, and determines that zero C14 exist in the creature, the evolutionist will not go by the Bible and understand that a canopy of water limited the quantity of C14 in the atmosphere. Thus, they will assume the creature slowly decayed from a full compliment of C14 at its death to trace quantity. They would be wildly off in their dating the creature to be at a minimum of 50,000+ years old. Then those same evolutionists go around teaching others that the Bible's creation account should not be read as plain text, but as an allegory.

Some examples of the inaccuracies associated with carbon dating: living sea mollusks have been dated at 23,000 years old.[67] One mammoth had been dated as 15,000 years old at the lower extremity and 45,000 years old at the higher limit.[68] Of course, the operator gathering the data simply threw out the high and low numbers to get a mean average.

There have also been blind studies done. For example, allosaurus bones (allegedly 140 million years old) were sent to the University of Arizona lab for testing to determine the age by the C14 method. The results were closer to the Biblical timeline; one sample was dated as 9,890 years old ±60 years, and the other sample was dated as 15,120 years old ±220 years.[69] Yet, evolutionists discount the findings by saying that "of course carbon dating isn't going to work with bone that old, but the date is still 10,000 years older than when your God supposedly created everything." Sure, the test results came in at 10,000 years older than the Bible, but they also were 140 million years younger than evolutionary timelines.

Chapter Summary: Carbon14 dating is inaccurate and becomes increasingly more inaccurate the older the item is that is being tested because C14 is forming in the atmosphere faster than it is decaying. C14 is virtually non-existent in dead life forms that died near the time of the Flood. The reason is because the canopy shielded the atmosphere from the high energy of the sun, that causes C14 conversion. Therefore, all life that dies before the Flood died with trace C14, and did not naturally decay to trace over 50,000 years.

---

67 *Science*, vol. 141, 1963, pg. 634–637.
68 Kent Hovind, Creation versus Evolution debate.
69 Angelfire.com/mi/dinosaurs/carbondating.html. Hugh Miller's blind study.

Chapter 15
Viscosity of Rock

Viscosity is the thickness of something in relation to its motion or fluidity. The lower the viscosity, the more fluid the item is. For example, water has a lower viscosity than molasses, and molasses has a lower viscosity than rock. Everything moves but at different speeds. The speeds vary greatly because they have different viscosity levels. Other items that move include stones, precious metals, jewelry, ice, and so forth. Glaciers seem to be solid and not moving, but with time-lapse photography, we can see glaciers (ice) move as a result of gravity. We do not see it live because the viscosity of glaciers is high, so the movement is too slow to detect with the bare eye. We can even change the viscosity of an item. For example, butter seems solid in the refrigerator. But put it in the microwave, and watch butter decrease its viscosity and liquefy as it heats up.

Increasing the temperature of an object lowers the viscosity by exciting electrons. Also, applying force to an object lowers viscosity. Both actions increase the fluidity.

Review: All objects are in motion, some faster than others. The amount of movement is dependent on the viscosity of the object, the temperature of the object, and the force applied.

How does this apply to the age of the earth? Since all objects are in motion, that means even rocks are moving. However, rocks have such a high viscosity that we do not detect their movements in a year, decade, or century. Their movements may be detected over several millennia depending on what type of rock they are. The harder the rock, the less movement. So how does this help us in determining the age of the earth? The moon has been hit by many asteroids, meteors, and comets, and those impacts have left craters. All rock moves, and the samples that astronauts have taken of the moon and impact craters tell us that the rock on the moon is basalt rock; it is not a hard rock by Earth standards. Granite is a harder rock than basalt. If the moon was billions of years old as some suggest, those impact craters would have been flattened out due to the gravity of the moon.

The lit side of the moon is 253°F, which is hot enough to boil water, which lowers the viscosity and increases the fluidity of rock. And the dark portions of the moon is −387°F, this change of temperature causes expansion and contraction of the surface rocks, which further causes basalt rock to become brittle. This causes rock to flatten out.

Also, consider the amount of space dust that lands on the moon each year. This space dust should have covered and smoothed out those jagged crater outlines if the moon was billions of years old. No solid data reveals how much space dust lands on the moon each year, but for the earth, it is estimated that the earth receives 40,000 tons of space dust each year (Peter Brown, meteor specialist, Uni. Western Ontario). Since the moon's rocks are basalt rock, which is not hard to begin with, there should be greater movement of rock formations if the Late Heavy Bombardment hit the moon 4 billion years ago. Therefore, the moon's craters should be smoother and less jagged, but since they are well defined, this suggests recent impacts within 5,000 years. *Photo credit: http://www.math.nyu.edu.*

Chapter Summary: Due to the viscosity of moon rock, the well-defined rocks and impact craters on the moon indicate recent impacts, not ones that are billions of years old. The impact craters would have flattened out if they had occurred eons ago. Ergo, impact craters tell us that every crater we see is relatively recent.

Chapter 16
Moon Dust

A known average quantity of space dust lands on the earth each year, which is around 40,000 tons. The moon's smaller size and less mass (weaker gravitational force), results in the moon accumulating fewer meteors, asteroids, and comets than the earth. But the moon does not have an atmosphere that burns most dust up to vapor and heat. Since the moon is near and travels with the earth, the moon has a proportionate amount of space dust accumulated each year per its volume and mass.[70]

When NASA was planning their missions to land on the moon in the 1960s, the scientists calculated how much space dust would be on the moon. Based on the moon being billions of years old, multiplied by the average amount of space dust collected each year, the moon should have 10+ feet of space dust on its surface. It should be noted that when NASA was initially planning on going to the moon they were worried about sinking because of the moon dust, but closer toward launch, NASA was no longer concerned about any sinking. Yet, NASA still utilized a space module's ladder set ~3 feet off the ground and large saucer landing pads to accommodate any anticipated sinking into the surface dust. The landing gear footpads were 37 inches in diameter and 7 inches deep. It is the same principle of walking in the snow with big snow shoes to prevent sinking. One scientist working at NASA wrote, "I get a picture, therefore, of the first spaceship, picking out a nice level place for landing purposes, coming in slowly downward tail-first and sinking majestically out of sight."[71] *Photo Credit: https://www.hq.nasa.gov/alsj/a11/a11.step.html.*

Surprise, when the astronauts landed on the moon, there was not enough space dust for the moon to be 100,000 years old; only enough space dust for the moon to be ~6,000 to 10,000 years old.

That's a problem for those who hold to the hypothesis that the moon is hundreds of millions of years old. How do cosmologists solve this dilemma? They do not, instead they hypothesize that the moon was a wandering small planet that collided into Earth 4.5 billion years ago. Then Earth's gravity held the impact debris in orbit, allowing the molten space debris to coalesce into the moon. This is speculative and comes with its own host of problems. For one, the collision was such a perfect glancing blow as not to destroy Earth and send enough debris into a near Earth orbit for the molten space debris to coalesce into the moon. Where is the left over debris? Conveniently, all the matter coalesced into the moon with no remnant matter orbiting the moon or floating just beyond the moon's orbit. This is a science fiction story. Also, if the wandering planet impacted the earth at a glancing blow, the scattered space debris would maintain a spin from the impact. Similarly, to how the planets of the solar system formed, the planets and galaxies still maintained their angular momentum of spin from the Big Bang and coalesced into planets with a spin, just like the moon coalesced together. However, the moon's rotational velocity is too slow to match a glancing impact theory and does not match the spin velocity of other planets. Where on earth is the impact crater and the moon's remnant impact material? Cosmologists contend the earth was liquid magma, and thus would not show an impact crater. This makes sense if there was not a Bible that declares the earth had water around it before the moon was finished forming, not liquid magma. Also, a lunar impact would have killed life on earth and been devastating from an evolutionary point of view. Cosmologists contend life had not started on the earth until after the impact theory. This makes sense if there was not a Bible that declares the earth had vegetation before the moon finished coalescing matter. This is just to name a few of the problems with

---

70 *Science*, issue October '93 by Love and Brownlee.
71 *Science Digest*, January '59, p. 36, by Isaac Asimov.

this impact hypothesis.

Those that hold to the impact hypothesis, explain that the rock samples NASA collected from the moon has a similar isotope to that found on earth. Suggesting there was a commingling of the material at one time—hence, the impact theory. The simple explanation of why similar isotopes exist on both the earth and moon is because they both coalesced matter relatively at the same time and distance from the coalescing sun.

It should be noted that when NASA landed on the moon, they sampled meteors and some asteroid rocks. What is interesting about this bit of information is that evolutionary cosmologists contend that those space rocks and fragments came from the late heavy bombardment about four billion years ago. However, very little dust accumulated on those rocks, and no dust piled up on the sides, suggesting that they impacted the moon recently, such as during the Genesis flood. If the asteroids were covered by space dust, it would provide evidence of millions of years. But not even a quarter of an inch of space dust covers the rocks. **Review:** A known amount of space dust collects on the moon each year. Given this current rate of collection, not enough space dust covers space rocks, and on the surface of the moon, to support hundreds of millions of years. However, the amount of lunar dust does support an age of less than 10,000 years.

Each planet gets space dust added to it. Well, this provides evidence for a young universe. Saturn is much larger than Earth and therefore attracts more space dust to it. Saturn also has a net or filter to collect the space dust, and that is the rings around Saturn. With the Cassini space probe, cosmologists have discovered that Saturn's rings are very brilliantly lit and very reflective. The reason is that most of the rings are made up of ice. If Saturn and its rings were old, such as millions of years old, the ice rings would be covered in dust and lose their reflective quality. Since the ice is clean, which is demonstrated by its high reflectiveness, the ice rings are not millions of years old, but less than 10,000 years of age.

Evolutionary cosmologists utilize the hypothesis that a comet recently collided into one of Saturn's moons and left a remnant debris of clean ice, free of dust. The problem with this hypothesis is that if a comet collided into one of Saturn's moons, the debris from the moon would also cover the surface of the ice to obscure the reflective capabilities. Additionally, the heat generated from an impact of a comet traveling 43,000 miles per hour would have melted or vaporized the ice and then coalesced with the debris again, similar to the moon impact theory. *Photo credit: www.exogeologyrocks.com/mineral-and-rock-samples/. Photo credit: www.abovetopsecret.com/forum/thread789691/pg1.*

Chapter Summary: Saturn's ice rings are clean of space debris, which indicates they have not been in existence for millions of years, but thousands of years. The rings lose their reflective ability as dust accumulates on the clean ice. The clean ice, free of debris, stands as testimony of a young universe. In addition, not enough space dust exist covering the surface of the moon to support hundreds of millions of years. The evidence support an age of less than 10,000 years.

Chapter 17
The Magnetic Field

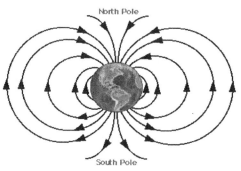

In the early 1970s, Dr. Thomas Barnes noticed a pattern of measurements of the earth's magnetic field spanning the last 150 samples. When the measurements were plotted on a graph, a pattern emerged that the earth's magnetic field has weakened over time.[72] Dr. Barnes calculated a half-life of only 1,400 years and concluded that the earth's magnetic field was less than 10,000 years old. He then surmised that the earth would have a parallel age with the magnetic field. Evolutionary geophysicists dismiss this claim by saying that the magnetic fields wax and wane over millions of years, so Dr. Barnes conclusion is only catching one phase of waning.

Dr. Humphreys revised Dr. Barnes' hypothesis in the mid-1980s. Dr. Humphreys concluded that as a result of the global flood, rapid pole reversals occurred during the Flood. He concluded the earth's magnetic field was created at creation. Then it slowly decayed for ~2,000 years, which weakened the magnetic field. During the Flood, the magnetic field endured rapid reversals, which weakened it. Following the Flood, the magnetic field experienced large fluctuations, which weakened it, and it has been slowly decaying ever since.

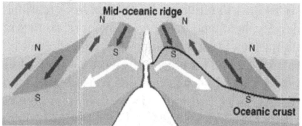

Dr. Barnes and Dr. Humphreys reject the evolutionary hypothesis that a dynamo effect occurs at the center of the earth to cause the magnetic field. With a flood model causing field reversals, the massive movements of tectonic plates, volcanoes, and magma spewing violently out of the earth, the central core would have had powerful heating because of the global flood. This would have accelerated the decay process of the magnetic field. Considering that the further back in time one goes, the stronger the earth's magnetic field, and considering the powerful core heating that occurred during the global flood to accelerate the decay process of the magnetic field, Dr. Humphreys concludes that the magnetic field is about 6,000 years old.[73] *Image Credit: www.cmspugliano.wikispaces.com.*

Since the magnetic field tends toward disorder and decays over time, the further back in time, the stronger the magnetic field. This means that we cannot go back too far in time; otherwise, the magnetic field will be too strong and cause intense heat on the surface that would vaporize all life.[74]

Some suggest that the poles reverse from time to time. Two evolutionists, Coe and Prevot, found evidence that suggests 50 rapid magnetic field variations from pole reversals.[75] The Mid-Atlantic Ridge; when viewing the positive and negative polar charge of the igneous rock that comes out of the divergent zone, a parallel zebra-like pattern emerges that suggests the magnetic field has reversed many times as the African and South American tectonic plates separated. As the magma emerged from the crust, it recorded the magnetic field at that instant before solidifying. *Image Credit:www.unc.edu.*

The sun has a magnetic field pole reversal every 11 years.[76] It is very chaotic and its surface is not rotating in sync with its core or mantle. This causes its magnetic field to twist and churn. The notion of twisting the magnetic field during the Flood saga because the crust was not in sync with its core or mantle, would seemingly simulate pole reversals, when in fact, the pole did not reverse, it was just the twisting and churning of the magnetic field during the catastrophic event of the Flood as the

72 Barnes, T, 1971, Decay of the earth's magnetic moment and the geochronological implications, CRS, vol. 8, pg 24–29.

73 AnswersinGenesis, "The Earth's Magnetic Field and the Age of the Earth, '91, Dr. Andrew Snelling.

74 Institution for Creation Research, Earth's Magnetic Field, by J.D. Morris, PhD.

75 Coe and Prevot, '89. *Earth Planetary Science Letters*, vol 92, pg. 296–297.

76 Newkirk, Frazier, '82. The solar cycle. *Physics Today*, vol 35, pg. 25–34.

crust moved independent of the core.

It is interesting to note that magnetic stripes on the ocean floor show that the field poles seemingly flipped rapidly many times during a quick catastrophic event in which the tectonic plates were moving quickly. This is in harmony with a Biblical global flood and in contradiction with the slow uniformitarian view that all things occur slowly over millions of years. A magnetic field pole reversal mirroring the cataclysmic event of the Biblical global flood is in harmony with the zebra-like striping (positive charge as black and negative charge as white) of the magnetic field imprints on the ocean floor. The evolutionary geologist hypothesis is that a dynamo effect exist at the center of the earth, and this spinning core slows down to a stop and then starts back up again in reverse. The problem with this hypothesis is that once the spinning iron core stops to 0 mph, another speculative large force is required to start the inner core spinning in the opposite direction. This process repeats itself frequently.

In physics, when a body comes to rest, it will stay at rest unless a directed force is applied. With the evolutionary hypothesis of a dynamo, what kick-started the dynamo once it stopped and came to rest? This is a problem with the dynamo hypothesis of frequently stopping and starting. The best solution is that during the first day of creation, as matter coalesced toward the core, this increased the density, heat, and pressure of the core, so that at the core there was liquid magma. With the core having liquid metal that is rotating, this caused electrons to flow. Similarly to a generator that causes copper to rotate and creates electricity with the flow of electrons. As the core increased in heat, it attracted more liquid metal that was charged, this abundance in charged metal and soil, generated the magnetic field for the earth, and in the same fashion is how each celestial body in the universe generated a magnetic field. The stored energy in the core from coalescing matter on the first and second days of creation, is how the magnetic field was generated. Since everything in the universe tends toward decay, so too does the magnetic field. *Image Credit: www.mvsdperiod6.wikispaces.com.*

Kent Hovind (creationist), and Dr. Walt Brown (author of "In The Beginning"), both present the best and simplest explanation of the zebra like patterns of the alleged pole reversals. They contend that <u>no pole reversals exist, merely as rock</u> <u>expanded at the Mid-Atlantic Ridge</u> <u>during the violent, fast moving</u> <u>tectonic plates of the global flood,</u> <u>cracks in the rock filled with cooler</u> <u>water and the temperature variances</u> <u>formed the alternating polarity in the</u> <u>igneous rock as it diverged out of the</u> <u>crust.</u> Their notion holds merit and

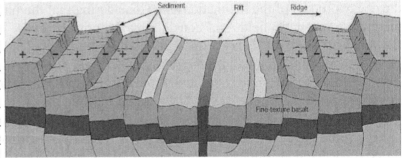

should be considered as a viable option to further be explored just like the other above hypotheses.

Chapter Summary: The magnetic field is decaying and gradually becoming weaker with a half-life of 1,400 years, which means that as we travel backwards in time, the magnetic field doubles in intensity every 1,400 years. This means that we cannot go back in time further than 10,000 years because the earth's surface would be disintegrated. Considering the mantle heat generated from the global flood, it would have used up magnetic energy and accelerated the decay process, which leads to an age of the earth of 6,000 years. Alternating polarity patterns exist in the igneous rock at the Mid-Atlantic Ridge. Is this the result of magnetic pole reversals from the Flood or simply cool ocean water contacting cracks in the hot igneous rock and the temperature variances formed the alternating polarity as it diverged out of the crust? I prefer the latter hypothesis because it is the simplest without having to explain a necessary force to cause reversals in the spin of the iron core, and it is in harmony with the fast tectonic plates (Psalm 104:8) of the catastrophic Flood.

Chapter 18
Polystrata Petrification and Fossilization

Polystrata Petrification: *Poly* means "many." *Strata* means "layers." *Polystrata* means "many layers." Layers of what? Fossils and petrified trees transcending many layers of sedimentary rock.

The soil of the earth is in layers. Petrification is when a tree is converted from wood to stone. We are told that this process allegedly takes 500,000 years. We must find out whether if that is true or just another tale to support the billions of years required for evolution. Science has broken down the mechanics of the petrification process by which wood changes to stone with the following: a tree has to be covered quickly (in hours to years) so that the tree does not decay to dust. Sediment containing moisture filled with minerals saturate the tree with silica or iron sulfide, and then the tree is baked with high heat and high pressure. *Photo credit: Ian Juby, ianjuby.org.*

The problem is that evolutionary scientists tell us that this process takes 500,000 years. If this is correct, the YEC have a problem.

How do they determine the age of a petrified tree? They can use relative dating, such as the rock layers determine the age of the fossils. But this leads to circular reasoning because the fossils date the rock layers (See chapter Layers of the Earth). They may use Carbon-14 dating, but this is flawed because the atmosphere had trace C-14 before the Flood because the canopy shielded the atmosphere from cosmic (high) energy from stars. All life lived virtually without C-14 before the Flood (See chapter Carbon-14 Dating). They may also use radioactive isotope algorithmic formula to determine the age:

$$\frac{\text{Pb (lead) ions}}{\text{Po (Polonium) ions}} \text{ X CRD} = \text{the age of the item}$$

The CRD is the tricky part because it assumes the aging process has always been constant (See chapter Radioactive Isotopic Dating). Old earth theorists contend that the rate of decay (radioactive and non-radioactive) has uniformly been constant through the ages. <u>The rate of how things age today, is the rate of how things aged in times past.</u> This is called the uniformitarian theory. All the dating methods are based on that theory, and 2 Peter 3:3–4 prophesied of this theory that has duped the world:

> In the last days mockers will come with mocking, following after their own lusts, and saying, '. . . <u>all continues just as it was from the beginning of creation.</u>'

The uniformitarian theory is a leap of faith because no one was there to observe the rates of aging (decay) in past millennia. This is one of the reasons that evolution is dependent on faith-based conjecture. Ample evidence shows that the rate of decay (aging) can be accelerated with trauma. Such as lightning converts oxygen into nitrogen instantaneously, which causes rainwater to naturally fertilize the soil.[77] Lightning and auroras are examples of how the slow radioactive decay rates are accelerated.[78] Both examples demonstrate that the current slow rate of aging (decay), may be accelerated under certain conditions. How do we know the rate of decay is not constant since we cannot go back in time to prove it? We can logically conclude this simply by observing that nature accelerates the aging process today via trauma, and mankind also accelerates the aging process with trauma. For example, we can accelerate the aging process of carbon to diamonds, and wood to coal, a process that allegedly

---

77 wikipedia/nitrogen cycle. and wikipedia/nitrogen fixation.
78 amendez.com/Accelerated Radioactive Decay, by Arnold Mendez.

takes 20 million years, in 8 months. We can accelerate the aging process of biomass to petroleum, a process that allegedly takes 50 million years, in 30 minutes. Mount St. Helens' volcanic eruption in 1980 accelerated the aging process of petrification to three decades. Also, solar flares cause uranium on earth to have monthly and annual variances in the rate it decays. Therefore, what evolutionary scientists are purporting to be an axiom is not even constant in our own generation, let alone for 16 billion years. Nature can accelerate the aging process of petrified trees in ~30 years. That is a serious acceleration of the decay process. Evolutionists argue that this is an acceleration of the petrification process, not an acceleration of the radioisotope. The connection is that by utilizing radioactive testing, evolutionists estimate the age through the process of measuring the amount of decay, compared to the rate of decay, from such things as the petrified trees, petroleum, fossils, coal, and so forth. This formula is a modification of the formula in physics used for estimating the velocity, distance, or time. Such as, $V = D/T$. But time is the variable we do not know, thus the formula is rewritten to $T = D/V$. Where the Distance is how much decay has occurred, with how many lead ions are present divided by polonium. Velocity is the rate of decay. Thus, this aging formula is a derivative of a simple mathematical formula that we use regularly. Any equation with false data, will produce false calculations. The false data in the formula used to determine the age of the item tested, is the "Constant Rate of Decay," and we have provided ample evidence that the rate at which things decay may be altered depending on the conditions. By altering the variables involved in the normal slow rate at which things decay, we may cause those things to accelerate their rate of decaying, establishing that any formula purporting the rate of decay has been constant, is mathematical fiction.

In addition, mankind has been able to accelerate the decay process of petrification in a lab as well. Pacific Northwest National Laboratory has successfully decayed wood to stone (petrified wood) in a matter of days. If mankind can petrified wood in a laboratory in days,[79] then there seems to be a problem with this evolutionary hypothesis that it takes 500,000 years to petrify wood. Any high school student can go into a science lab and accelerate the decay process of wood to coal in eight months, a process that is supposed to take 20 million years. By taking a piece of wood + trace clay + water – O2 + 150° Celsius + 8 months = 100% coal. This synthetic coal is indistinguishable from coal formed naturally by all testable techniques applied to it.

So what does this have to do with polystrata petrification? It establishes that nature and mankind can and have accelerated the aging process. Do not leap to the conclusion that petrified wood is a half-million years old. A superior, scientific explanation exist that is in harmony with the Bible as we will demonstrate shortly.

Review: Nature can accelerate petrification process to decades. Man can accelerate the petrification process to days. Therefore, do not believe for a second that it takes 500,000 years to produce petrified wood. And the radioisotopic dating formula based on the CRD, which is not constant, determines these items to be hundreds of thousands to hundreds of millions of years old; do not believe the CRD is constant. Lightning, high solar energy, chemicals, and trauma, accelerate the aging process (radioactive or non-radioactive).

For wood to be petrified, the wood must be covered quickly. Why? Wood that is not covered quickly by sediment starts to decay to dust. Arborists[80] teach that the base of the tree should not be covered up if you want the tree to survive because the bark of the tree will fall off, rot, and decay if it is covered by soil. Therefore, a tree will not wait around 100,000 years for one layer of soil to be deposited. The tree will start and finish the decay process long before one layer is completed.

---

79 Science News, February 13, 2005, "Want to Petrify Wood without waiting a few million years? Try this."
80 TheTreeTender.com, "Soil Level for Trees."

Evolutionary geologists claim that each layer of the earth takes 100,000 to a million years to form. No tree on the planet is able to wait around for the first layer to finish while not decaying, much less the many layers required. Once the tree has too much soil covering its base, it dies and the decay process immediately starts. Even petrified trees, when cut open, still have signatures of their annual rings. The rings usually count in the hundreds, not hundreds of thousands of years. Thus, further illustrating that the petrified trees were covered quickly by the soil. *Photo credit: www.geoclassica.com.*

Hundreds of petrified trees in the vertical standing position exist around globe that are transcending through many layers of sediment. Some of them pass through 30 layers of soil. Why is this a problem for old earth theorists?

We are being told that each layer of the earth takes hundreds of thousands of years to a million years to form. No tree would wait around for 10,000+ years for the first layer to form. When a tree gets too much soil covering its base, it starts to die immediately (within 10 years) in geological terms. What happens when a tree dies before the first layer is finished forming? The tree will rot and decay to a stump before the first layer is finished. Therefore, when hundreds of petrified trees are found in the vertical, upright position, transcending through many layers of sediment, that is evidence that the layers had to be formed quickly, as in less than one year. Sure, some trees are denser and may resist the decay process by decades, but to form a petrified tree or coal, that tree must be covered quickly before the tree decays to dust. This means that the evolutionary geologist's hypothesis that each layer takes 100,000 to a million years to form contradicts the observable evidence of layers of the earth being deposited quickly, not in one isolated accidental location, but around the globe.

When a creationist argues against the slow deposit hypothesis that says no commingling of the layers exist, the criticism is twofold:

1) Rain mixes the new sediment with the existing layers together and causes erosion. This prevents segregated, smooth layers of sediment. Since each layer of the crust is segregated and smooth, this represents that either no rain existed on the planet for hundreds of millions of years while each layer of the crust formed uniformly, which is not a tenable theory, or the layers formed quickly from a global flood and the slow deposit hypothesis of the uniformitarian theory is false.

2) When one studies the soil content of the crust, what becomes apparent is that the layers of the crust of the earth are different from each other. One layer is limestone, which is from ash, teeth, bone, coral, and shell that was broken down to their base form of calcium carbonate by acidic water and deposited. Another layer is compressed mud without organic material; it is called shale. Another layer is mud with organic matter (biomass), which is called black shale. Another layer is sand, and another layer is clay, and so on. This segregation of the layers is not a problem for the Biblical flood, as sediment and biomass mixed in floodwater always settle by their density according to the laws of physics and forms uniform layers. Additionally, with a global flood, a global tide twice daily sweeping across the globe unimpeded would have further segregated (a process called liquefaction) the sediment and debris by density: one layer of sand, one of mud, one of mud with biomass, one of only biomass, and so on. Uniformitarian evolutionists believe that each layer of the crust formed slowly over 100,000 to millions of years. Here is the problem with that: one type of layer is exclusively limestone, which is calcium carbonate deposited on the surface the earth, so for a million years, only limestone settled with no other sediment intermingling. One type of layer is mud with organic matter (biomass) exclusively deposited globally for a million years. Then another layer is mud without organic matter (biomass) exclusively deposited for a million years and then clay exclusively deposited globally for a million years. Then sand is exclusively deposited globally for a million years, and so on. Quickly, one sees that this is not a logical, rational conclusion based on observable evidence and testable means. Essentially, it is impossible to get such exclusivity in terms of the layers because the natural processes of soil deposition does not exclusively deposit only calcium carbonate for a million years, then exclusively deposit sand for a million years with no biomass, then exclusively deposit mud with no biomass for a million years and then exclusively deposit mud with biomass for a million years. Instead, the natural

process is that each type of sediment is deposited at the same time that dead creatures are deposited.

Putting arguments (1) and (2) together, means that the slow deposit over hundreds of millions of years without erosion from rain and with exclusive deposits for each layer for millions of years is simply faith based and illogical. It shows the extreme lengths people will go to stay away from the Bible, which records a logical explanation for the existence of the exclusive layers of sediment, and this is the catastrophic global flood. It was not a gentle clear water covering the land; it was a violent judgment with asteroids, volcanoes, fires, ash, debris, acid-rain, fast-moving tectonic plates that forced water out of deep caverns, and so forth. Putting all these pieces together reveals that the floodwater was filled with soil, vegetation, and dead creatures. YEC contend that the floodwater was not clear and was global, while theistic evolutionists contend the floodwater was potentially clear and regional. A salient point is the fountains of the deep that burst open. What was the driving force that pushed the water out of the deep caverns as fountains? YECs hypothesize that it was the fast-moving tectonic plates traveling at 1–2 mph that forced the waters and magma of the deep to burst violently open; however, theistic evolutionists and "gap theorists" are silent on this point, and both have to reject the words in the Bible that say that every mountain was covered under the heavens (Gen. 7:19–23) and reject the seven-day creation testimony of God (Exodus 20:11 and 31:17). They have to use a regional flood for their hypotheses to survive. This makes them guilty of annulling (setting aside or modifying) two major events of Scripture. Though a believer cannot lose their salvation—and plenty of saved believers are evolutionists or gap theorists—they could be called least in the Kingdom of Heaven (Matthew 5:19) because they set aside some Scripture to force the Bible into atheistic timeline of billions of years, and they teach others to believe the same.

What are the two major events that theistic evolutionists and gap theorists reject? They reject the notions that (1) everything was created in six literal days of creation and that God rested on the seventh (Exodus 20:11) and (2) the catastrophic global flood. "Have you not read?" Jesus asks in ridicule of people's lack of knowledge about creation (Matt. 19:4–5), and then Jesus directly quotes Genesis thrice (1:27, 5:2, and 2:24): "That He who created them from the beginning made them male and female, and said, 'For this reason a man shall leave his father and mother and be joined to his wife, and the two shall become one flesh?" God in the flesh, confirms the literal, historical record of the Genesis creation account, which is expected with a literal record but not if it is an allegory.

Since the evolutionary theory starts with, "the rains fell on the rocks and washed the minerals (amino acids) from the rocks into a pool of primordial complex chemicals, and from that life was birthed as a single–celled organism," then God spoke that evolution is idolatry in Jeremiah 2:27–28: "Who say to a tree, 'You are my father', and to a stone, 'You gave me birth.' For they have turned their back to Me and not their face. In the time of their trouble they will say, 'Arise and save us.' But where are your gods which you made for yourself? Let them arise, if they can save you in the time of your trouble." The Ten Commandments clearly record that God created everything—the heavens, the earth, the seas, and everything in them—in six days and rested on the seventh (Ex. 31:17). And Genesis clearly states that every mountain—all the high mountains everywhere under the heavens—were covered by water. The water prevailed by 15 cubits above every mountain on earth and every mountain under the heavens. And all flesh that moved on earth perished—all birds, all cattle, and all beast—and all human beings who were not inside the Ark died (Gen. 7:19–24). No way around these two facts recorded in the Bible. Both gap theorists and theistic evolutionists reject these verses as the clear, perfect truth of Scripture.

Of the two offenders that reject the perfect, sure, right, pure, clean, and true testimony of God (Psalm 19:7–11), evolutionists are the greater offender, as gap theorists at least accept the six days of creation. However, they accept it as a re-creation, not the creation. Both theories have believers, and both theories have attracted men and women who love God and who are useful for God, yet they have compromised the full extent of their usefulness to appear acceptable to atheists. Every time that mankind has done things its own way, or thought its own way, even though people wanted to worship

God, it has always turned out bad. Just ask Abraham about helping God to produce a son his own way; it resulted in Ishmael, the father of Islam, which has been a problem for the descendants of Isaac ever since. And just ask Aaron and the Jews, who decided to worship God in their own way and made a golden calf. This is analogous to evolutionists and gap theorists saying, "I'll worship God my way, and this is through the lens that the earth is billions of years old as atheists are telling us." They faithfully reject the accuracy of Scripture, which became flesh and dwelt among us.

Listen, the Scripture is clear that we are the representatives of God and should share God with others. This command is very serious; in fact, a penalty exist for refusing to teach others and for teaching error. Many theistic evolutionists discount the veracity of the Scriptures and just say that it is written by man alone, and thus it has errors, and worse, they teach others this blasphemous teaching. When one views the Bible to have errors, this results in little desire to read a book that is not supernatural. This leads to less knowledge, less obedience, and to sin and to stumbling in life. When a theistic evolutionist teaches others the same, they are causing people to stumble. Look at the warning in Matt 18:6: "Whoever causes one of these little ones who believe in Me to stumble, it would be better for him to have a heavy millstone hung around his neck, and to be drowned in the depth of the sea." That is how severe teaching error is, and that is how important it is to teach truth. Ezekiel continues the point that if you do not teach truth to one in error and they die in their error, their blood is on your hands:

> Son of man, I have appointed you a watchman to the house of Israel; whenever you hear a word from My mouth, warn them from Me. When I say to the wicked, "You will surely die," and you do not warn him or speak out to warn the wicked from his wicked way that he may live, that wicked man shall die in his iniquity, but his blood I will require at your hand. Yet if you have warned the wicked and he does not turn from his wickedness or from his wicked way, he shall die in his iniquity; but you have delivered yourself (Ezekiel 3:17–19).

Verses 20 and 21 give the positive side in terms of warning a righteous person that commits iniquity. It says that if we warn them and potentially deliver them, we definitely deliver ourselves from blood being required of us; if we do not warn them, they will die in their sin, and their blood is required of us for not sharing truth. Why? Life is in the blood (Gen. 9:4–6), and life for a life (Deut. 19:21).

Review: The smooth layers of the soil refute a slow deposit of sediment over millions of years because rain and erosion would have commingled with each layer as they were being deposited. Since no erosion marks exist between each layer, evolutionists are forced to believe that no rain occurred for hundreds of millions of years or to just ignore the point altogether. Additionally, the smooth layers are exclusive deposits, which is to say the layers are segregated. With this observable evidence, it is beyond rational thinking to believe that only a particular sediment layer was deposited for a million years, and then a different type of sediment layer was deposited for the next million years, and so on. All sediment and biomass settle according to their density when mixed with water. *Photo credit: In The Beginning: Compelling Evidence for Creation and the Flood; Dr. Walt Brown.*

Fossils also transcend through more than one layer. This would be impossible if the layers formed slowly over 100,000+ years. No organism would wait for more than a few months before decaying after death, let alone for 100,000+ years.

One evolutionist that I was talking to about a fossilized fish transcending multiple layers suggested that maybe a fish fell down a hole, then the hole got covered up, and that's how the fossil transcended multiple layers. More savvy evolutionists have argued, in regards to how petrified trees transcend through multiple layers of soil, that a couple of trees accidentally in the upright position transcending through multiple layers means nothing because they probably got disrupted from a mud flow. They say that volcanic mud flows from Mount St. Helens moved buried petrified trees from previous eruptions via lahars (mud flows) into the vertical position transcending multiple layers of soil. This would be a plausible argument if only a couple examples exited of petrified trees in the vertical position transcending through multiple layers, but thousands exist around the globe. Also this argument supports the YEC view regarding how layers of soil can be quickly formed from a flood. Which prior eruption did the mud flow reveal petrified trees from? It would be speculative as well to hypothesize which prior eruption caused the petrified trees to move.

Just take a bird's-eye view for a moment. Imagine that thousands of trees on multiple continents are in the vertical standing position transcending through 2 to 30 layers of soil. Can all of those trees be in an upright position because of lahars? That is a leap of faith and not logical to believe. The simple interpretation of the observable evidence is that the layers of soil formed quickly around the trees. This is strong evidence that the soil could not have been deposited 100,000 to a million years per layer.

The photo is of palm leaves and branches, which only last for several months once detached from the tree, and several other fossil types transcending through multiple layers of sediment. This is impossible if the layers slowly formed as evolutionists claim. *Photo credit: www.creationclub.com*

<u>**Review:** The old earth theory suggests that each layer of the earth takes 100,000 to a million years to form; it is proven wrong with petrified trees transcending through multiple layers. No tree would wait around for one layer to deposit, let alone 30 layers. The tree would have decayed before the first layer was finished depositing. Also, the layers of segregated and well defined sedimentary layers disprove a slow uniformitarian deposit hypothesis because erosion from rain would have commingled sediment. Thus, the evolutionary hypothesis requires millions of years with no erosion from rain. The old earth theory regarding the slow deposit of soil in the crust is also proven wrong with the exclusivity of the layers; no one in their right mind would believe that there was a million years of sand with no biomass mixed in, or only ash, teeth, bone, and shell deposited to form a layer with no other sediment. The exclusivity of the layers proves that the layers formed quickly from the Flood.</u>

The global flood record harmonizes with trees being covered with many layers of sediment in a quick amount of time. Not only did the water come down upon the earth in rainfall, but water burst up out of the earth. Look at Genesis 7:11:

> On the same day <u>all the fountains of the great deep **burst** open</u>, and the floodgates of the sky were opened. The rain fell upon the earth for forty days and forty nights.

We know that it rained for 40 days and nights, but were the fountains of the deep bursting open for a day, a week, or 40 days as well? The answer comes in Gen. 8:1:

> But God remembered Noah and all the beasts and all the cattle that were with him in the ark; and God caused a wind to pass over the earth, and the water subsided. <u>Also the fountains of the deep and the floodgates of the sky were closed</u>, and the rain from the sky was restrained; and the water receded steadily from the earth.

The fountains of the deep burst open for the same length of time as the floodgates of the sky: 40 days and 40 nights. With water and magma bursting out of the crust, through fault lines, of the earth for 40 days and 40 nights continuously, billions of tons of soil mixed in with the turbulent floodwater. This means the water would have high turbidity, so the floodwater would not be clear, but very dirty. A plausible cause of the fountains of the deep bursting open, is that Pangaea fractured from multiple asteroid impacts. The fragmented Pangaea released 1,600+ years of potential energy as fast moving kinetic energy, and the tectonic plates moved relatively quickly that caused the fountains of the deep to burst open. Fast moving tectonic plates is accompanied with volcanic activity, thus hundreds of volcanic activity occurred during the Flood saga. The fountains of the deep added soil to the waters, as did the volcanoes and asteroids. When the soil settled according to their density over the next year, this resulted in the layers of the crust.

Most theologians believe that the fountains of the deep (Gen.7:11) represent water that burst out of the earth for the global flood, but since a great deal of water is involved in volcanic activity, it is possible that the fountains included lava, magma, sediment, and debris that burst out of the deep from volcanic activity as well. The Hebrew word for deep is *tehom* (#8415), which means "an abyss, main sea, or subterranean water supply; deep place, depth." So it is possible that Gen. 7:11 could be read as the fountains of the abyss bursting open or fountains of the deep place bursting open, which leaves room for fountains of lava, ash, and sediment bursting out of volcanoes around the globe.

Review: The soil that covered the trees for petrification came from the fountains of the deep bursting violently open through the crust of the earth for 40 days and 40 nights as volcanic eruptions, sending massive amounts of ash and soil into the air, which then settled in layers.

The settling soil that was mixed into the floodwater explains why layers on the crust of the earth exist and explains how vertically standing petrified trees occurred transcending through 2 to 30 layers of sediment. The Biblical flood, from start to finish, took almost one year. This quick soil depositing process along with volcanic activity and high heat was necessary for trees to petrify. The observable evidence fits harmoniously with the Bible. The long evolutionary timeline of millions of years for layers to form to produce petrified trees does not fit with the observable evidence or with experiments of different soil mixed with water and left to settle.

Chapter Summary: Multiple polystrata petrified trees transcending 2—20+ layers of sediment have been found around the globe, and they are proof positive that the layers did not form over millions of years, but the layers settled quickly within a year's time.

Chapter 19
Distance to the Moon

Distance of the moon to the earth: 238,900 miles. Distance at which the moon cannot be any closer to earth or disintegration occurs: 11,500 miles. This is called the Roche Limit. The difference between the two is 227,400 miles.

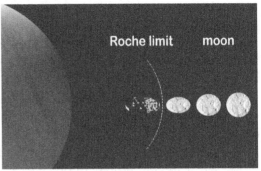

Some people have fun with the current rate that the moon recedes away from earth and try to determine the age of the earth-moon relationship. They use the fact that the moon is moving away from the earth at 1.5 inches (3.8 cm) per year and work backward to determine the age of the earth-moon relationship. They divide 227,400 miles by 1.5 inches per year and come up with 9.6 billion years. This is based on the notion from ungodly mockers that proclaim, "all continues just as it was from the beginning of creation" (2 Peter 3:3–4), called the Uniformitarian theory. This is a similar error that the radioisotope dating method uses; the rate of decay today, has always been constant. And this is the same error that geologists utilizes; the rate of soil deposit today, is the rate it has always been. But this is in error because the rate of recession was much faster in the past. The rate of lunar recession from the earth is progressively slower and slower over time. The further back in time, the greater the rate of recession. *Image credit: astronoo.com/.*

Others speculate what that rate would be using a sliding scale to compensate for larger recession rates of the moon away from the earth in the past and implement a mean (average rate of recession) of 3.94 feet (1.2 meters) per year. Calculating back to the Roche Limit (the distance at which the moon cannot be any closer to the earth or it would disintegrate), they come up with 305 million years (227,400 miles / 1.2 meters[81]/ 1 year = 305 million years). This seems like a more accurate process of determining the <u>maximum</u> age of the moon-earth relationship, and it debunks the evolutionary cosmological hypothesis that the earth-moon relationship started 4.45 billion years ago.

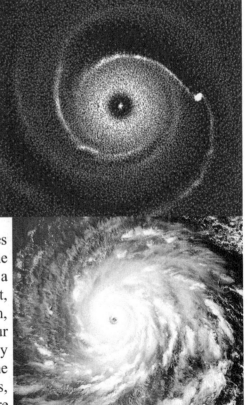

A few moons are formed from wandering asteroids that get caught in the gravitational force of a planet, but most moons were formed naturally, as hot matter coalesced to form an orbiting celestial body caught around a larger planet's gravitational force. This process of coalescing looks similar to the formation of a hurricane. Just like a hurricane that coalesces moisture as it rotates, a coalescing celestial body—during the burgeoning universe—gathered hot matter. At the core of a hurricane is a hole, but at the core of a coalescing moon, planet, or star, would be molten matter. Of the two ways to form a moon, the latter was the prevailing consensus for the formation of our moon until NASA landed on the moon and studied the soil. They observed evidence that the moon had been super hot at one time and that a similar isotope exist with earth. A creationist says, "Well, of course they should have a similar isotope; they were both made equal distance to the sun, from similar material, and at the same time at creation." An

---

81 Physicist Donald DeYoung explains, "One cannot extrapolate the present 4cm/year separation rate back into history. It has the value today, but was more rapid in the past because of tidal effects. In fact, the separation rate . . . was perhaps 20 meters per year long ago, and the average is 1.2 meters per year."

evolutionary cosmologist says, "They have a similar isotope because there was an impact that caused the commingling of the two impacting bodies and shared debris." Cosmologists hypothesize that the reason we do not see evidence of the impact of the moon hitting the earth is because it was completely disintegrated and then coalesced again over time from debris orbiting the earth. For some reason, it did not form a ring around Earth like Saturn's, and it did not leave any distant left over matter orbiting outside the moon's orbit as a calling card of the impact. It seems that whatever theory is best to fit the evolutionary time construct is what is acceptable. Evolutionists argue that Saturn's rings are a result of a comet hitting a moon. But the impact formed rings; it did not coalesce into another larger moon as our moon supposedly did. These are similar impact theories about Saturn and Earth; one scenario forms rings around Saturn, and one forms another spherical orbiting body called our moon. Saturn's rings are filled with ice that does not have dust covering the bright reflective sheen, thus the impact theory that formed Saturn's rings couldn't include another moon that included dirt. Therefore, not a likely scenario to have two moons collide and both contain only water. *Photo credit: NASA.*

However, the most damaging evidence against the lunar impact hypothesis, is the lack of evidence. We would suspect to find some matter that did not coalesce back into the moon. That the impact was severe enough that some matter had greater escape velocity to reach an orbit around the earth that is outside the moon. And we would be able to detect this matter. But as it is, 100% of the matter that got ejected into space around the earth formed back into the moon, this is beyond a leap of faith.

Anyone who believes in the Bible should see that the lunar impact hypothesis is contrary to the Genesis creation account. For at creation, the earth was formed from water, with an atmosphere and vegetation before the moon was finished forming, and the earth was not liquid magma from the third day on. The moon would have been hot at this point, so there's no problem there, but the earth could not have had an impact with the moon and still have sustained the water, atmosphere, and vegetation. Theistic evolutionists must say that the Bible is wrong and filled with errors or that the evolutionary impact hypothesis is wrong. They are mutually exclusive concepts, and either one is wrong and one is right or both are wrong, but both cannot be correct.

Let us get back to the discussion of the moon receding from the earth for a duration not exceeding 305 million years ago. Information is missing from the calculation, as starting the calculation at 11,500 miles to not violate the Roche limit, which would cause tidal surges too high to sustain life. Considering that the closer the moon is to the earth, the larger the ocean tides become, at some point life on earth would not be  sustainable because the ocean tides would drown out life trying to take root on dry land and would suffocate life that needs water to survive. For example, at the Bay of Fundy, the ocean tide is extremely large. The tide rises and falls 40 feet. Above the peak tide line, ample life exist, but within the chaotic tidal area, less life exist, a few crabs, sand dollars, algae, insects, and so forth. This demonstrates how too much of a change of tide is not conducive for life to thrive. *Picture credit: Thomas McGuire, www.epod.usra.edu/.*

The distance at which the ocean tides are too high is before the Roche Limit. A safe moon-earth relationship distance starts far outside the distance of the Roche Limit and outside the distance at which ocean tides become too large. Going back any further in time and the moon would be too close to the earth and gigantic ocean tides would rip the life from the surface of the planet. To actually put a date on when the moon-earth, relationship started and declare the date scientific would be speculative. Whether it is based on the current rate of recession and working backward or on a calculation using a sliding scale with gradually increased recession rates, the conclusions are at best conjecture, since they are not verifiable.

What causes the moon's recession away from Earth? The moon's gravity causes the ocean tides, the ocean tides take angular momentum out of the spin of the earth, and the moon uses that energy to move away from the earth. We do not know the exact rate of recession was in the past, but science proves it was not a constant rate of recession. The list below exemplifies that the further back in time, the greater the recession rate away from earth exponentially.

Year:	Present	1000 AD	0 AD	1000 BC	2000 BC	3000 BC	4000 BC
Lunar recession rate/yr:	3.8 cm	8 cm	24 cm	100 cm	500 cm	3 meters	21 m

Review: The moon's current distance from earth divided by a mean (average) rate of recession provides a maximum date that the moon began its relationship with earth, not billions of years ago, but 305 million years ago. However, the limiting factor is not the Roche limit for disintegration purposes, but the greater distance required between the earth-moon relationship where tidal forces would not disrupt life. Thus, the lunar tidal forces suggest a younger earth-moon relationship.

Is this a problem for YEC? No, because the starting location where the moon was coalescing matter on the first day of creation was not the place where God placed the moon on the fourth day. During the first day, the moon was close enough in proximity to earth that the outer coalescing material were probably in contact (this helps explain any similar isotopes). During the Big Bang/expansion on the second day, the distance between the earth and the moon was probably expanded out to ~200,000 miles from the earth. On the fourth day of creation, God finished coalescing the moon, sun, and stars. Thus, the distance of the moon to the earth, has natural explanations that are in harmony with a literal interpretation with the Genesis creation account.

The bigger problem is for old Earth believers in explaining how the moon first began its resonance with earth. Their best theory is that a wandering body (the moon) was traveling through space and got caught in the earth's gravitational force. The two bodies collided, and the moon has been caught by the earth's gravity ever since. This is a poor hypothesis because no residual matter left over exist floating in space as debris that did not coalesce into the moon. It is incredulous that 100% of the floating debris coalesced after the impact. With an impact hypothesis, one would suspect to find some matter that escaped to a greater orbital altitude from earth and remained separate as a ring similar to Saturn's rings. Also, no lunar sediment exist on earth from the impact either. In addition, the moon hit the earth with a glancing blow such that it did not become one with the earth, yet it was not too much of a glancing blow to cause the moon to float off into space. But the moon does not have enough spin to demonstrate a glancing blow impact. The same side of the moon always faces the earth.

Evolutionists address these problems by suggesting that when the moon collided with the earth, both entities were hot and in a liquid magma state, and this covered up the impact zone as matter transferred from the impact. And the moon would not show any impact crater because it was completely transformed into floating magma in space, which coalesced into the moon. This is a plausible explanation for why the moon does not show an impact, but there should be some left over debris that we can observe as a ring that is distal or proximal to the moon's orbit around Earth. If a planet was in a liquid magma state, an impacting planet that collided into it would also not show any impacting crater. It is fine to believe that, but do not call it fact. It is faith based to say that the earth got the moon from it colliding into the earth. One of the problems with this hypothesis is that the crust of the moon on the far side is ~40 miles thicker than the side we visualize.[82] Now the evolutionary cosmologists believe that perhaps two moons formed after the impact and then they later joined together as one. This is comical. It is best to accept that while the moon was more active, that because of its closer proximity to Earth, there was more tidal friction, which generated volcanic activity mostly on the side most effected by tidal friction—the near side to Earth. And both sides have impact craters, thus, this activity occurred prior to a bombardment of asteroids and meteors. In addition, the moon

---

82 http://moon.nasa.gov/about.cfm.

contains about ~6 billion tons of water ice,[83] which would be expected with each celestial body being formed from water as the Bible implies with "waters" being mentioned in Genesis 1:2, and that the earth was made from water and through water in 2 Peter 3:5. But one would not expect to find water still on the moon if it was billions of years old because of sublimation. Sublimation is the process of ice evaporating to a gas because of no atmosphere.

Review: The lack of a debris field, lack of lunar impact scar, and lack of debris on Earth from an impact coupled with a slow lunar spin put holes in the evolutionary hypothesis of how the moon began its relationship with the earth. But the origin of the moon is not a problem from a Biblical perspective, especially with the new discovery that ice water is on the moon.

Mars has two orbiting moons; one of the moons is called **Phobos** and is about one-third the size of our moon. Phobos is in a death spiral toward Mars and will eventually crash into Mars. The other moon, called **Deimos**, is smaller and farther away, and its escape velocity is greater than Mars' gravitational force; thus, Deimos is spiraling away from Mars and will eventually be free of the planet's orbit and will drift off into space to collide with Earth or Jupiter or come to some other fate.[84]

Cosmologists hypothesize that they both may be captured asteroids. This seems a likely scenario, considering their formless terrain looks similar to an asteroid. But cosmologists are not sure whether they are captured asteroids or actual orbiting moons. One contention is that they have asteroid impact marks on them similar to our moon. Either way, it does not matter. The point of bringing them up is that since one is spiraling into Mars and one is spiraling away from Mars, they both indicate a relatively short existence on an evolutionary time scale. They could not have been orbiting too long around Mars given the rate of Phobos' spiraling descent toward Mars and given Deimos' rate of recession away from Mars. When one works both trajectories backward, it represents a brief period of time according to an evolutionary time span. In an evolutionary model, there is no recent catastrophic event in the solar system on a scale that parallels with the capturing of two asteroids in Mars' gravity. From a creationist model, both wanderers fit well with the asteroid bombardment period that initiated the global flood, and they very well could be two captured asteroids from that time period. Or they could be moons from creation some 6,000 years ago just like our moon. Either way, a nice fit exist from a creationist point of view. But for anyone to argue that Mars captured two wandering asteroids some time in the past is questionable because their death spiraling orbit and break away orbit, suggest a younger existence.

Chapter Summary: The two orbiting bodies around Mars indicate a short existence in terms of orbiting Mars. Both moons have a limited shelf life for their respective orbits. The evidence—moon's distance from the earth, the lack of an impact mark, the lack of an exchange of sediment between the earth moon, the lack of left lunar material that did not coalesce into the moon, and the lack of appropriate spin—does not corroborate billions of years of existence for the moon. And the impact hypothesis with a molten, magma state earth, is contrary to the Bible that records that the earth was filled with abundant vegetation, seas, surrounded by an atmosphere, and a canopy, before the moon was finished coalescing on the fourth day.

---

83 https://nssdc.gsfc.nasa.gov/planetary/ice/ice_moon.html.
84 https://mars.nasa.gov/allaboutmars/

Chapter 20
Tyrannosaurus Rex Soft Tissue Found

The year was 2006, and Dr. Mary Schweitzer had a bright idea for performing lab experiments on dinosaur fossils. What she found inside a bone of Tyrannosaurus rex is impressive and should cause many to rethink their belief. T. rex is estimated to have existed 65 million years ago, but Mary Schweitzer discovered blood vessels and cells inside the bone[85] at a laboratory at North Carolina State University in Raleigh. *Picture credit: Dr. Mary Schweitzer.*

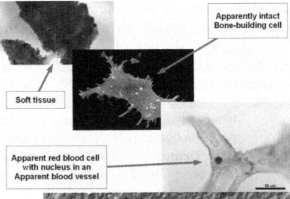

The evolutionary community claimed the find was contaminated. Why? Soft tissue cannot survive 65 million years, let alone 10,000 years. This is a problem for the evolutionists. Dr. Schweitzer, an evolutionist, flatly denies any contamination, and repeated her findings many times. This discovery is not an isolated aberration, others have discovered soft tissue in dinosaur fossils. Mark Armitage and K. Anderson observed soft tissue—osteocytes—in the horn of a Triceratops that he excavated from the Hell Creek Formation, Montana, USA.[86] Mr. Armitage documented his excavation, specifically that he found the triceratop's horn one foot from the surface, in the presence of insects, microbes, roots, fungal bodies, rodents, water, and oxygen. This is irrefutable evidence that dinosaurs did not die off millions–of–years–ago.

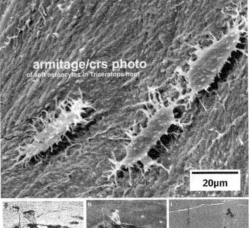

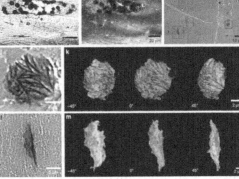

Unfortunately, as a result of him publishing his findings, Mark Armitage lost his job at California State University of Northridge. The persecution of anyone teaching the truth that exposes an old Earth as a lie, and reveals that science is in harmony with the plain reading of the Genesis creation and global flood continues. The evolutionists countered Mr. Armitage's findings with the notion that iron was the preserving agent for the 65–million–year–old dinosaur.

Dr. Schweitzer and Mark Armitage are not the only ones to find soft tissue in creatures that allegedly died 65 million years ago. A team of Taiwanese researchers found soft tissue in the rib of a sauropod dinosaur that allegedly died 195–million–years–ago.[87] The implication is that none of these dinosaurs died millions of years ago as preached by old Earth theorists. *Picture credit: Mark Armitage.*

Several other archeologists are finding soft tissue in dinosaur fossils. Such as, Bertazzo, et al., they found fibers and cellular structures preserved in 75-million-year-old dinosaur specimens. Nat. Commun. **6**, 7352 (2015).[88] *Picture credit: nature.com.*

In ideal conditions, red blood cells last only two years in a dead host. The fossilization and cold of Montana is the preserving factor for the soft tissue found in the T. rex by Mary Schweitzer. But how

85 wikipedia. Specimens of Tyrannosaurus#MOR 1125

86 Armitage, M.H., and K.L. Anderson. Soft sheets of fibrillar bone from a fossil of the supraorbital horn of the dinosaur Triceratops horridus. Acta Histochemica. https://www.ncbi.nlm.nih.gov/pubmed/23414624.

87 http://www.nature.com/articles/ncomms14220.

88 Bertazzo, et al., Nat. Commun. **6**, 7352 (2015).

long can soft tissue survive? Soft tissue is made up of cells, which is made up of proteins, which is made from the information in the DNA.

Therefore, a group of scientists (Allentoft et al.2012) calculated the limit beyond which no DNA (image of DNA with the nucleotides—A, T, G, and C) is likely to survive under optimal conditions. They analyzed mitochondrial DNA and determined that with a constant cold condition of -5°C in a protective sterile lab, DNA could last up to ~6 million years before the DNA would be broken down to one base pair (image of A-T base pair and G-C base pair).[89] This is the top estimate and under optimal conditions of slowing decay of DNA. For less durable anatomy, such as blood vessels and cells, as what Mary Schweitzer discovered, the decay rate is much faster. Under warmer conditions, the decay process would be accelerated. Therefore, since Mary Schweitzer's T. rex was discovered in Montana and not Antarctica, the decay process would have been accelerated because of periods of warmer temperatures in during the summer months and exposure to bacteria. Therefore, a 65-million-year-old T. rex could not have soft tissue still in its bone. Therefore, with Mary Schweitzer's T. rex still having soft tissue, this represents that the specimen is much much younger, such as 4,500 years old. Simply put, soft tissue does not last long.

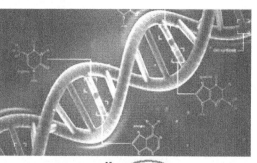

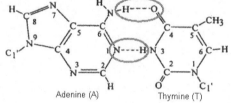

Adenine (A)   Thymine (T)

Guanine-cytosine base pair

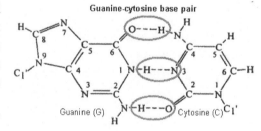

Guanine (G)   Cytosine (C)

That's not all they discovered about that T. rex; they discovered she was pregnant, which indicates that life on earth was vibrant and healthy for breeding at that time.

The sad fact of life is that no matter how much scientific evidence and Scripture is presented to some old Earth believers, they will mostly likely reject the truth, and interpret the Bible's creation record and the observable to fit the timelines and myths preached by atheists. We should not be surprised about this because 2 Timothy 4:3–4 prophesied this would occur. The primary forefather of this deception was renown atheist, **Charles Lyell**, and his Uniformitarian Theory. Charles Lyell is the one who deceived Charles Darwin away from the Bible. One of the things that breaks my heart is to hear a pastor say, "the age of the Earth is billions of years old." This reveals that (a) they have been indoctrinated by the world, (b) they do not know enough to discern the difference between an opinion given by scientists versus science, and (c) they do not fully trust the fidelity of God's Word.

Chapter Summary: The alleged time of 65 million years ago for when Tyrannosaurus rex roamed the earth has more than a serious hole with the discovery that a T. rex bone was found with soft tissue inside of it. The existence of soft tissue in the bone debunks the timeline of when dinosaurs roamed the earth. Soft tissue, such as WBC, RBC, and cells, have a short shelf life in a dead host. The cold and fossilization of the surrounding bone would slow the decay process down, but not even close to 10,000 years—let alone the evolutionary ages of 65 million years. The observable and testable evidence allows for a theory that the dinosaur existed ~4,000 years ago, and does not allow for an old Earth theory. Since she was pregnant, her mate also existed along the same recent timeline. This is in harmony with the Bible.

---

89 http://www.crystalinks.com/fossildna.html.

Chapter 21
Layers of the Earth

Evolutionary geologists tell us that each layer of the crust of the earth took 100,000 to a million years to form—based on the Uniformitarian theory by Charles Lyell. They say that this proves the earth is billions of years old because of all the layers. At first glance, considering the current rate of soil deposits, this old age of each layer and subsequent old age of the earth seem reasonable. But with careful analysis, problems exist with this hypothesis. Look at the layers of the Grand Canyon for a moment.

Have you ever wondered if it really took 100,000 to a million years for each layer to form, why are all the layers uniform? After all, there would be a lot of rainfall and erosion during each year that would cause mixing of the sediment. However, the layers are smooth and segregated. It is hard to believe that no rainfall occurred while each layer slowly formed to maintain the smooth, uniform layers. *Photo credit: www.bible.ca.*

The logic glares in our face that the layers had to form quickly to avoid erosion and commingling of the soil from rainfall. To believe otherwise is ignoring obvious evidence right in front of our eyes. Only one conclusion is reasonable, and that is that the layers were formed quickly. The other option is to believe that no rain and no erosion occurred for hundreds of millions of years.

We do not have to rely on sound logic alone. We can turn to the laws of physics and chemistry for clarity. All sediment mixed in water will settle according to their density 100% of the time. The reason is based on the amount of mass per volume (density), multiplied by gravity (acceleration), minus the buoyant force of the medium—water. Since each settling sediment had the same net gravity applied to it, the variable that determines the rate of descending to the bottom of water is based on the density. The more mass in a smaller volume, the greater the density, the greater the density, the faster the rate of descending to the bottom of water. Even different densities of liquids will settle according to the principle and form layers. If many different sediments are mixed into a container of water, and then the container is thoroughly shaken, when the container becomes motionless then all the different sediment will form segregated layers based on their density. With the densest sediment at the bottom, and the least dense sediment at the top. Vibrating the container will further segregate the sediment into more exclusive layers by breaking static friction, which frees "stuck" particles to a more low viscous state of free-flowing. This process is called **liquefaction**. During the Biblical flood, the vibration that further segregated the settling sediment was a twice-daily, global, and unimpeded, ocean tide, and earthquakes associated with the fast moving tectonic plates.

We are fortunate to have the Grand Canyon to expose the layers and the fallacy that each layer formed over 100,000 to a million years without rainfall commingling the layers. Unfortunately, if one goes to the Grand Canyon and speaks to park officials or reads the national park literature, it proclaims that the Grand Canyon was forged over millions of years by the Colorado River. This is in error as well because (a) the Grand Canyon has an average elevation of ~6,700 feet, and since rivers do not travel up hill, this ruins the notion that the Grand Canyon was slowly carved by the Colorado River, and (b) the existence of remnant green algae sediment on the upper level of the canyon that is exposed to the hot desert elements. Well, that algae only grows at the bottom of a freshwater lake. And guess what? The algae deposit pattern is in a saucer pattern that matches what lakes produce. The evidence tells us that since the Grand Canyon is at a high elevation of ~6,700 feet, a wall of the lake broke, and all the water stored in the massive lake rushed out quickly to form the Grand Canyon in about a week, not millions of years. When did this occur? It was probably 5 to 10 years after the Flood. The lake had to exist long enough after the Flood for algae to grow and deposit on the bottom of the lake, but not so long that the deposited layers of soil from the Flood that the lake was resting on would have hardened into rock (lithified).

Looking at the drawing, which was created by an evolutionary geologist, it is apparent that layers exist. The soil is segregated into homogeneous layers with homologous patterns, and those homogeneous layers lack erosion marks that are associated with a normal hydrological cycle. The young earth hypothesis explains the layers of the crust. The globe was covered with waters that were filled with debris, and that debris settled according to their density. This caused earth's crust to have different layers in regions around the globe. Because the sediment that burst out of the fault lines with the water was not exactly the same type of sediment around the globe. Some areas contained more sand. Also, some regions had turbulence and eddies, which pooled the debris together, such as sand in the area of Florida, and some massive dinosaur graveyards. But since all matter settles according to their density, the layers have a general outline of similar deposit history because sand settles in water at the same rate no matter where in the globe it is located. If one region has no biomass floating with the

sand and one region has massive amount of biomass floating within the sand, their rates of settling and the content settled would be altered. The final piece to the puzzle of sorting the different debris into like kind and forming layers was a global tide that swept twice daily around the planet, breaking static friction and allowing further segregation of the debris to like kind. This process is called liquefaction. Also, there were many earthquakes during the Flood caused by the fast moving tectonic plates (Psalm 104:8). These earthquakes produced liquefaction.

A young earth theorist has the Genesis floodwater filled with sand, mud, clay, silt, trees, plants, grass, ash, and corpses of all the creatures and humans that did not get on the ark. Therefore, the floodwater was filled with sediment, vegetation, and creatures, NOT clear water at all. The Bible directly says that every mountain was covered by the Flood, every mountain under the heavens, meaning everything. Also, the fountains of the deep

burst open violently, as the global flood of Genesis was a violent judgment with asteroids, volcanic activity, and tectonic plates moving fast at ~1–2 miles per hour. *Image credit: The Grand Canyon and the Moon, by Dr. Cowley, Univ. Mich. Univ.*

Review: The layers of the crust are segregated, homogeneous, and without erosion marks from the commingling of sediment that naturally occurs with the hydrological cycle. This fits perfectly with the violent chaotic judgment of the Genesis flood, with the waters not being clear, but filled with lots of different sediment, vegetation, and biomass.

One of the layers of the crust is limestone. **Limestone** is from broken-down teeth, bone, coral, shells, ash, and skeletons of plankton made up of calcium carbonate. A creationist has no problem with the evidence of a solid, exclusive layer of calcium carbonate from the many fires, and from the living beings that expired during the Flood. The waters roiled with all the sharp debris cutting, pounding, and breaking apart the flesh from the calcium-rich material and formed a layer of bones, teeth, coral, shells, and plankton skeletons equaling many layers of **calcium carbonate**. Some estimate that at the time of the Flood, there could have been 6 to 10 billion people alive, but that number pales in comparison to the number of land animals that would have contributed teeth and bone to form the limestone layer. As abundant as the land animals were before the Flood, that quantity of the mass of teeth and bone adding to the calcium carbonate layer pales in comparison to the tonnage of ash from the volcanic eruptions and fires, and also to the tonnage of shells and coral and plankton contributing to the limestone layer. I was debating an evolutionist, and he said, "There are not enough humans alive today to form enough calcium carbonate for the thickness of the limestone to have a global layer." I said something like,

> That's correct, but there were more animals than humans, and there were more shells than animals, and there was more coral than shells, and there was more plankton than all of them. Also, the teeth and bones of those that died before the Flood. They too would also contribute to form the limestone layers by having their grave sites disrupted by the violent catastrophe of the global flood. In addition, the many volcanoes and asteroids would have caused tons of ash from fires, this could have been an even larger contributor.

The evolutionary uniformitarian hypothesis has a problem with this observable evidence of exclusive limestone layers, as they are stuck with explaining away how a solid layer of limestone settled in certain regions of a continent with no other sediment deposited at the same time. Their belief suggests that for a period of roughly one million to hundreds of millions of years, the only deposited soil in several large regions around the globe was calcium carbonate (limestone) and no other sediment. It is illogical to exclusively see a layer of limestone, or a layer of sandstone, or any exclusive layer and listen to evolutionary geologists explain the slow formation of the different layers of soil; for a period of a million years, only sandstone was deposited in a particular region, or only limestone was deposited in a particular region and no other material. For example, in the southern part of the United States, there are limestone deposits hundreds of feet thick spanning several states. In England, massive amounts of chalk exist, unlike any region on earth. Many regions around the globe have massive amounts of marble. In addition, a slightly acidic body of water would be needed to cause the calcium carbonate and eventually limestone to gather together. They have to find several large bodies of acidic waters to handle the multiple large layers of limestone around the globe. However, acid bodies of water fits perfectly with a creationist's view of the catastrophic global flood, with hundreds of volcanoes erupting around the globe, and the entire saga commenced with several large asteroids.

The **limestone, chalk, and marble** all formed from calcium-rich material. The different end products—limestone, chalk, and marble—depended upon how much heat and pressure was applied to the material. But all three had to have slightly acidic water for the breakdown of the elements to occur. A catastrophic global flood with hundreds of volcanoes erupting would provide the necessary heat and sulfuric material to convert the waters in certain regions to a slightly acidic state.

Acid is required in combination with calcium-rich material to form limestone, chalk, and marble. Turbulent waters from a chaotic global flood with hundreds of global volcanoes, which would have been the source for the acid, would have created swirls in the waters that would have gathered together like material with like densities with a similar buoyant force, such as ash, bone, teeth, coral, and shell broken apart by the collisions with other debris in the water. If this pooling of the calcium-rich material was near an erupting volcano that sent enough sulfur matter in the air, droplets of rain would have combined with the sulfur matter to form sulfuric acid, which would break down the material to form calcium carbonate, or limestone, chalk, or marble. Evidence that massive amounts of heat generated from volcanic activity includes multiple locations around the globe of layers of soil that are bent, with sharp curves. The Gen. 7 violent flood is a perfect explanation of how and why sharp curves are present in rock that did not break or crack the rocks. The hot soil that settled in layers was still malleable because it was fresh deposit, and the hot water from being near volcanic activity. As the tectonic plates continued moving, they caused buckling and sharp bends in the soil before it solidified into hard rock.

Evolutionary geologists' explanation of how the crust has an exclusive layer of limestone is that a slightly acidic sea covered an area at some point in time, and coral, shells, teeth, and bone were broken down to their base element over millions of years and deposited at the bottom of the sea to form the limestone. And then, through tectonic plate movements, the sea shifted and no longer existed over the limestone. However, if this process really took that long, it would not be as pure as the data reveals. Other debris would have contaminated the purity. But if we took bone, teeth, coral, shell, ash, and plankton and mechanically broke them into smaller pieces because the Genesis flood was violent and soaked those pieces in slightly acidic water, it would not take millions of years to break down the items into calcium carbonate; it would not even take 100 years or even one single year. Those items would break down in several months, depending on the pH of the water. If a volcano was nearby and enough sulfur was released in the air,  it would rain low-pH acid rain in that general area. The young earth hypothesis of how we got segregated limestone in certain large global regions is in harmony with observable segregated layers, science, and the Bible. *Photo credit: Creation Faith Facts, by Rob Lester.*

Other exclusive layers exist, such as sand compressed to form sandstone. A creationist has no problem with this—all the sand that was disrupted during the Flood settled and pooled together with turbulent waters and formed layers of sand that was compressed by pressure to form sandstone. However, an evolutionist is stuck believing that for millions of years, only sand was deposited in a large region to form an exclusive sand layer, with no bone, no shells, no coral, no clay, no mud, and no organic material—just sand. Only sand was deposited in regions globally for a million years?

This is illogical, yet this hypothesis is ardently defended because the slow deposit theory (Uniformitarian Theory) provides large amounts of time. And time is the foundation for evolution. Remove the large amounts of time, and the evolutionary hypothesis fails.

How does a creationist handle the fact that gray, tan, yellow, and white limestone layers exist, and with layers of other sediment in between those layers. First off, when ash, teeth, bone, coral, and shell (the constituents that make up calcium carbonate, or limestone) are in their whole form, they each have different densities, though they are made up of the same material. Bone has more air in its trabeculae (tissue) and is less dense than coral. Therefore, the contributors of calcium carbonate in their original whole form each have different densities and settle at different rates. This is one cause of the different layers of limestone. The more the contributing factors are broken into smaller pieces, the more their densities are similar, causing them to settle at similar rates.

Another cause of the different layers are different impurities that may accompany a depositing layer. For example, some trace mud may mix in with a layer, sometimes a settling layer has some sand in it, sometimes a settling layer has some biomass or adipose in it, and sometimes a settling layer has some vegetation mixed with it. Though the limestone layers are predominately calcium carbonate, other soils are slightly mixed in at varying layers, and they affect the density and the settling rate. The different impurities cause limestone to be either white, yellow, tan, or gray. Those impurities cause several layers of limestone with different sediment in between them, not because there was one million years of calcium carbonate deposited, then one million years of sand deposited, and so on.

In addition, the Flood had many volcanoes globally erupting daily, so it is plausible that some

133

portion of the waters and rains were acidic, allowing the broken pieces of bones, teeth, coral, shell, and plankton to form into the base form of calcium carbonate. After the settling concluded, the immense pressure and heat was the final ingredient that determined the type of limestone formation, whether chalk (with the least pressure and heat), limestone, or marble (with the greatest pressure and heat).

When viewing the layers of the crust, another apparent observable piece evidence is that the layers are smooth with no erosion marks, with no evidence of a hydrological cycle. Evolutionists adhere to a hypothesis that suggests that the layers formed over hundreds of millions of years with no erosion marks, which means that there was no rain during the formation of each layer for hundreds of millions of years. Otherwise, sediment would commingle. A sand layer would erode and intermingle with the layer below, and each layer would have commingling. But this is not what happened based on the observable evidence.

At this point, I'm in awe of the evolutionists' fanatical adherence to their beliefs, while many "Christians" do not even adhere to the Bible with the same fervor. In fact, theistic evolutionists are forced to severely marginalize the accuracy of the Bible to force it to fit their evolutionary views. Evolution does not allow for a global flood, and the Bible directly records in Gen. 7:19: "The water prevailed more and more upon the earth, so that ALL the high mountains EVERYWHERE under the heavens were covered." No middle ground exist. Either throw out the Bible or accept the Bible, but do not cherry-pick the Bible just so you do not look foolish to evolutionists.

Continuing this lack of commingling of the layers discussion, there are layers of exclusive clay and layers of compressed mud without organic material (called shale) and other layers of compressed mud with organic material (called black shale). To believe that for millions of years, on a global scale, there was only mud with no organic material deposited on earth and no rain to mix the layers with erosion is illogical. For how could animals and vegetation not die and leave their remains in the million-year period, yet above and below that layer of mud are filled with remains of dead animals and vegetation? That is incongruous with uniformitarian hypotheses that suggest that there was a slow deposit of soil over millions of years. To have a layer with no biomass means that no life form died and mixed their organic material with that layer of mud deposit for a million years. This is impossible. According to the evolutionary belief in the slow deposit of sediments, there should be no layers at all in the crust, just one giant layer intermingled with limestone, shale, black shale, sand, clay, rock, vegetation, and biomass all mixed together. Evolution is all about randomness. Therefore, having uniform layers and exclusive deposits with millions of years for each layer and no rain to commingle the layers with erosion is incongruous with evolution because it demonstrates order. Something occurred to cause the layers, a force very large that was uncommon and no longer present. However, globally deposited uniform layers are in harmony with quick deposits from a catastrophic global flood.

Review: The uniform, segregated, homogeneous layers around the crust are contrary to a slow-deposit scenario because the natural process is not for each particular sediment to deposit for a million years. This takes too much faith to believe, but evolutionist are forced to abide by this construct to account for the large amounts of time required to evolve life.

Several chapters earlier, we discussed the core samples of the Atlantic Ocean and how there was only ~5,000 years worth of sand deposited on the ocean floor, representing that the **Sahara desert** has only been in existence for that period of time. Below the tan sand deposited on the Atlantic Ocean floor off the coast of northwest Africa, greenish sediment exist from a tropical forest that once thrived in the Sahara region before it became a desert. So ponder this, Egyptian soil layers include a layer of limestone from calcium carbonate and a massive layer of sandstone. Keep in mind that sandstone needs massive amounts of pressure to convert the sand into stone. Below that, the sandstone layer is igneous rock. So the slow uniformitarian hypothesis has sand being deposited for multiples of millions of years, given the thickness of sandstone, yet only ~5,000 years worth exist of sand blown into the Atlantic Ocean floor. This means that the observable evidence of ~5,000 years worth of sand existing in the Sahara region does not match the slow uniformitarian hypothesis of a process taking hundreds of millions of years. They do not go together. Therefore, either the Uniformitarian theory is wrong. The Bible is in harmony with the evidence.

Review: The observable evidence of when the Sahara Desert formed does not match up with millions of years of sand being deposited in northern Africa. Below the sand deposited in the Atlantic Ocean are deposits indicating tropical vegetation, telling us that the Sahara region was tropical before the Flood, not desolate for millions of years.

Evolutionists argue that the Gen. 7 flood was regional. As a matter of fact, they have to argue this point tooth and nail, for to give one inch of ground to the Bible being correct means evolution is wrong by default, since they are opposite constructs. If you ever wondered why evolutionists so vehemently argue that they will only allow a regional flood for the Bible legend, it is because so much at stake. If the Biblical account of the **global flood** is correct, billions of years of soil deposits attributed to the uniformitarian slow deposit theory are lost, and then evolution does not have enough time to evolve life, theistic evolutionists are exposed for believing a lie and persecuting creationists, and old Earth believers are guilty of annulling Scripture to fit Genesis into atheistic timelines, not trusting God's Word, and mocking young–earth–creationists. The entire evolutionary hypotheses hangs in the balance. This really is an all or nothing war on truth. The Bible declares the waters covered the earth in Gen. 7:19:

> The water prevailed more and more upon the earth, so that ALL the high mountains EVERYWHERE under the heavens were covered. The water prevailed 15 cubits, and the mountains were covered. ALL flesh that moved on the earth perished, birds and cattle and beasts and every swarming thing that swarms upon the earth, and ALL mankind; of ALL that was on the dry land, ALL in whose nostrils was the breath of the spirit of life, died. Thus He blotted out EVERY living thing that was upon the face of the land, from man to animals to creeping things and to birds of the sky, and they were blotted out from the earth; and ONLY Noah was left, together with those that were with him in the ark.

This is why each mountain has sea shells, and this is why the smooth layers of the crust are global. No way around this; it would be logical that it was only a regional flood if there were only regional smooth layers of sediment and if only regional mountains were covered with sea shells. This would be evidence of a regional flood, but that is not reality. The reality is that global smooth layers of sediment exist, and all mountains sea shells globally. Psalm 104 reveals that God caused the mountains to rise and the valleys to sink after the floodwaters; therefore, the Genesis flood occurred while the mountains were smaller than today.

Review: The smooth layers of soil around the globe of the crust of the earth without intermingled sediment proves the long slow deposit of soil required by evolution to be false. There would never be exclusively one type of deposit for a million years, followed by a different type of deposit for a million years, and so on. The smooth layers are evidence that corroborates the global flood record in the Bible, which suggests that the layers formed quickly, as in less than a year. The fact that the layers of sediment are global, and the sea shells on the tops of mountains are also global, corroborates the Bible that the Genesis flood was global, and not regional.

Additionally, **meteorites** are lacking in the layers of the crust. Since we observe today that around 200 meteorites land on the surface of the earth, in a preserved condition, every year. Then if a layer took 100,000 years to slowly form, there should be ~20 million meteorites in that layer. If a layer took one million years to form, there should be ~200 million meteorites in that layer. Since no factory produces meteors in space, and when a meteor collides with a celestial body it is gone forever, we may conclude that as we progress in the future less and less meteors exist, and as we travel back in time the quantity of meteors proportionately increases. Therefore, the logic suggests that each deeper layer should have more and more quantity of meteorites. As a result, we should expect to find billions of meteorites in the layers of the soil. But since we do not find meteorites in the layers of the soil, that is strong evidence that the layers were formed quickly, such as from a global flood, and not deposited slowly over billions of years.

A **fulgurite** is the byproduct of when lightning strikes the ground, and as a result of the tremendous heat transferred, the mineral grains in the soil fuse and vitrify. The changed matter has a distinctive hallow long tube with branches coming off the main core to fragmented bits of glass formed by the fusion of silica (quartz) sand or rock. Roughly 100 lightning strikes occur per second around the globe. If the layers took 100,000 years to millions of years for each layer, billions of fulgurites should exists in each layer, yet they are missing in the layers. This suggests that the layers formed quickly.

No animal or plant **burrow markings** exist in the layers of the crust of the sedimentary rock. If the layers were slowly deposited over millions of years, some plant roots would have burrowed through the layers or some evidence of animal burrowing before lithification occurred. But the fact that we see smooth layers without plant and animal burrow markings debunks the slow, Uniformitarian deposit hypothesis and is in harmony with a quick deposit theory.

From a Biblical perspective, all the ash, soil, vegetation, and creatures that were mixed in the turbulent floodwater from the Genesis flood settled at different rates based on their density over the course of almost one year. The Bible records that after the 40 days of rain and fountains, the waters prevailed over everything for 150 days, then it took another 5 months for the floodwater to recede into ice (glacial age) and dry up, as mountains rose and valleys sank (Psalm 104:5–9). The duration of the Flood saga is in complete harmony with all the sciences, though not in harmony with the opinions of evolutionary scientists.

Evolutionary geologists use the different layers of the crust of the earth as evidence for the large amount of time necessary for evolution. You see, evolution requires billions of years for random, unguided mutations to allegedly have enough time to evolve the genetic code for new functions and new kinds of creatures. Take away billions of years from the layers of the crust, and evolution is broken, right there. For that matter, the foundation for all old Earth theorists is broken.

An evolutionary hypothesis of how the many vast **salt deposits** formed is different than my hypothesis that fits a Biblical model. Take for example the Detroit Salt Mine; evolutionists believe that a basin (a hole in the ground) formed 400 million years ago, and ocean water poured into the basin, and then the water evaporated, leaving salt behind. This process kept repeating itself for millions of years until the vast deposits of salt were filled with only salt,[90] spanning 1,500 acres. So no other material deposited along side with the salt, no sediment, no vegetation, and no dead creatures? This hypothesis is accepted as fact but is lacking several logical components to the theory, most notably, the purity of the salt and the lack of other sediment that did not intermingle with the salt, for instance mud, clay, sand, trees, plants, animals, and so on. It does not logically resonate that only salt deposited for millions of years to fill a basin spanning 1,500 acres.

A hypothesis that fits with the observable evidence and science and is in harmony with the Biblical flood is that the glacial age resulting from the Genesis flood caused many of the **salt deposits** (the deeper salt deposits were formed during the high heat of the forming Earth that was surrounded by saltwater, the heat separated the salt from the freshwater via a process called evaporation, and this formed very large pure and deep salt deposits, and resulted in the fountains of the deep being

---

90 detroitsalt.com/history.

freshwater). When salt water has reached the saturation point, any additional salt added remains in a solid form, not diluted with the liquid. When the ocean waters during the Genesis flood started to freeze, only fresh water froze[91] and not salt water, which means that as the glaciers continued to expand, the product left behind that did not freeze was salt. As the glaciers expanded, the salt quantity increased proportionately. Since salt is denser in solid form than in ocean water, the solid salt sank to the bottom and formed salt deposits. This is actually very simple chemistry science, but the reason evolutionary geologists miss this or refuse to accept this is because they are forced to believe in millions of years to preserve the foundation for evolution. But this process did not take long. It started forming during the time of the waters prevailing over everything for 150 days (this is after the 40 days of rain), and the process continued almost a year. We may deduce when enough ice formed by the start of the wind. God started the wind immediately following the 150 days of waters prevailing over the everything (Gen. 8:1). For wind to occur, there needs to be a large change of temperatures from the freezing polar regions, to the hotter equatorial regions. The ice most likely began forming at the polar regions at the beginning of the 40 days of rain because we have to account for woolly mammoths frozen in the up right position in the Arctic Circle, and with undigested food still in their digestive track. But not enough ice formed to generate wind until after the water prevailed for 150 days.

The floodwater was salty, and after the 40 days of rain, toward the end of the 150 days of global flood, temperatures continued to plummet. This initiated the glacial age. As fresh water started to crystallize and freeze as ice, this left the salt that was in the water behind to settle at the bottom. With global floodwater at the saturation point near the glaciers, no more salt could be added; thus, the leftover salt went strait to a solid form.

Review: The lack of meteorites in the layers of soil debunks a slow deposit hypothesis. People have a choice to believe that salt deposits formed over millions of years from oceans pouring into a basin, or the salt deposits formed from the global flood, which left behind solid salt. As the glaciers expanded, the salt deposits increased proportionately, and this process took less than a year.

Let us discuss the layers of **oil reservoirs** at different depths. The biomass that lived before the Flood, settled at different moments during the Flood. The first and lower oil reservoirs were covered by the initial debris from asteroids impacting the earth, sending massive amounts of soil covering a lot of biomass. Then, as the floodwater rose, other biomass would settle and be covered up by later settling sediment. When the biomass was buried near heat, petroleum formed from the biomass. When biomass was buried without a heat source, it fossilized. Oil naturally collects together, so where cracks existed in the settled soil, the oil would collect. But back to the point of why oil is at different depths; biomass settles at different rates depending on the density of the material, so reservoirs from heavier material would be at a lower level and vice versa. For example, muscle is 3X more dense than adipose (fat), and they would settle differently, forming oil at varying levels. This is one reason petroleum exist at different levels from one global flood.

My concern is that it seems some evolutionists, even though they know that the natural decay rate of biomass may be accelerated and converted into oil in 30 minutes, reject the above hypothesis, not because it lacks merit, not because it is not plausible, but because it harmonizes with the Bible and debunks billions of years of time. This precious time is the most important foundation of evolution. Debunking the slow uniformitarian theory, evolution no longer has enough time to account for the diversity and complexity of life.

Review: The evolutionary hypothesis for oil production is that it takes millions of years for biomass to slowly decay into petroleum near a thermal heat source, and this occurred hundreds of millions of years ago. Considering that mankind can accelerate the decay process of biomass to oil in 30 minutes, validates the YEC hypothesis that oil came from biomass that was covered at varying intervals of the global flood saga by sediment, pressure, and heat.

We have discussed how the creation of **coal reserves** can be explained by the Bible. Let us

91 Water.usgs.gov/edu/earthglacier.

briefly review. The evolutionary hypothesis is that vegetation, near a heat source and pressure, was covered by a slow sedimentary deposit over 100,000 to a million years and decayed over a very slow process of 20 million years to convert trees and plant matter to coal. This, however, is contrary to observable evidence and tests, as we can convert wood into coal in eight months by mimicking the very same process of a buried earth scenario near heat and pressure.

Why believe a hypothesis of a slow sediment deposit when the process requires vegetation to be quickly covered by soil? Otherwise, vegetation would decay in short order and return to the soil as nutrients. Why believe a slow deposit hypothesis that suggests that only vegetation was deposited for a period of time and then layers above and below with no vegetation deposited?

Vegetation upon death, will not exist long enough for the slow deposit theory to cover it. Decay starts immediately, and most vegetation only last months; some of the sturdier trees may take decades to decay, but that still isn't enough time for the uniformitarian hypothesis. The earth is not filled with a layer of dead animals and vegetation that is waiting to be covered by the slow deposit hypothesis. No, upon death, organisms break down and decay to their base elements. That is why we do not see coal deposits being formed today. It is a race against time—will the dead vegetation decay to its base elements and become nutrients for the soil, or will the slow deposit hypothesis over 100,000 years cover the vegetation with enough heat and pressure to convert the vegetation into coal? The answer is obvious; vegetation always decays before the soil covers it. There needs to be a quick covering of vegetation with massive amount of soil, near heat, with enough soil weight to apply lots of pressure to convert vegetation into coal.

A hypothesis that is in harmony with observable evidence and science and the Bible is this: The Bible records there was lush vegetation before the Flood, enough vegetation to feed all the abundant herbivores (remember no carnivores existed until the fall of man). Some of that vegetation got covered up by debris early in the Flood saga by asteroid impacts, tectonic plate movements, volcanic activity, and water and sediment bursting out of the earth. Those activities sent massive amounts of soil in the air to cover some vegetation immediately, and it was buried adjacent to high heat and pressure, and that material was converted to coal in a short amount of time, forming the lowest layers of coal deposits. During the middle or later periods in the Flood saga, the vegetation covered by soil either turned into coal if it was near a heat source, or fossilized if it was not near a heat source.

It seems that evolutionists reject the above hypothesis, not because it lacks merit, not because it is implausible, but because they have to reject any hypothesis that debunks billions of years of a slow deposit hypothesis. For evolution's foundation is built on massive amounts of time; destroy that construct, and the entire evolutionary hypothesis crumbles. This is when it seems evolutionist are no longer seeking truth, but are seeking to support their beliefs at any cost.

Review: The evolution hypothesis of coal formation is that vegetation was covered by sediment over a period of 100,000 to one million years, near a heat source and pressure, and this caused a very slow decay process that converted trees into coal. However, humans can mimic the natural process and convert wood into 100% coal in only eight months. A young earth hypothesis for coal formation is that vegetation was covered quickly by sediment near a heat source and pressure during the varying stages of the global flood saga, and this caused a quick decay process that converted vegetation into coal with different depths. The bottom line is that decaying vegetation will not exist long enough for the slow deposit theory to cover them.

Another piece of evidence in the layers of the crust of earth that debunks the Uniformitarian hypothesis of soil deposited over 100,000 to a million years is the **fossil record** (bone mineralized into rock). The slow deposit of sediment over hundreds of millions of years is one of the backbones of evolutionary theory. The slow deposit hypotheses creates the large amount of time needed for random, unguided mutations, adaptation and natural selection to evolve life. However, the fossil record debunks this slow deposit hypothesis. Evolutionists say that sediment slowly deposits over dead creatures, covering them over hundreds of thousands of years. Once the creature is covered by enough layers of soil (100,000 to millions of years for each layer) and water so that the weight of the soil adds enough pressure, the fossilization process starts—and then that takes 500,000 more years. Could this be true? NO. Think of it is a race with time. It is a race between soil covering the creature and the rate of decay. The soil must preserve the creature for fossilization before carnivores, scavengers, bacteria, fungi, sun, oxygen, UV, and decay either consume the creature or reduce it to its base element as nutrients for soil. It is a race between the decay process of the creature versus the soil deposit rate.

Assume that a creature dies without a burial or a coffin and is just laying down on top of the surface. Immediately, the blood and fluids start to settle because of gravity. Then, within a couple of hours, the body stiffens in a process called rigor mortis. Anaerobic organisms within the digestive tract start to increase, bacteria starts to consume the creature from the inside out, and the body starts to putrefy. The methane gas from the bacteria causes the corpse to bloat. Scavengers arrive quickly to consume the corpse. How long does the slow deposit theory have to deposit enough soil to a) cover the dead creature and b) have enough soil weight to start the fossilizing process before the dead creature is reduced to its base elements, and nothing is left but dust and nutrients for soil?

The answer is that a dead creature immediately starts to decompose upon death and is reduced to fur, teeth, and bones in about two to six months, depending on temperatures and carnivores. The aroma of a dead corpse attracts carnivore scavengers (coyotes, foxes, lions, etc.) and insects (e.g., beetles, flies, etc.) to feed on the dead corpse. With further decay, the stench of a rotting carcass brings the final scavengers, such as vultures, maggots, dung beetles, and more to feast on the remaining flesh. All this is done within weeks of death when the temperature is warm or months when the temperature is colder. At this point, not enough soil is deposited to cover a hair of the dead creature. The only thing remaining of the creature is some fur, teeth, and skeletal structure. Then, the final stage of decay is accelerated by the sun. Bones left out in the open with no protection from the sun will start to dry and crack in one year and decay to dust in a couple of years. At this point, there may be one-tenth of a millimeter of sediment deposited, but by this time the dead creature has already been reduced to chemical nutrients for the soil. Nothing is left to fossilize. Therefore, every time a fossil is found in the soil, it is evidence that massive amounts of soil were deposited quickly from a catastrophic event, not from slow deposit over a million years.

Wait a minute. How do we still have mummies then? How do we still have skeletal structures of people buried from 2,000 years ago? Well, the mummies were embalmed to preserve there structures, and all internal visceral tissues were removed to preserve the external tissue. In both examples, the bodies were protected from scavengers and the destructive process of the sun. But animals are not buried in a memorial service by other animals or other humans. Every time you see a fossil, know that that creature or specimen was buried quickly by soil, not buried over 100,000 years. No dead creature would wait around long enough to be covered by one layer of soil—let alone the many layers necessary to generate enough weight for the pressure involved in fossilization.

This does not apply to only creatures, but also to leaves, trees, shells, crustaceans, and so on. When a leaf falls to the ground, it immediately starts to dry out and break into unrecognizable fragments from bacteria and fungi feeding on the nutrients of the leaf. No leaf would wait around for centuries for sediment to slowly deposit and cover the leaf. The leaf would decay to dust in months. Every leaf fossil is evidence against an old Earth and only allows the conclusion of quick soil deposit covering the leaf. Therefore, every leaf fossil cries out in support of the Biblical flood and testifies against the slow uniformitarian deposit hypothesis.

Look around—no fossils form today by a slow deposit theory. This should stop everyone in their tracks and pause for a moment. No fossils form today because the rate of soil deposited is way too slow to cover any organism before that organism decays to its base elements and dust. Evolutionists believe that "all continues just as it was from the beginning" (2 Pet 3:4), that the rate of deposit today is the rate it has always been. An obvious disconnect of logic exist with the evolutionary uniformitarian hypothesis and observable evidence and science. We observe and test the rate of decay, and the rate of soil deposit; the bottom line is that the rate of decay far exceeds the rate of soil deposit. Therefore, the only way to get soil deposited faster than the rate of decay is through a catastrophic event. *Picture credit: EP Minerals.*

Another problem with the slow uniformitarian hypothesis are the massive amounts of **diatoms** that have formed the quarries near the San Andreas fault line and other regions around the globe. Diatoms are tiny microscopic (one millionth of a meter) organisms in the oceans that sink to the bottom when they die and form a layer of diatomaceous earth. But they only form at a rate of a couple of inches every 1,000 years at the current uniformitarian rate. Finding pure, solid quarries of diatomaceous earth, without impurities such as sediment, vegetation, biomass, and so forth deposited, debunks the slow uniformitarian process because if the diatoms accumulated slowly then the quarries would not be pure. For this reason, this is strong evidence that during the global flood, superheated water burst violently out of the deep caverns (Gen. 7:11), and this instantly killed all the diatoms in those regions of eruptions that were covered by seawater and formed the pure quarries.

Also, recall the petrified clams that have been found with their mouths in a closed position. Since the clams are petrified in the closed position, they had to have been covered quickly by soil within days. Upon the clams petrifying, the mountains rose at the end of the Flood saga (Psalm 104:8) and produced the likes of Mount Everest and the Andes Mountains, revealing the clams were buried alive. Only a Gen. 7 flood explains this observable evidence, and this evidence debunks the slow deposit hypothesis. *Photo credit: Arturo Vildozola.*

Review: <u>Fossils can only be formed when soil is deposited quickly so that it covers the specimen before decay breaks it down to its base chemical elements. Every fossil is testimony that soil was deposited quickly, which debunks the slow evolutionary deposit hypothesis and supports the genesis flood. Diatom deposits accumulate by only inches over 1,000 years, so the existence of solid quarries of diatomaceous earth without other deposits, supports the concept of a quick superheated fountain of water shooting up into the sea. This fits the Bible and is contrary to the evolutionary slow deposit hypothesis. Giant clams fossilized in the closed position is testimony that they were covered quickly by soil and pressure, which prevented them from opening upon their death, and thus is evidence for the Biblical flood and against the uniformitarian hypothesis.</u>

One more arrow in the evolutionary quiver regarding the layers of the crust. The biology department holds on very tightly to all the dead animals at different layers in the soil that did not get converted to petroleum from the heat and fossilized instead. Evolutionary biologists call this the **geological column**. The geological column is the hypothesis that the deeper one digs down through the layers, the further back in time one goes; through viewing the layers, one can see the evolving of creatures from the primitive lower levels to more evolved creatures toward the surface. This goes back in time for hundreds of millions of years. When biologists see crustaceans toward the bottom and other seemingly simple life forms at the bottom and allegedly progressively more complex life forms closer to the surface, then this, in their minds,

THE GEOLOGIC COLUMN			Typical fossils
Eras	Periods	Millions of Years Ago	
CENOZOIC	QUATERNARY	2	
	TERTIARY	65	
MESOZOIC	CRETACEOUS	130	
	JURASSIC	180	
	TRIASSIC	225	
PALAEOZOIC	PERMIAN	275	
	CARBONIFEROUS	345	
	DEVONIAN	405	
	SILURIAN	435	
	ORDOVICIAN	480	
	CAMBRIAN	600	
	PRE-CAMBRIAN		

supports evolution because the billions of years of slow sedimentary deposits laid layers of soil in lockstep with the evolution of life. They claim that one can see the evolutionary chain of the different life forms as they evolved by looking at different layers of soil and seeing progressively more evolved creatures closer to the surface. *Photo credit: www.uncommondescent.com/creationism.*

As a side note, do not be alarmed when evolutionists say that Christians use **circular reasoning**. For example, "Believers claim the Bible is true because the Bible says it is true, and the Bible is the Word of God because the Bible tells us so." This is just a debate tactic to say that Christians do not use science and physics and logic. Though the Bible claims to be truth, anyone can study the Bible and find out what it claimed would happen and what has happened. After careful study, we find indeed that the Bible authenticates itself with fulfilled prophecies and accuracy in regard to doctrine, geography, archeology, biology, and all the sciences. Evolutionists are guilty of the very same thing that they accuse Christians of. They proclaim that one can determine how old a bone is by what level in the soil that the bone came from, and one can determine how old the soil is by what bone comes from that level in the soil. "The rocks do [sic] date the fossils, but the fossils date the rocks more accurately."[92] That statement is circular reasoning and not science, but that is one technique evolutionists will employ. They will accuse Christians of the very thing they are committing—circular reasoning. This dogmatic belief is so strong that the name *geological column* is often called the geological time scale.

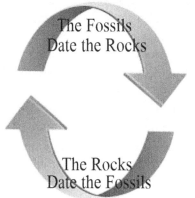

Why do creatures that did not get converted into petroleum at different levels in the layers seemingly create a geological column? The answer is twofold. First, the geological column is not exact; no place on earth exist where the geological column is complete. A few creatures exist at different levels in one place on the globe and different creatures at different levels at other places around the globe. No labels exist on the layers of soil that designates the age or on the fossils that designate their age. Evolutionists have created the column to provide evidence for evolution, but nowhere on earth is the geological column complete; it is a fabrication by evolutionists to support their hypothesis. Geologists have broken the layers down to 10 basic strata systems: Cambrian, Ordovician, Silurian, Devonian, Carboniferous, Permian, Triassic, Jurassic, Cretaceous, and Tertiary. But nowhere on earth do all 10 strata systems exist. In fact, Dr. Steven A. Austin, PhD, writes, "Data from continents and ocean basins show that the ten systems are poorly represented on a global scale: approximately 77% of the earth's surface area on land and under the sea has seven or more of the strata systems **missing**."[93] This is to say that nowhere on earth are all the layers represented, and 77% of the earth's surface only has three or fewer layers of the geological column. The only place where the geological column is complete is on the drawing papers from the minds of evolutionary geologists. When creationists say they are skeptical of the geological column that is dogmatically taught as fact, their objection is based on science.

However, even if creationists can prove that a hypothesis of evolution is wrong, it does not mean that creation is correct by default. Since creatures exist at different depths in the soil layers, let us deal with those creatures. The answer to solving the question of why creatures are at different levels of the layers of soil involves bacteria, methane gas from the bacteria, bloating of the host, subsequent changes in density, and buoyant force.

Logistically, creatures that were already living underground before the chaos of the Genesis

92 Dr. J. O'Rourke, *American Journal of Science*, "Pragmatism versus materialism", vol. 276, Jan. 1976, p. 51.
93 Dr. Steven A. Austin, PhD, "Ten Misconceptions about the Geological Column."

flood are more likely to remain at the lower levels. Just look around today—we do not see giraffes or elephants or lions living underground, we see seemingly simple creatures living underground. We do not see see crustaceans, worms, and the like living in trees, we see seemingly complex creatures living above ground. That explains why crustaceans and other underground living organism are found at deeper levels because worms and other creeping things were already living underground at the start of the Flood, just like they do today, not because complex life evolved from them while a slow deposit of soil accumulated along with the evolving life. This is observable and testable. For the record, nothing is simple about smaller life forms. If anything, life is more complex the smaller they are.

How to explain other creature buried at different levels, which supposedly supports evolutionary claims? It is actually simple. When the creatures died, the bacteria inside their digestive tract did not die. With no immune system interfering, the bacteria proliferated. What is the byproduct of bacteria after they eat? It is **methane gas**. This is a contributing factor to how methane gas or natural gas got trapped below the crust of the earth and where it came from. But that is not the end of the story. With all the dead creatures with bacteria thriving inside them, consuming internal tissue and defecating methane gas. This caused bloating of the host creature, which altered their density and buoyant force. The amount of resistance to bloating from the methane gas varies differently from creature to creature depending on their external structure and their diet. Those with hard shells would resist bloating more than a creature with elastic skin and would remain denser and sink quicker. Those with exoskeletons would mostly resist bloating and remain mostly at their original density. Those with tough, thick reptilian skin would moderately resist and lose some density. Those with a pliable hide but with fur would resist a little and lose more density. Those that had elastic skin with no fur would resist the least, and if they weren't buried by debris, they would float and decay to just bone and teeth in ~six months and further break down to their basic chemical component of calcium carbonate.

If you are struggling with bacteria producing methane gas and causing bloating and altering the densities of creatures to cause them to settle at different intervals, put your forensic hat on and think about a CSI (crime scene investigation) show. Or recall a story on the news in which someone was missing or murdered and their body floated to the surface about a week later.

During the global flood, the exterior of a creature was one determining factor in the amount of bloating that altered the creature's density and determined at what level of sediment the creature settled. Another factor is the type and amount of bacteria within the creature that produced methane gas. Those that had more bacteria within them had more methane gas produced and had greater bloating, which altered their density and influenced at which point the creature settled and what sediment the creature settled in. One of the final steps in decomposition (without heat) of biomass is methane gas.

Another factor that affected the density of a creature was the ratio of muscle to fat. Muscle is three times denser than fat. A creature that has a lot of fat would be more buoyant than a creature that has no fat. This sheds light on why the geological column has creatures at the bottom that a) already lived below the surface at the start of the Flood, b) had a shell to resist bloating from methane gas, and c) had little to no fat to make them buoyant. For example, top athletes that have very little fat and lots of muscle do not float in water; they sink. Conversely, an obese person with lots of fat and little muscle floats. This is all based on density and buoyancy.

When combining these facts about density and things that alter density, the geological column does not support the evolutionary claim that creatures evolved over billions of years as soil was slowly deposited. That would be contrary to observable evidence and tests. The geological column demonstrates that living things died during the global flood settled according to their density along with soil that settled according to its density, and this created the layering effect we observe today and the different levels of different creatures.

During the Flood, the turmoil of the waters caused eddies. These eddies would accumulate animals that ultimately would result in fossil graveyards. One of the eddies probably formed the whole peninsula of Florida with a large swirling eddy of sand. As the animals died in the water, some were swirling in eddies. Then their heads and extremities would fall off, and this would cause the large fossil graveyards of dinosaurs that we see today around the world. Another component is when the waters covered every continent and every mountain, no physical barrier existed to stop the tides. The global tide was unimpeded and roamed twice daily across the entire surface of the earth. With no continents to slow or stop the tides, this led to liquefaction as the tides rolled around the earth. This liquefaction was the final step of sorting all the soil, vegetation, and organisms according to their density. This is another component in forming the geological column and layers of the crust.

When the layers were formed and still malleable because of being hot from coming from within the earth, the tectonic plates were still moving relatively quickly, and they bent the malleable layers before they solidified into hard rock. Then the soil hardened into rock with the bent layers. Since the bent rocks were smooth, with no cracking or breaking, this indicates that the rocks were bent while they were warm and soft. The Flood solves this, and a slow deposit theory is debunked with this information because if the layers formed slowly, they could not fold because rock does not bend, instead it would crack. At the end of the Flood, the layers of the earth bent without cracks while they were all soft and warm; then they formed into rock. *Photo credit: www.allposters.co.*

Review: All organisms have bacteria in them. When hosts died during the Flood, the bacteria still lived inside them and consumed internal tissue, they became bloated from the methane gas trapped within them. This altered their densities and caused creatures to settle at different rates in different soils. Then upon resting, they either fossilized from the pressure (seemingly forming the geological column) or completely reduced to base chemical elements or converted to oil if they settled near high heat. The amount of bloating was dependent upon the makeup of creatures' exteriors and the type and amount of bacteria within them. The final step of sorting the soil, vegetation, and biomass was the tide that swept unimpeded across the globe, allowing the settling of sediment and decayed animals and plants according to their densities within the formed layers, seemingly creating the geological column.

Where does this leave the evolutionists who believe that the soil accumulated over hundreds of millions of years? Evolution requires billions of years to allow enough time for mutations of the DNA to randomly form new genetic code for new functions and new kinds of creatures. This results in evolutionists defending their theories at all cost, even turning a blind eye to the scientific method and worthy hypotheses if that construct interferes with the amount of time necessary for evolution. This leads to a faith-based hypothesis and leaves the realm of science.

Remember that the scientific method says that if a hypothesis is proven wrong, one should start all over with a new hypothesis, yet evolutionists still adhere to soil layers being deposited over hundreds of millions of years and look past the observable evidence.

We all make mistakes, and when someone points out a mistake, a wise person accepts the correction and grows in knowledge; a fool rejects the correction and mocks the sender of truth and thinks they know everything already.

Chapter Summary: The smooth layers of the crust of the earth around the globe reveal another violation of evolutionary constructs and reveal the Bible record to again be in harmony with observable evidence. The layers are smooth without commingling from erosion, so this is unmistakable evidence that the soil was deposited quickly, not over hundreds of millions of years.

Chapter 22
Transitional Fossils

Within the layers of the crust, trillions of fossils exist. They are not as rare as you may think. What is rare and does not exist is a transitional fossil demonstrating a change of kind. Every dead fossil shows that something died, not something that passed on genetic information. Evolutionists say they believe in evolution because of the preponderance of evidence in the fossils. But the fossil record does not support evolution at all; it merely records that something died and was quickly covered up in a brief moment in time and not over millions of years. The only things that support evolution are the interpretations of the fossils and the clay models that are created to represent what the archeologist's imagines their find looked like, once upon a time. However, any bone fossil found in the dirt only tells us that a creature died, and it is speculation to suggest that any of their genetic information was passed on. *Photo credit: www.livescience.com.*

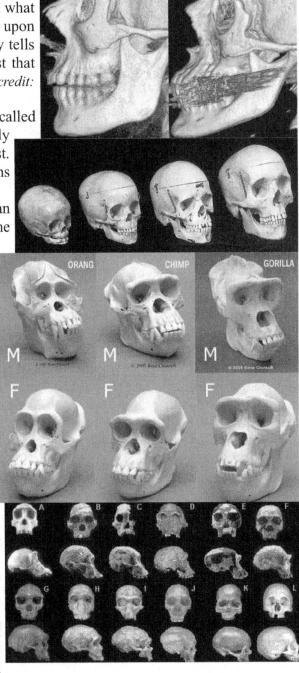

What about some of those pesky so-called evolutionary missing link discoveries that supposedly prove evolution and debunk creation? They do not exist. They are either falsified findings or misinterpretations because of a lack of knowledge.

When an evolutionist show you a skull of an alleged transitional fossil, ask them the gender of the skull, the age of the decedent at death, what strata was the fossil found in, and what percentage of the skull is fabricated to fit the evolutionary ideology? Why are these questions important?

When a creature is growing, differences exist in the cranial volume, skull size, and distinguishing features at varying ages of development. Keep in mind that though the human body stops growing vertically at a certain age, the facial bones never stop developing. As we age, the jaw protrudes, the eye brow ridges protrude, and so forth. We are able to see these developmental differences from a 20 year old face from a 70 year old face. How much more of a difference do you suppose we could visualize from someone living 900+ years, as in prior to the Flood. For this reason, knowing that the decedent was an adult is not sufficient, one must know the **age of the decedent**. *Photo credit: www.clinicalgate.com.*

The other critical bit of information is the **gender**. Differences exist in the overall size, cranial volume, and external features of the skull between the genders. Males have a larger skull, larger cranial volume, and more muscle attachments, which results in larger protuberances for those origin and insertion locations. Look carefully at the image of three primates (orangutan, chimp, and gorilla), and notice the differences between the male and female.

It is also important to know what **strata** the fossil was found in because according to evolutionary doctrine, the strata was deposited in lock-step with evolution. Thus, if an evolutionist won't tell you the strata the skull was found in, or no one knows, it is dubious to place skulls according to philosophical order. Lastly, it is vital to know what **percentage** of the skull was fabricated by an artist. If one adds putty to suit their preconceived philosophical views, and the public is unaware that the artists started with only a tooth, or a clavicle, or a jaw bone, and so forth, that is deceitful. *Image credit: www.theistic-evolution.com.*

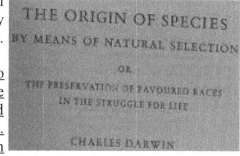

Review: Placing skull fossils in philosophical order to suit one's own preconceived ideology, without knowing the gender, age of the decedent, the strata the skull was found, and the percentage of artistic liberty taken by the artist is reckless. When an evolutionist shows you skull fossils placed in philosophical order to preach evolution, now you know why to question the age of the decedent, the gender, the strata depth, and the percentage of artist's putty.

Over the last 120 years or so, multiple alleged discoveries occurred that turned out to be fabrications, forgeries, errors in interpretations, and so forth. These hoaxes are on the same level as someone seeing tears coming out of the eyes of a Mary statue or someone allegedly seeing blood coming out of the thorny crown or the wrist of a Jesus statue. These are all lumped together as falsified hoaxes from fanatical zealots and dishonest people. Evolutionists that have falsified their archeological digs to say they found the missing link to prove evolution should be equally lumped together with those religious fanatics that falsify information. Let us look at a few falsified claims that set the world on fire for several decades; some textbooks still teach the falsified information.

Haeckel's embryo drawings: *Image credit: Wikipedia.org, Embryo drawing, a copy of the original.*
The first one is German scientist and atheist Ernst Haeckel, who successfully duped the masses in 1860 by falsifying embryo drawings of different species. He drew embryos of eight different creatures and drew them more similarly than they are in reality to make it appear that evolution is true and that we all evolved from similar ancestors. He drew a fish, salamander, tortoise, chick, hog, calf, rabbit, and human. All eight were drawn with nearly the identical heads, midsections (with gill slit folds), and tails. Haeckel drew the embryos in three stages of development. This set the world ablaze and fast-tracked the acceptance of evolution. His drawings were touted as gospel truth, and even though they were discovered as a lie, his fraudulent drawings eventually found their way into all school biology textbooks, where they still reside. They have duped the world for nearly 100 years. The folds in the skin of the embryos are not vestigial gill slits that have evolved away; they are folds in the skin that represent different neurological anatomy. *Image credit: yoursincerefriend.blogspot.com, by Harun Yahya.*

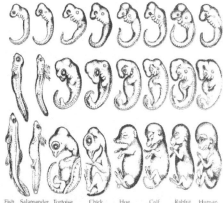

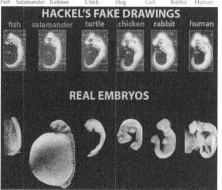

Noted evolutionist Stephen Gould had this to say about Ernst Haeckel's drawing[94]:

> Haeckel's forceful . . . books appeared in all major languages, and surely exerted more influence than the works of any other scientist, including Darwin . . . in

---

94 Natural History, March, 2000.

convincing people throughout the world about . . . evolution . . . Haeckel had exaggerated the similarities [between embryos of different species] by idealizations and omissions. He also, in some case—in a procedure that can only be called fraudulent—simply copied the same figure over and over again . . . Haeckel's drawings, despite their noted inaccuracies, entered into the most impenetrable and permanent of all quasi-scientific literatures[sic]: standard student textbooks of biology.

One of the fathers of evolution falsified information to push evolution on the public, and it worked. Imagine the outcry today if Jesus falsified His information to push God the Father. The Bible would be rejected. Combine this with the notion that the early fathers of evolution, including Darwin, erroneously thought the cell to be a simple protoplasm of ooze, and all that was needed for the cell to form was a crystallizing effect of complex chemicals to form the first single-cell amoeba. Darwin believed that a crystallization process was how the first living organism evolved from nonliving material because he did not understand the cell. They gravely wrong. Cells are immensely complex. Imagine if Jesus lacked knowledge about things He professed to be an expert on, and based whole theories on a completely wrong foundation as Darwin, the father of evolution did. Then the entire Bible would be completely rejected.

Also, the early fathers of evolution thought that some species of humans had evolved to a greater degree than other species of humans and that some humans were just barely past evolving from primates, while superior white people had evolved faster than their black human counterparts. Why on earth would any black person accept this lie, and for that matter, why would any God-fearing believer accept a hypothesis that suggests at its origins that one race was inferior to another by some evolutionary process. Imagine if Jesus was a racist as Darwin was; the implication is that the entire constructs of the Bible would be rejected. The Bible states that God is the Father of all, except the Nephilim, they come from demons. The races stem from the Tower of Babel (Gen. 10), from which God scattered them around the globe. But this is not so according to racist Thomas Huxley (an evolutionary forefather), who wrote, "No rational man, cognizant of the facts, that the average negro is the equal . . . of the white man."[95] **Charles Darwin** was so blinded by his racism that he titled one book, "The Origin of Species by Means of Natural Selection, or the Preservation of Favoured Races in the Struggle for Life." Very few people have heard the full title, most only hear it titled "The Origin of Species." Darwin wrote,

> At some future period . . . the civilized races of man will almost certainly exterminate and replace throughout the world the savage races. At the same time the anthropomorphous apes . . . will no doubt be exterminated. The break will be rendered wider, for it will intervene between man in a more civilized state, as we may hope, than the Caucasian, and some ape as low as a baboon, instead of as at present between the negro or Australian and the gorilla.[96]

Charles Darwin was certain that the white man would widen the evolutionary gap by exterminating the black man and the gorilla, so that the evolutionary gap between the white man and the next lower species would widen to the baboon. This list of racist quotes continues with Henry Fairfield (another evolutionary forefather): "The standard of intelligence of the average adult Negro is similar to that of the eleven-year-old-youth of the Homo sapiens."[97] Why would a woman believe in a man-made hypothesis that was fathered by sexist men who said,

> The chief distinction in the intellectual powers of the two sexes is shown by man attaining to a higher eminence, in whatever he takes up, than woman can attain—whether requiring deep

---

95 Thomas Huxley, Lay Sermons, Addresses and Reviews, New York: Appleton, 1871, p 20.
96 Charles Darwin, The Descent of Man, New York, 1874, pg 178.
97 The President of American Natural History Board, Henry Fairfield, Natural History, Jan 1926 issue, reprint 1980, p129.

thought, reason, or imagination, or merely the use of the senses and hands.[98]

The Bible states that all, including members of both genders, are to submit to everyone (Ephesians 5:21), and both male and female were created in the image of God (Gen. 1:27), and both genders are equally loved by God, and both genders may enter heaven (John 3:16). Imagine if Jesus was a sexist like Darwin, the father of evolution. The implication is that the entire Bible would be rejected.

This is not attacking an evolutionist's embarrassing mistakes. We have all made errors, but that is not the issue. When the ones committing acts of racism and sexism, expressing a lack of knowledge about the complexity of the cell, perpetrating fraud, and making gross misinterpretations happen to be the fathers of the evolutionary hypothesis, and they furthered their propaganda on the public because of fraud, deception, and misinterpretations, this is a severe indictment on the premises built by them. Although alleged Christians have committed acts of immorality, the Bible remains unchanged. It is not the forefather of Christianity (Jesus) committing these acts of immorality; it is the forefathers of evolution committing these sins. Thus, criticism of the racism, sexism, fraud, deceptions, and lack of knowledge, is valid and worthy criticism of evolution because the forefathers used those things to establish evolution. The converse against the Bible is equally true; if you find such things against God, then render just criticism against the Bible built on God, if you cannot find such things against God, then be silent against the Bible. *Image credit: Wikipedia.org. Neural development in humans.*

The truth about the folds in the embryo skin is that they have zero to do with gills from a fish; they are a development of the brain and nervous system, with the following functions: (1) olfactory, (2) optic, (3) oculomotor, (4) trochlear, (5) trigeminal sensory, (6) trigeminal motor, (7) abducens, (8) facial, (9) vestibulocochlear, (10) glossopharyngeal, (11) vagus, (12) cranial accessory, (13) spinal accessory, (14) hypoglossal, and (15) cervical n. I,II,III,IV.[99] It is easy to see that the folds have absolutely zero to do with gills.

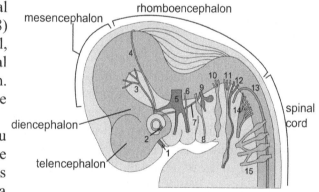

Do not let evolutionists continue to fool you by citing Haeckel's fraud. Evolutionists may continue to believe the brachial clefts are vestigial gill slits from ancestral fishes, but that is not science, that is a faith-based belief.

Review: Ernst Haeckel falsified his embryo drawings a 100 years ago and he has duped the world in fast-tracking the evolutionary acceptance. The early fathers of evolution were in error and thought a cell was a simple ooze of protoplasm, and life only needed to crystallize into forming the first self-replicating cell. The early fathers of evolution built the foundation of evolution based on lacking knowledge of the cell, racism, sexism, and forgery. If Jesus had done any one of those things, the Bible would be rejected. But instead of rejecting evolution because the forefather's prejudices and errors, evolutionists continue the ruse.

Piltdown Man:

A grand scale paleoanthropological hoax that surfaced to force the acceptance of evolution occurred with the alleged discovery of the missing link that bridged the fossil record of when primates evolved into humans. This discovery was called "Piltdown Man" and was found in East Sussex England, 1912. How long did this lie permeate academia? Until 1953—it took 41 years for it to be exposed as a forgery. Apparently, this archeologist took a jawbone of an old orangutan and combined it with a human cranium; the fragments were chemically stained to artificially age them, and the teeth were filed

98 Charles Darwin, *The Descent of Man*, New York, 1874, pg. 326.
99 Wikipedia.org, Neural development in humans, embryo nervous system.

down to add to the ruse.[100] It was a blatant lie. How many weak-minded people threw away their Bibles to accept this tall tale?

One of the notorious names involved in perpetrating the Piltdown man farce was Grafton Smith, the one who trained Dr. Black, who allegedly found "Peking Man."

Nebraska Man:

This was another scheme to artificially advance the cause of evolution and dupe the masses. The archeologist proclaimed to have found the missing evolutionary link in the fossil record that proves mankind evolved from primates. This wile was based on a single tooth—that's right, one single tooth—and from that, a whole theory supporting evolution was extrapolated that man evolved from an ape. The tooth was examined in 1922. *Photo credit: Wikipedia/Nebraska man.*

Later, in 1926, additional inquiries at the dig site occurred, and another identical tooth was discovered from the jawbone of a pig,[101] and the claim was retracted. But the damage was done. Evolutionists got their headline. How many heard the declaration and never heard the retraction? Often, the cover story is the proclamation, and the retraction is buried in another paper many years later. It makes one wonder how many people threw away their Bibles from this false tale.

How many drawings and even full-scale models cleverly created by some imaginative evolutionist to bolster their claim from this one tooth still appear in museums and textbooks to deceive the masses.

Java Man:

Dutch evolutionist Eugene Dubois set out to find the missing link in the fossil record that connected the evolutionary chain and prove man evolved from apes, such as monkeys, chimpanzees, and others. This was his mission; this is what he earnestly believed. This is important to know because he did not go to Java Island to search out different flowers and accidentally stumble upon this discovery. No, this was premeditated; in fact, he was a pupil of Ernst Haeckel, who was exposed for falsifying his infamous embryo drawings. *Photo credit: Wikipedia/Java man.*

In 1891, Dubois proclaimed to have found a transitional fossil that proved humans evolved from ape ancestors. The location of Dubois' alleged discovery was on the island of Java, Indonesia. He "found" a tooth, a skullcap, and a femur. However, it was not Dubois that was at the dig site. He was situated comfortably at headquarters and corresponded via written letters and took an occasional horseback ride to the dig site. When workers found bones, they brought those items to Dubois, who was off site, and he made the leap of faith that the bones were from the same dig site and connected each together. Dubois did not discover any of the bones attributed to him; nor did he see the bones in the dig site. The bones were brought to him at his headquarters, yet with his preconceived bias established, he determined that the bones were the "missing link," ignoring the possibility that the bones were from different dig holes and different layer levels. Compounding the problem, no geologist was on the site and no objective set of eyes to oversee the operation, just the subjective bias of Dubois labeling the specimens from off site. He already had his mind made up before he even went to Java as to what he would find. Is this a case of Dubois just misinterpreting the evidence or something more sinister? Considering that he concealed evidence to bolster his claim. For example, other bones were also found at the dig site by the workers, such as two skull caps, but he kept them away from public viewing and hidden because they were human, and that did not fit his timeline. And he stopped

100 Wikipedia, Piltdown Man.
101 Wikipedia, Nebraska man.

allowing others to examine his Java fossils, which meant it was his word alone, and no objective analysis by opponents of his view was allowed.[102]

Dubois argued that the specimen was the missing link and called it Anthropopithecus erectus, which is a type of specimen from Homo erectus, and declared an estimated 700,000 years of age.[103] His claim set the world on fire with the debate of evolution versus the Bible. Almost 80 books were written about this "discovery" in less than 10 years time. When the link grew tenuous, and because many knew this was not the missing link from apes to humans, many evolutionists shifted gears and just said that Java man was a primitive side branch of the evolving process or evolutionary tree of life, but they still held tight to their evolutionary views.

The femur was found a full year later about 40–50 feet away from the original skullcap. Dubois' failure to document the exact soil layer and dig site disqualifies his claim.[104] Many who examined the bones became skeptical of his claim, saying that "this creature was an animal, a giant gibbon, in fact. The thigh bones has not the slightest connection with the skull."[105] Dubois went into seclusion when skepticism rose, and when a German team of 75 researches went to Java Island to corroborate his claim, he refused to help. The team went to the alleged original dig site and unearthed bountiful amounts of soil and found 43 crates worth of bone fragments that were labeled and sent off to Germany for analysis. A geologist on the expedition refuted Dubois' claim and determined that his Homo erectus claim was a modern human fossil and regular primate fossil combined and not a missing link.[106]

Scientists seek truth, but when preconceived biases interfere with their judgment, objectivity is lost, and hypotheses are formed from subjectivity. Scientists are supposed to form theories based on observation and tests. But Dubois formed his beliefs prior to going to the island of Java, and either his preconceived bias clouded his judgment, or he took matters in his own hands and orchestrated a lie to support his belief system in an attempt to prove evolution correct and by default the Bible wrong. Only God knows. Compounding the problem, Dubois went on a lecturing tour to teach others about the proof of evolution. Sadly, today evolutionists cite Java Man as their evidence for evolution, and Java Man is credited as the first-ever discovered missing link by evolutionists, even though it was misleading to combine different dig site bone fragments as one species and ignore human fragments in the same dig site because they did not fit the timeline. The bottom line is that Java Man is not a missing link or a transitional fossil.

Peking Man:

Evolutionist Dr. Davidson Black did most of the studies in Beijing, China, until his death in 1934, and then Franz Weidenreich took over shortly after that. It is important to know something about the person who makes the claim of finding the missing link in the fossil record that supports the notion that humans evolved from primates. It is not that Dr. Black was out digging for seeds and happened to stumble upon this discovery; no, he had an agenda, a mission to prove evolution. He was a pupil of Grafton Smith, who was a known evolutionist and involved in the Piltdown Man fraud. Dr. Black already had his mind made up and was looking for bones to prove his beliefs.

The digs first find was a single tooth. After examining the tooth, Dr. Black concluded that it was two million years old and that it had likely come from a new and separate genus of man. He named the alleged new genus Sinanthropus pekinensis, which means "Chinese man from Peking."[107] Really, a separate genus of man, from a single tooth allegedly two million years ago? You can tell his beliefs were dictating his interpretations, just like evolutionists do today. In total, the site yielded 40 specimens and was a success for finding things that had once lived and had died.

102 Hank Hanegraaff, The Face That Demonstrates The Farce Of Evolution, 1998, pp. 50–52.
103 Wikipedia, Java man.
104 Hank Hanegraaff, The Face That Demonstrates the Farce of Evolution, 1998, pp. 50–52.
105 Wendt, Herbert, From Ape to Adam. New York: Bobbs-Merrill, 1972, P168.
106 CreationWiki.org/Java man.
107 Rahcael Bell, Dragon Bones: The mystery of the Peking Man.

The specimens were called Peking Man, though they had roman numerals to differentiate between them. The dates the specimens were discovered ranged from 1923–40, with the actual Peking Man being found in 1929, which was a skull cap in Beijing, China. A skull cap is the top portion or fragment of a skull. Peking Man was heralded as a missing link, which is a transitional fossil allegedly proving that mankind evolved from chimpanzees or monkeys (apes). As war broke out in WW2, the fossils were lost, and the claims were never verified by an objective team. The bones that were found were classified as Homo erectus, and even though they have been lost for almost 80 years, they have recently (March 2009) been aged at 750,000 years old,[108] based on notes and alleged plaster casts taken of the skull caps just prior to their timely demise. The accuracy of dating something that has been lost since the outbreak of WW2 is highly suspect at best, and basing them on casts that are not assured to be accurate copies or modified fabrications is highly suspect. Think of the remarkable forethought to make casts of a couple skull caps just prior to losing all the specimens a couple of days later; it is a bit coincidental. The fact is, no one will ever know the truth of what happened to the Peking Man or what it really looked like because the originals are gone, and with only one plaster cast of the specimen, we are not assured of its accuracy or if there was any modification to the cast. But imaginative evolutionists still created full-scale models of Peking Man for museums, and drawings of Peking Man litter the textbooks to further teach the masses about evolution.

Allegedly, the dig site found both human and ape bone fragments. A likely scenario to explain why the ape skulls are broken and fragmented is that ancient Chinese humans hunted and ate the apes. Another possibility is that both humans and apes were living relatively near each other, and when the global flood occurred, they were killed by water and debris fragmented their skeletal structures. Then, with the turbulent waters, they settled down together.

Orce Man:
This discovery was made in southern Spain in a town called Orce in 1982. It was proclaimed to be the oldest fossilized human remain ever found in Europe. This skull fragment was said to be a young 17-year-old male from around 900,000 to 1.6 million years ago. Evolutionists created drawings of what this person looked like, and of course they made him look like a transitional person halfway between an ape and a human. With the short brow and prolonged slanted jaw, it was very typical evolutionary propaganda stuff.

Now, when they say they found a skull fragment, they literally are talking about a fragment that is 3–4 inches in diameter and almost circular; we are not talking about a full skull or a complete bone of the skull. Extrapolating a story out of a bone fragment is not typical of honest evolutionist, but objectivity is strained to its limits when preconceived biases accompany well-meaning evolutionary archeologist on dig sites. Earlier, we talked about Dr. Black interpreting a single tooth and claiming it was an entire new species of a transitional hominid. That's the kind of loose claim pulled here; a skull fragment smaller than the palm of a hand and a hypothesis spun the size of Texas comes out of it that supports the preconceived beliefs already entrenched before the excavator even grabs a shovel. Then the unknowing masses go to a museum, and they see a fully developed skull or a fully developed face, or a full-scale model of an alleged Homo habilis or alleged Homo erectus, not knowing these fabrications are based off a single tooth or small bone fragment or falsely combined bones from multiple sites from different species to form one transitional species.

Dr. Duane Gish has a critical and devastating review of the evidence and logic that debunks the Orce man claim and reduces the claim to a young donkey's skull fragment, not human, and exposes the ridiculousness of basing a fictional tale from one skull fragment.[109]

Sahabi fossil:

---

108 Paul Rincon, March 11, 2009. "'Peking Man' Old than thought."
109 Duane Gish, "Evolution: The Fossils Still Say No!"

This is a collarbone discovered by Noel Boaz in the Libyan desert in 1979. Mr. Boaz claimed that this clavicle belonged to a primitive ape-man who lived around five million years ago. It is claimed as the oldest "ape-man" fossil in the world. He claimed that this ape-man walked upright. All this was from one bone? Again, this was an entire story extrapolated from one bone, and a presumptuous proclamation of five million years of age.

As it turns out, when objective analysis was performed on the alleged missing link, this "collarbone," was not "S" shaped like normal collar bones; no, it was "C" shaped like a rib and turned out to be the rib of a dolphin.[110]

Neanderthal Man, "The Old Man of La Chapelle:"
This discovery was made in 1908 in La Chapelle-aux-Saints, France. The bones of this specimen included a skull, jaw, most of the vertebra, several ribs, most of the long bones of upper and lower extremities, and some bones of the hands and feet.[111] Now here is the problem: the one who made the discovery wanted to find fossil evidence of evolution, so upon proclaiming to the public what he had found, he declared it to be a primitive creature about 60,000 years old and a transitional stage between primates and modern humans. When a model was made of what this specimen looked like, they made him look like a transitional being between gorilla and human to support evolution as much as possible. How many people bought this claim and the fabricated model of what this being resembled? This is unknown, but what is known is that this misinterpretation went on from 1908 until 1957, when an independent review of the fossil occurred. Over 40 years of misleading the masses occurred.

According to Dr. Rudolf Virchow, a top scientist from Germany who laid the foundation for modern pathology, studied the evidence and determined that "Neanderthal Man" was a feeble Homo sapien (just a human being), who had a head injury that disfigured his skull, deformities, arthritic conditions, and rickets.[112] Neanderthal Man was a really old man who had lived a long life. Almost all his teeth had fallen out, and regrowth of the mandible and maxilla had already set in as though there was a decade of eating food without teeth. Additionally, and here is the kicker, this person had very severe osteoarthritis. All the alleged changes in the bone structure that were associated to evolutionary modifications of the skeletal system were merely severe deformities from arthritic changes.[113] Nothing evolutionary at all, but if you go to an evolutionary museum, you will read all the "facts" about the missing links and see full-scale fabrications from a bone fragment.[114] In fact, the ability for the bone to adapt to variances of stimuli with arthritic changes is based on encoded DNA (adaptation), not variances in the bone from external stimuli results in enhanced DNA information (evolution). It is the preexisting DNA information that results in the body's attempt to stabilize a damaged joint with traction spurs, schlerotic changes, and joint fusing—which are arthritic conditions. The impairment of function does not add functional information to DNA code for any future new function or new kind of creature as evolution proclaims. This "Old Man of La Chapelle-aux-Saints" is not a stage in the transition from primates to modern humans, but a human being with a severe arthritic condition, which is adaptation.

Two modern day scientist, Dr. Straus, an anatomists from John Hopkins University, and Dr. Cave of St. Bartholomew's Hospital Medical College, reexamined these bones of Neanderthal Man in 1957. They concluded that Dr. Rudolf Virchow's finding were correct, and they affirmed his findings that Neanderthal Man was not a transitional fossil, was not a missing link, but was an arthritic old man, with a head injury and subsequent deformity, and rickets.[115] Addressing the arthritic condition of the "Old Man" does not give an explanation for Neanderthal. While humans age, their facial bones

---

110 I. Anderson, "Humanoid Collarbone Exposed as Dolphin's rib," *New Scientist*, April 28, 1983, p. 199.
111 La Chapelle-aux-Saints, "The Old man," Wikipedia.
112 Wikipedia, Rudolf Virchow, MD.
113 Evolutionisntscience.wordpress.com/evolution-frauds/.
114 Smithsonian, National Museum of Natural History, "What does it mean to be human?" Human Origins.
115 Creationism.org/books/TaylorMindsMe/TaylorMMh08.htm.

continue to develop. The Bible records that human beings used to live 900+ years before the Flood. This would have allowed for pronounced eyebrow ridges and jaws. The interpretation from the evidence is where things go haywire, preconceived beliefs of evolution dictate the interpretation. Neanderthal Man is not a transitional fossil, he was a larger human. A quick way to identify the skull is based on cranial capacity. The entire fossil record captured life when they were larger than their ancestors today. Neanderthal had a cranial volume of 1,600cc, today, our cranial volume has reduced to 1,200cc to 1,350cc, dependent upon male or female, this is a match for human ancestor. In addition, the old man of La Chapelle has 23 chromosomes just like you and I. Conversely, all primates, chimps, gorillas, and orangutans, have 24 chromosomes. **Neanderthal was just a larger human.**

Homo naledi:

The latest alleged transitional fossil is the discovery of Homo naledi in a South African cave. By now you should know that every creature in the fossil record is of a creature that was once larger and had to adapt to environmental changes resulting from the Flood. The Flood formed the oceans, which limits vegetation, which decreased O2 concentration, and the Flood decreased the buoyant force, which increased gravity, and all life lived shorter life spans and became smaller over time. Therefore, Homo naledi is a larger fossil of a smaller primate today, and not a smaller transitional fossil of the much larger human. Unfortunately, every evolutionists is blocked from accepting the logic because of their preconceived ideology that the Bible is wrong and we came from the created, rather than the Creator.

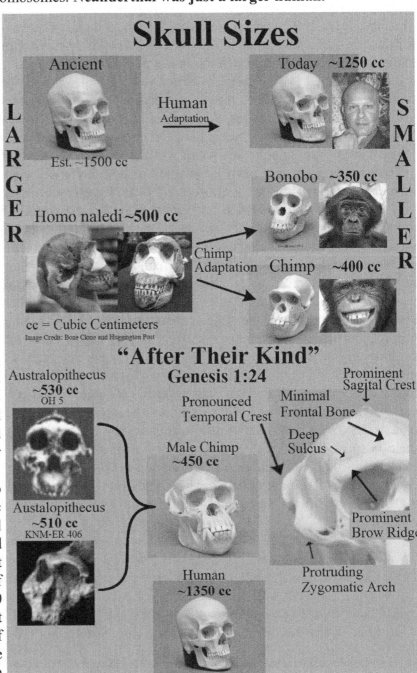

The cranial volume of Homo naledi (~500 cc = Cubic Centimeter) is close to the cranial capacity of the Bonobo (350 cc) and chimpanzee (400 cc) primates, but only ~40% of the cranial volume of humans (~1350 cc in men and 1150 cc in women). Since we know that life had to adapt to a reduction of O2 concentration in the atmosphere resulting from the Flood's formation of the oceans, the best interpretation of "Transitional" skull fossils is that they are transitional from the larger primates in the fossil record to a smaller primate today, and not a transitional fossil to the larger human kind.

152

<u>Australopithecus boisei: OH 5 (530 cc) and KNM-ER 406 (510 cc):</u>
All life was once larger and had to adapt to environmental changes resulting from the Flood. Those changes were a 1/3 reduction in O2 concentration, and a loss of the canopy that resulted in reduced buoyant force, which resulted in an increased net gravitational force. The empirical data that life was once larger is in the entire fossil record, and can be read in the Bible that there were once giants on the Earth.

Look at the image, notice the similar distinguishing features of Australopithecus and a male chimpanzee's skull (~450 cc). Specifically the prominent sagital crest, minimal frontal bone, deep brow ridge sulcus, pronounced temporal crest, protruding zygomatic arch, and prominent brow ridge. The entire fossil record illustrates adaptation (changes within their kind, called micro-evolution) and refutes evolution (changes to a different kind, called macro-evolution or Darwinian evolution).

<u>"Lucy," Australopithecus afarensis:</u>
Lucy was estimated to be 3.2 million years old and was discovered in Ethiopia in 1974. She consisted of an alleged bipedal upright gait. Countless models were fabricated to illustrate this missing link, and Lucy went into most of the museums and textbooks. The models made Lucy look like a chimp from the neck up, and a human female from the neck down, but hairy like a chimp and 3 feet, 7 inches tall. Evolutionary paleontologist Donald Johanson claimed that Lucy had 40% of a complete skeleton, but most of the bones were fragments. Some healthy skepticism exist regarding how wide-spread the bone fragments were from different dig sites scattered around the area, even as far away as 1.6 miles, and at different strata depths spanning 200 feet.[116] They find a bone fragment 1.6 miles away and conclude that this bone fragment belongs to that other bone fragments. Then, these excavators found a partial humerus in a different gully as well. Their excuse was that since none of the bones were duplicates, it had to be from one creature. Some evolutionists claim that Johanson found the bones much closer together and that when he said he found the knee 1.6 miles away that he was referencing a second knee. Look, even if the bones are found closer together, this is still not a problem for creationists. Why? Because the knee angle does not match a human knee, but matches a tree-limb walking creature, such as a gibbon. This does not prove evolution; it still takes the imagination of the evolutionists to spin the evidence to support their biased beliefs of what happened millions of years ago, which is not observable.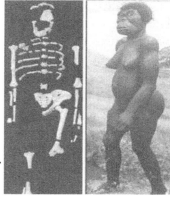

Donald Johanson said that the overwhelming subjectivity of wanting to find the missing link created a bias that he got tunnel vision. In his words, he said (Johanson and Edey, 1981, p. 257–258.),

> There is no such thing as a total lack of bias. I have it; everybody has it. The fossil hunter in the field has it. If he is interested in hippo teeth, that is what he is going to find, and that will bias his collection because he will walk right by other fossils without noticing them. . . . that is a healthy bias . . .other bias were not so healthy . . . there is a strong urge to learn more about where the human line started. If you are working back at around three million, as I was, that is very seductive, because you begin to get an idea that that is where Homo did start. You begin straining your eyes to find Homo traits in fossils of that age . . . Logical, maybe, but also biased. I was trying to jam evidence of dates into a pattern that would support conclusions about fossils which, on closer inspection, the fossils themselves would not sustain.[117]

I can sympathize with Johanson; we have all been there and done that on some level. However, that does not lessen the devastation that Lucy brought against truth. A lot of destruction against truth came

---

116 Wikipedia/Lucy, (Australopithecus).
117 Johanson and Edey, 1981, p. 257–258.

about from the forefathers of evolution, and their errors in understanding still permeates academia today. "Lucy" is not a transitional fossil or a missing link.

Authors Stern and Susman, who critiqued Lucy (American Journal of Physical Anthropology, May 2005), said, "There is no evidence that any extant primate has long, curved, heavily muscled hands and feet for any purpose other than to meet the demands of full or part–time arboreal life." Meaning Lucy has long curled hands and feet for tree climbing. In addition, Lucy has a locking mechanism in the wrists for knuckle walking, which humans do not have. A human knee has an angle of 9° genu-valgus, this allows us to walk upright without waddling from side to side to shift weight. However, a chimp and gorilla, both have a 0° genu-valgus, and this is why they waddle from side to side when they walk. So, the narrower the line for which a creature walks on, the greater the angle of genu-valgus to assist them walking on a narrow line. For example, to walk a tight-rope, it becomes easier with a greater knee angle, such as walking on tree limbs. That is exactly what Lucy has, a greater angle at 15° genu-valgus angle, which is ideal for being up in the trees walking on limbs. Thus, Lucy was unequivocally a knuckle walking, tree climbing, limb walking primate, and not a transitional fossil. Dr. David Menton goes into great details in "Lucy: She's No Lady!."

When Stern and Susman studied the pelvis of Lucy, they said, "The fact that the anterior portion of the iliac blade faces laterally in humans but not in chimpanzees is obvious. The marked resemblance of Lucy to the chimpanzee is equally obvious. . .It suggests to us that the mechanism of lateral pelvic balance during bipedalism was closer to that in apes than in humans."

Whenever an evolutionist wants to prove evolution, they will invariably cite Lucy as Exhibit A, yet Lucy is a spin on the evidence to support a paradigm. Lucy is just another primate and nothing more.

Coelacanth:

This was a fish that was thought by evolutionists to be the first fish that walked out of the ocean and eventually evolved to other creatures that evolved to humans. This fish was said to be extinct 70 million years ago, until a fisherman caught a Coelacanth near Madagascar in 1938.[118] This is just one of several misinterpretations based on preconceived doctrine by evolutionists that happens to be

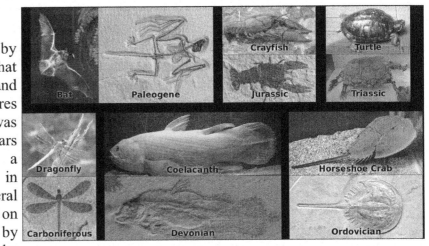

wrong. Many living alleged extinct creatures have not evolved in hundreds-of-millions-of-years in the minds of evolutionists. Why have they not evolved? Well, if you ask an evolutionist it is because they were caught in an evolutionary bubble. The obvious answer is that evolution is a myth, and these living creatures that have not changed in function or kind, but are just smaller than their ancestor, illustrates that evolution is a myth. *Image credit: www.sixdays.org.*

Archaeoraptor, Fake dinosaur-bird ancestor:

Evolutionists believe that dinosaurs evolved into birds because they have some similar aspects. Both lay eggs, have porous bones and about 20+ things I could add, such as clavicles, large orbits, teeth, a scapulae, and so on. But so do a lot of other animals. A missing link was needed to shore up this belief, as no evidence of a transitional fossil existed supporting this claim. Evolutionary archeologists needed to find a fossil proving this hypothesis and set out to find that elusive transitional fossil to support the

---

118 Gotquestions.org/fossil-record.html.

claim that dinosaurs evolved into birds. By the way, dinosaurs laid, as do reptiles today, a soft leathery egg. On the contrary, birds lay calcium-rich hard-shelled egg. From 20 feet away, it seems that they lay similar eggs, but up close they do not. *Photo credit: Wikipedia.org/archaeoraptor.*[119]

Saving the day for evolutionists was the discovery of a transitional fossil called Archaeoraptor that was "found" in China in 1997. The archaeoraptor was an extremely convincing fossil of a feathered dinosaur that researchers claimed was the missing link between birds and theropods. Published in *National Geographic* magazine, October 1999, this fossil was heralded as the missing link, proving dinosaurs evolved into birds. Oh, the tangled web we weave. In the year of publication in *National Geographic*, a CT scan was performed three months prior to publication, and the results indicated that the find could be a fraud, but decisions were made to keep that information silent. The lead team investigating this fossil, submitted a manuscript titled "A New Toothed Bird with a Dromaeosaur-like Tail" to the journal "Nature." The journal "Nature"

reported back that *National Geographic* was already prepared to lead with Archaeoraptor as the cover story and not enough time remained for peer review. Later, it was uncovered that Archaeoraptor was a fraud. Someone had glued three to five slabs of real fossils from different species together to make one alleged transitional missing link fossil to dupe the public.[120] After publication, *National Geographic* said that the fossil may have been a composite instead of calling it what it is, an outright fraud.

Let me help you put your mind at ease about whether dinosaurs evolved into birds; no, they did not. Even the exposure that Archaeoraptor was a fabrication will not persuade some evolutionists who are convinced and continue to use this fraud as a real transitional fossil. A fossil existed here, but it was a bird, not a transitional fossil. Do not get caught up in the fact that it has teeth; some birds have teeth, and some do not. Some reptiles have teeth, and some do not. Evolutionists proclaim that dinosaurs needed feathers, not to fly, but to keep warm. The evolutionary process of those feathers forming into wings evolved later, such as in archeopteryx. The traits of birds accumulated over time. A tree of evolution has the following steps: lobe-finned **fish**, primitive **amphibian**, most primitive **reptile**, an early archosaur (a "ruling reptile,") thecodont (primitive dinosaur), - another early dinosaur (a bipedal creature), a theropod dinosaur, another theropod dinosaur (one known to have "**protofeathers**"), a tetanuran dinosaur, a maniraptoran dinosaur (velociraptor), an avian dinosaur (most primitive known bird), Archaeoraptor (e.g., the above forged fossil), another avian dinosaur (i.e., another primitive bird) Confuciusornis, an advanced avian dinosaur (a neatly modern "enantiornithine" bird), a modern bird (pigeon), another modern bird (eagle), and so on. Therefore, birds are considered to be feathered dinosaurs. First off, all the above names are man-made, and none of the fossils come with labels. But let us look at protofeathers. *Photo credit: Wikipedia.*

Protofeathers are halo-like structures adjacent to a couple of reptile fossils that evolutionists interpret as burgeoning feathers. This accelerates evolutionists into believing that dinosaurs evolved into birds. Are there reptile fossils with "protofeathers" that represent the first stage of scaly reptiles having feathers? No. The fossils do not represent protofeathers—the pattern in the fossil may be from the scales fraying from the fossilization process, or from dinosaurs

---

119 MNN.COM, scientific hoaxes: archaeoraptor: Originally mentioned in *National Geographic* magazine.
120 Wikipedia.org/archaeoraptor.

that had some hair. During the fossilization process, the specimen undergoes tremendous pressure from the soil above, this causes the fraying patterns of the reptile's scales, and is not indicative of the beginning process of feathers. Since some reptiles today have hair in addition to scales, the fossils may be capturing this hair. This is because both hair, feathers, scales, nails, claws, horns, hooves, and so forth are made up of **keratin**. It is the DNA that determines the molecular shape of the keratin to determine the end product. The evidence does not indicate that reptiles evolved into birds. The Bible records birds were created before reptiles, and both came from the essence of God. Therefore, theistic evolutionists are calling the Bible wrong and proclaiming man's hypothesis of dinosaurs evolving into birds correct.

Unfortunately, the damage is done. Many people today believe dinosaurs evolved into birds and cite Archaeoraptor as proof of evolution. How many evolutionists became invigorated by this claim, and how many rejected the Bible as a result of this lie? I have talked to many theistic evolutionists and atheists who believe in evolution and cite fraudulent discoveries as proof. The evidence stands for all to view and judge for themselves. When you see a full-scale fabrication in a museum, do not assume that it is now fact because a museum has the information. Search out the evidence and see for yourselves what information or evidence was used to conclude an evolutionary link. Was it a single tooth that a whole theory was built upon? Was it bone fragments miles apart and at depths 200 feet different that led to a conclusion? Search for yourself, use your own mind, and do not rely on what others tell you.

Alleged Fusion of Chromosome 2:

Humans have 23 chromosomes, and all primates, such as chimps, gorillas, and orangutans have 24 chromosomes. This is a deal breaker. Researchers have studied the chromosome count of the alleged transitional fossils, and the chromosome count is important in the discussion of evolution. One would expect, since all life was once larger in the past, that the two largest skull fossils known as Neanderthal (cranial volume of 1600cc) and Denisovan fossil (cranial volume of 1800cc), which are both larger than the average human cranial volume today (~1350 cc in men and 1150 cc in women), that both the Neanderthal and Denisovan would have 23 chromosomes like us today, and they do. This establishes that they were just larger humans when oxygen concentration was once greater.

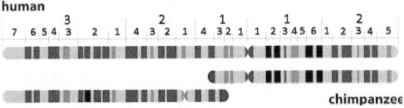

So how does an evolutionist handle this problem of humans having 23 chromosomes and chimps having 24 chromosomes? They contend that at some time in the past, date unknown, two chromosomes fused together to form one long chromosome for humans. The evidence that they use is called **apparent evidence**, which means that as something appears to be, so it is. That is the same evidentiary technique that the flat-earther's use.

From a distance the appearance of a fusion exist, but it is not evidence of a fusion because it is equally the same apparent evidence of a fission. That at some time in the past, date unknown, one long chromosome went through fission to form two smaller chromosomes for primates. In other words, no more evidence exist of a fusion than a fission. It is because of the evolutionist's belief system that the images of the two chromosomes supports their ideology of evolving from smaller chimps to larger humans. But again, that same technique of evidence is what flat earth believers use.

We have the capability and the technology to determine the chromosome count of all alleged transitional fossils, but no evidence is published regarding Homo naledi, Australopithecus, or other transitional fossil if they had 24 chromosomes as the chimps do today. The reason they will not publish this evidence is because it would undermine their claim. We would have confirmation that those alleged transitional fossils were just larger chimps. Just like they found out about Neanderthal and Denisovan were larger humans.

Also, we would have observed evidence today that evolution is still ongoing with some chimps having some evidence that their chromosome is fusing, and going from 24 to 23 in total. But none exists.

Another key factor in the discussion of the second chromosome alleged fusion. One would suspect that the human DNA adjacent to the location of the alleged fusion would have similar genetic information to the chimp. But they simply do not have similar coding on either side of the alleged fusion locus. The region surrounding the proclaimed fusion location was sequenced by Fan et al. (2002b), and it showed a large number of genes surrounding the alleged fusion sequence, all of which had no genetic match (synteny) to chimpanzee chromosomes 2A or 2B.

In conclusion, the lack of evidence beyond apparent evidence renders the discussion of an alleged fusion at chromosome 2 as fiction that only exists in the minds of those whose belief system starts with evolution. *Image Credit: Stephen M. Carr.*

Chapter Summary: Evolutionists can proclaim their belief, and they can shout louder than others and talk faster than others, but at the end of the day, their missing link fossils are either forgeries, misinterpretations, or misleading claims. From the fraud of Haeckel's embryo drawings, to Piltdown Man, to Nebraska Man, to Neanderthal man, and to Archaeoraptor, their claims of finding missing links that prove evolution, are wrong and only reveal biased beliefs that govern their objectivity. Claims come and go, yet the Bible remains unchanged and stands the test of time with the phrase that each kind (~Family) will produce "according to its kind." Both sides of the debate, creation and evolution, have admirable followers, and there have been forgeries, lies, and misinterpretations through the centuries on both sides, yet the Bible remains the same. You see, the Bible is not defined by followers. When a few wolves in sheep's clothing commit evil and hide behind the banner of Christianity, they are on their own and not following the Bible, which still stands as truth. But when an evolutionary forefather commits a forgery to build their doctrine upon, that is equivalent to Jesus committing evil to promote the Word of God. When Darwin builds a theory about spontaneous life from nonliving material because he has wrong information about the complexities of the cell, that would be equal to Jesus teaching error because He was lacking knowledge about biology. What the forefathers of evolution did to promote their hypothesis matters, just like it matters what Jesus did to authenticate the Bible. Human beings ever increase in intelligence, yet subjective bias can move the most honest evolutionist to misinterpret and force conclusions that support evolution.

Chapter 23
<u>Light</u>

The speed of light is 186,000 miles per second. This is incredibly fast, but considering the vast size of the universe, it still takes light a long time to traverse the galaxies and universe. The sun's light, though it is far from Earth at ~93 million miles, takes 8.3 minutes to reach us. Now, astrophysicists hypothesize that though the sun's light only takes ~eight minutes to reach the earth, those light particles took millions of years to reach the sun's surface from within the core. This is because it is believed that the sun consists of 91% hydrogen, 8.99% helium, and 0.01% carbon, oxygen, and so forth. Evolutionists argue that this is one reason that YECs are wrong, because when we see the sun's light, it is not just eight minutes old because that only considers the time for light to travel from the surface of the sun to earth. It is actually millions of years plus eight minutes old because that is how long it takes the light to travel from the sun's core to the surface to earth. *Image Credit: instructibles.com.*

How does a young universe hypothesis handle this? For one thing, the hypothesis that it takes light millions of years to traverse the sun's core is a hypothesis; it is not a proven fact. Even if this hypothesis is true, God did not created Adam and Eve as babies; He created them fully mature. Likewise, God created the sun fully developed, which means that immediately after the matter that would eventually form into the sun was created on the first day, it was spinning and coalescing matter together until the forming sun glowed hot on the middle of the first day of creation. By the fourth day of creation the sun coalesced enough matter that it ignited. The light emanating from the surface would be traveling to earth and not having to wait millions of years for light to leave the core. Therefore, since this occurred 6,000 to 10,000 years ago, we are currently viewing light that started just below the crust and worked its way to the surface and then to us from creation; we do not view light from the sun that is millions of years old and worked its way from the core. Adam and Eve viewed the same sunlight, however it was 6,000 years younger and they viewed the light through the filter of the canopy.

The Bible records that waters, specifically the "deep," which suggests salt water, was abundant in the small universe on the first day. And 2 Peter 3:5 states that the earth was made from water and through water, but Holman Christian Standard Bible and the Aramaic Bible in Plain English both interpret that both the heavens and the earth were made from the water and through the water. Thus, by means of the sun's spinning core of liquid metals (the battery in the image), this would cause the water, H2O, to separate by the process of **electrolysis** into H2 and O2, at a 2:1 quantity ratio. Given the immense pressure and heat, the diatoms of H2 and O2 converted to plasma. Therefore, since O2 is denser and heavier than H2, I contend that the outer plasma layers of the sun consists of a thicker, outer lighter layer of H2 plasma and a thinner, but heavier inner layer of O2 plasma. The implication is that with the inner, denser layer of O2 plasma, fusion does not need to only occur at the core and take millions of years to reach the surface, fusion may occur more distally and, thus, take less time to reach the earth.

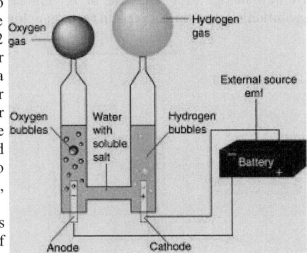

The process of electrolysis is a fast process that does not need much time. Once a spinning core of metals exist, this will generate a charge, and if H2O is in proximity to flowing electrons then electrolysis occurs. The greater the core, the greater the electromagnetism, the faster the process of electrolysis. Also, adding salt and other minerals speed up the process of electrolysis as well. The point being that the formation of the entire sun can be accomplished in four rotations of the earth, i.e. the fourth day of creation as written in Genesis.

What about other stars and other galaxies that are estimated to be billions of light-years away? A **light-year** is a measurement of distance and not time. A light year is the distance light travels in one year. By using triangulation calculations, we are only accurate up to 400 light-years for star distances; beyond that, we switch to utilizing starlight brightness to estimate the distance. This results in a compounding of the error rate to determine distances because we use nearby stars to determine the distance of stars farther away, which means the error rate increases the farther away the star is that is being measured. Just like a bowler that is throwing a ball down a lane, little errors at the beginning of the throw affect the accuracy down the distant lane; now imagine stretching the bowling lane out a couple thousand miles—those little errors at the beginning of the throw cause huge errors by the time the ball hits the pins. Therefore, potentially large errors exist in the number of light-years for the farthest distal galaxies. Notwithstanding, I think our universe is even larger than we can fathom. Do not get too caught up on reading that "x" galaxy is "n" distance away from the earth and the notion that this proves the universe is 14.6 billion years old. Why is this not a problem?

For one, humans are able to accelerate the speed of light impulses to 300 times the current velocity to 55.8 million miles per second.[121] Dr. Lijun Wang of the NEC Research Institute of Princeton has successfully increased the speed of light by 300 times. Just give mankind more time, and they will discover that they can speed up the velocity of light even greater. The implication is that the speed of light is dependent on the medium it traverses through. What was the medium for light during the beginning? No one knows. Therefore, no one should say that the speed of light we measure today was the same speed of light during the beginnings of the young universe. If the speed of light was faster during the beginning, the universe would be considerably younger.

To add to this theory, some scientists suggest that light has a decay element to its velocity. For example, in terms of the electromagnetism of planetary bodies, they have an ever-decreasing electromagnetic field. Dr. Troitskii wrote that "the speed of light could have been 10 million times faster in the past compared to what it is today."[122] This seems plausible, since everything in the universe is winding down and tending toward decay. Light could also tend toward decay and not be the only thing in the universe that is not decaying. This seems to solve the problem, but parts of other hypotheses are still applicable.

<u>**Review:**</u> <u>Light immediately started traversing from a star's surface instantly upon creation. Light did not have to travel from the core for a million years before the star began providing light. The speed of light can be accelerated 300 times current speed. If the speed of light has a decay process like everything else in the universe, this would certainly solve any problems with the distance across the universe.</u>

Measuring the distances of stars today does not mean they have always been at that distance. An unknown force is forcing the universe and each galaxy to expand away from each other at an ever-accelerated rate. This means that the universe is expanding faster and faster and not at a constant speed, indicating that the universe was significantly smaller in the past. This suggests that light did not have to travel as far to reach earth from its source because it started off closer in a much smaller universe. The Bible has several verses that discuss the universe being stretched out at creation and one that suggests that God continues to stretch out the universe. God "stretch<u>ed</u>" out the universe at creation on the second day of creation (Gen. 1:6–14-expanse, Isaiah 51:13). Also, according to Isaiah, God "stretch<u>es</u>" out the universe (40:22).

From the Biblical record, it appears that our solar system, though located at the edge of the Milky Way, could be near the center of the universe, as the Genesis record is from the perspective of Earth. This is just to illustrate that the earth is not at the edge of the universe, but is closer to the middle for distance purposes. In fact, cosmologists observe that an equal number of galaxies exist in every direction in the universe. The best way to shorten the distance for light to travel from one edge of the

121 Upheavals in Physics: The Speed of Light Exceeded, by Chuck Missler.
122 Dr. V. Troitskii, Astrophysics and Space Science, 139, 1987 p. 389–411.

universe to earth is to place Earth in the middle of the universe; now the distance is cut in half. But we still have billions of light-years to work with as YECs. How does a Big Bang theorist (basically all evolutionists) contend with the notion of the universe being 93 billion light years across, with only 14 billion years allotted from the Big Bang? Their solution is that the universe expanded faster than the speed of light[123] at the beginning, and then the expansion leveled off. This accelerated expansion is called **universal inflation**,[124] where the universe expanded by a "factor of 10^{90} in one billionth of a billionth of a billionth of a billionth of a second, according to" Lawrence Krauss, a theoretical physicist and cosmologist. This is like a grain of sand swelling larger than our sun and doing so faster than the speed of light. Creationists are interested in the notion of universal inflation, but we disagree when this rapid inflation occurred and the duration of the inflation. The hypothesis of inflation suggests that the universe has regions where it stops inflating, but it does not stop everywhere. Some evolutionists contend that after inflation expanded our universe, it continued on to expand another universe and another and is continuing to expand universes forever. This leads some cosmologists to accept a multiple universe hypothesis. The concept of universal inflation is the work of physicist Alan Guth. To a creationist, universal inflation, as far as expansion rates during "Let there be an expanse" and not multiple universes, fits well with creation and is simply a calling card that God expanded the universe on the second day of creation; evolutionary cosmologists accept the idea that the universe expanded faster than the speed of light, Creationists accept the same. Evolutionary cosmologists believe that so much happened during the first second of the beginning of the universe, the Big Bang, that Dr. Planck categorized the brevity of time in Planck units. Creationists view the universal inflation to have occurred at the beginning of the second day of creation, and lasted for several hours to a day. Utilizing an evolutionary construct of universal inflation and the Big Bang, creationists are successfully able to argue a young universe. A bit of irony there. What man has intended to explain away God by natural processes, winds up furthering support of a young universe. This seems a fulfillment of Romans 8:28, "And we know that God causes all things to work together for good to those who love God."

Since both sides accept the accelerated expansion hypothesis, where do they differ? It is in the amount of matter and volume of the universe "In the beginning" before the accelerated expansion, and the duration of the universal inflation. Evolutionist contend that zero matter existed because all the matter existed as energy and was compressed to a dot. Creationists contend that the first universal inflation occurred on the first day, and after God created the matter on the first day that the universe was compressed enough to allow water to exist in four forms (ice, liquid, gas, and plasma). God expanded the compressed universe during the second day of creation. This universal inflation concept is a plausible explanation of how we view stars from the earth in what appears to be a shorter period of time than what the average speed of light allows in a young universe hypothesis.

Creationists say that God created everything at a mature age free of defect, such as an adult Adam and Eve and tall trees, but this does not mean that God created anything with fictitious history. For example, Adam and Eve did not have belly buttons because they did not come from the womb. Tall trees did not have tree rings on the day they were created because they did not go through yearly growth to become as tall as skyscrapers. Nor did He fake a supernova explosion, so humans could perceive the remnant light. God did not create the universe to appear as though it had a fake history. God does not deceive and God cannot lie (Titus 1:2). God would not fake anything, and does not have too. The supernovas simply exploded when the universe was much smaller. Therefore, their light did not have to travel as far to reach Earth.

Another solution in physics that also adds to what we have talked about so far, and that is space travel. Physicists have theoretically shown that mankind may be able to travel 10 times the speed of light in a type of warp drive. The theory is based on the fact that space expands and contracts; if the space in front of a ship is contracted and the space behind the ship is expanded, a warp bubble is

---

123 Scienceline, How could the universe expand faster than the speed of light?
124 Alan Guth, Theoretical Physicist, 1979.

created, so it has been theoretically shown that we can move up to 10 times the speed of light. Well, if man may be able to do this with a ship (and mankind accepts that the universe expanded faster than the speed of light in the beginning), and if an expanding universe traveling faster than the speed of light also has the same warp bubble (with contracted space in front of light and expanded space behind the light), light could have traveled at least 10 times the current speed of light. If you are overwhelmed at this point, just know that scientists accept the notion that objects can travel 10 times faster than the speed of light. If light itself was that object, it too could have traveled faster than 186,000 miles per second. If you are still confused, think of a surfer riding a wave; this explains the concept of light traveling along the wave of universal expansion.

Review: The earth may very well be in the galaxy that is in the center of the universe. This cuts the distance light has to travel to reach Earth by half. Some scientists accept the notion that the universe expanded faster than the speed of light in the beginning. Since scientists believe that the universe already did this, it certainly should be acceptable for an all- powerful God to do the same. Since it has theoretically been shown that a spaceship can travel 10 times faster than the speed of light, what would limit God to do the same with light? Since man can accelerate the speed of light by 300 times, God can accelerate the speed of light.

Another aspect to the speed of light exist that is important. We have all been told that the speed of light is a constant at 186,000 miles per second (3 million meters/sec.) in a vacuum, but it turns out that the speed of light can be accelerated 300 times its speed, as discussed above, and now physicists are able to slow down the speed of light to less than the speed of a bicycle rider to a couple of miles per hour. Physicists are able to direct a laser beam of light into a medium called a Bose-Einstein condensate, and this medium is dense enough to slow the speed of light down to a couple miles per hour without any loss of information.[125] This is a reduction in the speed of light by a factor of 20 million.

Therefore, if light can be slowed down by a factor of 20 million and sped up by a factor of 300, an all-powerful God could perform the same acceleration of light. The creator of light may manipulate light how He seems fit. It is ironic that evolutionists use this light argument against YECs while touting the wonders of humanity at the same time for discovering that the speed of light can be slowed down or sped up, but then they limit the ability of God to do the same.

Evolutionists mock young universe creationists for not having enough time for light to travel such great distances in such short amounts of time, yet their own belief system only accounts for ~14 billion years of a universe that is ~93 billion light-years across and growing with each invention of a more powerful telescope. Think about that, mocking someone while indicting yourself at the same time. Several plausible explanations exist of how light has traveled so far in such a short amount of time for young universe creationists and for evolutionists. In the seemingly empty spaces between galaxies, vacuums in space are rarely found. Even the so-called empty spaces between planets and galaxies are hypothesized to be filled with dark energy. This dark energy pushes galaxies apart from each other at an ever-accelerating rate. This means that the distances measured today do not measure the distances that light had to travel in the past. Other theoretical discoveries have shown that light can jump from one locale to another in zero time; this is called a tunneling effect. The speed of light can be accelerated.

The Bible implicitly and at times explicitly records that God created matter in a small universe, with trillions of areas that immediately began coalescing (spinning and gathering matter together), until enough matter gathered together for magma to glow (light) at the middle of the first day. As a

---

125 Lene Vestergaard Hau, Harvard University, Using BEC to slow down light.

result, pressure built up until the Big Bangs, when God began stretching out the universe on the second day of creation and then enough coalescing matter ignited to form the sun and stars during the fourth day of creation. Immediately, light from the middle of the first day, from burgeoning stars, started traversing the distances of the small universal space. This scenario results in light traveling from the stars' initial location, which was much closer to the earth and not nearly as far as light has to travel today. Therefore, the light, from the burgeoning and coalescing stars that generated enough heat on the first day of creation to glow, had no problem traversing the entire universe because the universe was small. The light from stars that coalesced enough matter to ignite on the fourth day of creation, had no problem traversing the entire universe because the universe had just began expanding (Big Bangs) on the second day of creation. The distances today between the earth and all other galaxies is much greater than at creation. Really, this is a simple concept. The source of light was closer to the earth at creation than today, and the distance grows ever greater as galaxies move away from each other. In fact, Lawrence Krauss said, "In 5 billion years, the expansion of the universe will have progressed to the point where all other galaxies will have receded beyond detection. Indeed, they will be receding faster than the speed of light."

Evolutionists have accepted the idea that the galaxies are ever increasing in acceleration away from the earth, which corroborates that the universe was much smaller in the distant past, so light did not have to travel as far as it does today. But the easiest way to establish a young universe is with spiral galaxies because their spin rotation is too great for their gravitational force to maintain the appendages of the spiral galaxies. Therefore, every spiral galaxy has appendages because they have not been in existence long enough for the centripetal force generated from their spin to tear them apart. For this reason, evolutionists have to come up with an unseen force that is maintaining all the spiral galaxies together, called Dark energy.

The Bible declares that God finished forming the sun, moon, and stars on the fourth day and said, "Let them be for signs and for seasons and for days and years . . . and it was so" (Gen. 1:14–19). This indicates that God declared the stars were to be used as measurements of time immediately. If the stars were formed in the size of the universe today, it would take a stars' light ~four years (Alpha Centauri A and B) to millions of years to reach the earth, and God would have to wait for His Word to be fulfilled. But God supernaturally used natural means to cause light to traverse the small distances of space before creation was finished.

Dr. Raymond Chiao, a professor of physics (University of California at Berkeley), has reviewed Dr. Wang's work on accelerating light by 300 times and conducted his own experiments that indicate simultaneous multiple localities. Photons, the particles that constitute light, seem to apparently jump between two points separated by a barrier in what appears to be zero time. This is called **tunneling**. Should we be shocked by this? Was it not God who caused Philip to appear in one city sharing the gospel and then, poof, he was snatched away and appeared in another city (Acts 8:39–40)? Was it not God who snatched away Elijah (1 Kings 18:12) and Ezekiel (Ez 3:12,14, 8:3) and Paul (2 Cor. 12:1–6) to heaven and then back potentially without any time passing? Was it not God that walked through walls at His resurrection and just miraculously appears in front of Joshua (Joshua 5).

Why does mankind limit God's abilities? Yet, as mankind advances in knowledge, people are able to perform things that they use to mock God about. People mock believers who suggest that their God accelerated the speed of light for us to see distant stars, and now, humans can accelerate light. People mock believers who say that their God slowed the daylight in Joshua's day for a battle; now, humans can slow the speed of light down to a couple miles per hour. People mock believers that accept a young universe because of the distance of light, yet now, humans accept the idea that light can jump from one location to another location with a barrier in between in zero time. People mock believers that accept a young universe because of the distance of the universe, yet they accept the notion that the universe expanded faster than the speed of light near the time of the Big Bang. People mock believers who accept the idea that light from the stars was visible for Adam and Eve when the universe was smaller, yet now, scientists accept the notion that dark energy is pushing each galaxy away from each other at an ever-accelerating rate. People mock believers who accept that God created the sun, moon, and stars, yet some people believe that all the stars and planets and the universe evolved from nothing —that nothing exploded from nothing and formed everything. In this "nothing" at the beginning, at the Big Bang, allegedly no matter existed, but only abundant amounts of pure energy—and when the Big Bang exploded, that energy eventually formed into a more balanced state of matter and energy and then coalesced into the galaxies as we know it.

Science does not make it impossible to believe in God, but evolutionary scientists do try to explain away God with their theories, and it seems at times as an attempt to make it impossible to believe in God. In a sense, the more science we learn, the easier it will be for people to believe in God again. The old adage is that a little bit of knowledge can be dangerous; also, people perish for a lack of knowledge (Hosea 4:6). As knowledge increases, it is easier to see God. For example, some people mocked believers for accepting Jesus' virgin birth, yet mankind has achieved the same ability with artificial fertilization and cloning. The double standard continues. Atheistic evolutionists will mock all the way up until the heavens open up and meteors fall on them (Revelation 6:15–17) and in their time of trouble, they will say to God, "arise and save us." But God will say, "Where are your gods which you made for yourself? Let them arise, if they can save you" (Jeremiah 2:27–28).

Both evolutionists and creationists agree that the universe was smaller in the beginning. Using the notion of universal inflation, that the universe expanded faster than the speed of light in the beginning, a much smaller universe allows light to reach earth from the stars in a short amount of time, and as the universe expands.

Evolutionary astronomers believe and teach as fact, that it takes billions of years for stars to evolve from a red giant to a white dwarf. This is by faith alone, not science. In fact, ancient astronomers documented that Sirius—now a white dwarf—was redder than Mars. Paul Ackerman, author of "It's a Young World," listed the ancient astronomers that recorded Sirius as a red star: Egyptian hieroglyphs (2000 BC), Cicero (50 BC), Seneca, and Ptolemy (150 AD).

Chapter Summary: Since mankind can accelerate light and decelerate light, God—who created those clever humans and created the light in the first place—can accelerate light to a greater degree than lesser humans. Mankind has discovered that the universe is expanding at an ever-faster rate, which means that when God created the stars in the galaxies, they were closer to the earth, and their light did not have to travel as far to reach us. Scientists suggest that the universe expanded faster than the speed of light at one time and will do it again, which provides enough time for a large universe to have the light from the stars reach the earth when the universe was small. If the speed of light was a constant, both sides of the argument do not have enough time for light to reach the earth from such vast distances. Whether it is a young universe at 6,000 years or an old universe at ~14 billion years, neither has enough time for light to traverse a 93-billion-light-year universe based on light being constant. But the speed of light was not constant; nor was the expanding universe, there were times when both expanded faster than today's rates. Whatever theory evolutionists use to save their hypothesis and to explain how light sped up and the universal expansion was accelerated may also explain how God caused light to reach the earth so that we could see the light from the stars.

Chapter 24
Humans Lived 900+ Years and Adaptation from Origins

The Bible recorded that people from Adam to Noah lived 900+ years of age (Gen. 5:1–32). Then the global flood, and from then on, the length of life declined. Look at the life spans of the patriarchs:

Name	Life Span		
Adam	930	Ca. ~4004 BC, roughly ~6,000 years ago.	
Seth	912	born 130 years after Creation.	
Enos	905	born 235	"
Cainan	910	born 325	"
Mahalaleel	895	born 395	"
Jared	962	born 460	"
Enoch	365	born 622	" —God took him early to heaven, he never died.
Methuselah	969	born 687	"
Lamech	777	born 874	"
Noah	950	born 1056	" —at age 600 (Gen. 7:11)—**the catastrophic global flood.**
Shem	**600**	born 1556 years after Creation—at age 100—the Flood (ca. 2348 BC).	
Arphaxad	**438**	born 2 years after the Flood (Gen. 11:10–32).	
Salah	**433**	born 37	"
Eber	**464**	born 67	"
Peleg	**239**	born 101	" —In his days the earth was divided—the Tower of Babel.
Reu	**239**	born 131	" —around the time Job lived.
Serug	**230**	born 163	"
Nahor	**148**	born 193	"
Terah	**205**	born 222	"
Abraham	**175**	born 292	" (Gen. 25:7)—Noah dies 350 years after the Flood.
Isaac	**180**	born 392	" (Gen. 25:28)
Jacob	**147**	born 452	" (Gen. 25:26 and Gen. 47:28)
Joseph	**110**	born 543	" (Gen. 50:26)

Notice the enormous time that each person lived before the Flood. Then notice the gradual reduction of ages after the Flood as mankind adapted to the changes from the Flood. Not a sudden drop from 900+ years to 100 in one generation. What happened and how did the global flood reduce life's longevity, and is it possible for humans to live 900+ years of age?

Yes, it is possible. For one thing, no life was not cut short via disease or sickness. When Adam and Eve sinned (Gen. 3:23), the spiritual effects of their sin was immediate death. But the physical effects of their sin would take much longer to manifest. Such as the loss of the Garden of Eden, pain in childbirth, hard work for food, and so on. The physical effects from their sin would take generations to see, such as the judgment with a global flood and their distant heir (Jesus, Luke 3:23–38) having to die on the cross to pay the penalty for all sin. Sometimes the physical cost of our sin is not seen until later or even until our children bear the physical inheritance of our sins.

Also, no sicknesses from viruses, bacteria, or fungi that shorten lives because Adam's and Eve's immune system was working at optimum efficiency. No mauling from animals to shorten one's life. All animals, fish, and birds were herbivores (Gen. 1:29, 30). Yes, predators lived at that time, but they had not disobeyed God's command to only eat vegetation. No food poisoning existed to make one sick and die because they simply plucked ripe fruit and nuts off the trees in the Garden of Eden. Any fruit that fell to the ground and had too much bacteria in it, would be accompanied with the normal discoloration and odor associated with any fruit that has too much bacteria. Yes, bacteria, viruses, and fungi existed, but potentially harmful strains had not yet adapted to external stimuli, such as high-energy rays from space, and internal stimuli, such as sin. All that God made was very good (Gen. 1:31).

In addition, the oxygen concentration was 50% higher than today. This caused life to thrive. Also, the effects of gravity were reduced by ~20% because of the buoyant force from the canopy that hovered around the atmosphere before the Flood. Therefore, less strain on the cardiovascular system to circulate blood throughout the body, which prolongs life.

No obesity with early humans. How? No fast food, no soda, no fried food, no processed food, no canned food, no candy, no ice cream, and so on. People just ate natural fruit, vegetables, nuts, and grains. This meant that life was not cut short from maladies associated with diet.

All the above evidence is fine and dandy, but the reality is that if a person lives by the above dietary regiment today and is free from diseases, accidents, and the like, they still would not live 900+ years. Why? Some argue that God set the boundary of life expectancy to be 120 years. They will cite Gen. 6:3: "His days shall be one hundred and twenty years." But this cannot be correct because no one is recorded as dying at 120 years in the Bible. The best interpretation is that God gave mankind a warning to repent, for in 120 years judgment was coming; the Flood. God mostly uses natural means to carry out His judgment. As a result of the Flood, mankind's life expectancy gradually decreased from 900+ to around 90 years. How? The Flood significantly covered a bunch of land that once produced oxygen, so this physically reduced oxygen production and reduced the oxygen concentration over time. Life is dependent upon oxygen, so with reduced oxygen, life does not thrive as it once did. The Flood removed the canopy, which removed the buoyancy effect. Therefore, gravity now has a greater affect on life. This increased gravity puts extra strain on living beings. A greater strain on the life support systems of living creatures results in a greater reduction in life expectancy. Also, the loss of the canopy resulted in more harmful rays of the sun affecting life on the planet. This resulted in the creation of deserts and large global changes in temperature and polar ice caps. This led to tornadoes, hurricanes, and other storms that shortens life as well.

Review: One of God's judgments was that mankind would no longer live to extreme ages. God's judgment resulted in the fact that mankind would no longer live to extreme ages. But, this is not how it will always be. For God has decreed that He will undo the curse of sin and restore the longevity of humans again. When? It will be immediately after the battle of Armageddon, when Christ returns and crushes evil. Then, humans will live long lives again. Isaiah 65:20:

> No longer will there be in it an infant who lives but a few days, Or an old man who does not live out his days; For the youth will die at the age of one hundred and the one who does not reach the age of one hundred will be thought accursed.

This is describing a future time when living beings will live so long on average that if a few do happen to die at the age of 100, they will be considered dying as a youth. This means that life forms, not just humans, but all life forms will return to the same longevity of life that existed before the Flood.

Review: Life forms once lived 900+ years of age—not just humans, but all life forms on the earth. God judged mankind's wickedness, which resulted in a severe reduction in the number of years lived. God will restore the longevity of the life expectancy to 900+ in the future.

The event that single-handily changed the longevity of humans was the global flood. How? Let us go ~1,650 years before the Flood and look at the creation account of Gen. 1:6–9: "Then God said, 'Let there be an expanse.'" *Expanse* means to expand like a blacksmith would hammer out metal, with a violent force. This parallels the violent expansion concept of the Big Bang. The synonym *firmament* is used in the NKJ. Simply put, it is an opening, or an expanse formed by violent force via the process of cavitation. "Let there be an expanse in the midst of the waters, and let it separate the waters from the waters." This means that God violently stretched out the universe, and let the universe's violent expansion stretch out the atmosphere from the middle of the waters surrounding Earth. *Waters* is plural to represent both abundance and the four forms of water: liquid, solid, gas, and plasma. Verse 7: "God made the expanse (stretched universe), and separated the waters (seas) which were below the expanse (atmosphere) from the waters (canopy) which were above the expanse (atmosphere); and it was so." Notice that the *expanse* is singular. Verse 8: "God called the expanse heaven. And there was evening and there was morning, a second day." Verse 9: "Then God said, 'Let the waters below the heavens be gathered into one place and let the dry land appear'; and it was so, God called the dry land earth, and the gathering of the waters He called <u>seas</u>." Therefore, we know that this second expanse/heaven is the atmosphere. Also, notice that God now uses the plural form of *heavens*.

The purpose of reviewing Gen. 1:6–9 is that God made the atmosphere in between the waters. The waters below became the seas, and the waters above became the canopy of ice and salt water.

Review: <u>God made the atmosphere with the waters below that became the seas and the waters above that formed the canopy of salt water surrounding the atmosphere (See the chapter The Canopy).</u>

What is the purpose of this canopy of ice and salt water? It shields the earth from the harmful effects of the sun to prevent deserts, and creates uniform global temperatures to prevent polar ice caps, and this allows lush vegetation to grow in those places instead. Since the canopy rained upon the earth to form oceans, then prior to the Flood, no oceans existed but only smaller seas. This allowed for lush vegetation to grow instead. More vegetation equates to more oxygen. More oxygen equates to longer life span.

We discussed in detail how oxygen is vital to life in the chapter titled, "Oxygen Concentration." Without oxygen, we die within seven minutes. And that life thrives in an abundantly rich oxygen environment. Arizona St. University performed a series of tests. They raised insects in hyperoxia (high O2) and hypoxia (low O2) to determine if a change of life would occurred. They found that all the insects in their study were positively affected when raised in an hyperoxia environment, and all suffered some ill effect when raised in an hypoxia environment. The positive effects on the insects living in hyperoxia were that most grew larger and grew faster than normal.

Review: <u>We have evidence that the canopy resulted in greater vegetation quantity, and that vegetation produced greater oxygen concentration in the atmosphere, and greater oxygen caused life to thrive. Therefore, the canopy caused life to thrive.</u>

DNA, RNA, genes, and cells are adversely altered from ultraviolet rays, cosmic rays, X-rays, and gamma rays. These high-frequency light particles and wavelengths have an adverse effect on our lives and affect the accuracy of genetic duplication of DNA. Though genes have protein markers that correct errors and delete unwanted errors, occasionally errors in the gene code occur from ultraviolet rays, cosmic rays, X-rays, and gamma Rays. These random, unguided mutations always adversely affect functions, the host, and efficiency, and they never enhance functions or the host, and they never initiate a new function. It turns out that water is an excellent barrier to limit those harmful high-energy rays. Well, the canopy shielded against those higher energy light waves from adversely affecting DNA, RNA, genes, and life on earth. Before the Flood, the offspring of each generation from Adam and Eve were more accurate genetic copies of the first humans on Earth. After the Flood and the loss of the canopy, an increase in errors in genetic duplication occurred with each generation. Errors or mutations in the genetic code do not enhance function; nor do they create new functions. Errors or mutations in the genetic code always result in the impairment of functions or loss of functions because they destroy useful information. Mutated genes reduce the likelihood and sometimes prevent the host from having offspring, as all creatures are preprogrammed in their DNA to select the strong and not the weak and to select the genetically superior and not the genetically mutated. In addition, those with mutations are usually weak, so predators and climate kill them. Also, the genetically mutated are sometimes sterile to prevent passing on their mutated gene. It is an impossible uphill climb to support evolution, as evolution not only needs one example to show how mutated DNA enhanced a host, but it needs trillions upon trillions of beneficial mutations to occur for life to evolve into the complexities we see today. Yet, ask any brilliant evolutionist to show one beneficial mutation, and they will pause and say, "You are asking the wrong question, since the observable changes, such as fish to amphibians or primates to a transitional phase of humanity, occurred hundreds of millions of years ago."[126] This is an attempt to redirect you away from the lack of evidence of beneficial random mutations; it is smoke and mirrors and requires a leap of faith.

NASA has figured out that a canopy of water of a sort can protect astronauts from harmful high-energy radiation and limit those harmful rays from penetrating the hulls of spaceships. NASA is proposing to surround the hulls of spaceships with water to protect humans and vital instruments on long durations in space.

Review: The canopy of water indirectly caused more accurate copies of genetic information by limiting high-energy rays from space that can cause harmful mutations of DNA information and inaccuracies in copying genetic information.

Not only does water limit harmful high-energy radiation from penetrating the hulls of spaceships and onto the earth's surface, another benefit of the canopy is at the crux of the matter for longevity of life. But to get there, we need to lay a foundation of DNA. The DNA of all life is double helical and is composed of long threads of digital information of As, Cs, Ts, and Gs. DNA allows for the formation of chromosomes, which are located inside the nucleus of a cell. At the tips of the chromosomes are caps of DNA information that protect the rest of the chromosomal strand from fraying or splitting, sticking to each other, or losing information, all of which are harmful. These caps of DNA also allow cells to divide. These caps of DNA are called **telomeres**. For this reason, some teachers of genetics have likened them to the plastic tips on short shoelaces.

Unfortunately, a catch occurs with telomeres. Each time the cell divides, the end caps get shorter and shorter until they are no longer able to be reduced for cell division, and cell division stops. This causes the cell to become inactive, or it dies. For this reason, geneticist add to the plastic tips of shoelace example and say they are also like fuses for a bomb. No explosion occurs, but old age or cancer and death are associated with the ends of the burning fuses.

What is so important about cellular division from these telomeres? Cell division is responsible for the new growth of skin, blood, WBCs, nails, hair, bones, liver tissue, eggs in the ovaries, neurons, and synapses (for reflexes and memory). It also augments wound healing, pigment repair from damaged skin (from harmful sun exposure), elasticity of skin for sagging, the repair of damaged collagen (for wrinkles), ligament repair (to prevent sagging tissue and lax joints), reproduction, and so on. Just about everything we associate with aging is directly affected by the ability of cellular division from these telomeres. Another critical ability of telomeres is that they reduce in size when the cell divides, and this prevents chromosomes from reducing in size, preventing the loss of DNA information and mutations in offspring. To clarify for evolutionists, mutations are never positive, so when DNA information is lost and a child is conceived with parental genetic information in the chromosomes that is lost, this is not proof of evolution; this is a birth defect. To counteract the shortening of telomeres, the body produces a protein enzyme called **telomerase** that adds bases (As,Cs,Ts, and Gs) to the ends of telomeres to extend their life span. Unfortunately, as cellular division continues, the quantity of enzyme telomerase may not be sufficient to keep up with the demands of adding bases to extend the life of telomeres. This results in a loss of ability for the telomere at the tip of a chromosome to be reduced further with cell division, and subsequently, the cell becomes inactive or dies. This results in aging of the host of the cell. Geneticists have determined a link with those that die prematurely with having shortened telomeres as compared to those living longer lives. Also, they have noticed that the production of telomerase enzymes is associated with prolonged telomeres. Therefore, having a sufficient production of telomerase enzymes could be a causal affect of the longevity of life. A side effect is that high telomerase enzyme counts have also been associated with cancerous cells. Why bring this up here in this section of the book? Water limits the radioactive energy from penetrating into the human body and causing cancer. Therefore, the canopy limited the adverse effect from solar radiation

---

126 Quote from Richard Dawkins.

affecting life on earth and mutating DNA, mutating chromosomes, mutating genes, and causing cancer and cell death. Therefore, a link exist between the canopy of water preventing harmful high-energy rays from penetrating the earth's atmosphere and mutating cells, with the quantity usage of telomerase enzymes. For this reason, with the canopy protecting life on earth, less damage to cells occurred from high-energy rays, and therefore a reduced requirement for telomerase enzymes to keep the body young and repaired for maximum longevity of life.

Geneticist Richard Cawthon says that "one estimate is people could live 1,000 years."[127] If we could make a synthetic telomerase and implant the enzyme into the body, it would heal the body of almost all symptoms and conditions, and delay the progression of conditions that reduce the quality of life. No limit to what we could cure. It could cure cancer by using telomerase inhibitors that allow cancerous cells to continue with cellular division and grow. By blocking telomerase production to an isolated cancerous area, the cancer cells would not be able to sustain cell division and would die. Well, with a canopy of water, no harmful cosmic rays, gamma rays, x-rays, and ultraviolet rays penetrated the atmosphere to turn normal cells into cancerous cells in the first place, and no destructive tissue from high-energy rays from space. This means no wasted telomeres repairing destroyed collagen from ultraviolet rays, and no high-energy rays that damage tissue (which would use up the DNA telomeres caps), and therefore, more protein enzyme telomerase left over for prolonged life. The canopy could be the long-sought fountain of youth.

As a result of harmful cosmic energy that has been adversely affecting (mutations) the DNA for generations, then as we travel backwards in time, each generation would have less mutations from cosmic radiation. This is what geneticist, Dr. John Sanford, has discovered. In his book, *Genetic Entropy and the Mystery of the Genome*, he elucidates that the DNA is entropic with each generation, which means that the DNA is becoming more disorderly or prone to more harmful errors. This is completely opposite of the notion of evolution, that the DNA is becoming more orderly, more complex over time. Therefore, as we travel backwards in time, the DNA in life is less mutated until we reach a pair of humans with zero mutations, called Adam and Eve.

Review: Humans live longer with having longer telomeres DNA caps at the ends of their chromosomes. A link with more production of telomerase enzymes is also associated with the longevity of life. A source that depletes both telomeres and telomerase is high-energy radioactive rays from space. Water can block high-energy radioactive rays. Therefore, both telomeres and telomerase enzyme would positively be affected by a canopy of water that protects life from harmful high-energy rays, thus prolonging life.

Another benefit from the canopy of salt water. As mentioned previously, it would cause a higher atmospheric pressure and weight on earth, which creates a buoyancy effect and reduces net gravity force. Changes in gravity can have profound effects on the human body. Astronauts are susceptible to bone density loss with prolonged space travel. One study of the effects on astronauts in space revealed that 14% to 30% bone mass was lost six months on a space station.[128]

As a doctor, I have noticed that heavyset patients rarely suffered from bone density problems. In fact, when viewing radiographs, it is clear that heavyset patients have thicker bones than skinny patients. Sure, they tend to suffer from joint problems due to their extra weight, but their bones compensate for the extra weight by adding more mineral deposits.

The negative of this is true as well. Older patients that are too skinny have an increased risk of thinning of the bones. The propensity toward osteoporosis increases with weight loss and increased age. So what is osteoporosis? And what do reductions in bone mass, bone density, and increased porousness mean? They are all saying the same thing. They are caused when the cortex of the bone (outside portion) and the trabeculae of the bone (inside portion) get thin.

With increased load on the skeletal system, the brain responds by adding more bone mass to

---

127 Learn Genetics, "Are telomeres the key to aging and cancer?"
128 Www.space.com.

compensate. This load can be from increased weight or increased activity, such as from basketball, weight lifting, and sports in general.

The opposite is true as well. With less weight/loads and fewer activities, the brain responds by allowing a decrease in bone mass. This reduction of bone mass would be appropriate for the reduced stresses placed on the skeletal system.

When viewing radiographs (X-ray film) of patients' spines and diagnosing focal points of sclerotic white spots in the joints, it is clear to identify one side of a joint appears larger than the other side and represents an increase in mineral deposits. This particular increase in bone formation is usually associated with joints that do not share loads and ranges of motion. Therefore, one side of the joint has more load than the other side due to poor alignment, and the result is that the brain directs the body to build up strength in that region. The increased deposit of minerals to the joint appear thicker on the X-rays. The whole point is that the skeletal system is dynamic. This is to say that the skeletal system is alive and able to compensate for varying loads placed on the skeletal system. Increasing the loads equals increasing the density/mass of the skeletal system. Decreasing the loads equals decreasing density/mass of the skeletal system. It is a very simple concept. This does not happen overnight, but over a period of months and years.

Review: Because of pre-existing DNA, the body adapts to its environment; specifically, changes in weight bearing on the skeletal system affect the quality/density of the bones.

How does this play out for our discussion? Well, before the global flood, the canopy applied weight and subsequent pressure on the inhabitants of the earth. This greater weight increased the total atmospheric pressure on life on earth. This created a buoyant force that reduced the net effect of gravity by approximately ~25%. This is why dinosaurs had porous bones with such enormous tonnage.

Review: A direct link between reduced load on bones and the loss of bone mass (more porous). And a direct link between increased load on bones and increased bone mass. Similarly, a link between dinosaurs having porous bone structures with a weaker gravity.

How does gravity factor into the mass/density of the skeletal system? Both someone's mass and gravity put axial loads on the skeletal system. The brain is unable to determine if the extra strain on its skeletal system is via gravity or via weight gain. It does not matter. The brain will still adjust to both changes in weight and gravity equally by adding bone density. Force = Mass x Gravity.

The body adapts to its environment. We see adaptation today with the skeletal system. Dinosaurs are not here to tell us that gravity was weaker some 4,500 years ago, but their skeletal system is here, and it does tell us that gravity was weaker. Unfortunately, paleontologists do not know the skeletal system. They see porous dinosaur bones and porous bones in birds and say, "Hey, there are no more dinosaurs because they became birds." That really is silly. The most likely connection is that dinosaurs adapted to gravity and oxygen changes and grew smaller in size over time.

Review: The skeletal system responds to changes in gravity and changes in body mass equally. The brain is unable to discern between the two.

We have established the link with gravity and the skeletal system, so how did humans who once lived 900+ years start living less than 100 years? Several contributing factors exist.

The primary answer is a reduction in oxygen concentration. The advent of the global flood caused vast oceans that physically limit vegetation from growing. Today's current O2 concentration in the atmosphere is 21%. The concentration of O2 before the Flood was ~31%. Therefore, today's concentration is two-thirds of the levels prior to the Flood. Today the earth is 70% covered by water, 10% by deserts, and 10% ice, and 10% is usable land that can produce vegetation and O2. Potentially before the Flood, the earth was 30% seas (includes lakes), 0% deserts, 0% ice, and 70% usable land. With an increased concentration of 02 in the atmosphere, living beings get more O2 per breath with each tidal volume of air breathed in. Therefore, dinosaurs could have nostrils that were small in relation to their large size and still get enough oxygen. Why some dinosaurs had small nostrils compared to the volume of air they needed is a puzzle for some, but not for those scientists who are aware that O2 concentration was higher in the past.

Review: Reduced oxygen concentration in the atmosphere was the primary contributor to a reduction in the longevity of life.

The second way that life expectancy was reduced was via increased gravity. Reduced gravity allowed blood to circulate through the body with greater ease. And the extra atmospheric pressure allowed increased volumes of oxygen to be breathed in with greater ease with each breath. Imagine an athlete who takes in a greater volume of oxygen in less time (as in living before the Flood) than an athlete breathing in less oxygen (living after the Flood). It would be equivalent to blood doping[129] and allow an unfair advantage. The muscles would have been able to go longer before fatigue set in. Essentially, life thrives in an environment with increased oxygen and reduced gravity.

Also, creatures and humans would be stronger and able to lift objects that would defy our belief today. First, the objects would seem lighter because gravity was weaker. Secondly, the muscles would be stronger because of increased blood flow and increased oxygen. Conversely, with increased gravity, it is harder for life to sustain itself and for the circulatory system to deliver blood throughout the body. With the removal of the buoyancy effect and reduced pressure, it is harder to breath in oxygen today than it was prior to the Flood, and less oxygen flows into the lungs with each breath today.

Review: Increased gravity is a second contributor to reducing the longevity of life.

The third way that life expectancy was reduced was via genome adaptation to changes in the environment. The genome is a part of our DNA that we inherit from our parents, and it may be adversely altered by external and internal stimuli. This affects the body's growth, the number of years of life, and the quality of life.

Changes to the environment can involve any external or internal stimuli, ranging from ultraviolet rays, x-rays, cosmic rays, gamma rays, ice ages, global warming, volcanic eruptions, droughts, floods, influenza outbreaks, plagues, cigarettes, unhealthy particulates, poisonous food, sin, and so on.

Here's an example of how a mutated genome may affect future offspring: A male becomes obese and subsequently suffers from diabetes as a result, and he marries a woman that also becomes obese and subsequently suffers from diabetes as a result. They potentially have altered their genomes so that when they have children, they will have a higher propensity to becoming a diabetic than the average child. Why? The parents altered their genome and passed on their mutated genes, and this potentially affected their offspring because genomes are the inheritable traits of the parents.

The Bible repeatedly declares a cause and effect exist in terms of the quality and quantity of our years. For example, Jesus heals a doubled-over paralytic man who had been ailing for 38 years. Then a short time later the same day, Jesus saw the same man in the synagogue and told him to go and sin no more, lest a worse thing come upon him (John 5:1–14), thereby connecting this person's ailment to their sin.

The Bible directly warns people about their sins and indirectly warns about the genome effect on their heirs. God states in the Ten Commandments that He will visit the iniquities of the fathers to the third and fourth generations, while giving blessings to thousands that love Him (Exodus 20:4–6). Medical researchers have recently discovered the ill effect of worrying, anxiousness, and stress, on our body and genome. When someone does not trust in God, or know the power of God, they rely on their own devices to handle situations, and this manifests in worry, being anxious, and so forth—which is sin and has an adverse effect on our body. Therefore, the Bible was supernaturally ahead of medical science by 3,000 years, warning parents about the cause and effect of their sins affecting their genomes that are passed on to children. We can either pass down defective genomes resulting from our sin, or we can pass down blessings to our heirs with an obedient life to God. Look at Job; after everything was said and done, God blessed him with additional children: "In all the land no women were found as

---

129 Blood doping is adding extra blood to the vascular system just prior to a competition. The extra blood will carry more oxygen to the muscles and remove more lactic acid from the muscles. This increases endurance.

beautiful as Job's daughters" (Job 42:15). Our obedience to God will allow the most accurate duplication of the DNA, and result in the least amount of mutated genes, and benefit us with long lives and benefit our heirs with being beautiful and/or healthy. This is adaptation from internal stimuli from a spiritual realm that affects our physical realm. This is based on DNA already existing. This is not evolution, where new information in the DNA produces a new function or a new kind.

As mankind continued to sin and live after the fall of Adam and Eve, genomes became increasingly affected as a result. We see this today with inherited diseases of altered genomes passed down from prior generations. Mankind wants to blame God for this, but it is our own sin that is the blame. It is the same with natural disasters; before the fall of Adam and Eve, no tornadoes, hurricanes, and so forth existed.

The best DNA-coded humans were Adam and Eve; as sin continued and generations passed, the copies of the original Adam's and Eve's DNA code progressively increased in errors—mutations—which resulted in the decreased efficiency of function or impaired function. This was a result of life adapting to external stimuli from information already existing in the DNA code. The degrading of the DNA code from mutations never enhances/improves function nor results in new kinds of creatures.

Another type of adaptation is modification to a feature that is better suited to environmental conditions. For example, take the Galapagos finches; their beaks seemed adapted to reach seeds better, but they already had the information in the DNA code for the differently shaped beak. No new information added to the DNA code for a new shaped beak; no, this was from existing information in the DNA code from birth. Evolution requires new information that produces a new function or a new kind of creature. Finches with the dominate gene trait of a longer beak that better reached the hidden seeds, they thrived because of more food. Thus, when it came time for selecting a mate for reproduction, the mate selected—based on existing DNA that governed the choice to choose the best genetic copy—was the finch with the dominate gene that best reached the seeds. Their DNA dominated the population—this is adaptation, not evolution. If random mutations to the DNA code caused new information that produced a new function, that would be evolution.

Review: Genome adaptation is the third contributor to reducing the longevity of life. We pass our genome down to our heirs, which in turn affects our heirs' lives. Our lifestyle and obedience to God will determine if we pass down blessings (for example, fewest mutations in our DNA and the most accurate copy of our DNA) or pass down curses (for example, increased mutations in our DNA and a more inaccurate copy of our original DNA) to our heirs via our genome. For the purposes of this book, the genomes that were passed down from each successive generation post-Flood had built in less and less longevity of life due to the adaptation of environmental conditions (such as increased harmful solar radiation, decreased oxygen, and increased gravity), all of which were a result of God judging mankind's sins.

Evolutionists contend that the similarities in the DNA code from one kind to another kind proves we evolved from one common ancestor. Well, this sounds fine, but it equally means we have one common creator. Just like a car, plane, or boat may have similarities in terms of metal, wiring, bolts, and so on, it does not mean they came from the same manufacturing plant, but that humans created them. Chimpanzees having similar strands of genetic coding as humans, at first glance, seems to support the notion that humans evolved from primates. But with closer inspection, humans have similar strands of genetic coding to many creatures, not just chimpanzees and not just primates. Why? the genetic code instructs the body to produce proteins that have specific, exclusive, special purposes. Most of life share similar functions, such as respiration, reproduction, digestion, taste, smell, touch, CO_2 expiration, waste removal, and so forth. Different creatures also have similar mammary glands, skin, nails, teeth, blood, liver, hormones, hair, eyes, ears, muscles, tendons, ligaments, adipose, bone structure, and so on. Of course similarities in the genetic code exist for building 3D proteins that have similar specific, exclusive functions. Since a specific genetic code to build specific proteins exist to make, for example, tendons that attach muscle to bone, it makes perfect sense that the genetic code would be similar for all creatures that have tendons. Since a specific genetic code exist to produce blood from the marrow of the trabeculae in bones, well of course the genetic code would be similar for all creatures that produce blood from the marrow of bone. The inference is that we share similar DNA because we share similar proteins that perform similar functions. No mystery with that, this is not evolution. This is God being efficient with DNA that performs the same function in different creatures. Just like a computer programmer, utilizing the same operating system, would not write a new and different program that performs the exact same function of an already existing program. The software writer would simply copy and paste the functional information.

Therefore, similarities in the strands of genetic coding do not demonstrate that we evolved from primates. If so, we would not have similar strands of genetic coding with other creatures on a completely different evolutionary branch. What similarities in the genetic coding demonstrates is that one Creator created all life from and through Himself, so of course similarities exist in genetic code. The Bible calls this Creator God. Evolutionists call it "chance" or natural selection and random mutations. It is common to hear evolutionists purport that these similarities are proof of evolution, but the logic bypasses the fact that humans have genetic similarities with other creatures as well—even with nonliving things, such as bananas.

What evolutionists will not address are the dissimilarities in the chromosome count. Evolutionists look at general similarities, such as the fact that one animal has five bones in a limb and another has five bones in a limb, and draw the conclusion that they came from the same ancestor. But the most primordial information, the most empirical information, the most basic genetic factor of linking one kind of creature to another is the chromosome count. But when studying the chromosomal count of each kind and each species within the kind, an apparent widespread variety exist in chromosomal count. For example, Chorda algae have 56, and Cosmarium algae have 120, Bacillus fungi have 1, Saccaromyces fungi have 30, Amoeba protozoa have 30, Radiolaria protozoa have 800+, and on and on. Let me simplify my train of thought. Humans have 46 chromosomes, and antelopes have 46 chromosomes and lots of similarities. But hundreds of creatures have similar chromosome counts (or exactly 46 chromosomes); this does not prove or disprove anything. Evolutionists teach and preach that life evolves and becomes more complex, but this is contrary to humans having 46 chromosomes and white ash tree having 138 chromosomes or ferns having 480 chromosomes, as they preceded humans on the evolutionary tree. It seems more like entropy (a law that says that everything tends from order to disorder) rather than evolution.

Basically, creationists and evolutionists are looking at the same evidence, but the condition of the heart, soul, and spirit determines the interpretation. If one determines no God exist, all interpretations will be anti-Bible, anti-creation, anti-intelligent design, anti-young earth, and anti-God. If one determines that God exist, the interpretations will be pro-God.

Review: Similarities in genetic code point toward one creator. Creatures that have similar functioning things, such as tendons, blood, and muscles, have similar genetic codes. The dissimilarities in chromosome counts, which is as basic as genetic information gets, are contrary to the concept of evolution.

After the Flood, more solar radiation reached the earth's surface and oxygen concentrations in the atmosphere gradually declined and net gravity increased. They had adverse effects on the duration and size of life. This resulted in the genomes of all living organisms adapting to the new environment. This adaptation of the genome meant that each subsequent offspring would not live as long and grow as tall and as enormous. The genes being passed down to the next generation were affected with each passing generation until this process leveled out to the homeostasis we have seen in the last ~3,000 years.

Yes, this means dinosaurs would have been affected as well. With each passing generation, they too would have been smaller and smaller in size. Dinosaurs are reptiles, and they grow as long as they are alive. So if their life expectancy was cut shorter and shorter with each passing generation and

172

gravity was greater after the Flood, the emphasized genome that was passed down had information that allowed the once mammoth sizes to adapt. Yet, all the creatures on earth still have in their DNA code the necessary information to once again live 900+ years.

We know dinosaurs survived the Flood. How do we know this? God ordained that two of every kind of creature on earth, male and female, would enter into the ark (Gen. 6:19–20, 7:8–9, and 13–17). Noah did not physically gather every kind of creature in the Ark; that would have been impossible.

Some evolutionists resort to twisting what the Bible records, creating a "Straw-man" argument, to discredit the Bible. Such as, it is impossible that Noah got every creature on the tiny boat. The Bible records that two of every kind went on the ark, not two of every species, hundreds of species exist in a kind. For example, there was not thousands of dog species on the ark, there was probably a male and female hyena, wolf, coyote, and fox.

I have heard countless times from evolutionists: "It's physically impossible for Noah to gather two of every kind into the Ark. Therefore, the Bible is wrong." But this is just a debater's trick and is such a silly argument for evolutionist to use. For the text clearly states, in Gen. 6:18–22, " You shall go into the ark . . . two of every kind **will come to you** to keep them alive." Also, Gen. 7:7–12 says, "So Noah, with his sons, his wife, and his sons' wives, went into the ark . . . clean animals and unclean animals, and birds, and everything that creeps on the earth, two by two **they went** into the ark **to** Noah . . . as God commanded." And again in Gen. 7:14–16: "They went into the ark to Noah, two by two, of all flesh in which is the breath of life. So those that entered, male and female of all flesh, went in as God had commanded him; and the LORD shut him in."

Of course, the dinosaurs that went into the ark were younglings. This seems too obvious to point out. But evolutionists use this ploy to try in vane to invalidate the Bible by saying, "It's physically impossible to get full-grown dinosaurs in the ark." But when they are young, they eat less, poop less, and take up less space. Therefore, it is logical that most of the larger creatures would have been young.

Do we have additional evidence that dinosaurs survived the Flood? The phrase "two of every kind" should be sufficient for believers, but let us consider the book of Job. Job lived approximately six generations after the Flood. Yet, the book of Job describes dinosaurs in Job chapters 40 and 41. In Job 40:17, God talks about a **behemoth** with a tail like a cedar tree. Cedar trees in the Mesopotamian era grew 75–100 feet tall. That can only refer to a dinosaur. God also talks about the **leviathan** that fire came from his mouth. The whole chapter can only refer to a dinosaur. Why? Consider the bird's-eye view of the chapters in the book of Job. Do not overlook the point that God is making. God is saying that He is so much greater than any man because man cannot tame or conquer the greatest beasts that God created. Logically, the chapters of Job 40 and 41 refer to dinosaurs. God would be making a silly argument if He is saying that Job and mankind are so inferior that they cannot conquer the hippopotamus or the crocodile. Also, it is a worthless argument to reference something that the hearer does not know about to solidify ones point. Therefore, Job was fully aware of these dinosaurs, otherwise, God's illustration is pointless in referencing these creature to Job.

I have no problem taking these chapters literally—even the fire-breathing dragon. Why? Today we see the **bombardier beetle** as a small version of how this may have played out. The bombardier beetle has three separate fluid-filled chambers in its abdomen. When the bombardier beetle gets scared, it sends two of the fluid-filled chambers to drain into a distal empty holding tank; once the two fluids are mixed, a third reservoir that is filled with the catalyst enzyme drains into the holding tank. With the combination of these three different chemicals, the fluid starts to heat up to 200° F and boil under pressure, and then when the pressure exceeds the resistance threshold of its rear sphincter, a noxious boiling fluid bursts through the rear sphincter when a predator stalks the beetle. All this is done in fractions of seconds. The scalding hot noxious chemicals burn the unsuspecting predator with a chemical burn and temperature burn. While smoking hot, the predator flees. We see today how this could have been possible with a fire-breathing dragon (literally).

What is significant about this? God is talking about dinosaurs to Job, and for Job to understand

God's point, God discussed something Job could observe and understand. Therefore, Job knew what God was talking about. This is Biblical evidence that dinosaurs existed after the Flood and corroborates the Genesis account, which says that all creatures, including dinosaurs, went into the ark.

Therefore, dinosaurs had to go through the same adaptation as any other creature that lived in the post-Flood era, including humans. This suggests that as humans had to adapt and their longevity was reduced, so too the dinosaurs and all life adapted to less and less oxygen and adapted to increased gravity. They would have lived shorter and shorter lives. Since dinosaurs are reptiles, and we know reptiles continue to grow as long as they are alive, it makes perfect sense that as the dinosaurs lived shorter lives, they would have grown to shorter and smaller sizes with each successive generation. *Photo credit: www.bible.ca. by Stan Taylor.*

In fact, dinosaur fossil footprints have been found next to, and on the same layer of soil as human beings. This means that they both walked on the face of the earth during the same time frame. This is groundbreaking evidence that supports the Bible and a literal interpretation of the Genesis creation record and the Flood. They are in the Paluxy River near Glen Rose, Texas. Not just one footprint, but many of each. The human foot impressions are ~11.5 inches.[130] But since we do not know the gender or the age of the person that made those footprints, we do not know their height. But we do know, from the fossil record, that all life living before the Flood in an oxygen-enriched environment and weaker gravity would have had accelerated growth and prolonged growth.

Above, you can see dinosaur footprints going one direction and a human's going another, with a plaster cast made of one of the footprints. This is important for knowing what happened to dinosaurs. The findings of dinosaur prints and human prints is in harmony with the Bible but a problem for evolutionists. For 65 million years between dinosaurs and human existence, according to the evolutionary hypothesis. But the Bible has them both living at the same time.

Review: The Bible is in harmony with dinosaurs living in the post-Flood era. Gen. 7 declares that one male and one female of every kind of creature entered the ark. In Job 40 and 41, God tells Job that he and mankind are inferior to Him because they cannot conquer leviathan or behemoth, both being creatures that God made. God is talking about dinosaurs, as the behemoth had a tail as long as a cedar tree (75–100 feet), and the leviathan was a fire-breathing dragon.

Before the global flood, gravity was weaker. This would have had a profound effect on all skeletal systems of all creatures living in that environment. Their skeletal systems would have been more porous and had less mass/density than if they lived today.

Since dinosaurs had porous bone structure relative to their epic tonnage, this is evidence that dinosaurs lived in a gravitational environment that was weaker and explains why their bones were porous, which sounds much more plausible than the notion that they evolved into birds. By taking a simpler interpretation of the evidence, evolutionists do not have to go to great lengths to support their belief, such as falsifying evidence to support such a leap of faith. I'm speaking about Archaeoraptor.

The Bible records humans living 900+ years before the Flood, which means all life, not just humans, lived a very long time. With reptiles growing as long as they are alive, and living 900 years in an environment with weaker gravity, increased oxygen, less harmful solar radiation, and temperate temperatures; it is not hard to imagine that they would be huge, and we would call them dragons or

---

130 Www.bible.ca/tracks/talor-trail.htm.

dinosaurs. The Bible gives us the clue that humans lived so long, so we can infer that animals did too. This explains how we got dinosaurs/dragons on earth. Another interesting point is that humans have primary growth sites that fuse early, ending vertical growth, but secondary characteristic sites can continue to grow. Secondary characteristic sites include the brow above the eyes, cheek bones, and jawbones, and so on. Imagine humans living 900+ years and being about 10-12 feet tall and potentially having more pronounced brow ridges, cheek bones, and jaw bones, as they approached almost a thousand years of age, it certainly seems plausible those characteristics

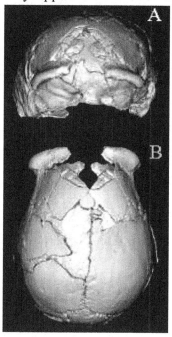

would become more pronounced. Evolutionists are claiming that humans were much smaller in the past, which is opposite to the fossil record, logic, Scripture, science and empirical data of oxygen concentrations. Evolutionists use skull fossils of larger male chimps (~530 cc), and call them transitional names such as Australopithecus, Cro-Magnon, and so on, and they will find skull fossils of larger female chimps (~500 cc), and call them Hominids, Homo naledi, and so forth, but they are not transitional to humans, they are merely adaptations to smaller chimps and bonobos. Humans would have adapted from a much larger skull fossil, such as **Denisovan fossil**, which has a cranial volume of 1800 cc, as compared to humans today that have a skull volume of 1350 cc. The Denisovan fossil fits perfectly as a human that had pronounced secondary characteristic sites due to prolonged life. Especially since Denisovan had 23 chromosomes; same as us. Remember, insects grow faster and larger in hyperoxia. All life forms would grow faster and larger, potentially including their secondary characteristic sites, such as brow ridges, cheek bones, and jaws. *Image credit: Zhan-Yang Li, et al, 2017.*

Chapter Summary: The evidence is that dinosaurs have porous bone structures. Given that bones respond to changes in loads (from atmospheric pressure and gravity) and that the canopy around the atmosphere reduced gravity, dinosaurs lived in a weaker gravitational system along with humans. Living things once lived 900+ years because oxygen was 50% higher and gravity was weaker. The global flood changed all that. The canopy rained upon the earth for 40 days and 40 nights, which eventually reduced the oxygen concentration and removed the buoyancy effect. As the genomes of DNA adapted to the changes in the environment, the maximum life spans declined with each generation. Dinosaurs are reptiles, and reptiles grow as long as they live, so when the dinosaur life expectancy declined, so too did their size. When gravity increased, their skeletal structures adapted.

Chapter 25
What Happened to Dinosaurs?

Did all the dinosaurs die off millions of years ago? No. The Bible describes that God sent one of each male and female of every kind into the ark. Gen. 6:19: "And of every living thing of all flesh, you shall bring two of every kind into the ark, to keep them alive with you." The dinosaurs would have been very young to accommodate for size, food consumption, and aggressiveness. Therefore, we may infer the Bible declares that dinosaurs survived the Flood. Those who claim to believe in God are faced with a dilemma. Do you believe the wisdom of men telling you that dinosaurs died off hundreds of millions of years ago, or do you believe in the inerrant Word of God that declares one male and one female of every creature went into the ark?

Review: An evidence supporting the notion that dinosaurs survived the Flood is from the Bible, which says that one male and one female of EVERY kind went into the Ark (albeit younglings). Dinosaurs lived after the Flood because God decreed "to keep them alive with you."

Now that we know the Bible indirectly tells us that dinosaurs survived the Flood, do we know that the dinosaurs lived long after the Flood? Yes. God talks about dinosaurs as being alive and in the present tense to Job to prove His point. God uses the words *leviathan* and *behemoth*. Through the ages and dialect changes, these creatures were called dragons and then dinosaurs. God makes a point to Job by using an illustration that is only valid if the listener is aware of His example. Therefore, Job would have been familiar with the leviathan and behemoth (Job 40 and 41). When did the conversation between God and Job occur? No direct date is provided, but enough clues are provided in the Scriptures that we may discern an approximate date. Job 22:15–16 (NIV) indicates that Job lived post-Flood, "Will you keep to the old path that the wicked have trod? They were carried off before their time, their foundations were washed away by a flood." Also, Job lived during the time of the patriarchs because as the head of his family, he offered up sacrifices to God (Job 1:5). Job 42:8 indicates that the friends of Job also offered up sacrifices to the Lord, a practice that ceased during Moses' time with the law given by God, and the priests performed the sacrifices on behalf of the people. Also, Job gave inheritance to his daughters (and sons), a practice that was only done in the absence of brothers (Numbers 27:1–11). Furthermore, Job's wealth was valued in the amount of his livestock, not in money (Job 1:3, 42:12). Lastly, the strongest bit of evidence is the length of years Job lived. Job 1:13–18 suggests that Job lived long enough to accumulate great wealth and have ten children old enough to be at the age of accountability and to drink at a party (Job 1:2,18). Also, Job 42:10–17 reveals that after everything was taken from Job, he lived an additional 140 years. Thus, putting the pieces together, Job lived 220+ years, about as long as Peleg (239 years), Reu (239 years), and Serug (230 years), around six generations after the Flood, or around ~one to two hundred years after the Flood. Therefore, the conversation between God and Job occurred around the time of ~2,200 BC.[131]

Let us take a closer look at the two chapters in Job that talk about dinosaurs to confirm that these creatures being described are not an elephant, hippopotamus, or whale. Let us set the scene: Job was a righteous man that God had blessed so much that he had ten children and honor, and he was the richest man of the East. God was so pleased with Job's obedience that God allows Satan to test Job and take away Job's children, his health, and his riches to demonstrate to Satan that Job loved God regardless of the blessings that God had given Job.

Satan kills Job's children, causes thieves to steal all his wealth, and afflicts Job's body with a host of sicknesses. Job is broken to the point that he questions God's plan, justice, and wisdom. Then God answered Job out of the whirlwind and said, (Job 38:1–3) "Who is this that darkens counsel by words without knowledge? Now gird up your loins like a man, and I will ask you and you instruct Me!" God asks Job a series of questions, all of which Job is unable to answer. God is establishing that His

---

131 Apologeticspress.org/ "When Did Job Live?"

ways are above our ways. God does not make mistakes ever, let alone with His plan, justice, or wisdom. Here are some of the questions God asks Job: Job 38:4:

> Where were you when I laid the foundation of the earth? [If you are as mighty as God, why weren't you there when I formed the earth?] . . . Who set its measurements? . . . who stretched the line on it? On what were its bases sunk? Or who laid its cornerstone, when the morning stars sang together and all the sons of God shouted for joy? [On the third day of creation, Job was not there and therefore does not know any of these answers.]

In verse 8, in reference to the global flood when the waters were bursting out of the earth, God asks, "Or who enclosed the sea with doors when, bursting forth, it went out from the womb; When I made a cloud its garment and thick darkness its swaddling band, and I placed boundaries on it and set a bolt and doors, and I said, "Thus far you shall come, but no farther; and here shall your proud waves stop?" Job was not there when the Flood occurred and cannot respond to the inquiry.

In verse 12, He asks, "Have you ever in your life commanded the morning, caused the dawn to know its place, that it might take hold of the ends of the earth, and the wicked be shaken out of it?" Job was not there at creation and therefore cannot respond to an all powerful God.

In verse 15, He asks, "Have you entered into the springs of the sea or walked in the recesses of the deep? Have the gates of death been revealed to you or have you seen the gates of deep darkness?" Job was not there at the creation of the seas on the third day of creation, nor has he seen Hell, so he cannot answer any inquisition.

In verse 18, He asks, "Have you understood the expanse of the earth? Tell Me, if you know all this." On the second day of creation, Job was not there to see how the atmosphere was created, so again he and all of humanity are revealed to be miniscule to an all powerful God.

In verse 19, He asks, "Where is the way to the dwelling of light? and darkness, where is its place, that you may take it to its territory and that you may discern the paths to its home? You know, for you were born then, and the number of your days is great!" God is making a clear point to Job that he does not know much because Job was not there when light was created. Job does not know the answers, and neither does humanity.

In verse 25, He asks, "Who has cleft a channel for the flood, or a way for the thunderbolt, to bring rain on a land without people, on a desert without a man in it, to satisfy the waste and desolate land and to make the seeds of grass to sprout? Has the rain a father? or who has begotten the drops of dew?" Humanity does not know the path of the thunderbolt; nor did Job.

In verse 31, He asks, "Can you bind the chains of the Pleiades, or loose the cords of Orion? Can you lead forth a constellation in its season, and guide the Bear with her satellites? Do you know the ordinances of the heavens, Or fix their rule over the earth?" Pleiades is a constellation that humanity can not bind with chains. Humanity also cannot release the gravitational grip that Orion has, and we do not know where our universe is in relation to other dimensions/realms or understand the extent of our own universe.

In verse 34, He asks, "Can you lift up your voice to the clouds, so that an abundance of water will cover you? Can you send forth lightnings that they may go and say to you 'Here we are?'" Job did not control the rain and hydrological cycle; nor do we. We command not where the lightning goes or when it comes.

In verse 36, He asks, "Who has put wisdom in the innermost being or given understanding to the mind? Who can count the clouds by wisdom, Or tip the water jars of the heavens, When the dust hardens into a mass and the clods stick together?" Job and all believers know that the wisdom of mankind comes exclusively from God; this is from James 1:5 and Colossians 2:2–3. Therefore, Almighty God is mightier than the created.

In verse 39, He asks, "Can you hunt the prey for the lion, or satisfy the appetite of the young lions, When they crouch in their dens and lie in wait in their lair? Who prepares for the raven its nourishment when its young cry to God and wander about without food?*" Job knew he did not prepare food for all of creation each and every day. Colossians 1:17 reveals that Jesus is the sustainer of His creation.

Job 39 continues with God illustrating how almighty He is and how insignificant Job is and by default, all of humanity. In each illustration God uses something Job can see and therefore understand God's point. But God is not done. He will use His grandest living creations, the leviathan and the behemoth (which we once called dragons and now call dinosaurs) to drive home His point.

Job 40: In verse 1, He asks, "Will the faultfinder contend with the Almighty?"

Verse 3: "Then Job answered the LORD and said, 'Behold, I am insignificant; what can I reply to You? I lay my hand on my mouth.'" Job gets the point that he is too insignificant to question God. But God is not done making His point.

In verse 6, He says, *"Then the LORD answered Job out of the storm and said, 'Now gird up your loins like a man; I will ask you and you instruct Me.'"* *Image credit: prehistoric-wildlife.com.*

In verse 8, He asks, "Will you really annul My judgment? Will you contend with Me that you may be justified? Or do you have an arm like God, and can you thunder with a voice like His? Can you adorn yourself with eminence and dignity . . . and look on everyone who is proud, and make him low. And Look on everyone who is proud, and humble him, and tread down the wicked where they stand?"

God describes His greatest land creature, the behemoth in verses 15–17: "Behold now, Behemoth . . . He bends his tail like a Cedar." Cedar trees that grew in the Mesopotamian era and region grew to 100 feet tall. This hardly fits the hippopotamus, with its very short tail, and it rules out the elephant. God would not use all these grandiose illustrations to then use the tiny tails of the hippopotamus and elephant. That is incongruous with all His prior examples.

In verse 19, He says, "He is the first of the ways of God." As far as the land creatures go, this animal is the most impressive. It was the first as in terms of strength,[132] not order, since all land creatures were created on the sixth day (Gen. 1:25, "great beast").

Upper estimate of *Argentinosaurus* compared with a 1.8 meter tall person

DIMENSIONS IN METERS   © www.prehistoric-wildlife.com

In verse 24, He asks, "Can anyone capture him when he is on watch, with barbs can anyone pierce his nose?" This does not fit elephants because man has tamed elephants and elephants have a trunk instead of a nose. Dinosaurs fit all the categories of the description in Job 40:15–24. The hippopotamus and elephant fit some of the descriptions, but not all. What animal would be the first of the ways of God? The great sauropod, Amphicoelias fragillimus, was 60 meters in length, (200 ft.), weighing in at a whopping 150 tons.[133] This is the largest relative of brachiosaurus.

Review: Job 40:15–24 indicates that the behemoth was a type of dinosaur. It seems congruent that God is describing one epic portion of His creation after another, one mighty thing after another when He then describes dinosaurs. Dinosaurs make mankind seem insignificant, just like all the prior illustrations God had used. But an elephant and hippopotamus do not make man feel insignificant. We have tamed elephants for millennia. But no man knows the ways of a

---

132 Col. 1:15–16 and Psalm 89:27 establishes first born as in title, not eldest, as King David was the sixth son of Jesse.
133 Wikipedia, dinosaurs sizes.

178

dinosaur, and no man has ever tamed a dinosaur. The long tail seals the deal that God is talking about dinosaurs. Ergo, the account flows with the rest of God's illustrations of demonstrating the mightiest of God's creation versus the insignificance of man.

The leviathan described by God is even more impressive than the behemoth. In Job 41, verse 1, He asks, "Can you draw out Leviathan with a fishhook? Or press down his tongue with a cord? Can you put a rope in his nose or pierce his jaw with a hook?" Mankind has captured every creature in the sea with some type of bait, hook, or net, but not a fire-breathing dinosaur. Therefore, this rules out the blue whale. Right off the bat, in the first verse, God is talking about something so monumental that the blue whale does not fit. This is in parallel with all the prior illustrations.

In verse 3, He asks, "Will he make many supplications to you, or will he speak to you soft words? Will he make a covenant with you? Will you take him for a servant forever? Will you play with him as a bird, or will you bind him for your maidens?" No dinosaur made a request to Job or spoke softly to him, and no human played with a dinosaur. Yet, we have many sea creatures in zoos for our pleasure. Even the killer whale is bound for our amusements.

In verse 6, He asks, "Will the traders bargain over him? Will they divide him among the merchants? Can you fill his skin with harpoons, or his head with fishing spears?" Again, this rules out the mightiest ocean dwellers we see today. For mankind has traded and divided the spoils of whale blubber for a millennium. But no man has ever captured or tamed Livyatan melvillei, with a head 10- foot long and teeth that were over 1-foot long. This fierce sea creature was like a killer whale but the size of a sperm whale. Or how about Megalodon? This was a remarkable prehistoric shark on steroids—the size of a school bus in length.

In verse 8, He says, "Lay your hand on him; Remember the battle; you will not do it again! Behold, your expectation is false; Will you be laid low even at the sight of him? No one is so fierce that he dares to arouse him; Who then is he that can stand before Me?" That is the salient point of God describing the greatest of sea creatures, rather than a whale. Only the prehistoric dinosaurs make man realize his insignificance versus the created, let alone versus the Creator.

God goes into details about this great sea creature that reveal clearly that this animal was unlike anything we see today, but alive and well in Job's time. In verse 13, He asks,

> Who can open the doors of his face? Around his <u>teeth</u> there is terror. His strong <u>scales</u> are his pride, shut up as with a tight seal. One is so near to another that no air can come between them. They are joined one to another; They clasp each other and cannot be separated.

The scales rule out large aquatic life, such as whales and dolphins, and fits a reptilian aquatic dinosaur. The terror around his teeth rules out the large aquatic creatures with baleen in their mouth. What kind of terror? In verse 18, He continues,

> His sneezes flash forth <u>light</u>, and his eyes are like the eyelids of the morning. Out of his mouth go <u>burning torches</u>; <u>Sparks of fire</u> leap forth. Out of his nostrils <u>smoke</u> goes forth as from a <u>boiling pot and burning rushes</u>. His breath <u>kindles coals</u>, and a <u>flame</u> goes forth from his mouth.

Clearly, this is unlike all creatures on earth today. The bombardier beetle has similar characteristics. As mentioned previously, the bombardier beetle can ward off predators by ejecting scalding hot noxious chemicals that burn the unsuspecting predator with a chemical and temperature burn. We see today that a fire-breathing creature, as described in Job 41, is within the realm of plausibility. In chemistry class, students learn that certain liquid chemicals create fire without matches or a lighter when mixed together. In the following examples,[134] only drops of chemicals are needed.

Chemical fire combination #1: Potassium permanganate + glycerin + <u>water</u> = <u>fire</u>. This is a nice fit since water is required. Remember that this particular leviathan that God is describing is in water yet sends fire out of its mouth. Potassium permanganate is a salt containing manganese and potassium; a mixture of manganese dioxide and potassium carbonate.[135] Glycerin is a sugar alcohol. A living organism, with the appropriate proteins, would be able to process ingested food, and fill separate chambers of Potassium permanganate and glycerin.
Chemical fire combination #2: Acetone + sulfuric acid + potassium permanganate = fire.
Chemical fire combination #3: Sodium chlorate + sugar + sulfuric acid = fire.
Chemical fire combination #4: Ammonium nitrate powder + zinc powder + hydrochloric acid = fire.

Who knows what method God used to form this dinosauric fire-breathing sea dragon. Before you think this implausible, remember that the bombardier beetle has a chamber filled with hydroquinone and another chamber filled with hydrogen peroxide. If you think it is impossible to house noxious chemicals inside a living organism, consider that humans have a chamber (stomach) of fluid in their body that holds hydrochloric acid. This is one of the deadlier known acids to man. If this acid comes in contact with any other body part, it can result in severe injury or death. Everyone has it in their stomach, and so do many other animals. Also, snakes have sacks filled with toxic venom in their skull without suffering any ill effects. Therefore, a fire-breathing leviathan is plausible. Matthew 20:26 says, with man some things are impossible, "but with God all things are possible."

Mankind has not yet identified a dinosaur fossil that matches the Biblical description of the fire-breathing dragon. However, if the bombardier beetle were extinct and discovered as a fossil, would we discern that the three chambers in the beetle's abdomen were used to generate a 100°C noxious gas that chemically and thermally burns a nearby predator in a fraction of a second? Probably not. Without modern-day chemistry, would we have known that potassium permanganate + glycerin + water = fire? Who would have thought that water was a requirement for a fire?

Review: Fire-breathing sea creatures are possible, and given the Bible's tract record of truth, I would elevate that from possible to certain.

Therefore, do not shy away from taking these verses about the fire-breathing leviathan as literal. For the verses and chapters prior to and the verses and chapters following are uniformly interpreted with a literal view. Just because the words describe a creature that we do not see or know of does not mean that they are not in harmony with the surrounding verses. Jumping to a figurative view may be appropriate at times, such as when the Bible says behemoth had legs like iron or a heart as hard as stone. It is not literally saying the legs were iron and it is not literally saying the heart was stone. But to default to a figurative interpretation of the Scriptures because a literal view causes one to be a fool in the eyes of others is not justification to do so. It may reveal a faith that is weak regarding the abilities of God and the infallibility of His Word. It is not as though the writer of the book of Job, even though inspired by God, got a little carried away with the pen at this point and only this point in the book. When in doubt on how to interpret the Scriptures, default to a literal interpretation. This will save you a lot of contradictions and troubles later on.

Review: the concept of a fire-breathing Leviathan (dragon/dinosaur) is to be taken literally.

In verse 25 we read: "When he raises himself up the mighty fear; <u>Because of the crashing they are bewildered.</u> The sword that reaches him cannot avail, nor the spear, the dart or the javelin. He regards iron as straw, bronze as rotten wood. The arrow cannot make him flee; Slingstones are turned into stubble for him. Clubs are regarded as stubble; He laughs at the rattling of the javelin. <u>His underparts are like sharp potsherds.</u>" This language describes no creature that we can identify today, but it fits

---

134 Chemistry.About.com by Anne Marie Helmenstine, PhD.
135 http://en.wikipedia.org/wiki/Potassium_permanganate.

dinosaurs. Just as some dinosaurs had protruding and jagged plates of scales, so too did this dinosaur.

In Verse 31 He continues: "He makes <u>the depths boil</u> like a pot; He makes <u>the sea like a jar of ointment</u>. Behind him he makes a wake to shine; One would think the deep to be gray-haired (mane). Nothing on earth is like him, one made without fear. He looks on everything that is high; He is king over all the sons of pride." The heat from the chemical fire proceeding from his mouth causes the water to boil, and the oily mineral this dragon uses to create fire, leaves an oily residue floating in the water behind him. With the total sums of all the descriptions, this could only be a sea-fairing dinosaur that moves through the waters, leaving a wake like a ship.

Review: <u>The Bible's description of the leviathan is clearly about a creature that was a seaworthy fire breathing dragon/dinosaur. But the writer of Job uses present tense grammar. Therefore, Job was able to see this leviathan and understand what God was talking about, which means that dinosaurs lived after the Flood.</u>

Therefore, the Bible is clear that dinosaurs not only lived with mankind but survived the Flood. If dinosaurs survived the Flood, where are they? When and how did they all go extinct?

We know that life thrives in an oxygen-rich environment with a reduced gravitational force, and conversely, we know that life suffers in an oxygen-poor environment with an increased gravitational force. Perhaps some species of the dinosaurs are extinct now, but perhaps many of them still live among us in an adapted state. Humans had to adapt to the changed conditions after the Flood; so too did all life have to adapt, and this includes dinosaurs.

For example: Take the saber-toothed tiger. It was much larger than tigers today, but what would happen if a tiger lived in a high-oxygen and weak-gravity environment for many generations? The tiger would live longer and grow larger. The teeth would also be larger. In fact, the canine tooth that distinguishes the saber-toothed tiger from other large cats would grow just as long on the tiger. Conversely, if the saber-toothed tiger lived today, its elongated canine tooth that makes it so distinguishable from other large cats would be reduced with each generation until it reaches the same size as the tiger's canines of today.

The saber-toothed tiger is the forefather of the current tiger. The only difference between the two is the environment they live(d) in. Just as our forefathers once lived 900+ years, so too did the tigers' forefathers once live, with long canine teeth that were a result of the environment and not because of evolutionary change. They merely adapted to changes in the environment.

This means that when oxygen levels and gravitational forces return to their pre-Flood optimal levels, so too would the tiger's canine tooth elongate over time to the length of its ancestors, the saber-toothed tiger.

Review: <u>The saber-toothed tiger could plausibly be the ancestor of the modern-day tiger, which means the saber-toothed tiger is not extinct, but living amongst us as the tiger. In an oxygen-rich atmosphere, life thrives. But in an oxygen-poor atmosphere, life suffers.</u>

Did the mighty Tyrannosaurus rex become extinct as well? When oxygen levels gradually declined with each passing decade after the Flood, T. rex would have gradually grown to a lesser height with each subsequent offspring, as it adapted to the changes in oxygen. The T. rex would gradually be reduced in size, strength, tonnage, and longevity of life. Since T. rex was a reptile, if we cut short its life span, we also cut short its size.

Now let us increase the gravitational force and see the effect that has on T. rex. Remember the example of the astronaut losing 30% bone mass because of the weightlessness of space. With the increase in net gravity after the Flood, an immediate change occurred. Though T. rex was very strong and powerful, and may have been able to resist this change for a generation of two, it was unable to endure the increased gravity and remain upright as a bipedal creature, so on its belly it went, adapting with modified means of survival and mobility. T. rex learned that mobility was easier in the water. Those that made it to the watery habitats survived and learned a new way of life. Being on his belly forced its head and neck up. It still possessed a large powerful tail, but this large powerful tail was no longer used for erect posture and balance, but was now used for mobility in the water. Does this sound like any creature we may know and see today? How about the alligator? do not they look like a T. rex that has adapted to two major changes in environment, reduced oxygen and increased gravity? It seems plausible that T. rex is not extinct, but living amongst us as the alligator. Likewise, the velociraptor, a smaller relative to T. rex, may also be living amongst us as the crocodile. The crocodiles have smaller jaws than the alligator, and velociraptor had smaller jaws than T. rex. Otherwise, they had similar characteristics. *Photo credit: www.bbc.co.uk/nature/life/Tyrannosaurus. by John Sibbick. www.pinterest.com/pin/526428643926665072. Also, Gavin Chapman/Barcroft Media.*

With the plausibility that the T. rex adapted to become the alligator and velociraptor adapted to become the crocodile, what are some of the similar characteristics? All four lay a leathery egg. They are vicious predators at the top of their ecosystem food chains and have short and weaker upper/forward

arms, stronger and larger hind legs, a long strong tail, an elongated snout, eyes perched on top of heads, and reptilian skin with ridges on their back and smooth underbelly. They also have a proportioned tail-to-body length; the list keeps going. Just stand back and take a bird's-eye view of both the T. rex and the alligator and the velociraptor and the crocodile. The similarities are awesome. If we were able to travel back in time and see how increased gravity and decreased oxygen affected T. rex and velociraptor, we would expect to see them forced on their bellies and crawling, utilizing the water to mitigate against gravity. They would be smaller in size because of a reduction in oxygen. And we would expect to see them look and act like our modern-day alligator and crocodile.

Review: It is plausible that T. rex is not extinct, but living amongst us as an alligator, and that velociraptor is not extinct, but living amongst us as the crocodile.

How about the mighty Megalodon? They had teeth 5 inches long, and their bodies were approximately 50 feet long—the size of a school bus, but with jaws. Now reduce the oxygen in the water from pre-Flood conditions of, let us say, 16%, to the current-day concentration of 7%–8% oxygen levels. This would decrease growth rates and affect the size of Megalodon, but it would adapt to produce 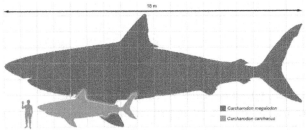 offspring that were smaller and smaller in size until we got to a size that is similar to our great white shark. Take a bird's-eye and a worm's-eye view of the Megalodon and the great white shark; they have the same features, proportions, and characteristics. It is quite plausible that Megalodon is not extinct, but living amongst us as the great white shark. *Image credit: comicvine.com.*

The great white shark still has the information in the DNA to return to Megalodon size. If we reversed the oxygen concentrations back to pre-Flood conditions and decrease gravity back to pre-Flood conditions, the great white shark would adapt and produce offspring that increasingly got larger and larger, until the size of Megalodon was restored.

Review: it is plausible that Megalodon is not extinct, but living amongst us as the great white shark. Take the mammoth, which is said to be extinct. But it has all the external and internal characteristics of our modern-day elephant. I contend that if we were living after the Flood and seeing through an accelerated time of several generations, we would observe the mammoth adapting to decreased buoyancy and increased gravity and decreased oxygen in the atmosphere. We would see changes to the following features through the generations: a shorter tusk (but consisting of the same tusk composite), the same short tail, the same trunk (but smaller), and basically the same image, but smaller. They would share the same likeness, personality, and diet. Essentially, if we watched the mammoth adapting to the changes in the environment through a time-lapse film, we would see the mammoth adapt to the elephant over a thousand-year period, not a changing of kind, but merely the same kind adapting.

What about the hair? The mammoth had lots of dense hair, and the elephant seems bald. Well, the elephant is not bald; it has the same type of hair, but it is just not dense. They adapted to the reduced oxygen by losing most of their hair. But they still have hair that is sparsely dispersed around their body. Is this so far-fetched that no one believes it possible? Before saying this is impossible, consider that losing hair is not impossible; some male humans lose their hair as they age. And all evolutionists believe that human beings shed their entire body hair heading into the ice age. Which seems less likely—that human beings shed their body hair heading into the ice age or that mammoths shed their hair from a lack of oxygen and adapted to the new environment as the elephant? It is foolish to think that through means of random, unguided mutations, humans shed their body hair while entering the ice age. We've already linked high oxygen levels with thriving life, and for the mammoth, that thriving life was represented by their large tusk, mammoth size, and dense hair. Elephants still have the tusk, size, and hair; they are just not as large due to the environment.

If one takes a bird's-eye view and a worm's-eye view of both the mammoth and the elephant and their similarities, one may conclude that the mammoth is not extinct, but living amongst us as the elephant. *Image credit: strangesounds.org.*

1: Songhua river mammoth
2: Columbian mammoth
3: African bush elephant
4: Woolly mammoth
5: African forest elephant
6: Asian elephant
7: Pygmy mammoth

My contention is that if we grew elephants in an oxygen-enriched atmosphere and reduced gravity and increased buoyancy, they would, based on information in their DNA, increase their tusk size and their overall size and grow dense hair again. This may not occur in one generation, but we would see slight changes with each generation that lived in a pre-Flood environment.

After all, male pattern baldness in men is due to a lack of oxygen supply to the hair follicle. Most people only hear that male pattern baldness is due to a lack of blood supply, but what does the blood carry? Oxygen. With a lack of oxygen, life suffers. But here, we are talking about the mammoth's hair. With a lack of oxygen, the mammoth's dense hair gradually declined in quantity and quality.

Review: It is plausible that the mammoth is not extinct, but living amongst us as the elephant. Everyone has seen drawings of **stegosaurus** (picture below), the dinosaur with the spinal plates on its back. Well, a small reptile exist in New Zealand, called a tuatara, has a distinctive features that are similar-looking, albeit much smaller, spinal plates or exterior spinal crest (fins) as the dinosaur stegosaurus. Tuatara's spinal plates point away from the center of the spine in an alternating fashion similarly to stegosaurus. The name *tuatara* means peaks on the back. *Photo credit: Wikipedia.org. Photo* *credit: www.thereptilereport.com.* The tuatara has similar skeletal and internal structures to stegosaurus and spinosaurus. It is plausible that either of those two dinosaurs adapted to the increased gravity and reduced oxygen and significantly reduced longevity of life and live today as a much smaller reptile. Any minor variances between the two are explained via the adaptation process over the generations from the pre-Flood conditions (low gravity, high buoyancy, and high oxygen) to the post-Flood (high gravity, low buoyancy, low oxygen) conditions. Spinosaurus seems to have similarities too. *Photo credit: Wikipedia.org. Photo credit: Alsipnursery.com.*

If we started with the tuatara reptile and raised it in a hyperoxia environment, with a high

buoyant force and weak gravity, the spinal plates of the tuatara lizard would enlarge to the size of a pre-Flood ancestor. Tuatara's size would enlarge over time as well with each generation. After several generations of the tuatara living in such an environment, it would adapt and could potentially become what we know as the stegosaurus or spinosaurus.

If we start with the stegosaurus and work forward in time to just after the Flood, the spinal plates on the back of stegosaurus living in post-Flood conditions (high gravity, low buoyancy, and low oxygen) would gradually get smaller and smaller, and so too would the size of the stegosaurus, until we arrived at the size of the tuatara or something similar. This means that stegosaurus or spinosaurus is potentially not extinct, but possibly living amongst us as the tuatara. The picture is of **spinosaurus** and a small reptile.

Review: it is plausible that the stegosaurus and spinosaurus are not extinct, but living amongst us as reptiles, possibly as the tuatara or some other lizard.

Evolutionists might critique this approach by noting that creationists do not believe enough time exist for evolution, yet they believe that 4,000 years is enough time for T. rex to evolve into an alligator or for velociraptor to evolve into a crocodile. No, that is not what I'm saying. If an alligator is indeed T. rex adapted over time to the post-Flood conditions, it would have similar DNA as a distant relative. Albeit the DNA would be slightly different because it is a copy of a copy of a copy, and so on. However, the identifying markers in the DNA depicting the kind of animal would be the same because the kind did not change. Therefore, plenty of time exist for adaptation to modify T. rex to an alligator.

The problem with evolution is not just time. It does not matter how much time is allowed, you can use billions or trillions of years, and it will not matter. Evolution utilizes random, unguided mutations of the DNA code for changes in function and kind. The odds of DNA code producing meaningful new functions that were not already in the DNA code is beyond possible. Remember that the odds[136] of random unguided changes to amino acids just for one single protein is 1 in 2 x 10^{195}. Evolution would need trillions of successful unguided changes to pull off some result in changes to different functions, let alone kinds. However, the DNA coding needed for adaptation is already embedded in the DNA code. This allows each life form to adapt to changes in the environment. When those changes are too much for that creature, guess what? It dies. It does not pass on any information to another creature to inform it to adapt differently. A common mistake by evolutionists is to see adaptation and confuse that with evolution. They are not the same. I was in a debate and an evolutionist proclaimed that I was playing games with semantics; he even used an illustration of driving a car, versus steering a vehicle. Let me be clear, this is not an exercise in semantics.

Adaptation does not require millions of year because the information to modify a feature, or adapt in some way, is already in the DNA code, and creatures always stay the same kind though man may categorize them as different species. With adaptation, plenty of time exist from after the Flood to before Christ to have T-Rex adapt to become an alligator and for velociraptor to adapt and become a crocodile. Therefore, an evolutionist using time as an argument is an ineffective means to support the premise of evolution because the problem with evolution is not time; they can have trillions of years, and it won't matter. The problem with the evolutionary hypothesis is a lack of information to begin with for the first living organism and a lack of information in the DNA code to change a function or kind of creature.

Ask evolutionists if they can name you one example of a mutation that increased genetic complexity. No naturally occurring example, evidence, or observation exist of a mutation that caused an increase in genetic complexity. Why? Mutations degrade the genetic code, not enhance it. It should be noted that evolution does not require just one lucky break in the billions of years for the success of evolution. Quite the contrary, evolution requires trillions upon trillions of random unguided mutations to enhance the genetic code for the successful occurrence of evolution, yet not one example in nature exist. This is a glaring fly in the ointment.

The concept of random, unguided changes to the DNA code is analogous to random, unguided changes to a software program, such as one that is designed to display a simple background color on a computer screen. Given enough time, would random changes in the code produce another functioning program, such as a word processor? The reality is that one single error in coding results in the entire program not functioning. That is what happens to life; when errors in the DNA code occur, the life form does not function properly. Instead, this results in stillbirths, sterility, premature deaths, physical mutations that prevent mating, weaknesses in defense mechanisms against predators, and so on. A mutation that has enhanced DNA coding has never been seen in nature. No one has observed mutations that led to a new function or that resulted in a new kind of creature.

If alligators are T. rex, they would be different forms of the same kind, and though mankind would classify them as different species, they would still be the same kind, with the same image and the same characteristics.

Review: If the alligators are a descendant of T. rex, they should have nearly similar DNA because they are copies of copies. This process would be through adaptation, which means the DNA necessary to adapt would already be in the DNA. The process of evolution does not have the information in the DNA to change and relies on the impossible means of random, unguided changes to DNA code to produce new functions and new kinds. *Adaption* and *evolution* are vastly different.

It is plausible that some dinosaurs are still living amongst us, but now they have been affected by reduced oxygen, increased solar radiation, decreased buoyancy force, and increased gravity and are

---

136 One out of 20 amino acids for a sequence of 150 chain is 20 x 20 x 20 x 20 . . . for 150 times. Some overlap exist in terms of 64 codons that make up the 20 amino acids, but we are not talking about the odds of making amino acids, we are talking about the odds of making a protein.

not as large as their fossilized ancestors. This explains why many cultures have dinosaur artifacts, drawings, engravings, and the like of dinosaurs before modern mankind had discovered such dinosaurs in archeological digs. While the dinosaurs were getting smaller and smaller, they were observed by ancient man and documented in carvings millennia after the Flood. People from different cultures chiseled replicas of dinosaurs out of stone after seeing those creatures. For example, in the exterior

Stegosaur
Depiction at Angkor Wat

walls of the **Angkor Wat Temple**, an identical replica of a stegosaurus was carved in the stone walls. It seems a plausible explanation that they knew what stegosaurus looked like because they saw it firsthand. People from a primitive culture would be more likely to replicate a stegosaurus because they saw a living one than it would be for them to discover the fossil remains and draw one. Without modern-day technology, it seems much more plausible that the Cambodians building Angkor Wat Temple saw a real-life version in front of them, and that is where they got the information to then chisel a replica on their walls. *Image credit: Sam at Samofindia.blogspot.com.*

Chapter Summary: Before the Flood, human beings lived 900+ years. After the Flood, the length of human life dropped dramatically with each generation. What changed? Oxygen levels, solar radiation was no longer shielded, the buoyancy force declined, and net gravity increased. This would also affect the dinosaurs. The Bible is clear that one of both male and female of every creature (including dinosaurs) entered the ark. Therefore, dinosaurs survived the Flood. And ~six generations later, in the Book of Job (chapters 40 and 41), two distinct dinosaurs are described in the present tense as alive and well: the behemoth and the leviathan. With the environmental changes, life span declined for all life forms, so dinosaurs did not live as long either. Since dinosaurs are reptiles, we know reptiles continue to grow as long as they are alive. Therefore, if a life is cut short, their size would dramatically be reduced as well. Their primary growth characteristics would be reduced and so too would their secondary characteristics. The saber-toothed tiger became the modern-day tiger. The mighty T. rex adapted and possibly became an alligator, and velociraptor adapted and possibly became a crocodile. Megalodon's size was reduced to the size of the great white shark. Mammoths slowly lost their hair and adapted to become the elephant. The size of the stegosaurus and its spinal plates were reduced to potentially a tuatara. The conclusion is that several dinosaurs are still living amongst us. They are not extinct; they just adapted to the new environment just like humans, who are also not extinct.

Chapter 26
<u>**The Big Bang and the Bible**</u>

Does the Bible support the "Big Bang"? Yes and no. The Bible explicitly records that God stretched out and stretches out the heavens, which means the Bible implicitly declares that the universe was small at one point in time. Consider Isaiah 40:22: "He who sits above the circle of the earth . . . who <u>stretches out the heavens like a curtain, and spreads them out like a tent to dwell in.</u>" Also, consider Isaiah 45:12: "I have made the earth, and created man upon it; I, even my hands, <u>have stretched out the heavens and all their host have I commanded.</u>" About 17 verses depict God spreading out or stretching out the heavens. It is clear in Scriptures that God spread out the heavens, which means that before He spread them out, they were closer in proximity. When was Isaiah written? About 700 BC, so this indicates that Isaiah supernaturally wrote that from the view of space, the earth appeared as a circle (the word *sphere*, or *sphaira*, was not invented until the Empire of Greece) and that the heavens were expanding, some 2,000 years before science confirmed this information. From deep space, no matter the angle from which one views the earth, it appears as a circle. Only a spherical planet will appear as a circle from every angle in space. Thus, through deduction, the Bible was ahead of its time by demonstrating that the earth was not flat as the scientist and early church once thought.

Some of the verses about God stretching out the universe are in the present perfect tense, explaining that what He did at creation is ongoing. This indicates a past event at creation in Gen. 1, that is also in the present tense, such as the universe is still expanding. Some verses explain that God stretched out the universe. Is this a contradiction? Can God have it both ways—that He has stretched out the heavens and is stretching out the heavens? It turns out that when God stretched out the heavens, this set them in motion, and astronomers have discovered what the Bible proclaimed 2,700 years ago—the universe is still expanding. Therefore, God did stretch out the universe and is still stretching the universe.

Does this violate physics? **Sir Isaac Newton** discovered a law of physics called the **first law of motion** (law of inertia and the conservation of motion). It tells us that an object at rest will remain at rest, and an object in motion will continue in motion with a constant velocity (that is, a constant speed in a straight line) unless it experiences an external force.[137] How did Isaiah know to write that God stretch<u>ed</u> out the heavens and God stretch<u>es</u> out the heavens? Isaiah wrote this in 700 BC, and Sir Isaac Newton did not pen the first law of motion till the early 1700s. Therefore, Isaiah wrote this 2,400 years before mankind new about the law. This is another illustration of the divine nature of the Bible.

The Bible describes the conditions of the universe at the end of the first day allowed for liquid waters. This was before the universe was stretched out and before the sun, moon, and stars were finished coalescing on the fourth day of creation. Gen. 1:2: "The earth was formless and void, and darkness was over the surface of the <u>deep</u>, and the Spirit of God was moving over the surface of the <u>waters</u>." For water to exist in the universe before the formation of the sun and stars, the universe had to be small enough to exert enough pressure to generate heat to keep the waters liquid. But the universe could not be too compressed because at the point of being anywhere close to a singularity (the point at which all the matter in the universe was the size of a dot eternally existing as energy) all liquid would have long since vaporized, and so too would all other matter at that point, leaving nothing but energy.

The Bible describes liquid water existing before God stretched out the heavens on the second day of creation and before the sun and stars were finished coalescing, which means that the universe was small enough to exert pressure that generated heat to keep some of the waters in liquid form, but not too small as to vaporize all water. What size would the universe have to be to have enough pressure to generate enough heat to keep the water liquid in space without any sun or stars? This is unknown; it could be the volume of hundreds of galaxies, or it may be the volume of a thousand galaxies.

It is interesting to note that scientists have just found out that the universe is expanding (in

---

137 Newton's first Law of Motion, *College Physics*, Serway & Faughn, pg. 56.

1925, Edwin Hubble), which means that the universe was smaller in the past. Also, mankind has recently, relatively speaking, discovered that exerting pressure generates heat (Guy-Lussac's Law), which melts ice. Also, that increasing temperature increases volume (late 1700s, Charles Law). Therefore, how did Moses, who wrote Genesis 3,500 years ago, know that the universe was stretched out violently on the second day—and that before the universe was stretched out and before the universe had the sun and stars—that water could exist in liquid form with a small universe exerting pressure to generate sufficient heat to maintain liquid water? I doubt seriously that Moses knew any of that. Many times in Scriptures, the writers had no idea what they were writing about. Daniel had to ask several times what the angel was showing him. Daniel 12:8: "As for me, I heard but could not understand." And Daniel 8:15: "When I, Daniel, had seen the vision, I sought to understand it; behold, standing before me was one who looked like a man. And I heard the voice of a man . . . called out and said, 'Gabriel, give this man an understanding of the vision.'" This demonstrates the supernatural divine nature of the Bible. The writers of the Bible wrote scientifically accurate information that is in harmony with physics some 3,500 years before mankind had any idea of the relationship between volume, pressure, and temperature. Moses likely did not know physics and chemistry. This leads the reader of the Bible to the real author, God. "All Scripture is inspired by God" (2 Timothy 3:16).

Review: The Bible implicitly declares that the universe was small before God stretched it out. The Scriptures record that the waters existed before the sun and stars finished coalescing matter, establishing that the universe was small enough to generate pressure and that this pressure was strong enough to generate heat to maintain water in a liquid state. But not too much heat to vaporize all the water. The Bible is at odds with the singularity and old universe hypothesis, but not with the Big Bang.

When did God stretch out the universe? The universe (the second heaven in relation to earth) was initially stretched with the creation of matter and energy that have volume, but this initial Big Bang was limited and brief due to the waters at the edge of the universe that did not have a heat source to keep them in liquid form. Thus, it is plausible that a shell of thick ice surrounded the universe by the end of the first day of creation, which allowed internal forces (heat, pressure, electromagnetism, and so forth) to quickly mount until God said, "Let there be an expanse in the heavens." This is the second Big Bang that violently stretched out the universe on the second day of creation. The expanding universe resulted in the atmosphere being stretched out. Note that the term *heavens* was pluralized in Gen. 1:9 (on the third day of creation). On the fourth day of creation, the sun, moon, and stars have coalesced enough matter for fusion by "let there be lights **in** the expanse of the heavens." The expanse of the heavens/universe seems to already be there for the sun, moon, and stars. It is clear though that on the fourth day the sun, and stars were ignited, and the planets and moons were finished coalescing.

Review: The Bible explicitly declares that God stretched out the heavens, which occurred on the second day, indicating that before God stretched out the universe, the universe was small.

The Bible does support that before the first Big Bang, the creation of all energy and matter, nothing existed. The Bible also supports that after the first Big Bang, at the end of the first day of creation, the universe was densely packed and small. But the Bible does not support that energy eternally existed as the singularity before the first day of creation. What is the difference between the Bible's Big Bang of "In the beginning God created" and "Let there be an expanse" versus the evolutionary "Big Bang"? The Bible has two Big Bang events. The first Big Bang is the violent creation of all the energy and matter, but that expansion was limited, which means the universe was densely packed at the end of the first day, which allowed water to exist in liquid form without the finished formation of stars to warm it. The second Big Bang is the violent expansion of the universe because of all the matter and energy. But where evolutionary Big Bang theorist go awry is that they remove God as the causal agent of the creation of all the energy and matter, and either say, "nothing banged, and out of that nothing came everything," or they say, "energy eternally existed as the singularity, and that Big Banged."

By observing that the universe is still expanding, we may infer that the further back in time we go, the smaller the universe becomes. But nothing in science or the Bible says energy eternally existed as the singularity. Only through philosophical views that God does not exist or that the Genesis creation account contains errors, does one start with energy eternally existed as a singularity. God directly testified, twice verbally and twice written in stone with His own hand, that He created everything in six days (Ex 20:11, 31:17). Therefore, no believer in God may accept the notion that energy eternally existed because this implies that God lied or deceived. All believers must accept that nothing existed before "In the beginning."

Although evolutionists and creationists agree on the premise of the expansion of the universe, neither camp can use science to prove the age of the universe. The reason is because no one knows the speed or duration of the universal inflation "In the beginning," and thus no one knows the volume of the universe at the end of the first day of creation (the first Big Bang, where God created all energy and matter by violent natural processes). Also, no one knows the speed and duration of the universal inflation during the second day of creation (the second Big Bang, where God expanded the universe by violent natural processes). Thus, by faith, creationists accept that God initially stretched out the heavens on the first day of creation, and additionally stretched out the heavens on the second day, and He did so with natural processes. Likewise by faith, evolutionists accept the idea that all the universe existed as a singularity and the universal inflation from the Big Bang was one billionth of a billionth of a billionth of a billionth of a second ($10X^{-36}$ second). All the estimations for determining a beginning point are man's conjecture, and seemingly, just to get us away from the Word of God.

How do astronomers determine that the universe is expanding? The year is 1925, and **Edwin Hubble**, utilizing the **Doppler effect**, determines that the universe is expanding. What is the Doppler effect? Austrian physicist **Christian Doppler**, in 1842, determined that a change in frequency exist for the wavelength of an object heading toward an observer versus the frequency for the wavelength of an object traveling away from an observer. For example, take a duck swimming in a pond. The waves of the water (wavelengths) in front of the duck are compressed (higher frequency and smaller distance of wavelength), and the waves (wavelength) behind the swimming duck are elongated (lower frequency and larger distance of wavelength). Therefore, just by looking at the waves the duck makes, one can determine which direction the duck is swimming.

Similarly, the sound of a siren on a police car traveling toward an observer has a higher pitch (sound waves are closer together, with higher frequency and higher pitch) versus the sound of a siren on a police car that is traveling away from an observer, which has a lower pitch of sound (sound waves are farther apart, with slower in frequency).

Similarly, light waves work on the same principle of physics. Light waves from a source traveling toward an observer are higher in frequency (blueish), and light waves from a source traveling away from an observer are slower in frequency (reddish). Utilizing Austrian physicist Christian Doppler's work, Edwin Hubble observed red and blue light emanating from different sources. Applying the Doppler effect, Hubble determined that since the source of a distant star is red shift, the source of the light is traveling away from the observer, leading to the idea that the universe is expanding.

<u>**Review:**</u> <u>The universe is expanding, which means that the universe is smaller as we go backwards in time. But how far back should we go, and back to what? All the way to God.</u>

How do cosmologists get to the notion that the Big Bang occurred ~14.6 billion years ago? They do it by estimating the relative distance traveled so far and dividing it by the estimated rate of expansion of the universe today to get an estimated origin date, and estimating a very brief universal inflation ($10X^{-36}$ second). The Bible partially agrees with this. The Bible declares that on the fourth day of creation, God finished making the sun, moon, and stars, and while creating those items, God placed them in a stretched-out heaven, in this case, the universe. Therefore, by working backward in time, one can surmise a smaller universe in the past using both the Bible and the Big Bang hypothesis. However, creationists contend the beginning was around 6,000 to 10,000 years ago. The problem is that no one knows the rate or the duration of the universal inflation that occurred from the Big Bangs. Also, no one knows the volume of the universe at the end of the first day before God expanded the universe for the second time on the second day of creation. Evolutionists contend the universe expanded faster than the speed of light (universal inflation) but for only one billionth of a billionth of a billionth of a billionth of a second ($10X^{-36}$ second). Their estimate of the duration is a guess, and if the duration of the universal inflation lasted a hours, the age of the universe would be very young, potentially 6,000 years old. This is because the universe would have expanded to an enormous volume, such as 90+ billion light years across, during those hours. Both evolutionists and creationists have the same precept of Big Bangs, though they use different nomenclature to describe similar events and accept a different duration for the universal inflation. But only the creationist has casual agent—God.

The "expanse" (raqayia) on the second day of creation, has a violent root (raqa) definition like a blacksmith hammering out iron. The imagery is of sparks flying, glowing hot metal, steam, violent force, and so forth. Thus, we may conclude that the Big Bang is a close representation of the expanse on the first and second days of creation. Amazing how the Holy Spirit guided Moses to choose that Hebrew word, that is associated with violent force, sparks flying, and rapid expansion. Creationists give credit to God for the violent expanse of stretching out the heavens, and evolutionists give credit to the natural processes of the Big Bang that stretched out the universe. A creationist will rightly argue that the design for the natural processes came from God, and this is where a theistic evolutionist smiles in agreement. Both creationists and evolutionists accept a moment of time of accelerated universal inflation immediately following the expanse or Big Bang. But they differ on the duration of the universal inflation and the starting volume of the universe on the second day of creation. A young universe premise does not conflict with science at any point. The only conflict of a young universe concept is with the man-made hypothesis called evolution, and the ~14.6 billion years required for evolution. For if the universe is young, evolution does not have enough time according to their slow evolving processes. The crux of the matter is this: Does one have faith that the universal inflation for the Big Bang was brief—a billionth of a billionth of a billionth of a nanosecond, which is 10^{-36} second, or does one have faith in God's Word with a small universe the size of ~100–1,000 galaxies by the end of the first day, and a violent expanse (second Big Bang) on the second day of creation, and a longer universal inflation duration, such as hours? Cosmologists provide their best estimates, in the form of a hypothesis, but they did not observe the duration of expansion in the beginning, and they cannot test the rate or duration of the expansion in the beginning, and neither can creationists. But most importantly, cosmologists do not know the starting point or the size of the universe when it started expanding. From what starting point did the universe start expanding? This is where evolutionary scientists are no longer practicing science, but a faith-based belief system. Both are faith-based as to the initial size of the universe, the date of the beginning, the rate of universal inflation, and the duration of the universal inflation. Creationists admit to having faith, and evolutionists try to say they do not have faith because it is fact. Both views cannot be correct, and the authenticity of both faiths hang in the balance.

At the start of the second day of creation when the universe started violently expanding, if that starting point was the volume of ~1,000 galaxies—and the duration of the universal inflation was minutes, the universe is young. If at the start of the second day of creation when the universe started violently expanding, if that starting point was the volume of ~100 galaxies—and the universal inflation was hours, the universe is young. If at the beginning of time when the universe first stated expanding from a singularity, if the duration of the universal inflation was $10X^{-36}$ second, the universe would be around ~14 billion years old.

A key to unraveling this mystery are the waters in Gen. 1:2. For waters (solid, liquid, gas, plasma, and abundant) to exist in the universe before God stretched out all the matter and before He formed the stars to warm it, the universe would have had to be small enough to generate heat and pressure to keep water in a liquid state, but not too small as to generate too much heat and obliterate all water. This leaves us with the notion that at the end of the first day of creation the universe was expanded to make room for matter and energy, but still densely compact so that waters could exist. Potentially the volume of 100–1,000 galaxies combined. With waters existing before the second Big Bang, that is, before the expansion of the universe on the second day of creation, means that the rapid expansion of the universe on the first day (the first Big Bang) was not exactly as evolutionists teach because water would sublimate to gas unless the first Big Bang was contained or limited. Therefore, to maintain water after the first Big Bang (the creation of all matter and energy) there had to be something natural that contained the universe from expanding with empty space in between the celestial bodies, and allowed waters to exist between all the celestial bodies (2 Peter 3:5). The solution seems to have a two part event to the expansion.

If the rate of the universal inflation did not cease after the creation of matter and energy, water would not be able to exist because of the rapid reduction of pressure would convert the water to gas, and the rapid reduction of temperature would sublimate the water from ice to gas, and that would result in no water existing during the first day. Since the Bible has water in abundance throughout the universe, and cosmologists accept water once existed throughout the universe, and every celestial body shows scars of remnants of water, the only theory that solves all the problems is the water at the perimeter of the universe, because there would be no pressure or heat around the outer circumference of the universe, a shell of ice surrounded the universe. This thick shell of ice would prevent continual expansion from the first day, and allow for natural internal forces to increase on a cosmic scale for the violent expansion of the universe on the second day of creation. The thick shell of ice allows water to exist during the first day of creation.

The size of the universe is a fine-tuning measurement—too small and dense of a universe at the middle of the first day of creation and water could not exist because of the intense heat and pressure. Too large with empty space in the universe at the middle of the first day of creation and water could not exist because of a lack of pressure and heat. Therefore, the volume and density of the universe at the first day of creation had to be just right to allow water to exist in a solid, liquid, gas, and plasma forms. Just picture this as the "Goldie Locks" scenario. The initial volume and density of the universe has to be within a range for water to exist in four forms—too small and then all the water is vaporized, and too large and then all water freezes to ice and sublimates to gas. The plural form of waters (ice, liquid, gas, and plasma) and which form they existed in was dependent on its proximity to a burgeoning, coalescing celestial body. The amount of energy provided to the water determined its state. All four states of water played a key role in expanding (second Big Bang) the universe. This is potentially why the Bibles pluralized *waters* in Gen. 1:2. Such as:

Ice: With no heat source on the outer rim of the small universe, the water located there would be ice. The ice acted as a thick outer shell to the universe, forcing pressure to build internally. Without this outer shell of thick ice, potentially thousands of miles thick, no pressure would build up, and then there would be no Big Bang on the second day of creation and no rapid release of pressure of the water that surrounded the early earth, and thus no atmosphere would have been formed on the second day of creation either.

Gas: The water near to the burgeoning, spinning, hot, coalescing stars, vaporized to gas. This process applied pressure inside the tightly packed universe for the Big Bang on the second day of creation. Without this water near the forming stars, there would be no gas, and no pressure, and no Big Bang. Therefore, without water, the universe would still be tightly packed, and all the trillions of individual coalescing stars would combine into one molten mass, with no individual stars, and no galaxies, just one gigantic molten core that was slowly expanding and slowly cooling.

Plasma: This is the highest state of water, with the most energy in it. Plasma existed by being within coalescing future stars and received the most energy.

Liquid: The water in between all the spinning masses that was far enough away to not vaporize, but close enough to remain liquid, provided the supply for either converting liquid to gas to increase the pressure nearest a heat source, and supplied the conversion of liquid to ice to seal in the pressure

191

furthest away from the heat. In this liquid medium of water, filling the tightly packed universe at the location of a formless and spinning earth that was void of life, we read of the Holy Spirit hovering over the deep in Gen. 1:2. The four states of water were made possible by trillions of spinning, coalescing masses (the future stars) at the beginning of the first day, though darkness was everywhere. With each passing minute on the first day of creation, trillions of coalescing masses gained mass and heat, until enough matter coalesced and enough heat was generated, that the future stars started to glow hot at the middle of the first day with, "Let there be light" (Gen. 1:3). The process of converting liquid water into gas by trillions of coalescing masses pressurized the small universe, and this pressure was sealed in by an external shell of thick ice. This was a key component of the Big Bangs (second day of creation). With the trillions of glowing hot coalescing masses spinning, they caused a flow of electrons, and this process resulted in a buildup of unstable amounts of positive and negative charges on a cosmic level. This process is similar to an alternator, generator, or thunderstorm that builds up electric charges. However, this was on a cosmic scale. When the pressure was near an unsustainable load and the electric charges were at an unstable level, God said, "Let there be an expanse in the midst of the waters," and lightning sprang forth throughout the universe; this was the final component, and this action on the second day of creation caused the Big Bangs. This rapid release of pressure from the Big Bangs caused our atmosphere to form on the second day of creation by a process called cavitation. This process can be observed by opening a new soda bottle. The spinning, coalescing masses (the future stars) continued adding mass until the fourth day, when they coalesced enough mass to ignite after God said, "Let there be light in the expanse of the heavens." Thus, God supernaturally used natural processes to fulfill His Word.

Review: Since God created all energy and matter on the first day of creation, theists must reject the theory that energy eternally existed as the singularity. Since waters is present on the first day without a star to warm it, the volume of the universe was large and densely packed, potentially the size of 100–1,000 galaxies. This allows for the four states of water; ice, liquid, gas, and plasma, which reveals the mechanisms that violently expanded the universe on the second day of creation. Evolutionists and creationists both accept universal inflation, they differ on its duration.

No one knows how fast the universe is expanding. People can only surmise that the universe is expanding from viewing the galaxies separating. But no one knows what the ratio of universal expansion (outer edges) is compared to galactic expansion (inner material). It is not a one-to-one ratio; it is more likely a sliding scale of faster expansion the closer to the edge of the universe. It is an unknown because no one can see the edge of the universe. But we might have a smaller scale model that may help us. When a grenade explodes, the highest velocity of matter are the initial particles traveling away from the central location, with a sliding scale of the slowest particles the last to leave the central location. Thus, the closer we visualize the outer edges of our universe, the higher the velocity of galactic expansion should be. This is exactly what Edwin Hubble discovered. When he viewed distant star light, he observed that the farther away a star, the more its light had a reddish hue. This indicated that the star with the redder hue was moving faster away. Thus, he applied the red-shift Doppler effect to the expanding universe and this is called, **Hubble Constant**.

It is interesting to note that the creation record is told from the perspective of Earth. Therefore, it is plausible that our galaxy, the Milky Way, could be near the center of the universe. Cosmologists have determined that every galaxy is expanding from every other galaxy. Even though this is accepted, there still has to be a center of all the expansion. That center could be our solar system in our galaxy.

Does the Big Bang theory conflict with the Bible? Not exactly. The Big Bang theory suggests that all matter (as energy) was compressed to the size of a dot and exploded some 14.6 billion years ago. This explosion set in motion all the natural processes we see today, meaning that everything we see today is explained by natural processes, and a God is not required. The Bible is in direct opposition to the singularity premise that energy eternally existed by declaring that all things were made in six days. The Bible is in direct opposition to the evolutionary time-line by saying that God created everything in six literal rotations of the earth (day) and rested the seventh day, with the genealogies suggesting that God's creation occurred some 6,000 to 10,000 years ago. And the Bible is in conflict with the order of the Big Bang with waters existing on the first day of creation, and we may infer that the conditions of the matter caused the second Big Bang/expansion. Otherwise, the idea of a Big Bang is fine as they sort of parallel the violent creation of energy and matter on the first day and the violent expansion on the second day of creation.

Can believers in God believe that God created everything through the Big Bang some 14.6 billion years ago and that the Bible is not exactly accurate, but merely exists to give us general ideas of what happened? They can believe this, but then they are calling God's Word a lie because God in the flesh declared that not one jot or tittle would pass from the law. God gave details of His creation in Gen. 1 and 2 and repeated it (twice verbally and twice written in stone) with a general summary of how long it took God to create everything in Exodus 20 and 31. The Bible says that the Word of God became flesh and dwelt among us (John 1:1–18). That is Jesus, the co-creator, the second member of the one God. Therefore, those who claim to believe in God, but declare His Word to not be accurate, are going against Jesus. Jesus said you are either for Me or against Me (Matthew 12:30), so those who claim that the beginning of time happened according to how evolutionary cosmologists say how and when it happened and not how God testified how and when He spoke them into existence are calling God a liar.

God testified that His Word is perfect, sure, right, pure, clean, and true (Psalm 19), so when God says He made everything in the heavens and on earth in the six days of creation, it is a litmus test of one's faith. But take heart because my hypothesis of interpreting the Genesis creation account will make it easier for you to accept a literal genesis creation account. For example, utilizing how scientists at the C.E.R.N. Hadron Collider converted energy into matter, is a plausible explanation for how God created matter on the first day of creation. Also, the principle in physics called cavitation to explain how God made the atmosphere from the pressurized water, that once surrounded the earth, on the second day of creation. Also, utilizing geologist's explanation of how land is rising today with Post-Glacial rebound, to explain how God gathered the waters together and made the dry land appear on the third day of creation. And the light at the middle the first day of creation with molten, liquid matter as the sun was coalescing matter, until the fourth day when enough matter had coalesced that the sun was able to fuse hydrogen.

When God created all the matter in the small universe on the first second of the first day of creation, all the matter, and energy came directly from God, from His actual essence (Colossians 1:15-17). The small universe had countless regions of spinning mass that began coalescing (growing in mass). This generated enough heat to maintain water in liquid form (Gen. 1:2). However, since the outer portion of the universe also had water but was not near a heat source, a thick frozen shell surrounded the small universe (the volume of ~1,000 galaxies). Potentially, the ice surrounding the small universe was tens of thousands of miles thick. At the middle of the first day of creation, the countless spinning and coalescing future stars accumulated enough mass and density that they began to glow hot from liquid magma upon God declaring, "Let there be light." As water vaporized near those countless spinning, and coalescing balls of magma, the pressure built up to unmeasurable amounts. In addition, the liquid metal cores that was rotating, caused electrons to flow and built up electromagnetism for each coalescing mass and built up electrical charge on a cosmic level. Until the internal pressure exceeded the tensile strength of the external frozen shell, as God declared, "Let there be an expanse in the midst of the waters," the small universe expanded with countless Big Bangs that stretched out the universe at the speed of light on the second day of creation. This universal inflation caused cavitation due to the sudden drop in pressure, converting water into gas that surrounded every planet in the universe, thus expanding the atmosphere on the second day with water below and water above our atmosphere. The universal inflation expanding the universe at the speed of light, slowed down throughout the second day by the gravitational force of each coalescing mass that would eventually form a star, and their gravitational forces slowed the universal inflation to the velocity we see today. With the earth spinning, and a sudden release of pressure and weight and reduction of heat on the soil from the recent expansion and from the distance from the coalescing sun increased, God spoke on the third day, and the soil expanded, and formed topography as seas moved to lower elevations because of Earth's gravity, and granite froze capturing polonium halos. By the fourth day of creation, trillions of spinning future stars collected enough mass and density to generate fusion that God spoke, "Let there be lights in the expanse of the heavens" just as the spinning balls of mass ignited into stars, and others finished coalescing matter together and formed planets and moons. The creation of life on the earth all came from God's essence as well and explains why we all share similar DNA.

Therefore, a believer in God can accept the expansion of the Big Bang, but not the concept of the singularity, or that matter did not exist prior to the expansion/Big Bang (second day of creation), or the old earth/universe hypothesis. In fact, scientists have discovered signatures in the universe as cosmic microwave background radiation that suggests past explosions. The prevailing hypothesis is one Big Bang, but viewing the ubiquitous nature of the **cosmic microwave background** radiation[138] indicates that the one Big Bang was comprised of trillions of simultaneous smaller Big Bangs.

Chapter Summary: It all comes down to the size of the compressed universe before God started expanding it. If the universe was the size of 1,000 galaxies combined, the duration of the accelerated rate of universal inflation was shorter. If the universe was the size of 20–50 galaxies, the duration of the accelerated rate of universal inflation was longer. Either size is acceptable, as long as the compression of a small universe generates enough heat to keep water in a liquid state, but not too compressed to vaporize all matter. Both rule out the singularity of the Big Bang hypothesis.

---

138 Science.nasa.gov/astrophysics/focus-areas/what-powered-the-big-bang/.

Chapter 27
The Big Bang Versus Physics

Does the Big Bang conflict with physics? A law exist in physics that says everything goes from order to disorder, from complex to simple, and heat flows toward a cooler object. This abstract notion from the **second law of thermodynamics** is called **entropy**.[139]

Big Bang theorists believe that the Big Bang exploded from the spinning hot massless energy of the universe, which was the size of a dot, and from that, all the natural processes we see today evolved. Everything—even the complexities of the DNA code, the information to form life, consciousness, and morality—came from chaotic disorder. To have all the universe squished to the size of a dot could be considered order on a gargantuan scale. Exploding the universe could be considered significant disorder. So far so good, right? But we have skipped a step. How and where did all the energy come from in the singularity? What is the intelligent source required to squish the universe to an orderly dot? This formation of all the energy and matter of the universe squished to an orderly dot is a violation of entropy. Before the Big Bang, everything went from disorder to an orderly dot of pure energy, spinning at high velocity called the **singularity**. That is backward to the law of entropy, which states that everything goes from order to disorder. The Big Bang hypothesis that everything in the orderly singularity explodes and goes from the disorderly explosion at the Big Bang to the orderly formation of all the galaxies is another violation of entropy. Going from disorder to order is backward and violates entropy.

Instances do exist of going from disorder to order in a smaller system, when an outside source (we'll call this outside force "A") applies a force to that disorderly system (we'll call the disorderly system "B"), but the overall entropy of both systems combined tends toward disorder. Also, the force being applied by the outside source "A" requires intelligence to utilize the force to cause the disorderly system "B" to be more orderly. As a result of source "A" applying force to another system, it becomes more disorderly, and the disorderliness of "A" is greater than the new orderliness of "B." Therefore, the net sum of the two systems is net disorder, which is in harmony with entropy. If we applied fictitious numbers to this principle of physics, it would look like this:

A: The outside source applying order is "A." Value: 100 equals highly ordered.
B: The disorderly system being modified is "B." Value: 10 equals disorderly.
C: The combined overall value is 110.
D: The cost of applying order is a two-to-one ratio.

Where "A" (the outside source with a value of 100 units of force) applies 20 units of force to "B" (disorderly system with a value of 10), the resultant change to "B" is +20 units of force, resulting in "B" having a value of 30. The cost to "A" applying the force equals –40. Therefore, the changes are:

Outside source "A": Value of 100 reduced by –40 = net 60, a decrease in order.
Disorderly system "B": Value of 10 changed by +20 = net 30, an increase in order.

The combined overall value is 90. Entropy increased as the two systems combined has less order. Therefore, although system "B" became more orderly, the overall combination of both systems tended toward disorder, which is in accordance to entropy. Creationists need to stop saying that order cannot arise from disorder because if an outside system applies energy, it is doable. What creationists should say is that even though order may increase when a force is applied, the overall order will always tend toward disorder. Hence, entropy always increases—but, and this is a big caveat, only when a design is already in place, when intelligence is involved in the process. We'll discuss this portion later.

To most honest evolutionary cosmologists and theoretical physicists, the enigma of the Big

---

139 *College Physics*, 2nd Edition, Serway/Faughn, pg. 324–331.

Bang is an unknown. The most honest explanation for the belief in the Big Bang comes from theoretical physicist **Michio Kaku**, who said, "We do not know <u>why</u> it banged, we do not know <u>what</u> banged, and we do not know <u>how</u> it is banging."[140] Honest evolutionists admit they do not know the "why, what and how" of the Big Bang; however, most evolutionists do not speak in such honest terms —instead, they proclaim evolution and the parameters of the Big Bang as fact. Take for example Lawrence Krauss, a cosmologist who explains the Big Bang not as a hypothesis, but as fact—as "the moment when everything we see, all hundred billion galaxies, each of which contains a hundred billions stars, all that material, was compressed in a region that was infinitely small."[141] This is a summary of the singularity, which is in complete opposition to the Bible that records that God created all things in six days, that includes energy (Ex 20:11). Also, that waters and dirt existed before the second Big Bang, before God stretched-out the heavens and created space in between celestial bodies. This is one reason a believer in God cannot be a theistic evolutionist. They must choose either to believe the likes of Lawrence Krauss who hates God or believe the Word of God.

Where and what is the orderly force that applied order to the disorderly universe that just exploded from the Big Bang? Some evolutionary cosmologists solve this problem by saying "We do not know yet. But just because we do not have the answer, does not mean the Bible is by default correct." Or they suggest the existence of multiple universes and say these other universes applied the necessary force to our universe. Big Bang theorists attempt to solve their problems by adding a large enough time coefficient and/or some unknown, non-observable, non-testable multiple universes. Often, I have read suggestions from evolutionists, such as given enough time, what is impossible becomes possible, and the possible becomes probable, and the probable becomes certainty, and the certainty becomes fact. What evolutionists are saying is that they concede it is impossible, but given enough time, the impossible is not only probable, but it becomes fact. It never ceases to amaze me the faith that atheists have. Sometimes their faith surpasses the faith of those who believe in God. The two belief systems are similar, as the Bible says, "With man this is impossible, but with God all things are possible." If this was not such an important topic, it would be comical how similar they are at times; both require faith, and both are a belief system. Christians admit they have faith and a belief in God, and atheists pretend they have no faith and no belief system—just unbiased science and empirical data and facts. The funny thing is that believers in God see that atheists utilize extreme amounts of faith and have a very strong belief system, but atheist cannot or won't see it.

The Bible foretold of mankind pursuing myths and legends of creation and rejecting the Bible's Genesis creation account (Romans 1:18–23) and chasing after their own desires and positioning teachers to teach them what they want to hear to tickle their own desires (2 Timothy 4:3–4). The Bible describes that God allows them to pursue their own desires and hands them over to a depraved, non-functioning mind (Romans 1:24–28). When debating an atheist who pulls out the multi-universe card as an explanation and says, "Given enough time, the impossible is not only probable, but certainty and fact," just remember the verses above, and if they won't hear science and Scripture, potentially they may be fulfilling the above verses; your best option is to gently and lovingly give them the seed of the Gospel and pray for them because their mind may be closed, and they potentially would rather believe evolution and the singularity construct even if it is shown to be false.

When one studies science and Scripture, without the influence of the uniformitarian theory, they realize that the entire Bible does not violate any laws of physics, including entropy, in regard to any aspect of Genesis creation, but specifically as it relates to the origin of the universe. In fact, entropy is supported in the Scriptures. It appears almost a millennium before science caught up to speed. Isaiah 51:6 and Hebrews 1:11 both explain that Heaven and Earth will wear out like an old garment:

You, LORD, in the beginning laid the foundation of the earth, and the heavens are the works of

---

140 How the Universe Works, "The most important second in history which seals the universe's fate."
141 Ditto.

your hands; They will perish, but you remain; and they all will become old like a garment . . . But you are the same, and your years will not come to an end.

Also, 2 Cor. 4:16 explains the outer man is decaying, which is entropy in a nutshell. This is another supernatural occurrence of the Bible talking about sound physics and knowledge of entropy 1,000 years before mankind had a clue. This is further evidence that the Bible was written by the inspiration of God. Isaiah wrote 700 years before the birth of Christ, that the entire universe, galaxies, and everything on Earth was wearing out in accordance to entropy. This was beyond human ability for anyone to know during Isaiah's time.

Does the Bible's creation account violate entropy by going from the disorder of all the water and dirt being formless and void of life in Gen. 1:2 to God creating extreme amounts of order through six days of creation? No. God is the outside source applying force to the disorderly system. Then, does God reduce in order? No. God is infinite and all powerful, infinity does not reduce (God's order). If we applied fictitious numbers to this scenario, it would look like this:

A: The outside source applying order is God. Value: infinite.
B: The disorderly system being modified is creation. Value: 0.
C: The cost of applying force is a two-to-one ratio of cost versus change. The overall value of the two systems combined is infinite.

Infinite God (the outside source) applies 30 units of force to B (the disorderly system, creation) with a value of 0). The resultant change to B is +30 units of force, resulting in B being at a value of 30. The cost to A applying the force equals –60. Therefore, the changes are:

A: God: infinite value reduced by –60 = net infinite.
B: Creation: value of 0 changed by +30 = net 30.
C: The overall value of the two systems combined is infinite.

It is a simple mathematical model, but when something is infinite, no changes to its value occurs. That is why the Bible is consistent with physics when the Bible declares that God is the same yesterday, today, and forever (Hebrews 13:8)—that God is infinite. All that God created is subject to entropy—the law is not, the truth is not, and the Word of God is not.

I was asked in a debate, "Does God have to trim His toenails and hair?" The answer would be no. Those things tend toward decay and disorder. God does not tend toward disorder. God the Father is invisible, and the Holy Spirit does not take on flesh, so we are only talking about God the Son here, and His hair and toenails stay the same length with His eternal immortal body. However, when He was born of Mary, Jesus trimmed his toenails and cut His hair because He shed His immortal flesh and took on mortal flesh.

I was asked, "Do we have the same DNA as God?" Since all of creation was made from God, everything would have some signature of God, some more than others, with humans having the closest DNA autograph. Since we are copies of copies with respect to DNA, the further back in time, the less mutations in our code and the closer our DNA gets to God's, with Adam and Eve being the closest replica of God's DNA. This is also in compliance with entropy.

Review: *Entropy* means that all things tend toward disorder. The singularity of the Big Bang hypothesis violates entropy by the idea that energy eternally existed, and the universe organized itself into an orderly singularity (a spinning dot); that's going from disorder to super orderly, which is a violation. It explodes into disorder (which is acceptable) and then proceeds to the order of all the galaxies we see today; that is another violation of entropy. But the Bible is in harmony with entropy and discusses the concept of entropy (that the heavens and the earth will wear out like a garment) almost 2,000 years before mankind found out about this law of physics.

Another aspect of entropy that the Big Bang theory violates is the design or intelligence involved in the application of force to move from disorder to order. Entropy states that all things tend from orderly to disorderly. The only way to go backwards, from disorder to order, is to have an outside intelligent source apply a force or intelligence involved in utilizing the force.

Why does design or intelligence have to be involved in the process of adding more order? Have you ever tried to clean your room by throwing a stick of dynamite in the room? Energy without intelligence is always destructive. Nothing organized can come out of an unintelligent force without design involved. But that is exactly what Big Bang theorists believe. The Big Bang, which is an unintelligent, non-designed force, fostered all the natural processes of nature that are intricately fine tuned—even the laws of physics—to form the galaxies and eventually all of life as we know it.

Big Bang theorists argue that this is a straw-man argument. In other words, I have set up a theory that Big Bang theorists do not believe, and then I have proven wrong a theory they do not believe as though they did believe it. However Big Bang theorists want to play with synonyms, they believe that an unintelligent explosion set in motion all the natural selection mechanisms (which is all governed by intelligent information called DNA) and all the complexities of life and order we see. This is a violation of entropy; something cannot go from disorder to order without an outside source and intelligence utilizing the force applied. How do evolutionary Big Bang theorists get around this? They cite the multiverse. They believe that an outside source from our universe is the fuel source for our universe to go from the disorder of the Big Bang to the order of the laws of physics, chemistry, cosmology, math, and biology and the complexities of life.

It should be noted that a multiverse is not observable, and cosmologists provide no explanation of the origins of the other universes affecting our universe. It seems that they use whatever their imaginations can come up with to support their established views and that is contrary to the Bible, and then they mock creationists for their alleged blind doctrinal faith and ridicule them for allegedly going against science. The atheists cry for tolerance and more tolerance, but they are intolerant of creationists. I have had atheists tell me that they openly and blatantly mock Christians for being idiots for believing in some magical God in the sky. The reality is that creationists and the Bible never go against science, but they frequently go against evolutionary scientists regarding creation and the origin of life.

What is sad is to hear of so-called believers in God proclaiming that they believe the ideas of mankind and their theories versus the Word of God. Yet, the Word of God is the one in harmony with physics by declaring that all of God's creation obeys entropy (Isaiah 50:6 and Hebrews 1:10–11).

God gives His own testimony to what He did and saw through His Word. To reject His testimony, yet claim to love and trust Him, is only fooling oneself. The eternalness of the singularity and the billions of years from the Big Bang, violates the Word of God and entropy.

The law of entropy explains that all things wear out, and all things tend from order to disorder. Does that mean the Bible violates entropy by saying God never changes and God is eternal? No. God is infinite. This means in mathematical terms and in physics that an infinite source will never reduce, never run dry, and never tend toward disorder, and therefore it is not in violation to entropy. The Bible is again in harmony with physics, and physics is in harmony with the Bible. The problem is the heart of man, who utilizes his own intellect to interpret data instead of the mind of Christ (I Corinthians 2:16). That is the problem; the problem has never been science. Science is a dear old friend to a creationist in the search for truth. Since science means to know, and physics is for us to understand all the workings in the universe, Proverbs hits the nail on the head with, "The fear/reverence of the LORD is the beginning of knowledge (science)," (Proverbs 1:7). Proverbs 9:10 says, "The fear/reverence of the LORD is the beginning of wisdom, And the knowledge of the Holy One is understanding." Therefore, the first steps to know and understand all the workings of God's creation, one must fear/reverence the LORD. Even a child that accepts the Genesis creation account, can speak profound knowledge with understanding, that is beyond the atheistic, erudite elites—just from simply reverencing God.

Review: The Big Bang theory violates physics by going from the disorder of the Big Bang to the orderly fine-tuned universe, utilizing no intelligence in the application of an outside source to evoke the necessary order we see in the fine-tuned universe.

Energy comes in many forms, such as light, heat, radiation, chemical, electrical forms, and matter.[142] The **first law of thermodynamics** says that energy can change forms, but it cannot be created or destroyed, and therefore, the total sum of energy and matter remains constant throughout the universe. In other words, if energy is decreased, matter increases, and vice versa, so that no change occurs in the total sum. Thus, it is called the **conservation of energy**.

How is this a problem? Also, where did the energy come from to compress the universe to the singularity and spin it, and where did the energy come from that made up the singularity?

This is a problem for evolutionists and Big Bang theorists because they either have to believe by faith that all matter and energy in the universe spontaneously evolved at some point in time or all matter and energy existed eternally.

<u>**Nothing existed:**</u> Some evolutionists believe that nothing existed before the Big Bang, and then the Big Bang and everything evolved out of nothing. This hypothesis has an increase in the total sum of energy. This belief is a violation of the first law of thermodynamics because this law states that the total sum of energy and matter cannot increase or decrease. Therefore, this belief is not based on science.

<u>**Energy and matter eternally existed:**</u> Some evolutionists believe that all matter and energy eternally existed before the Big Bang, then who/what created them, or where did it come from? Since energy and matter are observed and tested to not be eternal, and the second law of thermodynamics, Entropy, states that all things decay, all things go from order to disorder, then this belief is faith-based like a religion and is not science. Let that sink in for a bit. We know it is hard enough to squish a car to the size of a dot, let alone all matter and energy in the universe. All the matter in the universe was compressed to the size of a dot, and the amount of energy and design/intelligence required to compress all the matter in the universe is beyond calculations, and the heat generated from such a compression would consume the matter that was compressed. In other words, the matter would be used up to generate the heat because heat cannot be spontaneously created without something being used up. In this case, at the singularity, the matter would have been used up to generate the immense heat. The heat generated from the insane amount of pressure would be in the order of around 5.5×10^{28}°C to 1.0×10^{31}°C.[143] This would incinerate the matter and turn all the matter to heat and inert ash. Remember that with the conservation of energy, if the amount of energy (in this case heat) goes up, the amount of matter goes down, so the net sum does not change.

We all know that to do something, to move something, or to squish something down to a tiny dot requires fuel. One cannot have a motor move something without consuming some fuel to power the motor. One cannot perform a task without consuming some calories (fuel) in the human body. It is an axiom we all know that you do not get something for nothing, or from nothing. So the concept that all the matter in the universe, or "the fuel," did not get used up to generate the energy to squish the large universe into the size of a dot violates logic.

<u>**Energy eternally existed:**</u> Some evolutionists believe that only energy existed at the time of the singularity, and as a result of the Big Bang, then massless particles colliding at the speed of light formed all the mass of the universe

142 *College Physics*, 2nd edition, Serway/Faughn, pg. 312–314.
143 Wikipedia/Orders of Magnitude of temperatures.

we see today.

Big Bang theorists have thus shifted their concept such that—at the moment prior to the Big Bang—only energy was compressed down to the size of a dot and zero matter. All the matter in the universe, including all the stars, planets, and so forth, was compressed together so tightly that all matter existed only as energy and not as matter. In physics, matter and energy really are the same thing, so this hypothesis is acceptable in physics. The singularity hypothesis is only theoretical and not observed and has not been tested. What has been tested and observed via the **Hadron Collider**, is that trace amounts of matter can be converted from enormous amounts of energy. The **Higgs boson** particle establishes that massless particles can collect trace amounts of mass as they pass through a field of protons that have just collided into each other near the speed of light. When I say trace amounts of mass, I'm talking about the mass equivalent of 125 gigaelectron volts, which is 2.29×10^{-22} grams.[144] To put that in perspective, the average raindrop weighs about 2.0×10^{-1} grams, and a grain of sand weighs 4.4×10^{-3} g. Physicists have used energy to form mass that is 1.0×10^{-19} times smaller than a grain of sand and with an alarming amount of energy and intelligent design required to do so. To give an indication of the amount of intelligence involved, it is estimated that >10,000 scientist and engineers were involved in the project.[145] Not only that, they utilized 140 computing centers (which was the largest computing grid in the world, comprised with over 170 computing facilities) to analyze tens of petabytes (which is a million gigabytes). To illustrate the amount of resources involved, the estimated cost is ~$13 billion (as of June 2012) to find the Higgs boson, and $1 billion per year since the discovery. It takes ~180 MW (equal to about ~180,000 homes) to operate the facility at peak operation.[146] The magnets are 100,000 times more powerful than Earth's gravitational force on a per scale basis, which means if the magnets were the size of the earth, their strength would be 100,000 times Earth's gravity. All of this intelligence, design, force, and energy to operate one Large Hadron Collider, to collide two massless particles together at nearly the speed of light, and only produce 2.29×10^{-22} grams of matter. Thus, they have a long way to go to form something as large as a grain of sand and an infinitely longer way to go to account for all the matter in the universe. What they have established is that it takes intelligence to achieve what they have done—not random chance. Their work, intended to establish natural means of forming matter and to suggest that no God exist, has only firmly supported intelligent design. The large amount of energy/power required to collide two massless particles into each other and form miniscule amount of matter, establishes that only an all powerful God could have enough force, energy, design, and knowledge to create the amount of matter that exists in the universe.

Where did the energy come from? And what caused the orderly design of the singularity? This violates the first law of thermodynamics with the initial creation of the intelligent energy that formed the singularity and the creation of the energy contained in the singularity. When evolutionists argue that the energy eternally existed, this violates Entropy and is a religion.

Remember, nothing comes from nothing. The evolutionary response, is that just because they do not know where the energy came from, does not mean the theory is wrong, nor does it mean that creation is correct. Evolutionists solve the origin of the energy with a belief in multiple universes provided the energy. A multiverse is a leap of faith, the existence of only energy as a singularity is a leap of faith, and believing all matter formed from the Big Bang's energy is a leap of faith. This is fine to believe, but do not call it fact or science; a multiverse is not observable or testable. And we are back to the same problem, where did the energy come from to form the singularities and fill those singularities with energy in all the other universes. Eventually, evolutionists are left with a faith based hypothesis and violate either the first or the second laws of thermodynamics by believing that an increase in the total sum of energy and matter occurred at one point or everything came from nothing.

Big Bang theorists want people to believe that all the energy to squish the universe to a dot, and

---

144Http://en.wikipedia.org/wiki/Electronvolt#Mass.

145Http://en.wikipedia.org/wiki/Large_Hadron_Collider.

146 Http://en.wikipedia.org/wiki/Large_Hadron_Collider.

heat the dot, and spin the dot, and explode the dot, not only survived, and did not produce inert ash, but formed all the matter in the universe with ample energy left over. This energy somehow spontaneously evolved or came from an outside source, such as other universes. This is where science morphs into a faith-based endeavor and departs from the observability requirements of the scientific method.

Review: The Big Bang theorists that believe everything came from nothing violate the first law of thermodynamics, which states that the sum of energy and matter remain constant. The Big Bang theorists that believe that the energy eternally existed violate the second law of thermodynamics, which states that everything decays, everything goes from order to disorder, that no [created] thing is eternal. Therefore, Big Bang theorists violate the laws of physics from "In the beginning" just to reject God. It is science that exposes them as having a faith based religion.

How many times in your life have you had to try and try to get something correct? Rarely does something work out perfectly on the first attempt. Take a beginning golfer that has for the first time stepped onto a golf course—and let us make this the toughest golf course on earth. How many times will it take the novice golfer to achieve a hole in one? Take a beginning piano student—and set Beethoven's Fur Elise in front of the amateur. How many times will it take for the student to get it correct? Are you seeing the picture yet? Take a child just learning to ride a bicycle for the first time or to solve an algebraic math problem. The examples are endless. Rarely does anything or anyone achieve perfection or get something right on the first try. Using the scientific method, we observe that in almost everything we do requires some practice, some repetition, some redoes, and some failures to get it right, but not with the Big Bang. Oh no, on the first try, the Big Bang perfectly laid the foundation and set in motion all the laws, constants, and natural processes that eventually led to spontaneous life. Boy, we sure are fortunate to have gotten lucky with that accidental perfection. Imagine what kind of pickle we would be in if the Big Bang was too little of a bang or too big of an explosion.

This perfection on first attempt does not seem realistic. Even God had a redo with destroying mankind with the Flood and sending His Son to die on a cross for the sins of mankind. That seems to be the case, but it was mankind that needed the redo, not God. God actually planned out prior to creating anything that His Son would die for mankind to redeem mankind from their sins. God, with foreknowledge, knew that mankind, with free will, would fall short of His glory and be deserving of the penalty of sin, which is death. This demonstrates the mercy of God to withhold instant judgment on sinners who are deserving of instant death; this demonstrates the justice of God in rendering righteous judgments. This demonstrates the love of God in sending His unique, one-of-a-kind begotten Son to bear the full cost of sin for those who love Him. This demonstrates the grace of God to give freely, full forgiveness of the cost of sin to those who ask of Him. Where is it that God predetermined to crucify His Son before time began? Acts 2:22–23: "Jesus the Nazarene . . . delivered over by the predetermined plan and foreknowledge of God, you nailed to a cross." God does not increase in knowledge because He knows all things, so the predetermined plan was in place before God determined to create everything in six days.

The universe consists of finely tuned laws. Slightly altering one aspect of the fine-tuned laws would collapse the other finely tuned laws, which would eventually collapse the entire universe as we know it. Scientists place all the myriads of fine-tuned laws within our universe in a "Goldie Locks" scenario. Every parameter, every law, every constant, every element, and everything needed for life on earth was "just right." Take for example the mathematical form within nature. Albert Einstein had this to say after observing the mathematical precision and harmony of the universe and all that is within it:

You may find it strange that I consider the comprehensibility of the world (to the degree that we may speak of such comprehensibility) as a miracle or an eternal mystery. Well, a prior [deductive, derived by reasoning from self-evident propositions], one should expect a chaotic world, which cannot be in any way grasped through thought . . . The kind of order created, for example, by Newton's theory of gravity is of quite a different kind. Even if the axioms of the theory are posited by a human being, the success of such an enterprise presupposes an order in the objective world of a high degree, which one has no a priori right to expect. This is the miracle which grows increasingly persuasive with the increasing development of knowledge.[147]

Dr. Walter Bradley, who has a PhD in material science and a B.S. in engineering science, while discussing the strong nuclear force of atoms, had this to say:

> If the **strong force** which binds together the nucleus of atoms were just five percent weaker, only hydrogen would be stable and we would have a universe with a periodic chart of one element, which is a universe incapable of providing the necessary molecular complexity to provide minimal life functions of processing energy, storing information, and replicating. On the other hand, if the strong force were just two percent stronger, very massive nuclei would form, which are unsuitable for the chemistry of living systems. Furthermore, there would be no stable hydrogen, no long-lived stars, and no hydrogen containing compounds.

Even the expansion rate of the universe is finely tuned, says Gregg Easterbrook:

> If the expansion were slightly less, the universe would have collapsed back onto itself soon after its birth. If it were slightly more rapid, the universe would have dispersed into a thin soup with no aggregated matter. The ratio of matter and energy to the volume of space at the birth of the universe must have been within about one quadrillionth of one percent ideal![148]

The amount of matter also reveals how finely tuned the universe is. If you have too much mass, gravity, and density, the universe begins to collapse upon itself. Or if you had very little matter, you would have less gravity, and the universe would have continued expanding and would be freezing. A critical density is required for equilibrium to prevent the universe from freezing to death or collapsing upon itself, and to paraphrase Michio Kaku, Theoretical Physicist,

> That critical density is ~5 hydrogen atoms per cubic meter average throughout the universe. If there were more hydrogen atoms, then the universe would begin to collapse; if we had fewer hydrogen atoms, then the universe would expand to super freeze death.[149]

The finely tuned universe cries out precision, order, intelligence, and design, such that only an all-powerful God, knowing exactly the measurements necessary and requirements for life to be sustained, could have created everything. Psalm 19:1–3: "The heavens are telling of the glory of God; And their expanse is declaring the work of His hands. Day to day pours forth speech, and night to night reveals knowledge. There is no speech, nor are their words their voice is not heard." Since mankind has refused to cry out and acknowledge God, the universe stands alone and testifies for the almighty creator. Forever living in shame, mankind denies God and says that trillions of universes have undergone trillions of Big Bangs, and this one we happen to live in was the one that got it right.

> **Review:** "God's invisible attributes, His eternal power and divine nature, have been clearly seen, being understood through what has been made," Romans 1:20. The fine-tuned universe testifies day to day of the glory of God.

Scientists theorize that dark matter fills what was previously thought of as empty space between galaxies. Two teams of scientists studied 42 supernovas over an eight-year period and discovered something remarkable. When the stars exploded to cause those supernovas, the matter continued accelerating after the explosion as though something was propelling it faster and faster. We do not know why or what caused the acceleration, but scientists hypothesize that a new type of matter is the

---

147 Albert Einstein, 1956, Lettres a Maurice Solovine.
148 Gregg Easterbrook, Besides Still Waters: Searching for meaning in an age of doubt.
149 Michio Kaku, Theoretical Physicist, How the Universe Works.

cause. We cannot see it or touch it. Scientists call this alleged matter, "**dark energy**" or "**dark matter.**" It does not reflect light, it does not absorb light—thus the name dark matter. Further discoveries have suggested that dark matter has a repulsive gravity—a kind of anti-gravity in space that pushes all galaxies away from each other, accelerating the rate of universal expansion. As this acceleration continues, dark matter in space allegedly increases proportionately; as space doubles, dark matter doubles in mass and volume and causes more acceleration as it pushes galaxies farther away from each other. Some estimate that dark matter makes up 6X more weight than regular matter in the universe.[150] Additionally, cosmologists have determined that all the galaxies spin too fast to maintain their spiral appendages and shape, and should have flown apart by now because gravitational force and the distance between stars are not strong enough to keep galaxies together. The galaxy's spin generates centripetal force, which is greater than the gravitational force generated by the center of the galaxies. Therefore, if the universe is old then an unknown force is keeping the galaxies together because they should have spun apart by now—hence the invention of dark matter to save their belief. However, a creationist simply argues that the reason spiral galaxies have not spun apart is because they are young. Those who believe in an old universe at any cost, will invent a force to keep galaxies together and call their beliefs science.

Review: One of the oddities of the Big Bang theory is that on the first and only try, it perfectly laid the foundation and set in motion all the laws of physics, biology, astronomy, and chemistry. After violating the first and second laws of thermodynamics, then all the laws of physics were perfectly in place. Yet, the backbone of Darwinian evolution is that random, unguided mutations eventually, after billions of tries, got it right. The two polarizing theories conflict with each other. Mankind will go to the ends of the universe to say God does not exist.

Another law in physics that applies to this discussion is a principle called the **conservation of angular momentum**. This states that the energy, linear momentum, and angular momentum of an isolated system all remain constant. In other words, the direction of an object will remain heading in the same direction until another force alters its original direction. Big Bang theorists contend that at the moment of the Big Bang, the singularity was spinning ultra fast. Thus, matter that came out of the Big Bang should have conserved the angular momentum of the singularity and all spinning in the same direction.

For example, if a bunch of kids were spinning on a merry-go-round, and it spun so fast that the kids spun off, the kids would spin off with the same spin direction of the merry-go-round. Why? The outside portion of the kid's mass (the aspect farthest away from center of the merry-go-round) would be spinning faster than the inside portion of the kid's mass (the aspect closer to the center of the merry-go-round). The kids conserve the angular momentum of the merry-go-round and rotate in the same direction. How does this work for the universe and the Big Bang hypothesis? Cosmologists theorize that at the moment of the singularity, when all the energy and matter in the universe and the universe itself were squished to the size of a dot (existing only as energy), it was spinning at a tremendously high velocity. This means that at the Big Bang, all the matter that spun off to form the galaxies maintained the same directional spin as the source. The galaxies should be spinning in the same direction to not violate physics' law of angular momentum. But this is not exactly the case; some galaxies do not spin in the same direction—some counterclockwise, some with a 90° tilt, and so on.

How do evolutionary cosmologists get around this? They hypothesize that chunks of matter bounced into each other and altered their original angular momentum. Upon any explosion, the outer portion of the explosion will have the highest velocity moving away from the center. Then the next layer in will have a slightly slower velocity moving matter away from the center and so forth. With each fragment or layer getting closer and closer to the center of the Big Bang, the matter will have a slower and slower velocity leaving the center. This is exactly what Edwin Hubble observed, that the farther he viewed into space, the greater the red hue shift of the star's light. This discovery is called the

150 Dr. Andrew Benson, Theoretical Astrophysicist, How the universe works, Alien Galaxies.

Hubble Constant. This means that as the initial fragments of matter (which would become the size of a galaxy) spun off the singularity at the Big Bang, those initial fragments would be traveling faster than the next set of fragments. The **Cartesian coordinate system** elucidates locations in space. The system utilizes "X" for vertical coordinates, "Y" for horizontal, "Z" for depth, and "T" for time, and may help us understand this principle. During the Big Bang, fragments that came off simultaneously would not share the same X-Y-Z coordinates because they would be exponentially spaced apart from each other as they receded away from the singularity. And no two fragments from the Big Bang that would come off sequentially would be on the same X-Y-Z-T coordinates because their accelerations would differ.

Therefore, it is less likely that the galactic fragments would have collided, which means the theory of the singularity and Big Bang, as taught by evolutionists, needs some modification. Because if there was only one central spinning singularity and due to the violent expansion inherent in the Big Bang theory, then all the celestial bodies would be spinning in the same direction and not have the timing and proximity to collide with other celestial forming bodies to alter their angular momentum. This leads to the notion of how Scripture solves this problem.

When the universe was created on the first day, it was densely filled with all the matter and energy. Trillions of burgeoning spinning galaxies existed with future planets, moons, and stars coalescing matter, with no empty space between the spinning galaxies or celestial bodies. With a tightly compressed universe during the first day of creation, this is when, where, and how some galaxies collided and altered their original angular momentum. Then as the universe was violently expanded on the second day, this further altered the angular momentum to today.

As the Big Bang theory is postulated today, with empty space between matter from the Big Bang, it does not hold merit that galaxies bounced off each other to alter their original angular momentum. For this reason, creationists rightly use the Scriptures for clarity that the universe was tightly compressed with all the matter and water filling all the gaps between celestial bodies, which coincides with the theory that some matter colliding into each other during the first day of creation while the universe was densely compact before the violent expansion of the universe on the second day of creation. This explains why not all galaxies are spinning counterclockwise.

Some Big Bang theorists contend that matter did not exist at the time of the Big Bang, and the formation of matter occurred through time as energy collided together. And eventually, the matter coalesced <u>over time</u> to form planets, stars, and galaxies. To have matter coalesce, there needs to be a rotation at the core of the matter. Coalescing matter like a hurricane coalesces moisture is an excellent explanation of how we got all the planets, moons, and stars. This theory is accepted by both creationists and evolutionists, though they differ on the amount of time it took to form celestial bodies. But to have the coalescing component, there needs to be angular momentum—rotation. To argue that energy formed mass <u>over time</u> removes the closeness concept of the singularity that is essential to force massless particles to collide. The CERN Hadron Collider demonstrates the amount of intelligence, energy, and order required to cause massless particles to collide together in close proximity. The farther apart energy particles get from other energy particles, the less likely they could impact each other. Thus, the <u>over time</u> component actually undermines the hypothesis that the energy in the singularity formed matter.

The universe might take one of these shapes

Flat

Negatively curved

Positively curved

<u>**Review:** Big Bang theorists contend that the singularity was spinning ultra fast. Therefore, matter that came from the Big Bang should have conserved the angular momentum of the singularity. However, the galaxies that we observe do not all spin in the same direction, indicating that many collisions occurred while galaxies were in close proximity to alter their angular momentum, which supports that the universe was densely compact after the creation of all matter and energy.</u>

NASA has suggested that the universe is not spherical, but is flat like a throw rug or with sides curved downward, like a saddle on a horse.[151] Some cosmologists suggest that this presents a problem for Big Bang theorists because both of these shapes represent that the Big Bang had designed order.

Why is a flat universe a problem? When objects explode in a vacuum without resistance, they explode in a spherical fashion, which means the universe should be spherical, not flat. In other words, there had to be some type of design involved in the singularity of the Big Bang so that when it occurred, it did not obey a natural spherical explosion, but a flatter expansion. Any solution with an idea that the north and south ends of the singularity had more integrity, more stability than the equator of the singularity, constitute a designed order to the singularity. And any mention of a design of the singularity is not acceptable for their hypothesis. With an explosion, the place of the first displacement of matter would be at the weakest link, so even if they try to solve the flatter universe with an explosion following the weakest link at the equator and with the poles holding their integrity for a Planck time longer, it still means that the singularity had design, and that is a problem for Big Bang theorists. *Drawing credit: www.flatuniversesociety.com.*

When fireworks explode, they can cause the explosion to be spherical, circular, square, triangle, and so forth, but this presents design. No flat-designed firework explosion occurs by a natural, explainable process. Intelligence and a designer is involved. This leads back to a creation model and not random unguided events to bring about the order of the finely tuned universe.

Other cosmologists hypothesize that the flat universe that we perceive is just one morsel or thread of cluster galaxies, like a vast webbing of filaments, and our galaxy is in a tubular channel along with millions of other galaxies that make up one of trillions of tubular networks of connector threads or connector filaments. They suggest a bird's-eye view in which our galaxy is a  nano-speck in one giant neural structure of a brain-like structure that we call the universe. If this theory is correct, this also suggests order and design in the positioning of each galaxy, as the galaxies are positioned together to form clusters in an elongated tube like formation, and these channels of filaments connect other clusters of galaxies. The computer simulation models indicate lots of order, design, and formation. This is perfect for the creationist, but there should be randomness according to evolutionists. In the drawing, the measurement "Mpc/h" is megaparsecs or one million parsecs. The distance to nearest galaxy to us is ~one parsec.

Review: The Big Bang hypothesis leads to the notion that the universe is more spherical, as would be expected from a natural explosion, but some theorize that the universe is flat. Some contend that the notion of a flat universe suggests designed. Other cosmologists hypothesize that the flatness of the universe is merely one observable filament of millions of galaxies that make up millions of filaments called the universe. Both views have design and order as their foundations.

What does the Bible describe regarding the shape of the universe? Isaiah 40:22: "Who stretches out the heavens like a curtain, and spreads them out like a tent to dwell in." Curtains are flat. Also, the Bible clarified the solution 3,500 years ago. How?

When God created the universe, He stretched out the universe in a way that revealed His design, and He inspired Moses to write about it. Look at Gen. 1:6:

Then God said, 'Let there be an expanse in the midst of the waters, and let it separate the waters from the waters.' God made the expanse, and separated the waters which were below the expanse from the waters which were above the expanse; and it was so. God called the expanse heaven. And there was evening and there was morning, a second day.

---

151 NASA, Universe 101, Big Bang Theory, What is the Ultimate Fate of the Universe?Dec '12 Dr David Chuss.

The direct result of God creating energy and matter on the first day of creation, the first Big Bang, may have formed the filament clusters of galaxies, and God stretching out the universe on the second day, the second Big Bangs, is the creation of the space in the universe, which formed our atmosphere as well. The KJV and NKJV use the word *firmament* for expanse. *Firmament* and *expanse* are synonyms. The Hebrew word for "firmament/expanse" that God inspired Moses to use is *raqiya* (#7549), which means firmament or visible arch of the sky or expanse. Note that the visible arch of the sky potentially refers to the canopy that hovered around the atmosphere and/or the spiral appendages of the Milky Way Galaxy. *Raqiya* is derived from the root word *raqa* (#7554). The root word *raqa* means to pound the earth (as a sign of passion), by analogy to expand (by hammering), by implication to overlay (with thin sheets of metal), beat, make broad, spread abroad (forth, over, out, into plates), stamp, or stretch.

Moses wrote that when God began stretching out the universe, God expanded it like a blacksmith expands metal to make a sheet of thin metal, with violent force, sparks flying, hot glowing metals, and steam from vaporized water. This is the Big Bangs on the first and second days of creation.

It is ironic that NASA hypothesizes that the universe is flat or has many flat sections like threads, which fits the Word of God and the notion that God expanded the universe like a blacksmith would hammer out thin sheets of metal from one lump. Mankind has just recently formulated the Big Bang theory, and creationists resist this notion, but the words Moses wrote 3,500 years ago, indicates a violent expansion with force, sparks, glowing hot magma, water, and steam, but on a cosmic level—all the things that would be associated with a blacksmith expanding matter. Creationists should not reject the Big Bang, but consider the violent root word of expanse of creation and how it parallels a violent Big Bang (but rejecting the eternal singularity premise. This reveals that the Word of God was supernaturally written because Moses could not have known that the atmosphere was flat and thin on the spherical earth, or that the universe contained flat portions or is flat entirely, or that the expansion was a violent force. Imagine the problem for creationists if Moses had written that God expanded the universe with gentle separation; modern man would jump all over that error, but no error exist in the Bible, and no conflict with any of the sciences. Only now, as science catches up with the Bible, do we understand why some of the words in the Bible are there. This is truly remarkable evidence that the Bible was supernaturally written.

Review: Some theorize that the universe is flat or contains flat components to make up the whole, and the atmosphere is flat and thin around the earth, and God's word alludes to them as such 3,500 years before mankind even knew anything about the universe, providing more evidence of the divine nature of the Bible.

So far, we have discussed the notion that the singularity of the Big Bang goes against logic, physics, and the Scriptures, but the Big Bang has many workable notions that are acceptable. Big Bang theorists believe their event occurred ~14.6 billion years ago, and the Bible clearly says that God created everything in the universe in six days. The Bible clearly repeats that God twice gave Moses a verbal summary and twice gave Moses written summary in stone of His creation time frame (Exodus 20 and 31). Utilizing the genealogies in Genesis, it is apparent that the Bible supports a young earth and a young universe of approximately 6,000 to 10,000 years of age.

Chapter Summary: The singularity of the Big Bang hypothesis violates the first law of thermodynamics (the conservation of energy), the second law of thermodynamics (entropy), the first law of motion, (the conservation of angular momentum), and the Word of God. The Bible is in harmony with the laws of physics, and they are in harmony with the Bible.

Chapter 28

Evolution versus Mathematics

Chemical evolution (**abiogenesis**) is the theory that all life stems from one single-celled life form, which evolved from nonliving material in a complex chemical pool of amino acids. **Darwinian evolution** suggests that everything in nature can be explained by the natural processes of survival of the fittest and random, unguided mutations. From these natural processes, simple life forms gradually became more and more complex over time. Therefore, God is not needed. We will study Evolution versus Physics, Chemistry, Biology, Mathematics, and the Bible.

First, let us look at abiogenesis from a mathematical point of view. Sometimes when things get too complicated, one should go back to the basics. In math, any number multiplied by zero equals zero. Even if the number being multiplied by zero is very large or even infinite, it still equals zero. Assuming ∞ = infinity and 0 = zero, then $0 \times \infty = 0$. Therefore, life from nonliving material is impossible. Addressing this evolutionary dilemma of violating Louis Pasteur's discovery that no living thing comes from nonliving material and spontaneous life cannot occur, listen to the words of George Wald:[152]

> The important point is that since the origin of life belongs in the category of at-least-once phenomena, time is on its side. However improbable we regard this event, or any of the steps which it involves, given enough time it will almost certainly happen at least once. And for life as we know it, with its capacity for growth and reproduction, once may be enough. Time is in fact the hero of the plot. The time with which we have to deal is of the order of two billion years. What we regard as impossible on the basis of human experience is meaningless here. <u>Given so much time, the "impossible" becomes possible, the possible probable, and the probable virtually certain. One has only to wait; time performs the miracles.</u>

George Wald, speaking on behalf of the evolutionary community is saying, "With time being so large, the impossible becomes certain." This violates a simple principle of mathematics. Zero times any number, no matter how large, still equals zero. But evolutionists adhere to this erroneous formula: non-living material (zero) x long-enough time = life. Even a fourth-grade math student knows this is incorrect. But here is what evolutionists do to make their hypothesis seem viable: they add some important sounding words like *primordial* (first created/developed, original state) and *abiogenesis* or *biopoiesis* (life from nonliving material) and call the theory fact. Also, whenever anyone objects to this obvious violation of mathematics, they ridicule and mock them saying, "Christians reject science."

George Wald said, "One has only to wait; time performs the miracles." At least he admitted to a miracle. He just did not believe that God performed the miracle; "time" performed the miracle instead. On a Biblical level, this violates the first law of the Ten Commandments, "Thou shalt have no other Gods before me." George Wald, speaking for all the atheistic evolutionists, is unwittingly saying that "time" is the god that performs the miracle. This is blasphemy. And guess what? All those who claim to have faith in this belief that "life came from nonliving material" are failing at the rudimentary level of science, and that is observability and testability. Since this is not observable and fails basic math, the hypothesis should be scrubbed, not dogmatically believed in by atheists and believers alike.

It is sad to hear those who believe in God accept as fact this unproven, unobservable, untested, and failed belief system that says that spontaneous life came from nothing. They should believe in God's Word as fact. Otherwise, they are saying God's Word has errors.

Review: <u>Evolution's spontaneous generation of life from nonliving material violates basic mathematics: zero x any number = zero. Therefore, nonliving material x 4.6 billion years = nonliving material, not life.</u>

Let us go to an even simpler mathematical law to see how evolution violates math. Consider that any number plus zero equals the original number, represented by $n + 0 = n$. Let us say "n"

---

152 George Wald ,1958, wrote "Innovation and Biology" in *Scientific American*, Volume 199.

represent the primordial soup of complex chemicals and lightning and whatever condition evolutionists can come up with as the sum of nonliving materials. And let us say "0" represents the absence of life. We come up with the equation: nonliving material + absence of life = nonliving material.

Even if we wait and wait (which is "time" multiplied by "0"), the answer is still the same, (absence of life x 4.6 billion years) + nonliving material = nonliving material existing for 4.6 billion years. No matter how long one waits—and 4.6 billion years is a long time—the answer is still the same. Spontaneous generation of life does not exist.

Review: Evolution's notion of the spontaneous generation of life coming from nonliving material violates the most basic mathematical formula: $n + 0 = n$.

How do evolutionists get around this violation? Some have suggested that alien life initiated life on Earth—that literally, a living alien being came to earth and initiated life. But we are still back to the same question—instead of who/what initiated life on earth, now it is who/what initiated life on the alien home world that initiated life on earth. The violation still continues, but now it is more in a mythological realm.

Some, such as Richard Dawkins,[153] hypothesize that a meteor/asteroid (the alien) potentially brought just the right amount of amino acids to the planet. These building blocks then formed proteins and ultimately DNA in the primordial pool and initiated life. This is called **panspermia**.

Either way, this is still a violation of the simple mathematics of something from nothing: life from the nonliving. Evolutionists like to point out that mankind has made excellent strides in almost creating life from nonliving materials. But let us say that mankind did successfully create life from nonliving material. Would that validate abiogenesis? No. That would only validate that a creator was required for the creation of life, and not random, unguided chance. It would be mankind making life based on understanding science, technology, and knowledge and acting as God creating life. Mankind would then be the intelligent designer of the creation. It is a no-win situation for spontaneous life believers. Either they fail to prove life can come from nonliving material, or they are successful, which authenticates that a creator is required.

Do I think mankind could eventually create life from nonliving material? Yes and no. No, not in the sense of abiogenesis, with a single-celled organism that evolves from nonliving material without intelligence guiding the process. But yes, in the sense of intelligent design, guiding the process of creating a single-celled organism from nonliving material via science and technology. This will happen in the near future. Researchers are already working on isolating and repairing mutated recessive DNA codes that lead to diseases, and other researchers, like Craig Venter, et al., have taken simple single-celled organisms and taken out genetic code to find the base genetic code for life and self-replication; this is the tip of the iceberg of what mankind will be able to do. At this pace of accelerated knowledge and technology, whatever mankind can dream up will be tomorrow's reality. Why? Gen. 11:1–9, in reference to the Tower of Babel says:

> Now the whole earth used the same language and the same words . . . They said to one another . . . "Come, let us . . . make for ourselves a name, otherwise we will be scattered abroad over the face of the whole earth." The LORD came down to see the city and the tower which the sons of men had built. The LORD said, "Behold, they are one people, and they all have the same language. And this is what they began to do, and **now nothing which they purpose to do will be impossible for them**. Come, let Us go down and there confuse their language, so that they will not understand one another's speech." So the LORD scattered them abroad from there over the face of the whole earth; and they stopped building the city.

---

153 Richard Dawkins, leading evolutionist from a philosophical aspect and an elite mind in my opinion. I disagree with his beliefs, but highly respect his intelligence.

It seems we are approaching a similar point in the history of mankind again. Mankind has returned to the point of being of one voice and rejecting God. Mankind has returned to the point of using the same words, and those words seem to say that we evolved from nonliving material through evolution. Mankind has returned to the point of being one-minded by using resources and money in an attempt to support evolution and disprove the Bible and therefore disprove God. God said that when the people are one, "Nothing which they purpose to do will be impossible for them." Therefore, mankind is right now at the point of being successful in whatever endeavor it chooses to embark upon. In Strasbourg

France, people have built what seems to be a symbol of the Tower of Babel, with production posters that read, "Many tongues, one voice." Mankind is again at the precipice of repeating their actions of the Tower of Babel, that is of making a name for themselves and trying to take away from the name of God. But this will only repeat the same result and bring the return of the Lord with His judgment. *Image credit: Left to right: A painting of what the Tower of Babel may have looked like during construction. Painted by Pieter Breugel in 1563. The middle drawing is a poster used by the European Union while constructing the European Union Parliament Building in Strasbourg, France (image on the right).*

So evolutionists are in a no-win situation. Their attempt to support that God does not exist and make a name for themselves is only storing up wrath for themselves and will only fulfill Scripture and bring God down to Earth with His judgment as it did for the people of the Tower of Babel.

Wisdom says that if one does not learn from the past, they will repeat it. Look at the parallels: At the Tower of Babel, mankind had one voice and one language and used the same words; people pooled their financial resources to make a name for themselves and take away the name of God. They brought judgment and brought God to come down to the earth. We are at the same moment of historical precedence, just ~4,000 years later. Mankind has built such facilities as the CERN Hadron Collider to find proof of the "God" particle that started everything and that God is not needed to perform the miracle of the Big Bang. Mankind has spent billions of dollars on searching the stars, not to marvel at God's creation, but to find life on other planets to explain how life began on earth, without any necessary miracles and without God to start it all. This is a repeat of the same moment in history, the same thinking that mankind had at the Tower of Babel. And the result will be the same: judgment, the fulfillment of Revelation and all the "end time" prophesies and the return of the Messiah to judge.

The promise of God is that through the evil of mankind, God will make good come out of it for those who love Him (Romans 8:28: "And we know that God causes all things to work together for good to those who love God"). This is best exemplified with the crucifixion of Jesus (Act 2:23–24) and best summarized with this verse: "You meant evil against me, but God meant it for good to bring about this present result, to preserve many people alive" (Gen. 50:20).

<u>**Review:**</u> <u>Evolution violates the simple laws of math that say that zero times any number equals zero and that any number plus zero equals the original number. Mankind is on the verge of repeating the same mistake that humans made at the Tower of Babel, and the same outcome awaits them.</u>

Does the Bible violate the same mathematics when God created Adam and Eve? Let us take a look. God said (Gen. 1:26–27): "Let Us make man in Our image, according to Our likeness . . . So God created man in His own image; in the image of God He created him; male and female He created them." Then God gives us more detail of the creation of man with Gen. 2:7: "And the LORD God formed man of the dust of the ground, and breathed into his nostrils the <u>breath of life; and man became a living soul</u>." Did God violate mathematics and the law that says that anything multiplied by zero still equals zero? Let us break down the key words of the last bit of detailed information:

> *Formed* (#3335): *yatsar*: to press, squeeze into shape, to mold into form, as a potter.
>
> *Man* (120): *Adam.*
>
> *Dust* (#6083): *aphar*: dust, clay, earth, or mud.
>
> *Ground* (#127): *adamah*: soil redness.
>
> *Breathed* (#5301): *naphach*: to puff, to inflate, or blow hard; expiration.
>
> *Nostrils* (#639): *aph*: nose, nostrils; hence the face, a person.
>
> *Breath* (#5397): *neshamah*: a puff, as in the wind, angry or <u>vital</u> *breath*, divine inspiration, <u>intellect</u>. or an animal, (that) <u>breath (-eth)</u>, inspiration, <u>soul</u>, or spirit.
>
> **_Life_ (#2416): _chay_**: <u>alive, (as a noun) life, or living thing.</u>
>
> **_Living_ (#2416): _chay_**: <u>alive, (as a noun), life, or living thing</u>
>
> *Soul* (#5315): *nephesh*: a <u>breath</u>ing creature, i.e. animal or <u>vitality</u>, bodily or <u>mental</u>, soul, mind, desire, heart, man, him, her, me, one, own, person, self, or will.

A salient point is the similarities between *life* and *living*. Both words are defined by Strong's Concordance (#2416) as *chay*: alive, (as a noun), life, or living thing. This clarifies that from the Living thing, man became a living thing, or from the Life, man became a life. This clearly sums up that man did not come from nonliving material, but man/Adam came from living life, from God Himself. This means life begot life, not that nonliving material begot life as in the evolutionary model. This leads to the next part, which is what became alive? And that is the soul, the breath of man. What has always been the source of the soul and the breath of life? Well, that would be the Breath of God—the Holy Spirit. Similarities exist between the definitions of *neshamah*/Breath (#5397) and *nephesh*/Soul (#5315), and the root words they are derived from are similar as well. Both definitions share the meanings of *breath, mind, vital, and soul*. Thus, we may infer that the Breath of God begot the breath of man, and the Soul of God begot our soul. The Bible is in harmony with science again, that our mind, breath, vitality, consciousness, and soul, came from God's mind, breath, vitality, consciousness, and soul. Evolution stands alone in contradiction to biological and medical science with the hypothesis that life came from nonliving material. Science affirms that no living thing can come from nonliving material.

How did God make up the *life* that made man, shaped from red clay, *alive*? This is splitting the Trinitarian hair, but here it goes. When God (Elohiym = plural form of the one God, i.e., Father, Son, and Holy Spirit) created everything, He spoke everything into existence. The breath that came out of God's mouth as He was speaking was the moving of the Holy Spirit, and the Holy Spirit entered the man, who was shaped from red clay, and from *Life,* Adam became *alive.* How do we know of the Trinity that this was the Holy Spirit? When God breathed the *Breath of Life*, the word for breath was *neshamah* (#5397); that is, <u>wind, angry/vital breath, divine inspiration, divine intellect, soul, spirit</u>). The Hebrew word for *spirit* (as in the Spirit of God moving over the surface of the waters; Gen. 1:2) is *ruwach* (#7307), which means <u>wind, breath, violent exhalation, spirit</u>. They have very similar definitions. Ruwach is closely associated with *Neshamah/Breath*. In fact, *ruwach* is sometimes used as the Holy Spirit (Gen. 1:2) and sometimes used as breath (Gen. 6:17). Therefore, when God shaped man and then spoke him into being alive, it was because God the Spirit, the breath of Life, moved and entered Adam and made him alive. Life begot life.

Review: <u>The Bible indicates that the Breath of God begot the breath of man, and the Soul of God begot the soul of man, and the life of God begot the life of man. All that have the breath of life came from a living God. Only evolution stands firm in direct violation of biological and medical</u>

science that life cannot come from nonliving material.

Some debate as to whether mankind consists of two parts, such as dichotomy—body and soul/spirit, or has three parts, such as trichotomy—body, soul, and spirit. The confusion may be because the spirit of mankind came from the Spirit of God, and the soul of man came from the Breath of God—the Holy Spirit. Both the soul and spirit of man came from the Holy Spirit. It is true that upon being conceived, when the embryo (physical) is fashioned in the womb and the spirit is joined to the embryo, the soul is made and never separated from the spirit going forward. Therefore, the dichotomist are partially correct that a material aspect to man—the body, and an immaterial aspect to man—the soul and spirit exist. However, more information needs to be consider.

Medical science knows the difference between a joint versus the marrow within the bone. Also, we have all tried to explain the difference between our thoughts and our intentions (actions) when being misunderstood. But God always knows the line between the joint and the marrow, and between our thoughts and intentions. In fact, Hebrews 4:12–13 says, "The Word of God is living and active and sharper than any two-edged sword, and piercing as far as the division of soul and spirit, of both joints and marrow, and able to judge the thoughts and intentions of the heart." Therefore, the soul and spirit are different and distinct entities. Know this, that the Bible never wastes words, so if the Bible uses *soul* in some locations and uses *spirit* in other locations, a purpose exists. We may not fully know why for each verse, but that does not negate that the two closely associated, albeit different words, *soul* and *spirit*, have different applications and meanings.

Considering the above, and that the spirits of all life were created on the first day of creation and the soul/breath of life for Adam was made on the sixth day of creation, there seems to be a definable difference. The bird's-eye view of Scripture suggests that the spirit of mankind connects the body and soul to the spiritual realm. Ephesians 6:10–20 elucidates the point, "our struggle is not against flesh and blood, but against . . . spiritual forces of wickedness in the heavenly places." The flesh obviously is the body, and since God does not waste words, the blood adds additional information. The blood carries oxygen, which is from our breath, and our breath comes from the breath of life, which made us a living soul (Gen. 2:7), the blood represents the soul. Thus, we may interpret Ephesians 6:12 that we do not wrestle against human bodies and human souls, but against spirits in the spiritual realm. Therefore, our spirit connects our soul and body to the spiritual realm. Our spirit is either of the Light—alive without sin, and this influences our soul and body to bear Godly thoughts and actions, or our spirit is of the darkness—dead in sin, and this influences our soul and body to not bear Godly thoughts and actions. A dead spirit never ceases to exist. We have no power to raise a dead spirit back to life. This is where the Bible tells us that God is our source for faith and resurrection, and through God we have power over the spiritual realm. Our spirit may be considered our subconscious. This is why salvation is exclusively by God alone and no work can earn or improve on salvation (Ephesians 2:8). We can obey God's law to prevent our spirit from dying in the first place (Ezekiel 18:20,30), but all have sinned and fallen short of living without sin (except Jesus).

The soul (a breathing, conscious life) of mankind seems to connect the body to the spirit. Spiritually speaking, without the Holy Spirit we are dead in our sins though still breathing, and our soul will only desire for our body to carry out self glory, self worship, greed, only evil, we are alienated and hostile in mind toward God (Col. 1:21–22). With the Holy Spirit, we are alive in Christ, and our soul desires for our body to be morally obedient to God, to submit to the authority and ownership of God, and to revere God. This is where the Bible tells us to put effort in, to be diligent, seek truth, read the Scriptures to grow in wisdom, knowledge and understanding, sober minded, die to self, become more obedient, strive to sin less, to repent, and so forth. This is our part in doing work that authenticates that our spirit is saved (James 2:14–26). Physically speaking, without the Breath of Life, we are dead and dust we shall become. With the Breath of Life, we are alive to think, act, breath, have desires, and so forth. This is where the boy Jesus studied the Scriptures and increased in wisdom (Luke 2:52).

The body of mankind seems to connect the soul and spirit to the physical realm. The physical body manifests and represents the condition of the soul and spirit that dwells within the body. The body is a temple (I Corinthians 6:19), and either God dwells there and we see that manifested in our actions and words, or it is a temple without the Holy Spirit or with an evil spirit dwelling within, and we see the lack of Godly actions and words. Note that God purchased every body (temple) with His blood, but the free will of the soul must accept God through faith alone.

Review: The Scriptures suggest that life is made up of a body, soul, and spirit. A triune human made in the same image of a triune God (Gen. 1:26).

Now back to the question: Did God violate mathematics and the law that anything multiplied by zero still equals zero? No, because God breathed the breath of Life into Adam's nostrils from His own essence, and man became a living being. Adam became a living soul with a spirit from God the Spirit, as God the Father gave God the Son the Words to speak (three aspects of one God). Essentially, man was created from the very essence or a part of God. Not only were we created to look like God, and not only were we created to have some of God's characteristics (Gen. 1:26), but God gave us the breath of life from His very being (Gen. 2:7), exactly as when we perform CPR (mouth to mouth resuscitation). Therefore, the Bible does not say that Adam came from nonliving material—no, quite the contrary— the Bible says Adam came from "The Life Source," from God's breath (breath = ruwach" = Holy Spirit) of Life. Therefore, God breathed from Himself, from His Spirit, Adam's spirit into Adam, and Adam became a soul/alive. Man came from a living God. Life begot life.

The notion that Life begot life is supported in the genealogy of Luke 3:23–38: "Jesus the son of . . the son of David . . . the son of Judah, the son of Jacob, the son of Isaac, the son of Abraham . . . the son of Adam, the son of God."Adam was the first son of God. So the formula looks like this:

God spoke x (nonliving material red clay shaped into the form of man + Holy Spirit) = living man with the Holy Spirit dwelling inside man = God spoke x (0 + Breath of Life) = life.

Adam was the first son of God. This does not contradict the statement, "Jesus is the only begotten Son of God" (John 3:16) because Jesus has the title of being "First Born" (Colossians 1:15), but Jesus has always eternally existed (Hebrews 13:8 "Jesus is the same yesterday, today, and forever") as the co-creator of all things (John 1:1–3, Gen. 1:1, Colossians 1:15–17). This is rectified by understanding Old Testament, Abrahamic, and Davidic ways. The title of "First Born" usually goes to the first born son who was physically and literally born first. But instances occurred where the title went to a younger son, such as with Isaac (Gen. 21:13), Jacob (Gen. 25–27), King David (I Samuel 16:10–11 and Psalm 89:27), and even the kingdom of Israel (Exodus 4:22). They were all given the title of "First Born," but they were not physically born first. Isaac was younger than Ishmael, Jacob was younger than Esau, King David was younger than seven other brothers, and many kingdoms existed before God declared Israel His "first born."

When Jesus was born in Bethlehem 4,000 years after Adam, it had nothing to do with when Jesus came into existence. For Jesus has eternally existed as God in the flesh. However, Jesus shed His immortal flesh and put on mortal flesh and literally and physically was the offspring of God the Father, as was Adam. That is why Colossians 1:15 declares Jesus the first born of all creation; this is saying that Jesus has the title of being the First Born of God the Father physically, and spiritually over the real first born of God, Adam.

The change from immortal flesh of God the Son to the mortal flesh of God the Son (yet still maintaining His immortal soul and spirit inside), through the birth of the virgin Mary, was for the purpose of fulfilling God's Word with the final blood atoning sacrifice for all of Elohiym's creation— not so that Jesus could earn a new title of first born. Jesus already had the eternal title "First Born" in the spiritual realm before Jesus in Gen. 1:1 co-created everything with His Father and the Spirit. Now, at Jesus' physical birth, He revealed that He has always been the worthy possessor of the title of "First Born" of all of creation over the physical realm as well as over the spiritual realm.

Do not let anyone try to convince you that Jesus was a created being because He is physically and spiritually the possessor of the title "First Born" of all creation. Although Adam was the first physically begotten by God, the eternal God the Son has always possessed the title of "First Born" of all creation, without being a created being. It is simple; one cannot be created when you are the creator of all things (John 1:1–3 and Colossians 1:15–17).

Review: The Bible is in harmony with mathematics, as man was created from Life. Life passed on life. Life begot life. That's why Adam was the first born of God, but Jesus is the worthy possessor of the title "Firstborn of all creation" because all things were made through Him.

God has finished creating all things (John 1:3) and is now sustaining His creation (Colossians 1:17). All the spirits of every human and every moving thing that has the breath of life and angelic hosts were created during the six days of creation. I contend and will show later that our spirits began on the first day of creation. When a baby is conceived, the spirit is not created. This means that with each conception of a life/soul in the uterus, the spirit is not created, it is united or joined with the energy carrying "unit" passed down by the parents, called the body, and becomes a living soul. At conception, the spirit joins the newly fertilized egg in the womb and becomes a living soul and wait nine months for birth. That is why abortion is murder and continues on the pagan worship of the Ammonite god, Molech.[154] That is why a new birth is God sustaining His creation, not still creating, as He did on the first six days of creation.

The body, soul, and spirit are from God's essence. The spirit of man is one of the things created with the light on the first day without the sun, moon, and stars being created until the fourth day of creation. God is light, and He took some essence of Himself to create the spirits. That is why the souls and spirits and angelic hosts are immortal because God is immortal. So essentially, Life begot life, God begot the souls and spirits from Himself. The formula for the creation of Adam would be as follows:

Shaped man of the red clay, but not alive = 0.

God = Infinite = ∞.

God's Spirit/God breathed = infinite = ∞.

(Formed from the clay but not alive + God's Spirit) x God spoke = Adam, a living being with a soul and spirit, joined to the body. $(0 + \infty) \times \infty$ = Adam.

Now according to this formula, this would make a portion of Adam infinite, or in other words, immortal, and a portion of Adam mortal. That is exactly what mankind is, a mortal temporal body with an immortal soul and spirit. The mortal aspect of our body is exemplified with the paraphrase, *from the dust you came and from the dust you shall go* (Gen. 3:19 and Ecclesiastes 3:20). Eventually, humans will be clothed by God with an immortal body to house our immortal soul and spirit, but currently we have a mortal body. When everyone gets their immortal body, the source will be divine, and some will worship God with that eternal immortal body, but most will suffer in the Lake of Fire with that eternal immortal body.

The Bible says, "Jesus is the Way, the Truth and the Life" (John 14:6). All those that are not with Jesus are dead in their sins. Is John 14:6 only referencing the spiritual aspect (as far as salvation), suggesting that Jesus is the Life for salvation only, and not also physical life? Maybe, but I'm thinking it also represents the physical. How about John 1:3–4: "All things were made through Him (Jesus), and without Him nothing was made that was made. In Him was life." Jesus is the "life" giver in that Jesus was "life" from the beginning. Thus, as Jesus spoke, He breathed His "life" force, the Holy Spirit, went into Adam, as the Father gave Jesus the Words to speak creation into existence. Therefore, Elohiym (Father, Son, and Spirit) created everything.

Review: The Bible is in harmony with mathematics because the life found in the first man was from a living God. The Bible explains that life on earth came from Divine Life and that life begot life, which is in harmony with math. However, evolution is in violation of math by suggesting that life came from nonliving material.

Even the most basic mathematical formula (n + 0 = n) is in harmony with the Bible. Remember

---

154 Lev. 18:21, Jeremiah 32:35: They would sacrifice their children to appease their god Molech.

that evolution violated mathematical addition with: Nonliving material + time = life. However, their formula should be: non-living material + time = very old nonliving material, not life.

Review: Evolution violates the most basic mathematical formula of n + 0 = n (nonliving material + absence of life = nonliving material, not life), no matter how long one waits. However, the Bible is in harmony with n + 0 = n (God is life + nonliving material = life (Bible records that chay + nonliving material = chay).

What about all the animals? Does the Bible indicate how they were created, and does the Bible violate the same math that evolution's spontaneous life violates? Let us take a closer look. The Bible gives us some general information about the creation of all matter in the universe, though void of life and formless, with Gen. 1:1: "In the beginning [time] God created the heavens [space] and the earth [matter]." Then God gives us some detail with Gen. 1:20:

Then God said, 'Let the waters teem with swarms of living creatures, and let birds fly above the earth in the open expanse of the heavens.' 21 God created great sea monsters and every living creature that moves, with which the waters swarmed after their kind, and every winged bird after its kind . . . 24 Then God said, 'Let the earth bring forth the living creature according to its kind; cattle and creeping thing and beast of the earth.'

Then we get a little more detail about the creation of the animal kingdom with Gen. 2:19: "**Out of the ground the LORD God formed every** beast of the field and every bird of the air." Then we get some more clarity with Leviticus 17:10: "And whatever man . . . who eats any blood, I will set My face against that person who eats blood . . . For the life of the flesh is in the blood, and I have given it to you upon the alter to make atonement for your soul, for it is the blood that makes atonement for the soul." And then finally Gen. 6:17: "I am bringing the flood of water upon the earth, to destroy all flesh in which is the **breath of life**."

Putting the pieces together, every life that has the blood and breath of life on earth—the creatures became living souls: (a) God formed them out of the ground just like God formed man; (b) and God breathed the breath of life in them, just like God breathed the breath of life in man. The same concept applies, that everything on earth that has the blood of life in them came from the breath of Life, a living God. Life came from Life. The Bible is consistently in harmony with mathematics, even with the creation of the animals. This is why all creatures on earth share some similar DNA. All that have the blood of life in them originally came about via the same breath of Life (Holy Spirit) entering their oldest ancestor. This is why the Levitical law required life for life. This law in Leviticus was for governments to rule the people, not for people to exact their own revenge. Jesus clarified for the individual to turn the cheek and allow God and the government to render justice according to the crime.

Some naysayers may argue that the text does not directly say that God breathed the breath of life in the animals. But, no one can talk without the breath of life flowing through them. Try talking without any breath; it cannot be done. We were created in His likeness. Just imagine God saying, "Let there be," with His voice having the "Breath of Life" (Holy Spirit) flowing through Him. With His Word, He created everything. His words are powerful, and since we are an essence of Him, our words have power. With our words, we confess God as Lord of our lives unto salvation (Romans 10:9); with our mouth, we can edify our brethren or cut down our brethren (James 3). God used His Word to call into existence life from His breath of Life as He breathed into their nostrils/face/personage.

It should be noted that all of creation shares the same 20 amino acids, which are the building blocks of proteins from the DNA that determines what does what and what looks like what. Evolutionists argue that because everything has the same amino acids, it is proof that we evolved from the same single-cell organism. But no observable evidence exist to support this, so it fails the scientific method. The Bible reveals why everything alive shares the same amino acids and similar DNA: we were created by the same God and in a similar fashion. God formed living things from the clay of the ground and breathed the breath of life into everything that has the breath of life (blood). Everything was made from and through God.

The Scientific Method requires a hypothesis to be observable and testable. Always, 100% of the time, we observe and test that life always comes from a prior life. By the way, the very same scientific method applied to the origin of the DNA results in the same conclusion. Always, 100% of the time, DNA for life comes from a prior life. Never has it been observed or tested that the DNA for life has come from non-living material. Therefore, only two logical conclusions exist. Either this concept of life from a prior life repeats for eternity past, which cannot be because we know the earth is finite and had a beginning. Or at some point in time in the past, an immortal life begot life on Earth. Those are the only two options from what we observe and test. A hypothesis that must be fully rejected based on the scientific method, is that at some time in the past life came from non-living material because that has never been observed or established by tests. For this reason, only the Bible is in harmony with science. Only the hypothesis that evolutionists start with is a violation of science. Therefore, the study of modern medical science of genetics proves the Bible is the only one in harmony with science, and proves that only evolution is in violation with the science of genetics.

To split the Trinitarian hair; Jesus is the one doing the talking (Gen. 1:26, Colossians 1:15–17, John 1:1–3). The Father gives all the Words for Jesus to speak into existence (John 12:49), and the Holy Spirit is the breath that moves and enters the newly formed being to begin life (Gen. 2:7 and Gen. 1:2). All three aspects of the one God were equally involved in creation as one God—just like a human being has three aspects to make up one person: body (Jesus) that is the image of the mind, the mind/soul (Father) that gives the body the words to speak and connects the body to the spirit, and the spirit (Holy Spirit) that connects the mind and body to the spiritual realm. That is why, in Gen. 1:1, "God" in Hebrew is "Elohiym," which is the plural form of the singular God, the Trinity. This is also the same reason that Gen. 1:26 has God saying Let Us make man in Our image according to Our likeness. God is using plural personal pronouns to describe again the plural form of the singular God (The Father, Son, and Holy Spirit as one).

It is sad to hear about believers in God, who reject what God said He did at creation to form life and believe the schemes of man on how life began (abiogenesis), but put the tag on it "God did it" to make themselves think they are not guilty of annulling Scripture (Matthew 5:19). Man's way is proven to be a mathematical violation of "something from nothing" and is a violation of biology and medical science of "something from nothing." God's way has life coming from Life, and since God is infinite and all powerful, "something came from everything." This is completely against man's view that "something came from nothing." The two views are polar opposites. Do not think you can believe a little of both. It is either all of one or all the other. An in-between position does not exist, no lukewarm spot, no partial scatterers, and no partial gatherers; you are either all for the Word or all against the Word. One cannot even say, "This isn't my fight; I'm not involved." No middle ground exist either (Matthew 12:30).

Review: Evolution's spontaneous life from nonliving material (abiogenesis) violates the most basic   mathematical formula (zero x any number = zero). The Bible is in harmony with mathematics because the life found in the first man was from a living God. The Bible explains that life on earth came from life. God begot Adam (Luke 3:38). Life begot life with the formula of God x (nonliving material + Holy Spirit/*chay*/breath) = life. Evolutionists believe something came from nothing, while creationists believe something came from everything.

Evolutionists believe that unguided, random mutations made meaningful changes to the DNA code that provided new information to evolve life into greater complexities and completely new kinds of creatures. What the general public does not know is that the human DNA code is so complex that if the DNA code was typed out on paper on the front and back sides and the pages were stacked on top of each other, the pile of pages would be as tall as the Washington Monument. Displace one small section of coding and malfunctioning mutations would occur, including disease, impairment, stillbirths, early death, or sterility.

Any computer programmer will tell you that when writing software programs to perform a simple function, if one error occurs, the program will not work properly. Computer software programs are similar to DNA coding in that errors in both result in malfunctions of the program. Both systems require a specific design to be able to function, and if left alone, will not add extra code. But evolutionists believe that random, unguided, mutations made meaningful changes in code to create new coding that was not there before for new functions or a new kind of creature. The odds of this is beyond the realm of possibility. The odds of random, unguided mutations producing meaningful changes to proteins that are not life threatening to an organism—let alone producing a series of proteins and their accompanying genes and let alone producing a whole section of DNA coding having meaningful changes of kind—are beyond the threshold of possibility. Any computer programmer will tell you that random, unguided changes to coding are more likely to degrade the code rather than enhance the code. A computer programmer writes simple programs compared to the DNA code, and one code written wrong in a computer causes the whole program to fail. Yet, the simplest living organism is trillions of times more complex than a computer program. To know that a simple computer program fails with one mistake in software coding, yet still believe that random, unguided mutations to a complex organism creates meaningful changes and leads to a new kind of creature, is an amazing leap of faith.

As a doctor, I can tell you that mutations accelerate the death process; they do not enhance life. When a mutation occurs and kills the host, no information is passed on to a surviving neighbor to tell them not to mutate a protein of the DNA coding in the same area. Since evolution is based on random, unguided chance, when a mutated DNA strand occurs that leads to death, no intelligent being is taking notes of the error and trying a different sequence of the DNA code to change the poor result to a more beneficial result. This is what intelligence does; it sees poor results and modifies things to achieve a better result, but unguided, random mutations do not have that process. Let us say that one change in the DNA code results in a modified protein that does not kill the host, but the next random change does kill the host, the information is neither shared nor passed on to another. Usually, the body dies from a mutation; most of the time, the body rejects the mutation and wars against it. Sometimes, the mutation causes the body to be sterile. Most of the time, mutated creatures are rejected by the opposite gender as being unworthy to reproduce with. Sometimes, a mutated creature is rejected and killed by the same gender. Usually, the harshness of the weather kills off mutated creatures. The mutated creature is always weaker and more prone to sickness and poorer health. If the weather does not kill off all the mutated creatures, the predators get them. Mutated creatures are always slower and less coordinated, with less endurance and less strength. As a result, they are easy prey for predators and are the first to be killed.

Here are the obstacles for a mutated creature to overcome:

1. Mutated creatures are often born dead.

2. Mutated creatures often die shortly after birth.

3. Mutated cells accelerates death (e.g., cancer).

4. The body rejects mutated cells and wars against them; this leads to frequent sickness.

5. Mutated creatures are often sterile and are unable to pass on any inherited modified DNA coding.

6. Mutated creatures are rejected by the opposite gender and therefore cannot pass on DNA.

7. Mutated creatures are rejected by creatures of their own genders as unworthy members of society and killed.

8. Weather kills off most mutated creatures because mutated creatures are weak and frail and prone to sickness and disease.

9. Predators kill off the remaining mutated creatures. Mutations make a creature slower, weaker, with less endurance, and less strength; sometimes mutated creatures have all these deficiencies.

An even greater problem for natural selection proving evolution is that natural selection is based on a preexisting DNA code; one cannot argue for evolution based on natural selection when the DNA code built into each creature for natural selection has no origin, but just an existence.

When one takes the sum of the problems that mutations have to overcome to evolve a new function or to evolve from one kind of creature to another kind of creature, it becomes an impossible feat. The probability for survival is such a small number that it renders the hypothesis implausible. MIT graduates can calculate the odds to be more than $1/10X^{400}$ or whatever extremely small number, and computer programmers can tell you that random mutations ruin a program, not enhance it. But the bottom line is that if people take a bird's-eye view of the problem mutations have to overcome, they will see that the evolutionary hypothesis of random, unguided mutations being able to beneficially change a function of a protein or change the kind of creature is implausible—just based on the survivability of mutated creatures. This does not even consider that no information exist in the DNA code to establish a meaningful change of function or change of kind. In other words, without the DNA information already being in life, no way exist to get the code in without an intelligent designer putting it there. The hypothesis of utilizing natural selection to pass on genes that have undergone random unguided mutations turns a blind eye to the probability of the creature being sterile, stillborn, weak, and so on.

Mathematically, evolution is impossible. For when a mutation occurs, too many obstacles exist to overcome. The altered DNA would still have no information for creating a new kind of creature; all that the altered DNA would have is a degraded DNA code of the original host creature. As much as evolutionists want to believe that mutations build on other mutations to eventually generate a wholly new kind of creature, it is implausible. Do not confuse mutations with adaptations; they are different.

A mutation is a change from a normal cell to an altered cell by inherited trait or biochemical change in the genetic material, with abnormal function and/or impaired function. This change is not hardwired into the DNA, and the cells that mutate are foreign to the body. This causes the host to suffer on some level. These changes are random and unguided. But evolutionists believe that random mutations that are unguided can alter the DNA in a meaningful way and build upon the changes to create a new kind of creature; this is not what happens. Any unguided change to the DNA code produces an adverse effect, not a beneficial effect. In addition, any altered cells from an outside source still does not have the DNA information to utilize the alteration and build upon it. It is like tossing a splinter at a large building and believing that splinter will cause the building to evolve into a new structure given enough time. Mankind will soon be able to make guided changes to the DNA code to produce a beneficial effect, such as removing a mutated disease code in the DNA. This, however, establishes that intelligence is required to change the DNA code, not unintelligent, random, unguided mutations.

Adaptation or specialization is a small change(s) to conform to a new environment. The ability to adapt is already hardwired into the DNA, and the cells that adapt remain normal to the body, and the DNA remains the same. Why? In the words of Grady McMurtry: "The Laws of genetics are conservative, not creative; these laws only allow for the copying or rearranging of previously existing information which is then passed on."[155] Such as the Galapagos finches, they already had the information in their DNA from their ancestors for a particular beak shape, and if their beak shape better suited the environment, they will thrive and reproduce more offspring that also has the information in the DNA for the beak that allows them to thrive in a particular environment. Thus the DNA information for that particular beak dominates the population, through a process called natural selection. But this is based on information already existing in the DNA code, not new information embedded in the DNA code. This is not evolution, this is adaptation.

DNA code can change, such as combining chromosomes from parents. But this is not evolution either. A creature will adapt over time to form different species of the same kind, and this is all based on existing information in the DNA and the kind of creature will never change because the information changes occurs in the epigenome, whereas the DNA remains unchanged. This is how the wolf adapted

---

155 Grady McMurtry, "Nine great proofs for evolution and why they are all false."

through many generations to be related to the common house dog. A process of natural and artificial selection but always based on exiting information in the DNA. This is a process is called adaptation, not evolution.

Another way of changing the DNA or genome is with random, unguided mutations from external stimuli, such as chemicals (toxic chemicals, drugs, etc.) and high-frequency energy (UV rays, X-rays, Gamma rays, etc.), and this always results in a loss of functional DNA information, which results in either impairment of function or a loss of function; never ever does a mutated DNA result in the gain of new functional information that results in new function or a new kind—ever. Only in the science fiction movies, will chemical or solar energy, result in an improvement of the DNA. This is evolution. This is the error of evolutionists; they want to believe that adaptation is evolution, but the two concepts are vastly different.

Another means of changing the DNA code is with internal stimuli. Such things as stress, obesity, and other sins, may adversely alter our genome; the spiritual realm affecting the physical realm. Exodus 20, the Ten Commandments, God says He will visit the iniquities of the fathers to the third and fourth generations of those who hate God. Sin adversely alters our genomes, and when we reproduce, our chromosomes may contain the mutated genome that resulted from sin. Thus, a sinful parent, may pass down defective genomes in their chromosomes for fertilization, that passes on the effected genome from our sin. For example, say a father abuses alcohol and on a spiritual level, he is worshiping himself with his lust for physical satisfaction, and adversely affects his genomes for the internal organs. Now when he has children and passes on his mutated genome, his heirs have a higher propensity of organ failure. Therefore, fulfilling the Ten Commandments of having no other god before God, or else God will visit the iniquity of the father to the third and fourth generation. In this example, this resulted in a loss of efficient information in the DNA code. On a genetic level, a further deviation away from Adam's DNA, and since Adam's DNA 100% came from God's DNA, then the sin of the father, altered his DNA further away from a copy of God's DNA, and the father therefore, caused his heirs to be further away from God. By the way, this example can be illustrated with all the acts of sin that may adversely affect our genome. Even stress can adversely affect our genome. Stress is a result of not trusting in God. When one trusts in God, they will have no fear though they walk through the valley of the shadow of death (Psalm 23). When someone trusts in the Lord, they will receive a peace that surpasses all understanding (Philippians 4:6–7). However, God is merciful and full of grace. Offspring can break some inherited curses from sin, and that is with forgiveness of sin and obediently following the precepts in the Bible. Forgiveness of sin and obedience to God causes the spiritual realm to beneficially heal the physical realm. Such as with the body being free of sinful lifestyle that adversely affect the genome, the body can repair the damaged genome with protein markers that are designed by God and embedded in the DNA to hunt down mutations and repair them. This is adaptation, not evolution because the information already exists in the DNA. This is why the Ten Commandments follows the warning to the fathers with; "but showing lovingkindness to thousands, to those who love Me and keep My commandments" (Exodus 20:5–6).

The adaptation aspect of genetics has limits as to how far and to what extent life can adapt. It allows a closer copy of the original DNA to survive and be passed down. Changes to the genome are designed and guided by DNA coding. Evolutionists see adaptation and mistake this for evolution. But that is an error in deduction, as the ability to adapt is already in the DNA code, so it is not the DNA that changes, it is the body's response to the outside stimulus that is modified because the preexisting DNA tells it to, and this all occurs in the epigenome. *Image credit: Understanding Evolution, UC Berkeley.*

Evolutionists are notorious for showing examples of creatures that have lost a function because of mutations and proclaim this proves evolution, that mutations gain new information over time. For example, they cite flies with four wings and say, "See, evolution." But what they do not tell you is that the fly cannot fly, so it is an example of a lost function; other flies will not mate with it, so no genes get passed on, and sometimes they are sterile. Another notorious example that evolutionists use is the fruit fly drawing, with different colored bodies because of adaptation. But what they won't tell you is that (a) it is a drawing, (b) they are still fruit flies, and (c) all adaptation is based on DNA already being encoded. Therefore, their drawing of fruit flies changing body colors would only be possible because the information to do so is already in the DNA and this adaptation occurs above the DNA in the epigenome.

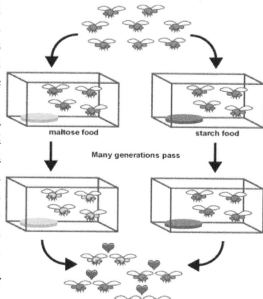

maltose food   starch food

Many generations pass

Review: The kind of creature will not change with adaptation (governed by preexisting DNA); only a different aspect of the DNA code is predominately displayed via natural selection. DNA will change with mutations from sin, chemical, or high-energy radiation, and this always results in a loss of functional information that results in an impaired function or loss of function, and natural selection (governed by preexisting DNA) results in mutated creatures not being selected for mating.

Stephen Meyer, a super bright fellow and author of *Darwin's Doubt* and *Signature in the Cell*, has written about overwhelming evidence regarding the improbability of random mutations evolving new genetic DNA to form new functions or new kinds of creatures and about intelligent design in the DNA code. He has utilized the scientific method and the peer-review process to authenticate a time-tested hypothesis that says that all life has intelligent design, and therefore an intelligent designer brought forth life, rather than the unlikely hypothesis of random, unguided mutations of evolution.

Chapter Summary: Random, unguided mutations are more likely to ruin the DNA of the host and kill the host than enhance the DNA and result in a different kind of creature. The odds of mutated creatures surviving and procreating to pass on their altered DNA code is impossible. There is too much to overcome: stillbirth, very short life span, sickness, weakness, malfunctioning vital organs, reduced immunity, sterility, rejection by the opposite sex, rejection by the same gender, weather, and predators. The odds are against evolution, and this demonstrates the extent of evolutionists' faith.

Chapter 29
Evolution Versus Physics

Evolutionists believe that billions of years ago, when the earth was hotter, rain came down upon the earth and formed pools of complex chemicals of amino acids, the building blocks of life. Then, given the right conditions (no UV rays and no oxygen because they degrade proteins, cell components, and amino acid and nucleotide sequences for proteins) and enough time, life came from nonliving material and that the first life form was a single cellular organism. Via the means of random, unguided mutations, some form of a proto-RNA replicating entity evolved into the first prokaryote life form, and the complexities of life that we see today came via a natural selection process called the survival of the fittest and random, unguided mutations.

The hypothesis of evolution violates the second law of thermodynamics (entropy). Entropy suggests that all things go from order to disorder, from complex to simple. Going from a simple single cell to the complexities today is in violation of entropy. The evolutionary counterargument is that outside forces applied energy to allow the smaller system to tend toward more order. This is a valid argument on the surface. However, intelligence must be involved in the process for that to occur. For example, the sun's energy is a standard source that an evolutionist uses to support how more order occurred. The problem is that if life does not have the necessary information already in the DNA to utilize the sun's energy, only destruction results from the sun's energy. Take the human body; we already have information in our DNA code that allows us to utilize the sun's energy to produce vitamin D; we also already have melanocytes in our dermis that have information about how to protect us from the sun's harmful ultraviolet rays and that reduce the amount of UV rays that penetrate our skin to damage our collagen and adversely affect our genomes. Without the necessary DNA code, humans would only decay from the sun's energy. Case in point, in the vinyl roof of a car, no intelligence exist to utilize the sun's energy, and the roof obeys entropy as it tends toward decay. Look at botanical life forms; they have the necessary DNA code to utilize the sun's energy for photosynthesis. Without already programmed DNA code, the sun's energy is never utilized to tend toward more order. The sun's energy is only harmful and destructive.

Review: The concept of evolution, of going from a simple single-celled organism to the complexities of today, violates physics; the second law of thermodynamics (entropy).

Even $H2O$ already has a design inherent in its structure, which allows water to form and bond together due to the covalent bonds of $H2O$ at a 109.5° angle. Sophisticated evolutionists use a clever argument of a snowflake to support the idea that things tend toward order as evolution tends toward more complexities.

Evolution's answer to their violation of the second law of thermodynamics is with a question; they'll ask, "Can order come from disorder?" All untrained students will say no. Then the evolutionist will show pictures of a snowflake, with the inference that order arose out of the chaos of random raindrops. Then they demand that you can never say that evolution violates the second law of thermodynamics and entropy.

But it is a trick question! The question should be, "Does order come from disorder without intelligence?" Then the answer is always no. Let us take a look at this snowflake trap that evolutionists use on people. The question, "Do water molecules frozen into a snowflake demonstrate going from disorder to order?" The answer is yes, but with an overall loss of energy as the molecules slow down with more and more loss of energy as they cool. Thus, although the order increased in the crystallization of the snowflake, the overall system tended toward entropy with the loss of energy/heat. The salient point is the molecules are positioned according to their designed structure—the intelligent design. Within the design of a water molecule, the position of the "H" atom with the "O" atom causes the location and positioning of other molecules to become attached. The snowflake indicates design because of how the molecules are positioned according to the 109° angle of covalent bonds and how they crystallize based on altitude, pressure, and temperature. The evidence of design is inherent in the water molecule, and this design is what shapes how a snowflake is formed. It appears that a snowflake is more orderly, but it is based on the preexisting design order of a water molecule that dictates the order of a snowflake, and the overall system results in the loss of energy, so even a snowflake is in harmony with entropy, as are all things.

Evolutionists also argue that adding energy results in less entropy and more order and that the sun's energy is the outside source that is applied to the earth. Thus, they say that evolution tending toward more order is not in violation of the second law of thermodynamics—entropy. But adding energy does not add order unless intelligence is involved in terms of how to utilize the energy. Energy is purely destructive by itself without intelligence to utilize the energy. Evolutionists may cite a plant as evidence of random glucose transforming into an orderly state. However, with closer inspection, an overall lose of energy occurs, and intelligence is intricately involved in each process. The plant took a lot of energy to absorb the CO_2, water, nutrients, and sunlight, and the DNA in the plant orchestrated each process. The bottom line is that intelligence is required to utilize energy; otherwise, energy is destructive.

Review: Moisture going toward the orderly shape of a snowflake is not an example of evolution being allowed to violate the law of entropy because an overall loss of energy occurs as the moisture cools, and the formation of a snowflake is based on the intelligent design inherent in the angle at which the hydrogen atom bonds to the oxygen atom. This angle and the altitude, barometric pressure, and temperature determine the finished design of a snowflake and cause no two snowflakes to be alike. Evolutionists cannot use the snowflake as an explanation that evolution does not violate entropy. The DNA of a plant is intelligently designed and utilizes the sun's energy. Energy by itself without intelligence is destructive. Thus, evolution still violates entropy, a law of physics.

Evolution violates another law of science. This law was first discovered by **Louis Pasteur** in the late 1800s. Pasteur discovered that life has not and cannot be spontaneously generated from nonliving material. He proved that life only comes from life. This is called biogenesis, which means "all life from life." Evolutionists use several methods to get around these violations of the laws of science, as listed below.

1. Time

Evolutionists argue that "Given so much time, the 'impossible' becomes possible, the possible probable, and the probable virtually certain. One has only to wait; time performs the miracles."[156] This violates simple mathematics, which says that any number multiplied by zero equals zero. Saying that "time performs the miracles" reveals that the hypothesis of evolution is a faith-based belief system.

For evolutionists to say that they believe in the miracle of time, which assures an extraordinary event that has never been done before or since, is leaving the world of science and entering into the realm of a faith-based belief system and mythology. When they argue that they have science to back them up and that they do not believe in a fairy-tale god, they are forgetting that their belief is unobservable and has failed all scientific tests. Observability and testability are the two bedrocks of the scientific method.

2. Terminology

The idea is to bury any violation of the laws of physics or logic in scientific terminology that confuses the populace. For example, Darwinian evolutionists will not say they believe in spontaneous generation of the first life, but they will say they believe in abiogenesis. What? This is double talk, as abiogenesis is life that comes from nonliving material; they have the same definition. It all sounds very technical and scientific, but it is really just fancy words for saying that one believes that life spontaneously

---

156 George Wald ,1958, wrote "Innovation and Biology" in *Scientific American*, Volume 199.

spawned—that life came from nothing. Some evolutionists have even used debating tricks, such as abiogenesis has nothing to do with evolution because evolution is only about life evolving. However, the concept of life evolving cannot occur unless life exists. According to evolution, the first life came about by abiogenesis. Thus, evolution has everything to do with abiogenesis, albeit chemical evolution.

How about the phrase, "ontogeny recapitulates phylogeny," by Ernst Haeckel in the late 1800s? Let us break down these fancy words. *Ontogeny* is the growth (size change) and development (shape change) of an individual organism from an embryo to an adult. *Recapitulate* is to restate briefly or summarize. *Phylogeny* is the evolutionary history of a particular group of organisms, as depicted in a family tree. Ernst Haeckel is a well-known scientist who so dogmatically supported Darwinian evolution that he falsified the similarities of embryonic development of different creatures into his infamous embryonic drawings. Although his notorious drawing has been rejected by modern biologists as a lie, it still exists in some textbooks for students to learn how evolution works and how one kind of creature evolves into another kind of creature.

In a debate class that I took in college, I learned that the one speaking truth does not necessarily win a debate. Sometimes, the winner of a debate goes to the one who uses bigger words. I enjoy listening to Richard Dawkins (evolution philosopher) speak, he has a razor sharp intellect, but that does not mean he is on the side of truth. The reality is that sometimes the simplest answers are on the side of truth. That is why pearls of wisdom can come out of the mouths of babes. Matthew 21:14–16 discusses "children who were shouting in the temple, 'Hosanna to the Son of David.'" These children were talking about Jesus the savior and rightful King of Israel. But the erudite Pharisees, in their superior piousness and prowess of intellect, became indignant at the thought of children who were so unworthy to speak about this information—let alone in the temple—and rebuked the children and shooed them away. But Jesus rebuked them back for not understanding the Scriptures by saying, "Have you never read, 'Out of the mouth of infants and nursing babies You have prepared praise for Yourself'?" Since God is King of the Jews (I Samuel 8:7) and King David wrote Psalm 8:2—in which Jesus quotes that God prepares praise for Himself out of the mouths of babes—Jesus was declaring Himself to be God in the flesh, the representative of the invisible God the Father, by accepting the praise of the children and the idea that Jesus was the Hosanna (the one to save now) and the heir to King David. Jesus was declaring that He was the Savior, King of the Jews/Israel and God in the flesh.

3. The half truth tale and the unknowing hearer

The law of entropy states that the sum of everything in a closed system will tend toward disorder. This means that some things can tend toward more order, but only when something else is applying a controlled force, with intelligence involved. However, the total sum tends towards disorder.

For example, my daughter's room tends toward disorder; in order for the room to become organized, a controlled intelligent force needs to be applied. She cannot just throw a firecracker in the room and expect a "big bang" to organize everything. She also cannot just start a fire in the room and apply unintelligent energy. My daughter needs to expend energy, with intelligence, to put order into her room. This expenditure of energy comes at a cost; she needs to eat to gain the fuel to have energy to clean her room. After she has cleaned her room, she has spent more energy cleaning than is actually applied to the actions of cleaning and organizing. Therefore, the overall net sum tends toward disorder, even though her room has been cleaned.

Evolutionists argue that life evolves toward more order and more complex kinds of creatures because another outside system is applying force, which causes the reversal of entropy. The outside system is either the sun, which provides energy for life on earth, or other universes that have applied a force to create order within our universe. Evolutionists argue that the earth is not a closed system.

However, the sun's energy is destructive unless intelligence is involved. Imagine if my daughter tried cleaning her room by removing the roof and letting the sun's energy clean her room. Since the sun is not an intelligent force applying energy in exact locations and in guided directions, then the sun's energy that is applied to her room would cause more entropy. Similarly, the sun's energy to the earth accelerates disorder more than it advances order. Every time advances in order occur, intelligence is always involved. Therefore, this outside source utilized by evolutionists to say evolution does not violate the law of entropy is merely a well-constructed argument based on half truth.

The sun can send destructive solar flares that are harmful to life on earth and that increases entropy tremendously. Also, ultraviolet light that accelerates the aging process, which is code for increasing disorder, increases entropy. Also, a whole lot of entropy exist in the Sahara Desert and many other deserts across the globe that results from the sun's unintelligent energy. These deserts cause very hot wind to move, and when that heated air comes across moisture, severe destructive weather patterns can occur. A whole lot of entropy is created in the aftermath of tornadoes and hurricanes. Even the moon is taking angular momentum from the earth and increasing entropy. The sun applies unintelligent energy to the earth, the moon steals energy from the earth, and the cold of space takes energy from the earth via heat transfer. Other destructive energy includes gamma rays, cosmic rays, asteroids and comets, bring their own destructive energy to the earth to increase disorder and to increase entropy. Without intelligence to utilize the sun's energy, there would be zero increased order. The sun is slowly dying, losing energy. One day in the distant future (billions of years from now), the sun will no longer provide light, heat, or energy. This means that the sun is tending toward decay, increasing entropy. Thus, even though the sun provides energy to the earth, and intelligence applies that energy toward more order, the overall sum of entropy increases.

Since the earth as a whole is moving toward more disorder and is increasing in entropy and since the sun's energy is unguided, unintelligent, and impartial, one cannot argue that life on earth is using the sun's energy to generate more order and more complexities without intelligent design to utilize the energy. Thus, the primordial soup of complex chemicals that lacked intelligence in the form of DNA, could not utilize the sun's energy to increase order into the first replicating single-celled organism. Since the earth is moving toward disorder and a less complex system, life on earth would also move in the same direction if intelligent design was not behind the existence of life.

Review: The sun's energy is unguided, unintelligent, and impartial and is more destructive than constructive; it is an outside source assisting the planet to move toward more disorder and more entropy, not less entropy and more complexity. Therefore, one cannot count on the sun to save evolution from its violation of the second law of thermodynamics—entropy. Evolution violates physics and tries to cover up this violation with half truths.

4. Argumentum ad hominem

Argumentum ad hominem is a Latin phrase that means arguing against the person versus the ideas of the person. Evolutionists personal attacks against nonbelievers of the hypothesis of evolution versus arguing against the evidence against evolution. Personal attacks include being called a fool, idiot, and so on. This stifles a reasonable, logical debate.

Since many believers in the Darwinian evolutionary theory are atheists, they are not subject to absolute morality from a higher authority that commands obedience to the concepts of kindness, gentleness, self-control, humility, patience, peace, joy, and love. Therefore, the personal attacks can be quite severe, with nothing to restrain the verbal assaults. Some Christians have lost their jobs for voicing their concern about the theory of evolution.

Of course, this is a two-edge sword. There have been ample wolves in sheep's clothing that claim to represent God that do all kinds of atrocities on humanity. Of the two types of offenders, the one who proclaims to be a believer in God, yet is not and commits evil, is the worst kind.

Chapter Summary: Evolutionists cover up the fact that their hypothesis violates the laws of physics by saying that time saves the day and by using Latin terminology, half truths, and argumentum ad hominem (personal attacks).

Chapter 30
Evolution Versus Science

Science means having knowledge in an area or knowledge that is an object of study, covering general truths or the operation of general laws, especially as obtained and tested through the scientific method.[157]

A valid question from a scientific point of view is where did God come from? The Bible records God's existence is infinite/eternal. Does this violate science? No, it is acceptable to have something be infinite. For example, the space that the universe is expanding in is said to be infinite and immeasurable. In mathematics, the numbers to the right of the decimal point continue on forever, and an infinity symbol exist: ∞. In astronomy, the edge of the universe that is expanding is boundless. In geometry, a line is infinite. Most things are finite, meaning they do not go on forever, so it is extremely rare to find something that is infinite. Evolutionists are trying to determine if some elements, some matter, and some laws of physics have existed forever. Why couldn't God be infinite, especially since He declares He has existed eternally?

Does evolution violate science with the belief that life and the DNA information within all life spontaneously generated from nonliving material? In 1958, George Wald wrote,

> Throughout our history we have entertained two kinds of views of the origin of life: one that life was created supernaturally, the other that it arose "spontaneously" from nonliving material . . . This great controversy ended in the mid-19th century with the experiments of Louis Pasteur, which seemed to dispose finally of the possibility of spontaneous generation. For almost a century afterward biologists proudly taught their students this history and the firm conclusion that spontaneous generation had been scientifically refuted and could not possibly occur . . . Conceding that spontaneous generation does not occur on earth under present circumstances, it asks how, under circumstances that prevailed earlier upon this planet, spontaneous generation did occur and was the source of the earliest living organisms . . . Given so much time, the "impossible" becomes possible, the possible probable, and the probable virtually certain. One has only to wait; time performs the miracles.[158]

Is there a violation of science with the evolutionary belief in abiogenesis, the spontaneous generation of life from nonliving material? Let us dive into the science and determine whether evolution or the Bible violates science. Scientists have created a basic template for which a hypothesis (an idea to explain a phenomenon) is measured to determine if the hypothesis is worthy to be considered a scientific theory (an idea accepted by the scientific community).

The scientific method has specific steps of solving scientific problems:
* Make an observation.
* Ask a question.
* Form a hypothesis.
* Conduct an experiment/test.
* Analyze the data.
* Either accept or reject the hypothesis.

Evolutionists claim to be on the side of science, but the very first step of the scientific method is to "make an observation." George Wald, speaking on behalf of evolution, states, "Conceding that spontaneous generation does not occur on earth under present circumstances, it asks how, under circumstances that prevailed earlier upon this planet, spontaneous generation did occur." There has never been an observation of spontaneous generation of life from nonliving material, and all the

---

157 Merriam-Webster Dictionary.
158 George Wald wrote "Innovation and Biology," 1958, in the *Scientific American*, Volume 199, p. 100.

experiments to support the idea of spontaneous generation from nonliving material have failed. The two most important steps of the scientific method, observing and testing, have failed. Therefore, the hypothesis of spontaneous generation must be rejected. But instead of rejecting the hypothesis, it is taught as fact. The assumption that "conditions must have prevailed upon the earth to generate spontaneous life from nonliving material given enough time" is not science; it is a leap of faith.

Two leaps of faith an evolutionist must take: (1) since spontaneous life does not occur today, the conditions that prevailed upon the earth to generate spontaneous life from nonliving material were significantly different than today, and (2) this difference allowed abiogenesis to violate the laws of biology because of the length of time that performed the miracle of life. One of the differences they assume is no oxygen existed on the planet at the time of this spontaneous generation of life. This is not observable, and to compound the error, evolutionists assume that conditions were perfect to have spontaneously generated life that would not have spontaneously generated in earth's current conditions. Building upon those two leaps of faith, spontaneous generation was certain to occur given enough time. The time aspect is testable, but unfortunately, people interpret data and set up tests to support their preexisting beliefs in regard to an old earth, rather than actually seeking truth. Remember that the flawed testing of time is based on a constant rate of decay (CRD) that is not constant, and this is how they determine the earth to be very old.

This next quote from a college biochemistry textbook that illustrates the nomenclature of speculation that is used to lay a foundation on which to build facts.

> It has been <u>suggested</u> that all living organisms <u>may have</u> descended from a single primordial cell line. Thus the first cells to have arisen on earth and survived <u>may have</u> been built from only a few dozen different organic molecules <u>which happened</u> to have, singly and collectively, <u>the most appropriate combination</u> of chemicals and physical properties for carrying out the basic energy transforming and **self-replicating** features of a living cell . . . But here we have a dilemma. Apart from their occurrence in living organisms, organic compounds, including basic biomolecules, occur only in traces in the earth's crust today.

This evolutionary author is espousing the belief that life spontaneously generated from an abundance of nonliving material, acknowledging that the nonliving material exists in trace amounts today. Where did all the primordial complex chemicals go that allegedly formed life? Since each component of a cell needs all the other components to form simultaneous because each component is interdependent on the other for life, and because O2 and UV breakdown proteins and tissue for quick cell death, and because a cell only lives hours to days in a protective environment, the first cell needed to replicate within the days of life. Therefore, it needed to evolve a precise DNA code by random, unguided errors for binary fission or cellular mitosis (self-replicating) within the first moments of existence before cell death. It is fine to have a belief, but do not call it science. The textbook goes on:

> It is <u>believed</u> that the earliest living cells eventually used up the organic compounds of the seas, not only as building blocks for their own structures but also as nutrients or fuel, to provide themselves with the energy required for growth. Gradually, through the ages, the organic compounds of the primitive sea were consumed, faster than they were created by natural forces. As organic molecules disappeared from the seas, living organisms <u>began to "learn"</u> how to make their own organic biomolecules. <u>They learned</u> to use the energy of sunlight through photosynthesis to make sugars and other organic molecules from carbon dioxide; they learned to fix atmospheric nitrogen and convert it into nitrogenous biomolecules, such as amino acids.[159]

We cannot see the primordial chemical soups because the initial organisms used up nearly all the organic compounds? How convenient, and the proof that abundant amounts of primordial chemical

---

159 *Principles of Biochemistry*, Lehninger, Ch. 3, pg. 59–62, sixth printing, 1988.

soups once existed is that they are in trace amounts today. The reason they are in trace amounts is proof that the organisms ate them. This is mythological, not science. This is a classic ploy of reverse logic, that because the primordial soup is in trace amounts and is not natural to Earth, it proves that it got consumed and initially was abundant. The premise starts with the conjecture that it was there to begin with and then argues from there. That is the proverbial cart before the horse. This opens the door to any speculative hypothesis, such as little green people started life on Earth and evolved into other life forms, and proof that they evolved is that we no longer see the little green people. This is comical pseudoscience. The mistake of believing that a few organic elements, such as nitrogen, carbon, hydrogen, and oxygen, could form together to make a functioning cell with programmed information in the form of DNA. This is the equivalent of dirt that has all the compounds of a car; given enough time, the car emerges under the right conditions and consumes all the remaining leftover compounds as fuel and then learns to consume a different fuel source. This is beyond the realm of possibility. Even debating where the information came from for the living organisms to learn to consume a new fuel source and to learn how to utilize the sun's energy via photosynthesis is going beyond the threshold of the possible—let alone discussing spontaneous generation of life. Also, where did the complex code come from for asexual reproduction? The huge leaps of faith include the following.

A. Organic molecules occur in trace amounts naturally, so to presume an abundance existed at one time for life to spontaneously spawn is faith based.

B. To cover up the loophole by espousing that the reason organic molecules occur in trace amounts is because the early life forms used it all up is faith based.

C. The idea that after using up all the organic molecules, life evolved the ability to find and consume a new source of fuel is faith based.

D. The notion that the first cell, with a brief shelf life of hours to days, some how formed the intricate DNA code for self-replication before its brief life was over is faith based.

Then after these faith-based assumptions, evolutionists proclaim they are on the side of science and do not require faith, and utilize uniformitarian theory and arithmetic fiction to support the evolutionary belief system (See chapters Radioactive Isotopic Dating and Carbon-14 Dating).

Review: The scientific method requires observations and tests to determine if a hypothesis can be a theory. Evolution repeatedly relies on faith-based assumptions and then builds on that.

Evolutionists proclaim that the natural selection process (survival of the fittest) and unguided, random mutation of DNA remove the necessity for God. Also, that these two natural processes cause all life forms to become more complex and diverse. Several problems exist with this hypothesis; one is that natural selection gets rid of the mutated to preserve the better genetic copy of the original. All mutations produce a loss of a function that leads to frailty, weakness, sterility, stillbirth, and so forth because all mutations result in a loss of functional information in the DNA code. Natural selection is actually designed to limit errors in the genetic code from being passed on, to ensure that the closest exact copy of the original genetic code is preserved by getting rid of creatures that have errors in their genetic code. These concepts that form the very foundation of evolution actually prevent evolution. It is Satan's routine to take what God has created (natural selection) and twist it for his benefit?

By the way, it should be noted that natural selection—which allows a predator to seek out the weak and kill it amongst a herd of the strong and implants the desire of the female to only mate with the best genetic copy of the original—is already built into the DNA. No new information occurs; in fact, the existing DNA information is designed by God to prevent new information that could result in a new kind or a new function. A bird offspring with a beak that adapts better to grab food better is based on DNA that already exists in its code from a parent. When I talk about a new function, I'm talking about (for example) a bird evolving baleen teeth or some photosynthetic skin cells, which would mean that the bird would no longer need to eat with a beak.

Review: Natural selection eliminates creatures that have mutations in their DNA code. Random, unguided mutations in the DNA code always result in a loss of function or an impairment of function,

226

and then natural selection eliminates those mutated creatures to preserve the DNA. Never does a mutation enhance genetic code. Mutations that are small enough go undetected, otherwise, all creatures with mutations are either weak, frail, sterile, stillborn, and so on, and natural selection eliminates them. Natural selection is a creationist's argument, not an evolutionist's argument.

The ability of a life form to adapt to its environment occurs in the epigenome, and is accepted as fact by creationists. But limits exist as to how far adaptation can go. When the edge of adaptation is reached, the limitations are set with stillbirths, sterility, and deformities, and these limitations are determined by the DNA in terms of how far a particular kind of creature can adapt to external conditions. Adaptation is observable and accepted as fact, but the creature adapting always remains the same kind of creature. Never has there been an observation of a kind of creature adapting so far that another kind of creature is formed. God has established in the DNA that each kind of creature remains the same kind.

Review: God has determined the boundaries of adaptation, and that boundary is hardwired in the DNA code. Also, natural selection is one of the means that God uses to rid the world of mutations. Both the preexisting DNA code and natural selection prevent evolution from occurring.

A well-known ongoing experiment involving **Escherichia coli bacteria** to determine how E. coli bacteria adapt to different stimuli and to ascertain how/what bacteria can evolve into. This experiment is frequently cited by evolutionists as proof that evolution is fact. The end result after 50,000 generations (which is more than all humans and primates combined) of E. coli reproducing is . . . (wait for it) bacteria! Brilliant. After 66,000 generations, E. coli bacteria is still E. coli bacteria, with different adaptive characteristic.[160] This is not evolution; this is adaptation. Now, if the test started with E. coli bacteria and finished with a blade of grass, a fruit fly, a ground worm, or a fungus, then evolutionists would have something. But after 66,000 generations, bacteria are still bacteria, which proves the creationist viewpoint that all kinds remain the same kind. Living things have the ability to adapt to changes in the environment, yet limits exist in terms of how far life can adapt and survive.

Science is always welcomed by the Bible. Physics is the Bible's old friend, and biology is a dear neighbor. No creationist fears science, physics, or biology, as they are obedient servants to God. One will never find the Bible in violation of any laws of physics, principles of science, or tenets of biology. Bilateral harmony exist because the God that fine-tuned the universe, created life within it and recorded His actions by the pen of mankind through the inspiration is God of all and creator of all, and that includes the laws of physics. He is not just the creator of man and life, but also of all the laws of physics and biology and chemistry. Do not confuse man's discovery of these laws with the origin of these laws; they were there before man had the ability to understand modern science and to discover these laws; that's why—as man progresses with science—we still find hidden truths in the Bible that are in harmony with the sciences.

I was debating an evolutionist about natural selection, intelligent design, and creation versus evolution, and he argued that theists believe that only intelligent design can breed sheep together to produce woollier animals through breeding (artificial selection), but a series of very cold winters would also create woollier sheep as well, via survival of the fittest and random mutations that alter the genetic code. He argued that intelligent design proponents need a breeder to get to different breeds of sheep. He claimed that natural selection could achieve the same result. But this is not what intelligent design proponents are arguing, as they are not saying that woollier breeds can only be created through breeding. Intelligent design proponents are saying that the information necessary to produce a woollier sheep was already coded in the DNA way before any breeder came along and way before any winter came along and caused natural selection. The information was in the sheep's DNA at birth, from its parents, and their parents got their DNA from their parents, and so forth, until you get to creation. It is not that cold winters over several thousand years produce new DNA code to produce woollier sheep. That's not how it works. It is that the cold winters kill off the sheep that had the thinner coats of wool,

---

160 Widipedia.org, E. Coli long-term evolution experiment.

and the woollier sheep thrived and breed. Thus, producing a population of woollier sheep.

Similarly, the potential for new species within the same kind of creature via adaptation, whether by natural selection or artificial selection, is also already coded in the DNA. Therefore, arguing that natural selection rules out any God is a poor argument. Creationists accept as scientific fact that adaptation occurs, and given the same parameters of cold winters, the sheep with a woollier coat would survive, and when they reproduce, they would pass on a genome with information for a woollier coat already embedded in the DNA from their ancestors, not from a new DNA code produced because of cold weather.

Dr. Stephen Meyer is on the cutting edge of using the scientific method for authenticating intelligent design. His book *Signature in the Cell* is a must read for anyone willing to fully understand the improbability of evolution and the conclusive deductive reasoning behind intelligent design. Dr. Meyer says that all information, whether it be from newspaper, books, computer program, or in binary form, is exclusively acquired through intelligence, especially in regard to information that has a function. This is exactly what DNA consists of: digital and functional information. Therefore, based on all experiences, whenever we see information, especially functional digital information, we always assume intelligence, and we are always correct.

Review: A herd of sheep adapt to cold and become woollier through the generations because the information is already hardwired into the genetic code. No random, unguided mutation of the DNA code causes sheep to be woollier. Natural and artificial selection do NOT create new information in the DNA code. Adaptation and evolution are not the same; adaptation already has the DNA information to adapt, and evolution allegedly makes new code via random, unguided DNA changes that produce a new function or a new kind.

Evolutionists argue that the proof that man evolved from chimpanzees is that we have an almost identical genetic code, with only a 1% difference in the DNA between humans and chimpanzee. Even professors sneak this information out to unprepared students and into debates. When believers in God hear this, they are left thinking, *well then, maybe they are correct*, and students who do not know God, are all the more convinced of the viability of evolution. How do evolutionists justify that we share 99% similarities in the DNA? By teaching that when a dissimilarity occurs in the DNA between chimps and humans, they discount this DNA as non-functional junk DNA. However, according to geneticists **Dr. John Sanford**, non-functional junk DNA strands do not exist in the code, and thus, we only share ~50% similarities in the DNA with chimps. By the way, genetic researcher Craig Venter, et al., the team responsible for taking out genetic code in a single-celled organism to find the code responsible for its life and replication, stated, "junk DNA has functional switches that tell certain genes when and where in the body to turn on." Notwithstanding, even if we falsely assume non-functional junk strands of DNA exist, Dr. Grady McMurtry explains,

> Evolutionists are not telling the whole story because the claim that we share 99% DNA is based on comparing only 2.7% of the DNA code from humans and chimps. Yes, the human DNA code has been 100% mapped out, but not the chimps'. Now, why would one make a bold claim that we evolved from chimps, while leaving out 97.3% of the information?

According to Dr. Grady McMurtry, chimps and humans do not share 99% as evolutionists claim. Only 83% of the DNA is similar. But 88% of the DNA shared by humans and rats is similar, and humans share 60% with bananas, and sea squirts (marine invertebrate creatures living near coral that look like tubular flowers) share 88%.[161] The claim that we have nearly (99%) identical DNA with any creature is false. The reason similarities of DNA strands exist is because we literally came from the same creator—from the same essence through God. Also, processes within living things share similar necessities and functions, and those similar properties or components result in similarities in the DNA

---

161 Dr. Grady McMurtry, CreationWorldView.org.

code.

For example, all creatures that have the breath of life in them breathe oxygen and have blood running through their bodies have similarities in the DNA code because they have the same protein that makes RBCs, the same proteins that make up the vascular system, such as the heart, arteries, veins, and so forth. It is like asking a painter why so many paintings have similar colors. Likewise, all life forms that have similar functions have a similar DNA code. This does not mean that we evolved; it means that we came from the same creator that copied and pasted information.

Review: The argument that we share 99% of chimps' DNA is false. The empirical data is that we share only ~50% similar DNA, and not just with chimps, but with many creatures. Creatures that have similar characteristics have some DNA similarities by default. This illustrates that we did not evolved, but that we came from the same creator who was efficient with using the same DNA code that produced similar functions in many life forms.

In life, when something appears obvious, do not overthink it. But with evolution, a tendency occurs to come up with outlandish leaps of speculative faith to explain a phenomenon, and the explanation must be contrary to what the Bible records. For example, Richard Dawkins said, "Biology is the study of complicated things that give the appearance of having been designed for a purpose."

The question is, is there an appearance of design, or is there really design in life? How did the concept of intelligent design get downgraded by those in the late 19th and early 20th centuries, and why was it removed from science? We have all been down the road in life at some point in time, when we thought or said something was one way or another, and we went to great lengths to try to prove we were correct, yet all the while regretting that we took the stance we did in the beginning. But the ball was rolling, and we were stuck with it. We see this in sports frequently when a team hires a coach to lead them to championships. But the coach takes the team down a different path, and the owner tells the media how great the coach is doing. The owner has faith in the coach, but season after season of losing makes the owner regret that he took the stance of hiring the coach. Well that's what evolutionists' forefathers of the 19th and early 20th centuries did. They formulated theories on spontaneous generation without full knowledge of cells, amino acids, proteins, DNA, nucleotides, and so on. For example, the idea that a single-cell organism could spontaneously generate from nonliving material was spawned by a misunderstanding of the complexity of cells. They did not understand cells at all. They thought the primordial pool of complex chemicals simply had to crystallize for life to form the first single-cell living organism, called a prokaryote (which is in the Amoeba family). For example, in 1870s, Ernst Haeckel said, the cell is a simple "homogeneous globule of plasma," a gooey ooze of the same structureless substance. This type of erroneous understanding was the basis for thinking that life could evolve from nonliving material. Today, evolutionists still cover up this error concerning the spontaneous generation of life; they still try to prove that their belief is still a valid hypothesis, even though it has never been observed and has failed every test. But they opted to force their hypothesis by skipping the scientific method and going straight to saying, "It's fact." Anyone who says otherwise is going against science.

Review: The forefathers of evolution perceived cells to be chemically and biologically simple, which made the process of going from simple amino acids to a living cell simply through crystallization seemingly plausible. But reality couldn't be further from that error.

Dr. James Watson and Dr. Francis Crick discovered DNA, and now we know that DNA has digital-like characters arranged according to a preexisting code that tells the building blocks how to form a protein and where to go and what to do. That preexisting code came from the initial fertilization of parental DNA. Therefore, we have to keep going backward in time to find the origin of the information. To the evolutionist, the first single-cell prokaryote got its information from nonliving material via the spontaneous generation of information. To the creationist, the first man got his information from an all-knowing God (life begot life). God infused Adam with parts of God's knowledge. Evolutionists say that life was spontaneously generating from nonliving material, suggesting that genetic information also spontaneously generating from nonliving material. Without the information in the DNA code, there would be no life, there would be no knowledge about how to find food, consume food, process food, mate/replicate/reproduce, defend oneself, get rid of waste, walk, and so on. This is a huge problem for evolutionists, but they just shrug it off and proclaim that the information evolved through random mutations over time. This is faith based.

Review: Information from DNA is vital for life; without information to know how to innately function on a macro- and micro-cellular basis, life would not exist. The spontaneous formation of DNA information for the first living thing is another faith-based leap for evolutionists.

When the early pioneers of evolution postulated that life spontaneously generated from nonliving material, not much was known about a cell, DNA, epigenome, and so forth. The hypothesis was formed with the knowledge equivalent of science as a fifth grader today. Thus, some gentleness for their ignorance. But modern-day evolutionists carry on this idea, even though evidence, logic, and science expose the errors in the hypothesis of evolution. Belief in evolution is not based on ignorance, but a willful choice to accept half truths and huge leaps of faith, instead of seeking truth.

Ernst Haeckel and Darwin and the early evolutionary forefathers were ignorant of the complexities of a cell. For example, they did not know that four elements make up an amino acid: oxygen, hydrogen, nitrogen, and carbon. Also, they did not know the 20 amino acids common in proteins: glycine, alanine, valine, leucine, isoleucine, methionine, phenylalanine, tryptophan, proline, serine, threonine, cysteine, tyrosine, asparagine, glutamine, aspartic acid, glutamic acid, lysine, arginine, and histidine.[162] Also, that the 20 amino acids, to form a protein, are in a precise sequence order of about 150 amino acids long; this order is based on a predetermined, preprogrammed DNA to form a single protein. One amino acid out of place results in malformation, which adversely affects the function built upon that protein. The DNA information is stored in digital form, which means it is similar to a computer program that determines how the amino acids are formed to create the three-dimensional shape of proteins. One error in the sequencing for a protein formation alters its shape, and it won't fit into a receptor site to carry out its function. Preexisting DNA information from a prior life determines the sequencing of the amino acids that form proteins. Proteins are vital for functions within the cell and the entire body. Since the chain of the 20 amino acids to form a protein is ~150 long, and since evolutionists believe that random chance evolved the first protein and not DNA, the odds of random, unguided chance getting one protein correct with all the sequences in correct order is 1 in 20^{195} (this is logically impossible). Winning the lottery is ~1 in 10^7. *Photo credit: https://worldofweirdthings.com.*

DNA consists of four nucleotides: adenine, guanine, cytosine, and thymine. This is where the A, G, C, and T letters come from when one sees a DNA helical structure. It is important to note that the double helical structure of DNA, from what we have studied so far, is always in the clockwise formation. This represents design and order, whereas with an evolutionary model, a more random pattern should exist. With the random, unguided mutations hypothesis, different formations should exist, such as, hexagon repeater shapes, layered taffy-like shapes, film reel shapes, fishing line spool shapes, fragmented and individual segments (like blades of grass with each having a specific function), and so forth. All the order we see in the DNA code has zero to do with randomness; it screams order and design and that all life came from one creator. And that creator sealed His creation to remain as He intended it from the beginning. The Bible records that each creature was to reproduce after their own kind, which means each creature will remain the same kind as they have always been.

Review: The design and order of the DNA code suggests intelligence designed it. With the evolutionary hypothesis, there should be a random display of shapes and patterns in the DNA code of living things.

---

162 Biological Science, Keeton & Gould, pg. 58.

Each nucleotide (A, C , G, and T) building block, as discovered by Dr. Rosalind Franklin, has a five-carbon sugar on the outside, a nitrogenous base, and a phosphate group. They make up the DNA code, which determines the precise order of the above 20 amino acids that form the 150-long chain needed to make one single protein. With random, unguided mutations forming the DNA coding, there would be errors in the DNA. These errors would adversely affect the sequencing information that instructs the proper order of the 150 long chain (consisting of the 20 amino acids) that are needed to form one single protein. Without a precise sequencing of the amino acids to form the protein, then a complete loss of structure and function of the protein occurs. The protein is a precise, complex 3-D shape that fits other molecules like a hand in a glove and that carries out exact functions—one amino acid in the wrong order would cause a total failure of the protein because there would not be a perfect fit with the other molecule that it is designed for to carry out the exact function. Therefore, nothing occurs—no function, no catalyzed reactions, no building structural parts, and no processing of DNA. This is just like a computer program; make one coding change randomly, and the entire function is broken. Where does the information come from to put together the exact order of the amino acids to form one single protein? The DNA code has the information for which to build the different proteins that perform different functions for the cells.

What are the odds of 20 amino acids properly forming a 150-chain sequence to produce one single protein? The calculation is 1 in 20 x 1 in 20 x 1 in 20, for 150 times. That equals 1×10^{195} odds. That is one with 195 zeroes. Therefore, the odds are ~1 in 2×10^{195} for random, unguided chance to form one single protein. To put that in perspective, the average six-number lottery with 1–49 numbers to chose from is 49 x 48 x 47 x 46 x 45 x 44, but since it is in any order, we divide by 6 x 5 x 4 x 3 x 2 x 1 = 720,[163] so the odds are one in 1.4×10^7 to win the lottery. However, protein formation requires a specific order, not any order, which decreases the odds of forming one protein by random chance, and this does not include the more complex process of forming DNA structures. Which one do you have more faith in, winning the lottery or winning the evolutionary hypothesis lottery to form one protein?

The odds to form one protein through random, unguided mutations is astronomically low; we do not need one successful event for the first life; we need this random, unguided chance to be successful 250–500 times for each cell because each cell on average has that many proteins. The odds get worse; each protein has around 1,500 genes in proper sequence. Four nucleotide (A, G, C, and T) options exist for a sequence 1,500-chain long. Therefore, the odds of random, unguided chance forming the proper gene for one solitary protein is ~1 in 2×10^{903}. Plus, add the ~1,500 properly sequenced genes for each of those 250–500 different proteins, and you quickly start to see the problem. A lot of information is required. With 1,500 properly sequenced genes needed to build one protein, multiplied by 250–500 proteins for each cell, and a cell has at a minimum of 375,000 sequences that have to be precisely in the correct order, or the cell dies. Now multiply that by how many cells the human has, but forget those crazy numbers. Focus on the first self-replicating living cell. After the first cell evolves out of the primordial soup of complex chemicals, it then needs to evolve the complex genetic code for cellular mitosis (asexual reproduction), and it needs to get this information evolved within days because a cell only lives one hour to days in the protection of a host. The odds of random chance forming the necessary information to form one cell is beyond possible. The odds of random, unguided mutations forming the DNA code for life, which has vastly more information, and then evolving the complex code for mitosis for replication, is beyond impossible. This is why chance via random, unguided mutations in the DNA code would most likely degrade a code rather than enhance it. Think about it; the DNA code is where the information comes from to sequence the 20 amino acids in proper order 150 times to form one single protein, so without the DNA, no information exist to guide the sequencing order. This is where faith in evolution takes over science.

Additionally, if an evolutionist argues that the nucleotides (A, G, C, and T) are attracted to each other because of charge, and thus, no need to rely on the low odds of random chance to form the DNA

---

163 Wikipedia, lottery mathematics.

sequence, this is not accurate. For the sugars and phosphate that form the backbone (or structure or exoskeleton) of the helical DNA structure are chemically bonded by electrical charge, but they carry no information, zero. A chemical bond exist between each nucleotide to the sugar-phosphate back of DNA, but <u>no bond and no attraction exist among the nucleotides (A, G, C, and T)</u>. The sugar-phosphate bond allows any one of the four nucleotides to bond with it. Therefore, one cannot argue that the DNA

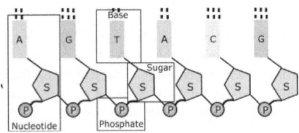

sequence of the nucleotides is based on attraction. No attraction between the nucleotides that result in the DNA sequence holding information.[164] This means that evolution is stuck with random, unguided chance to form the first DNA sequence and to form new information for new functions and for new kinds of creatures. This is an untenable hypothesis. *Image credit: National Human Genome Research Institute.*

But it gets worse for evolutionists, as we have not discussed the odds of a select few elements, randomly with no guidance, forming together to form an amino acid to begin with. They say that nitrogen, oxygen, carbon, and hydrogen randomly came together from the first rains on the rocks on the earth some four billion years ago. Therefore, if the select elements (N, O, C, and H) formed together by random unguided chance to form the 20 amino acids, the odds get worse factoring in the formation of the 20 amino acids. Then we have to calculate the odds of random chance forming the elements in the first place. The odds are never in the evolutionist's favor.

How does an evolutionist sidestep this problem? They say that given enough time and enough multiple universes, life is bound to begin in one of them and form new functions and new life through random, unguided mutations. They just bypass the reality of the impossible odds and just regurgitate the evolutionary doctrine, like a chanting monk. Another more astute evolutionist would agree that chance by itself is not sufficient, but what cannot be accomplished via chance could be accomplished through natural selection.

The problem with this is that for natural selection to work, sexual or asexual reproduction must exist. For reproduction to occur, there needs to be a specific DNA sequence with specific proteins to carry out reproduction, and this information needs to evolve before the first cell dies within its hour or week of life. Therefore, the information is required first. The information is what causes reproduction and natural selection. Natural selection does not provide the information or cause new information, but it can prevent bad information. But believing that natural selection helps shape or form new information in the DNA code is putting the proverbial cart before the horse.

As discussed earlier, no bond exist between each nucleotide to other nucleotides. Therefore, no law of attraction explains how the sequence of the DNA is formed. For this reason, the theory that says the law of attraction, given enough time, will form the DNA sequence is completely false. Zero attraction occurs for the sequencing of the letters that form the DNA code. This poses a question: "Where did the information come from to form the DNA sequence in the exact proper order of 1,500 sequential chain of nucleotides to form one single protein, multiplied by 250–500 times to form the number of proteins in one cell?" Always, this information comes from a prior life, and that is where God comes in. God is the one who provided the knowledge, but the evolutionists are left with faith in an erroneous view that suggests that chance and time provide the miracle. The Bible declares that chance does not exist and that even the outcome of the lot that is cast (like dice) is of the Lord (Proverbs 16:33).

<u>**Review:**</u> <u>The odds of winning the lottery: 1 in 1.4 x 10^7. The odds of evolution winning the amino acids that form one protein lottery: ~1 in 2 x 10^{195}. The odds of evolution winning the genes that form one protein lottery: ~1 in 2 x 10^{903}. The complexities of 20 amino acids forming a long chain with 150 amino acids to make one protein is based on information predetermined by DNA coding. The</u>

---

164 Stephen Meyer, *Signature in the Cell.*

complexity of generating DNA code is beyond comprehension as compared to creating a single protein. Putting this information together reveals the impossibility of random, unguided mutations forming a single amino acid, let alone a chain of 150 of them to form a protein, let alone for nucleotides to form genes for each protein and the even more complex DNA code, which is where the information comes from to form the sequencing of amino acids that form proteins in the first place. This illustrates the faith-based required for evolution's abiogenesis of life and information.

The cell that Ernst Haeckel erroneously hypothesized to prove evolution is not a gooey blob of plasma at all; it has complex mechanisms. An amoeba cell—which may be similar to what evolutionists believe was spontaneously generated out of nonliving material as the first prokaryote cell—moves by pseudopodia and has a genome the size of 290 billion[165] base pairs, or DNA units, which is 100 times larger than what a human has. Though the amoeba genome is very complex, it does not have the number of genes that a human has.

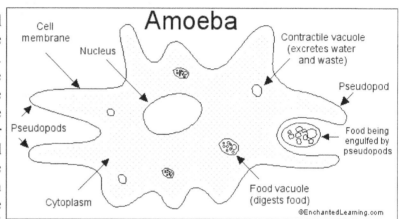

An amoeba is complex. A cell must have a cell wall and a membrane around each vital organ within the cell. A cell wall that is semipermeable allows some things in and out of the cell; the wall is dynamic, with the ability to engulf foreign objects for consumption (endocytosis and phagocytosis) and expel waste (exocytosis). Programmed information allows it to know the difference between harmful and beneficial objects. Cellular life forms have to have a means of locomotion to pursue food and flee danger, and they must have preprogrammed information to know the difference. A cell must have a power source (mitochondria for animals and chloroplasts for plants) to provide energy to get food, process food, and so on. All these functions are because of preexisting DNA information. A cell must have a place to bring food into the cell (vacuole), a processing plant to convert food into energy, and a place to store processed food for future needs. This requires preexisting DNA information to accomplish. A cell must have a waste-processing plant (vacuole) to expel used waste; otherwise, the cell would become toxic from waste buildup. This requires preexisting DNA. A cell must have a central information control center (nucleus) to provide information for all the necessary functions, and this requires preexisting DNA information. A cell must have a means of asexual reproduction, such as splitting into two via binary fission (cellular mitosis). Equal DNA information in both new cells requires preexisting DNA. Without any of the above, the cell will die. Without the required DNA coding for the organ to exist and function, the cell dies. All of these processes and information are necessary for the operation of each function. Furthermore, and I cannot stress this enough, all the above components of a cell are interdependent. If a cell is missing one component then no life exist. Therefore, all proteins, all components of a cell, and all the DNA had to be simultaneously generated for the first life form.

The error of the forefathers of evolution to think the simple single-celled amoeba was a simple homogeneous ooze that merely had to crystallize from a primordial soup of nonliving material could not be further from the truth. The evolutionary model suggests that not only did the first living organism spontaneously generate from nonliving material, but so too did the DNA that is required first before the single-celled organism can be alive. Therefore, one can see that evolution is a leap of faith, not science.

Review: The cell is very complex and not a globe of homogeneous plasma ooze, as the forefathers of evolution believed. The odds that the information needed to form the functions within a

165 Wikipedia, Amoeba. *Image Credit: https://en.wikipedia.org/wiki/Amoeba.*

one-cell amoeba or a primordial single-cell prokaryote could be spontaneously generated from nonliving material are too low to consider a possibility. Life and the DNA for life, always come from a prior life.

When one takes a bird's-eye view of where the information came from to instruct amino acids to form certain sequences for certain proteins to form all the necessary functions within a cell and to form the genes that go with each protein, one is left with the same problem: establishing life and the information to form life from the spontaneous generation of nonliving material is beyond possible.

Every attempt to explain the origin of information through evolution by chance, necessity, and time still comes down to information spontaneously generated from nonliving material, from nothing. The notion that given enough time, random chance and the need for information brought about the information is faith based. This is not rational, but it is obedient to the methodology that God is not required to start life and provide the information necessary for life, and everything can be explained without God.

How do evolutionists solve the dilemma of where DNA comes from? Their answer is that **mRNA** did it. mRNA plays a vital role in gene expression and in coding, decoding, regulating, and catalyzing biological reactions, such as protein synthesis, by directing the assembly of proteins and by transferring amino acids to the ribosomes for manufacturing amino acids together to form proteins. However, a huge gap exist between the formation of a protein and DNA formation. The salient point is that there needs to be DNA information to instruct mRNA. Therefore, where did the information in the RNA come from to send the amino acids to the ribosomes to manufacture proteins? This leads us back to requiring DNA. Another question is where did the information come from for the formation of ribosomes factory, which is based on protein formation? Again, this leads us back to requiring DNA. We are still back at the same starting point, which is that information cannot be spontaneously generated. This is impossible, but it is the beginning point of evolution. A source or causal agent is required for the information to occur.

Review: The information required for life is too complex for random, unguided sequencing of amino acids in a primordial pool to form a basic entity, such as a protein, let alone to account for the complexities of the DNA code in the simplest single-cell prokaryote life form.

All the parameters and quantitative values of the universe, such as those relevant to the laws of thermodynamics, motion, electricity, electromagnetism, light, energy, equilibrium, solids and fluids and gases, sound, heat, and so forth, require precision and finely tuned constants. If subtle changes were made to the laws of attraction, gravitational force, the elements of the periodic table, the constant nucleus force required to hold onto electrons, the ratio of fundamental forces, the expansion rate of the universe, or covalent bonds, life would be impossible. This indicates that a superintelligent being set the parameters to make an environment in which life could be sustainable. The degree to the fine-tuning of the universe and in all the properties of physics, chemistry, biology, and mathematics, the logical conclusion is that life does not happen by random chance, but by the hand of an intelligent being—God.

The simple reality that our DNA is held together by hydrogen bonds (intermolecular forces) is indicative of fine-tuning. If DNA were held together by covalent bonds or ionic bonds (both intramolecular forces), this tighter bond would hinder the reproduction via cellular mitosis. Hydrogen bonds are weak enough to allow their helical structure to split apart for reproduction, but covalent bonds are very strong and can keep diamonds together. Without chromosomes being split into two equal pairs, cellular multiplication for conceptional life development would be hindered. This is another example of fine-tuning within the universe but on a molecular level.

When evolutionists realize that the spontaneous generation of life and information are impossible, they try to solve this problem with multiple universes. Thus, they speculate that a multiple-universes theory provides an opportunity where a single universe does not. Why cannot a multiverse theory work? For one thing, what and where is the universal generating mechanism or factory? In other words, where did all the universes come from? String theory is their answer, but it is a speculative hypothesis and possibly explains how the universe became fine-tuned with all the laws and constants of physics, but not the initial conditions. Evolutionists have also introduced "universal inflation," which is another theory that explains how the universe expanded so fast in a short amount of time, but not the fine-tuning of the laws and constants of physics.

Therefore, they utilize speculative postulates to explain away what the Bible records as the work of an all-knowing creator, who set in motion all the initial conditions of a fine-tuned universe and is currently sustaining all that He created (Colossians 1:17). Both the string theory and inflation theory require prior fine-tuning to set up or prepare the way. Therefore, they are back to the same problem, which is who/what did the fine-tuning? It is a circle that won't end. When the improbability of evolution is too much to overcome, often the evolutionist will resort to a redirect away from their failed hypothesis by posing a question, "Where did your God come from, who created Her?"

The Bible records that God is eternal. Does this violate science that nothing can come from nothing? No. It is not that God came from nothing, it is that God is infinite, eternally existent. Infinity is an acceptable term in science, but it does require a measure of faith. The amount of faith required is inversely proportional to the amount of knowledge. The more knowledge, the less faith required. For example, since science allows for the notion of something being infinite and eternal, do we observe that God decays, or that God can be decreased or increased? Remember, this is why energy cannot be eternal because we observe that it is not eternal, it obeys entropy. To corroborate the claim that God is eternal and infinite, and reduce the amount of faith required to accept this claim, the evidence to authenticate the Bible's claim of God being eternal is the Bible itself. Not in the sense that God is infinite because the Bible says so, but that we can test His Word to determine if a divine nature exist to His Word. The Bible's divine accuracy is tested and confirmed by archeology and observed with its harmony with the sciences. The Bible has endured the toughest of scrutiny from the most ardent opponents, and still the Bible is without contradiction, without error, without violations in the sciences. Only divine inspiration could have 66 different authors spanning three thousand years writing in perfect harmony of doctrine, biology, modern medical science, cosmology, and so forth. The more than two thousand fulfilled prophesies authenticate that something beyond human ability wrote the Bible. The apostles who committed their lives to follow Jesus illustrate that they saw many miracles. Since Jesus required celibacy or monogamy, acknowledged that He was poor and His followers would not get rich following Him, and promised persecution, this means that the apostles followed Jesus knowing they were not going to get women, fame, or money, but were promised persecution. Not to be superficial, but Isaiah records (~700 BC) that Jesus was not good looking, and He had no physical form that would attract people (Isaiah 53:2). The only way to get them to follow Jesus was for Him to perform miracles and rise from the grave. If Jesus couldn't substantiate His claims with miracles, the apostles would have stopped following Him. If Jesus fooled them with some fake miracles, then upon His death on the cross, the apostles would have been scattered and given up because of the life of no women, no fame, no money, and promised persecution. That is exactly what happened when Jesus died. The apostles scattered and gave up. Thus, only a resurrected Jesus, after being dead for three days, could have brought the apostles back to following Him in a life of no women, no fame, no money, and promised persecution. The only conclusion is that Jesus rose from the grave, and only God could have performed this miracle. Therefore, combining the evidence of the perfect accuracy of doctrine from cover to cover, the fulfilled prophesies, the harmony with the sciences, and the lives of the apostles and Jesus' resurrection, leads to knowing that when God claims He is eternal and infinite, it is truth. The faith required to accept this is reduced as knowledge increases.

Review: The fine-tuning of the universe, all the laws and constants and parameters to make an environment in which life could be sustainable, strongly suggests a designer. Applying logic to what Jesus promised the apostles—persecution, and what they had to give up and endure for the sake of following Jesus, forces the conclusion that Jesus did miracles, died, and rose from the grave.

How does the Bible handle the beginning of information and life? The Bible records that God created life from Himself. Luke 3:38 records that Adam was begotten by God with "Adam, the son of God." God spoke life into existence with "God formed man of dust from the ground, and breathed into his nostrils the Breath of **Life**; and man became a **living** soul (Gen. 2:7)." Remember that *life* and *living* are represented by the same Hebrew word, *chay*. The Bible is repeatedly and explicitly saying "life came from life." This is why we were created in the image and likeness of God (Gen. 1:26) because God created us from and through Himself (Col. 1:16). This also explains that the information in the DNA code came from the very essence of God. Therefore, our DNA code came from parts of God's DNA code, and since God created all the other things from His essence, they too have parts of His DNA code. Thus, similarities in the DNA codes exist between creatures.

Does the Bible violate the scientific method? The Bible states that the life of everything living came from God Himself, which is in harmony with the science that shows that life does not come from nonliving material, just as Louis Pasteur proved in the late 1800s. But where is the observable portion of God? Stephen Meyer is on the cutting edge of this topic. Besides *Signature in the Cell*, I also recommend that you read *Darwin's Doubt*. Is God observable? It seems like a tall order, but it is a lot simpler than one would imagine. If the Bible is true, and since the Bible recorded that God made mankind in His image and likeness, then by looking at humans we may observe the Father of humanity. But not every human. For God strictly said for those with sin to depart from Him for He never knew them. Therefore, we must look at those who are without sin, those whom Jesus said we should be like because theirs is the kingdom of heaven (Matt. 19:14). I am speaking of all the children. Just look at their joy, innocence, humility, peace, love, gentleness, and kindness.

Man has spent billions of dollars and countless hours searching the heavens for evidence of life to potentially explain how life began on earth. What are some of the indications in the heavens that mankind is looking for? Astronomers look for anything and everything, from complex machinery to straight lines to curved lines. Can a straight line or curved line indicate life? Yes. How? The existence of life often includes things in geometric shapes, such as parallel straight lines, circles, and triangles. When cosmologists find a straight line or circle, this indicates intelligence. Something or someone with intelligence put things together to form a geometric shape. This isn't restricted to space; the same application applies to almost every science. When archeologists stumble upon a circle of rocks, they know that man likely placed those rocks in a circle or that intelligent life did it. When archeologists or geologists see geometric shapes after digging down into the ancient past, they conclude that intelligent life formed the geometric shapes. They never assume that stones in a circle can evolve into a circle given enough time.

Whenever we see a watch on the ground, we know that a watchmaker (intelligence) made the watch. It does not matter if we found the watch in the ocean or in the desert, we would come to the same conclusion. Everyone knows that a watch cannot form by itself, even if it has an infinite amount of time. Every human on earth knows that when they see a calculator, or a rubber door stopper, or any item, they know that the maker of the item was a human being (an intelligent designer and creator). No one believes that all the things we see in life, from a simple rubber door stop to a complex car, came into being because of random events over a great deal of time. No one believes that a printing factory can explode and produce a new work of literature, even if we exploded a billion factories a billion times a day for a billion years. The odds are zero, zilch, and nada.

When we observe items that have a design, function, and a purpose, we know by repetition, pattern, and history that a designer and a creator was involved with the item. We innately know the item did not evolve by random chance, an explosion, a primordial soup of complex chemicals, or any amount of time. This is our first clue toward an intelligent designer behind the design of humans.

Review: Observable evidence exist of intelligent design in the things we see in life. We can test it and confirm it. When we see what seems like intelligent design, indeed an intelligent designer exist.

Now, let us delve into the observable and testable portion of the scientific method to determine whether a designer and creator was involved for human beings.

In life, we see that humans will do certain things to protect what they feel is precious to them, especially when it comes to things they created. For example, when sculptors create something, they put their seal on the image/sculpture with a signature to protect their creation and let everyone know it is theirs. When authors write something, they put their seal on it by copyrighting it to protect their creation and let everyone know it is theirs. Inventors similarly patent their inventions, and parents give their children their name.

We are created in the image (shape) and likeness (character) of God (Gen. 1:26), and when we create something, we are performing the very same actions that God performed ~6,000 years ago when He created life after His own image by begetting Adam, His first physical son (Luke 3:38). How did God patent His invention? Did He sign His sculptures, copyright His information, and give His name to let everyone know that He is the designer and creator of mankind? Yes, through the command multiply *"after their kind."*

The human female ovum (egg) has a shell around it to seal and protect the chromosomes of the female from being fertilized by the wrong kind. This shell surrounding and protecting the ovum must be dissolved for fertilization to occur. For the shell to dissolve and create an opening, it needs a specific enzyme from an outside source (from the male) to come in contact with the ovum shell. The female ovum shell is receptor specific; in other words, it will only allow one type of enzyme from one kind of creature to dissolve the shell for fertilization and reproduction. To make matters more exclusive, the means of contact for fertilization is only by means of a chromosome-carrying device that has its own source of locomotion and its own energy source. The ovum is deep within the body and protected by gravity and acidity. Spermatozoa have a flagellum tail for locomotion to swim against gravity; they utilize a high-pH serum to neutralize the acidity of the initial reproductive tract of the female. In addition, multiple spermatozoa are needed to dissolve the ovum shell; in fact, hundreds of spermatozoa must reach the ovum to have a sufficient number of acrosome granules (enzymes) to dissolve the shell.

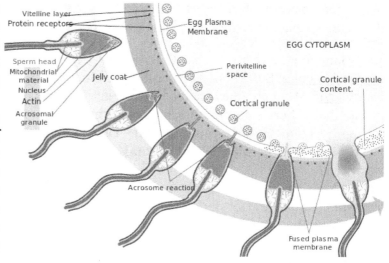

Well, that's where one of the seals of God comes into play. Only one kind of creature on earth that has the proper enzyme to dissolve the human female ovum shell for fertilization. It is the human male. At the tip of the human male spermatozoa is an acrosome granule; its sole purpose is to dissolve the shell of the ovum for fertilization. The male spermatozoon is also receptor specific for only one kind of creature on earth and only one kind of ovum. No other tissue that the spermatozoa comes in contact with will cause the spermatozoon to release the acrosome granule prematurely. Only the human female ovum has the correct protein receptor sites to trigger a release mechanism on the spermatozoa to release the acrosome granules for shell dissolving. Imagine the disaster if spermatozoa released the acrosome granules upon contacting any tissue. No fertilization would ever occur, and all kinds of creatures would become extinct in short order. *Image credit: Wikipedia.org.*

No other creature on earth besides the human male has this specific acrosome granule to dissolve the female human ovum shell for the fertilization of the chromosomes. Also, no other creature on earth besides the human female has the protein receptor-specific sites to trigger the male acrosomal enzyme release and accept the granules of the human male spermatozoa for fertilization. This is two-way specificity that establishes exclusivity. Do not be fooled by websites claiming that mankind has been cross-breeding different kinds for years; that is a switch of terms. Mankind has been cross-breeding different species of the same kind, but no one has cross-bred two different kinds of creatures.

So how is this a testable scenario that proves the hypothesis of God being the intelligent designer and creator of human beings? Well, it is a dubious test, but through the debauchery of mankind and the unfortunate sin of bestiality, mankind has on multiple occasions and over many millennia performed this "test" that determines if different kinds of creatures can crossbreed with the human kind. The answer is emphatically "No."

Since God created us in His image and likeness, He sealed us to protect us from ourselves to keep His creation in the form that He intended it. God gave Adam His name to claim him by claiming Adam as His son (Luke 3:38) and giving Adam the Breath of Life from the Holy Spirit. God made it so that each kind of creature could only reproduce with the same kind of creature. That is why in the Gen. 1 creation account, one reads nine times the phrase "after their kind." God created each creature "after their kind" (Gen. 1:11, 12, 12, 21, 21, 24, 24, 25, and 25), from grass to plants, to trees, to fish, to birds, to beasts, to mankind; all are created after their kind by God to reproduce only with their own kind. All life on earth can only reproduce after their kind. This is an amazing seal and an amazing signature by God that reveals the exclusivity of His creation.

It should be noted that evolution by definition would not allow such exclusivity of kinds of creatures. Since evolution is based on random and unguided mutations and survival of the fittest, exclusivity of kinds would not exist; quite the contrary, crossbreeding of kinds[166] would be encouraged to determine the best kind of creature. Even the famed movie *Jurassic Park* has a line that says that one cannot make evolution exclusive—evolution cannot be boxed in. Evolution would not allow such exclusion of kinds. Evolution would find a way to cross the different kinds. Remember in the movie where the scientist of chaos Dr. Ian Malcom learns that the creatures in the park were all female dinosaurs so that the owners could control the population? Below are quotes from the movie.

John Hammond: I've been present for the birth of every little creature on this island.
Dr. Ian Malcolm: Surely not the ones that are bred in the wild?
Henry Wu: Actually they cannot breed in the wild. Population control is one of our security precautions. **There's no unauthorized breeding in Jurassic Park.**
Dr. Ian Malcolm: **How do you know they cannot breed?**
Henry Wu: Well, **because all the animals in Jurassic Park are female.** We've engineered them that way.
Dr. Ian Malcolm: But again, how do you know they're all female? Does somebody go out into the park and pull up the dinosaurs skirts?
Henry Wu: We control their chromosomes. It is really not that difficult. All vertebrate embryos are inherently female anyway; they just require an extra hormone given at the right developmental stage to make them male. We simply deny them that.
Dr. Ian Malcolm: John, **the kind of control you're attempting simply is, it is not possible. If there is one thing the history of evolution has taught us it is that life will not be contained. Life breaks free; it expands to new territories and crashes through barriers, painfully, maybe even dangerously,** but, uh, well, there it is.
John Hammond: There it is.
Henry Wu: **You're implying that a group composed entirely of female animals will breed?**
Dr. Ian Malcolm: **No, I'm, I'm simply saying that life, uh finds a way.**

Dr. Ian Malcolm tells them that they cannot confine evolution. Evolution will find a way. And guess

---

166 Crossbreeding of kinds is not crossbreeding of species. Many species exist within a kind.

what, evolution does find a way in the movie, and everything goes crazy shortly thereafter. Why? According to evolution, exclusivity does not exist; nature will find a way to crossbreed kinds. Nature will find a way to reproduce new kinds of animals and a way to evolve new kinds. Transitional creatures that are half of one kind of animal and half of another should be normal to see around earth, not 100% of humans being humans, 100% of apes being apes, and 100% of each kind being the same kind. But no evidence exist in the past or present of any dog becoming any other life form. Why? God sealed His creation from the beginning by coating female eggs and providing only the same kind of male creatures with the enzyme to dissolve the coating for fertilization. Also, from the beginning, God sealed the hormone receptor neurons of males to only be receptive to the same kind of female hormonal release of pheromones. Therefore, hormone production is to attract the same kind.

"Once you eliminate the impossible, whatever remains, however improbable, must be the truth."[167] I am suggesting that the exclusivity of reproduction with only the same kind of creature, eliminates the evolutionary hypothesis of unguided randomness and only allows a creator hypothesis. Why? The existence of too much order and design governing the exclusivity of the reproductive process of all living things on Earth.

The evidence of the Creator is out there for all to see, but how the evidence is interpreted is where the disconnect is. This is the heart of man interpreting the evidence that science uncovers; it is not science that is against God. It is this mindset in which so-called unbiased evolutionists interpret evidence and come up with theories that are anti-God. It is not that science is anti-God; quite the contrary, science is in harmony with the Bible.

By the way, it should be noted that each male dog has the correct enzyme for each female dog, from the wolf to a Maltese dog. Each male cat has the correct enzyme for each female cat, from the tiger to a tabby cat. Logistics make it unlikely that a male tabby cat could fertilize a female tiger, but it is possible. But no male cat has the correct enzyme to dissolve the shell to allow the fertilization of a female dog. It is like this for each creature. Each kind of male fish can only fertilize the same kind of female eggs, and each kind of male bird can only fertilize the same kind of female egg. Please note that a "kind" is a larger grouping of animals. For example, all breeds (varying species) of dogs may have descended from the wolf are of one kind of animal.

Review: God sealed each creature to only be able to reproduce with their own kind. Medical science proves the exclusivity with reproduction and that each kind of creature can only reproduce after their own kind, which proves the Bible correct and proves evolution is wrong and in violation of medical science. This is testable evidence of the existence of God.

Evolutionists believe that mankind shed its fur because "6–8 million years ago apelike ancestors of modern humans had a semiaquatic lifestyle based on foraging for food in shallow waters."[168] Then, mankind had to kill other creatures so that they could put on heavy coats to survive the ice age. What an evolutionary bummer that we lost our fur heading into the ice age. The theory is that humans lost their fur so that they could swim better. And proof of this is our remnant webbed hands and feet. This is a fanciful, wild hypothesis that is faith based, yet it is acclaimed by evolutionists as fact.

This leads us into the discussion of **vestigial organs**. A vestigial organ is something that has no function and has lost its original purpose. Vestigial organs are offered as proof that we evolved from another creature. For example, the most famous alleged vestigial organ is our tailbone. Evolutionists cite the tailbone as proof that we once had a tail like our forefathers, the primates. Here are the problems with that: (1) Again, evolutionists want to show a loss of something to prove that we gain information via random genetic mutations. This is backwards thinking; why would we lose something that is functional? This is the fanciful dream world of evolution. They never see any human with a partial tail, but they assume we all had a tail millions of years ago. (2) The coccyx is not called a tailbone; it is called the **coccyx** because of its resemblance to a cuckoo's beak, and it is not a remnant

167 Arthur Conan Doyle, 1890, Sherlock Holmes, "The Sign of the Four", Ch. 6, (Doubleday, p.111).
168 *Scientific American*, "Latest theory of why humans lost their body hair?"

tail. It has a function and a purpose. The function is to allow the attachment of many muscles, ligaments, and tendons. The purpose is as a structural support for all the visceral organs, and more importantly, for the sphincter control of involuntary muscles, so we can defecate at the appropriate time. Without the coccyx, feces would just ooze out via peristaltic motion without control. Thus, if any evolutionist proclaims the coccyx to be a remnant tailbone, they do not know anatomy, nor anatomical functions.

The other famous vestigial organ is the **appendix**. The appendix allegedly proves that we evolved from another kind that once used the appendix. Since the appendix allegedly has no function and no purpose, it proves we evolved. Well, this is antiquated thinking, and frankly, it is a hypothesis based on ignorance. Medical science has finally caught up to the bizarre wild claims of evolution. Several decades ago, we did not know what the appendix was for, but now we do. The appendix stores bacteria that are necessary for the breakdown of food for fuel. When humans eat something bad, or when their bodies are overwhelmed with foreign bacteria that cause diarrhea, the healthy bacteria in the large intestines needed for the final breakdown of ingested food for nutrient absorption get flushed out of the intestines. Well, guess what? The appendix, which stores the good bacteria for the intestines, is there to save the day. The appendix releases stored bacteria into the intestinal system and reconstitutes the healthy, needed bacteria into the intestines. Without the appendix to save the day, humans would get diarrhea and die of dehydration. Therefore, the appendix is involved in immunity. Do not think for a second that the appendix has no function and no purpose. The appendix is not from an ancestral creature that we evolved from. Again, evolutionists want to use the logic of losing something as evidence that we gain new function and new kinds via random, unguided mutations of the DNA code. It is illogical to show a loss of a function as proof that we gain new functions and new kinds. Whenever, an evolutionist proclaims the appendix proves humans evolved, know that the only thing their wild claims prove is that they do not know medical science.

As discussed previously, evolutionists use the term *pharyngeal gill slits* to describe the folds in the skin on a human embryo. They proclaim that these folds are vestigial in nature, indicating that man evolved from fish. Creationists and those familiar with anatomy know that each fold of the tissue of an embryo grows into a different aspect of the human nervous system; in no way do these folds in embryonic tissue represent that we once had gills from ancestral fish. This is really just a lack of knowledge on the part of those who suggest that the folds in the tissue are from prior gill slits.

I have even heard an evolutionist use the **pineal gland** as evidence of evolution because the gland has no function. Well, mankind has recently found out its function and that it is responsible for hormone production for such things as sleep inducement. The pineal gland produces melatonin, which is a serotonin-derived hormone that influences sleep. A full night's rest is important for decelerating the aging process. What was thought of as a useless vestigial organ, which supposedly proved evolution, actually aids in sleep regulation and youthfulness.

Are **wisdom teeth** vestigial? No, they have a purpose. Imagine living 900+ years, the teeth are useful to force the other teeth together to close gaps when another tooth is lost. Also, the skull size of humans before the Flood was larger than today. The Denisovan skull, is a human skull with a cranial volume of 1800 cc, which is 38.5% larger than the average male, and ~57% larger than the average female. This would allow ample room for wisdom teeth to grow. Many people do not get their wisdom teeth extracted. They are not vestigial.

Lastly, we come to the alleged vestigial thigh bone in whales. It is said that the bone is from when the whale used to have a leg and that it no longer has a function. On the contrary, the bone is used for mating and reproducing. It shouldn't even be called a femur; it is part of the pelvis. The label for the bone came from evolutionists trying to provide evidence to support their beliefs. The bottom line is that the bone is part of the pelvis and is useful for mating and reproducing offspring.

Medical science has caught up to the wild claims by evolutionists. Now you are more informed about these alleged vestigial organs that are really based on not knowing how the body works and forcing fanciful ideas to fit their beliefs. In fact, not one single vestigial organ on any creature alive or dead to show that any creature evolved into another kind or from another kind. No need to go through each fanciful tale of supposed vestigial organs; at some point, it is not logical to chase an endless trail of wild claims. What is sad is that theistic evolutionists buy into vestigial organs based on illogical deduction and theories based without knowledge of anatomy that reject Biblical claims. Theistic evolutionists try to appease both sides in the war on truth, and God declares you are either 100% for Me or 100% against Me. You cannot believe 50% of the Bible and 75% of evolution. They are exclusively on opposite sides of the war on truth.

One animal actually does have a partial vestigial extremity, but it does not support evolution; instead, it authenticates the Bible. You will never hear an evolutionist mention this. The snake does have a rudimentary extremity that represents a time in the past when the snake once had full extremities and crawled on limbs instead of slithering on its belly. Gen. 3:14 explains that as a result of a particular snake allowing Satan to possess it and subsequently being an agent of the Devil to deceive Eve, the snake lost its ability to crawl on legs and was forced to slither on its belly. The snake still has small, leftover partial claws, from when it once had limbs. The snake still uses those claws for mating but no longer uses them for mobility.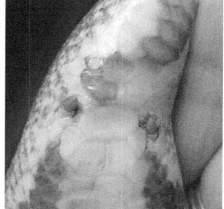

Three functions once existed at creation but have been removed because of sin. One is the legs of snakes that were once used for crawling. Yet, they still have a function, and that is for mating. The other two are not tangible things that we can observe: they are that, potentially, humans used to be able to see in the spiritual realm and animals used to be able to talk to humans. The last two are discussed toward the end of the book, but they deal with Balaam and his donkey in Numbers 22 and the snake in Gen. 3.

Review: Evolutionists' claim of vestigial organs that prove creatures evolve only prove evolutionists' lack of knowledge regarding the organs that they think have no function. Logically, the hypothesis of evolution does not get credit for showing something that allegedly has lost function to prove we gain new functions and new kinds. These are illogical, wild claims just to disprove God.

Someone reading may still be wondering what evolution is. To break down the theory of evolution into lay terminology versus Ernst Haeckel's "ontogeny recapitulates phylogeny," it is the compilation of tiny changes in organisms via mutated DNA over time, adapting to an ever-changing environment and stimuli, coupled with natural selection to assure that the best mutations survive. Those subtle and tiny changes accumulate over time and build on each other with each passing generation, and this is how life evolves from a single-cell organism to a human being after 1–2 billion years of evolution. It is illustrated by the following series of shapes as a crude example:

! ! Ĺ Ł ķ Ķ ƛ Ý Y´ Ÿ V V̈ Δ ◊ △ ¤ ۞ O O C̃ G̈ ω ∞

From the schematic above, you can see how an exclamation mark evolved into an infinity sign through subtle and accumulative changes over time. This sounds reasonable, and on the surface, it does make sense. Is this truly how it is? This is where the debate of evolution versus adaptation occurs. Adaptation (or specialization) is accepted by creationists as fact. Adaptation occurs in all life forms, from animals to botanical life. Subtle changes occur due to adaptation to the environment, but the "kind" of creature remains the same. A creationist would say that the above illustration may start off as an exclamation mark, and it may become larger or bold, turn into italics, or change font, but in the end, it is still an exclamation mark and cannot evolve into an infinite symbol. For example:

! ! / / ₁/ !! ! ! !

The different types of exclamation marks represent species from adaptation, yet they are still the same "kind" because the DNA code for "kind" remains the same. It is the epigenome that causes the changes by directing the genome (DNA) by turning off or on certain genes. The information is still there in the

DNA, but as the epigenome reacts to external and internal stimuli, it marks genes to either turn off or on or controlling protein production in certain cells.[169] This is where the adaptation occurs, on top of the DNA, not within the DNA. The epigenome markers on the DNA results with a different emphasis on the information when mitosis occurs, and it can be passed down to generations. Also, adaptation occurs with combining parental DNA and environmental conditions. When a mutation occurs to the question mark and it loses its function, it becomes an indistinguishable blob, and a loss of function or information occurs, not an enhancement of information. Evolutionists always use adaptation to show that evolution is real, but adaptation and evolution are different. Adaptation is based on information already in the DNA code, and the DNA code limits how far a creature can adapt before death or sterility occurs. Adaptation already has defined limits set by the DNA code, and it is impossible to evolve to different kinds without new DNA coding that was not already there. It is analogous to a computer software program having changes done by random keystrokes by blindfolded monkeys who accidentally improve the software program, not just once for one benefit, but trillions of trillions of times. Evolution requires the DNA to get new information for the changes to occur for new function or new kind. The two (adaptation and evolution) are very different; one does not authenticate the other.

At the end of the day, at the end of the century, at the end of the millennium, the creature is always the same kind, even though it has adapted to its environment. Since we observe that adaptation is limited and no one can observe the alleged evolutionary changes millions of years ago and since it is so slow today that no one can observe a change of kind today, that's where science ends and faith takes over.

A problem for evolutionists is the alleged sudden explosion of complex and diverse creatures during a brief Cambrian period. An evolutionary explosion of creatures did not occur, it is just a vast array of diverse life buried in this sedimentary layer resulting from the global flood, that evolutionary geologist call the Cambrian rock layer. Evolution is defined as being very slow; however, embedded in this rock layer are many new complex creatures, which suggest that they seemingly evolved in too short a time period given the slow hypothesis of evolution. A very clever evolutionist might explain this rapid evolution by demonstrating how a bipedal creature quickly grew a brain that was three times larger than a human brain two million years ago. Can biologists take a mammal, such as a mouse, and experiment with varying stimuli, such as protein inhibitors, beta genes, and so on, to explain the alleged accelerated brain growth of transitional Australopithecus to a more advanced Homo Erectus? It turns out that the beta-catenin gene, which coats a protein, helps cells regenerate and causes cells to get bigger. By regulating the beta-catenin gene in the central nervous system, biologists inactivated the amino terminus, which is a component to keep the gene active. Then, they made an enhancer and put it in the mouse and raised the mouse under those conditions. The result: the mouse brain was twice the mass, with increased sulci. Evolutionists say the mouse adapted and evolved a larger brain, just like earlier primates evolved to have larger craniums and to eventually become human. However, no evidence exist that this benefited the mouse or if the mouse thrived or died prematurely. This is just a mouse artificially adapting as though a DNA code was instructing the regulation of the beta-catenin gene, not a new function and not enhanced brain power, and no epigenome marker established to pass on to other generations. No information was increased in the DNA code, and no offspring were produced that had an increased brain size. This is not evidence for evolution; this is evidence of adaptation by intelligent design of the scientist. Now, if the mouse became slightly smarter, or if the mouse's DNA added new beneficial information, evolutionists would have something, but that is not what happened. No additional information added to the DNA, and no new function resulted from the artificial test. Therefore, the test merely demonstrates intelligent design to artificially illustrate the ability of the body to adapt and not the ability of the body to evolve a new function.

Review: Adaptation does not lead to or authenticate evolution; they are different. Adaptation utilizes the epigenome to turn on or turn off information in the DNA code to modify features. The DNA

169 Www.genome.gov/about-genomics/fact-sheets/epigenomics-fact-sheet.

for kind never changes. Whereas evolution relies on random, unguided changes to the DNA code that produce new functions and eventually new kinds. Evolution is impossible, and evolutionists erroneously use adaptation to save themselves.

Take Darwin's Galapagos finches; they had DNA code allowing them to be finches with beaks. Through adaptation, their beaks slightly elongated by a couple of millimeters, but they were still finches. The DNA of a kind remained the same, but the genome got modified by the epigenome that sits on top. The finches that had DNA from birth for elongated beaks that better suited that environment, thrived and dominated the population. This is exactly how every species of human, though sharing the same DNA from Adam and Eve, but because of environmental conditions, sin, and so forth, humans have different color of hair, shape of hair, color of eyes, color of skin, tall, short, and so forth.

The information to adapt to the external stimulus was already in the DNA code; it was not new information being added into the DNA to allow beak modification. In other words, take Adam and Eve, they both had the DNA information for all the differences we see today in humans. Yet, every human is the same kind, made in the image of God, sharing DNA with God, and God is their physical Father. The epigenome turns on or off certain features based on environmental conditions, and those markers are passed on via the chromosomes. That's a big difference from saying that random, unguided mutations altered the DNA, and this caused the beaks to alter shape—and those whose beaks were altered poorly died off, and those whose beaks were altered appropriately for the terrain survived.

Suppose that Noah took a set of male and female wolf pups on the ark. After millennia of breeding, migrating to different regions on the globe with different environmental conditions, and adaptations governed by existing DNA, we now have hundreds of different species of dogs, from the wolf to white fluffy Maltese, to beagles, and so on. But guess what? They are still dogs. Why? A protective coating exist surrounding the egg of a female dog, and only one kind of creature on earth has the necessary enzyme at the tip of the male sperm to dissolve this coating for fertilization to occur. Guess what that creature is? A DOG! Again, why is this? Because God has sealed His creation from the beginning for plants and animals to produce after their kind. This exclusivity of breeding is for each kind of creature.

Also, in the hormonal makeup of each kind of animal, specific pheromones attract only the same kind of animal. When a female dog goes in heat and she is ready for a mate, she releases pheromones to attract a mate. Why is it that other kinds of creatures do not come to fertilize her? Humans do not get excited and court the female dog. A male cat does not get excited and court the female dog. God has sealed His creation so that all plants and animals produce after their kind. In fact, the pheromones that the female dog release to attract a mate have no biological affect on other kinds of animals, except the male dog. This deals with DNA. No other animal has the appropriate protein receptors that are specific to receive the female dog's pheromones and translate the stimulus into a mutual hormonal mating response, except a dog. This is similar for every animal, fish, bird, and human. That is why no crossbreeding of kinds is possible and explains why 100% of dogs are 100% dogs, and 100% of humans are 100% humans, and so forth.

Evolution never knows where it is going; it is a free-running, random, unguided program, with survival of the fittest kind of guiding its steps along the way. By definition, we should be able to observe creatures making evolutionary progress, and survival of the fittest should either allow new transitions to succeed or eliminate them. We should still be able to see this random, unguided process occurring. We should be able to observe a human devolving back to a chimp because of unguided, random mutations, and we should be able to see chimps evolving. But we do not. Evolutionists conveniently say that the process is too slow to see. The changes occurred hundreds of millions of years ago, yet evolutionists do not know that. Each day, each year there should still be those changes that evolutionists proclaimed happened 300 million years ago. It is a nice way to hide their lack of evidence.

Evolutionists might say, "Hey a horse and a donkey produce a mule, and a lion and tiger produce a liger." Yes, but the mating occurred between the same kind to produce a variation within the same kind, and those offspring are always sterile. Thus, stopping the alleged evolution process and proving that boundaries exist to adaptation. The horse, donkey, and mule are the same kind, and the mule is sterile. Likewise, the lion, tiger, and liger are all the same kind, though different species. And the liger is sterile. Thus, limitations exist to how far a creature can adapt before the DNA ends the adaptation with such things as sterility. This is observable evidence corroborating the Bible's version of creatures can only produce after their kind, and it debunks evolution.

When did God seal the grass to remain as grass and the plants to remain as plants and the trees to remain as trees? It was on the third day of creation with the phrase "after their kind" in Gen. 1:11–13. God repeats this phrase three times to drum home the point for botanical life. Why? Because plants needed to be told? No. Because God knows the mind of man. God knew man would think that mankind evolved from other created things. The world wants you to believe Darwin was the first to postulate the idea that life evolved from rocks, trees, and the like. Consider Jeremiah 2:27:

> Who say to a tree, "You are my father," And to a stone, "You gave me birth." For they have turned their back to Me, And not their face; But in the time of their trouble they will say, "Arise and save us." But where are your gods Which you made for yourself? Let them arise, if they can save you in the time of your trouble.

You see, this is an age-old tactic to remove God as creator. To say we evolved from a rock is to say that one rejects the Words of God. Darwin is not the originator of this movement. Nor is any other human for that matter. Now wait a minute; no one thinks they literally came from rocks, do they? Well, let us trace the evolutionary tree backward. Where did humans come from? Primates (apes, monkeys, and so forth)—and where did they come from? You keep going backward until you get to the beginning, where it rained on rocks, and the minerals from the rocks pooled to create a primordial soup of chemicals. Voila, rocks are the starting point. If evolution is false and deceitful, it may be from deceitful spirits and thereby a doctrine of demons (I Timothy 4:1). Evolutionists would be wise to ponder the implications if this be true—that the concept of evolution is purely an attempt by Satan to keep humans away from the Word of God, thus trapping them in the slavery of sin and eternal death.

Chapter Summary: Evolution violates medical science with the belief of crossbreeding of different kinds, which is proven to be impossible by the exclusivity of the fertilization process. Evolution violates the scientific method by believing in something that is not observable and not testable, with notions such as the spontaneous spawning of first life, the spontaneous forming of DNA coding, mutations enhancing the genetic code, and on and on. Evolution violates logic with a bait-and-switch scheme by noting what is observable, such as adaptation, and using that to suggest that what is not observable is true. Evolution violates logic by vestigial organs as an apparent lost function to demonstrate that we gained new function, and each reference to an alleged vestigial organ only points out the lack of knowledge of anatomy.

Chapter 31
Evolution Versus the Bible

Many Christians believe in evolution, but they suggest that God performed or initiated the process. It is God's creative act that allowed the first single-cell life form to exist and to eventually evolve into all the complexities of life via mutations and natural processes. Can the two be in harmony? Can a believer in God believe that God orchestrated the evolutionary process over billions of years? Or does a theistic evolutionist's beliefs lie in complete conflict with the Bible? What does the Bible say?

The Bible puts the death knell in the concept of evolution in Romans 5:12, "Therefore, just as through one man sin entered into the world, and death through sin, and so death spread to all men, because all sinned . . . death reigned from Adam." Since death did not exist in the world before Adam sinned, fossils did not exist before Adam sinned. Since the notion of evolution is accompanied with a series of failed attempts, death, and fossils as man evolved. Then God completely obliterates the notion of evolution by saying that death did not exist in the world before Adam sinned.

Furthermore, God says in Jeremiah 2:26–28:

> As the thief is shamed when he is discovered, so the house of Israel is shamed; They, their kings, their princes and their priests and their prophets, who say to a tree, "You are my father," and to a stone, "You gave me birth." For they have turned their back to Me, and not their face; But in the time of their trouble they will say, "Arise and save us." But where are your gods which you made for yourself? Let them arise, if they can save you. In the time of your trouble.

Israelis were theistic evolutionists and God declared they were committing idolatry and were shamed. Even Jesus quotes Genesis, indicating that He believed in a literal interpretation of creation, that God made mankind male and female from the beginning. Those who want to believe that man evolved by evolutionary means are faced with Jesus' own words, (Matthew 19:4-6) "Have you not read that He who created from the beginning made them male and female, and said, 'For this reason a man shall leave his father and mother and be joined to his wife, and the two shall become one flesh'?" For those who think they can believe in God and evolution, "Have you not read?" Jesus 100% ruled out the possibility that God created a single-cell prokaryote that evolved into other life forms and eventually humans.

God is merciful, and He knows that people have been taught—from all of academia to every television show and to every friend and from a young age all the way to adulthood—that evolution is fact. God has special verses for those who are without knowledge of the Bible or reject the Bible and the notion that every mountain was covered under the heavens for a global flood (Gen. 7:19–23) and for those who are without knowledge of or reject a seven-day creation and accept a re-creation or evolution (Exodus 20:11), which make them guilty of annulling or setting aside or modifying or neglecting some of Scripture. A believer of Jesus cannot lose their salvation (Rom. 8:38–39) and will enter the Kingdom of Heaven, but those who set aside some Scriptures to accept evolution will be called least in the Kingdom of Heaven (Matthew 5:19). Those who hold the Scriptures in low esteem will be held in low esteem by Jesus. A harsher warning for those that lead (teach) people astray with false doctrine, such as with evolution (Matthew 18:6).

Review: A believer in God will not call His Word a lie or inaccurate because Jesus is the Word. It is possible for a believer to make errors, such as believing in evolution, but once this information has been brought to a true believer's attention, they will mourn for doubting God's Word and reject evolution because God rejected evolution in Jeremiah 2:26–28 and Matthew 19:4–7.

Some people believe in the singularity of the Big Bang theory and God, but the two concepts are mutually exclusive. The Big Bang theory suggests that all that exists in the universe was compressed into a tiny dot and existed eternally as energy. Yet God's testimony in stone is that He made everything in six days; that includes energy. Big Bang believers do not allow for water to exist in abundance in the expanding universe immediately following the first Big Bang. Yet before God expanded the universe and the atmosphere on the second day (i.e., the second Big Bang), the Bible records "waters" were abundant, indicating that the volume of the universe was smaller before the violent expansion on the second day of creation, but not too small to prevent water and dirt from existing. Also, all Big Bang believers are pressured to reject the Biblical record of the global flood.

A big problem for humans is that they are being staunchly told that the earth is billions of years old by seemingly the smartest people on the planet who use sophisticated science to allegedly prove it, with such things as radioactive decay dating methods. Most people think that scientists are telling them the truth, which makes God's Word non-truth. Why do evolutionists take the leap of faith and believe that the earth is billions of years old? The evolutionist does not accept the notion that they believe in anything. They say it is fact, and radioactive dating is just one part of the proof. But they do not know or wont believe that the foundation for radioactive dating is based on a "Constant Rate Decay," which must always be constant. And this belief starts with the assumption that "all things continue just as it was from the beginning of creation" (2 Peter 3:4), which is the Uniformitarian hypotheses. We have shown that the CRD is not constant. Why are many evolutionary scientists and believers still adhering to their beliefs in evolution?

It is fair to argue that errors made in the beginning of a theory that have other ideas built upon them will cause greater and greater error margins with each chain of hypotheses built upon the erroneous foundation. And that is what creationists say is wrong with the hypothesis of evolution; it starts wrong with the origin of life, the origin of information, and the origin of energy and matter, and increasingly gets further from the truth with each progressive thought built upon the foundational errors. The evolutionary model is a set of errors built upon initial error.

From a medical perspective, the hypothesis of evolution is like a sick patient with increasing symptoms and different ailments that are becoming more chronic, with new and more acute symptoms flaring up with each increase in mankind's knowledge of life and understanding of the universe. What is the root cause of why people believe in evolution? Two answers exist: the voluntary realm and the involuntary realm.

The voluntary realm.

For the evolutionist: This is a willful attempt to justify sin. Take the atheistically motivated Charles Lyell[170] for example; he rejected God, and therefore the Bible had to be wrong. For this reason, when he looked at the layers of the crust of the earth, and because he rejected the Biblical record of the global flood as the explanation for the layers of the crust, he chose an interpretation that was against God's testimony. He rejected the notion of a catastrophic global flood, and therefore the layers accumulated slowly because "all things continue just as it was from the beginning of creation" (2 Peter 3:4)—Uniformitarian theory. An assertion that the rates of operations today have always been constant, and therefore explain all the former changes to the Earth's surface. Thus, Lyell attempted to justify his atheism because the Bible was wrong, based on the deep time established through the Uniformitarian paradigm. However, not all evolutionists are atheists, but all theistic evolutionists link arms with atheism by accepting Lyell's theory and rejecting God's testimony of the six days of creation and the global flood.

Take Charles Darwin for example; he believed he was of a superior race. Therefore, he interpreted empirical data based on this foundation. Thus, Darwin attempted to justify his superiority and that his species had evolved further than other human species of color—through evolution. Evolution was designed to justify the sin of racism. However, not all evolutionists are racists, and for this reason the voluntary realm needs a broader explanation, such as by drawing conclusions from the

---

170 Charles Lyell wrote, "Principles of Geology," ca 1830. The book that turned Charles Darwin away from the Bible.

empirical data that fit their own beliefs as the standard or foundation on which to formulate such conclusions by conscious choice. For example, when one believes humans eventually evolved from a single-cell organism, and fish were one of the evolutionary steps, then when they sees folds of skin on a human embryo, the folds look like gill slits from when our ancestors were fish. This is a voluntary choice to interpret data that fits a preconceived belief. This is called apparent evidence, which is the evidentiary technique that flat earthers use to support their view. When one rejects God, the standard of morality becomes relative and subjected to lustful desires. For this reason, one makes a voluntary choice to interpret the observable evidence so that it aligns with allowing one to live without the absolute morality of the Bible. The root is that God does not exist, and the data is interpreted to support that conclusion. Thus, the result is denying God the honor due Him, and giving man the highest rank by evolutionary means. For this reason, evolution is linked to self-worship, human glory, and sin. Scripture addresses this with Romans 1:19–23:

> That which is known about God is evident within them; for God made it evident to them. For since the creation of the world His invisible attributes, His eternal power and divine nature, have been clearly seen, being understood through what has been made, so that they are without excuse. For even though they knew God, they did not honor Him as God or give thanks, but they became futile in their speculations [about creation], and their foolish heart was darkened. Professing to be wise, they became fools, and exchanged the glory of the incorruptible God for an image in the form of corruptible man and of birds and four-footed animals and crawling creatures.

For the creationist: This is drawing conclusions from the empirical data using God's wisdom as the standard or foundation on which to formulate such conclusions by conscious choice. Proverbs 3:5–6: "Trust in the LORD with all your heart, and do not lean on your own understanding. In all your ways acknowledge Him, and He will make your paths straight. Do not be wise in your own eyes." Creationists accept the Word of God, which says that all life came from God as He wrote it through the inspirational writings of Moses. However, this is not blind faith, for the Bible instructs us to test everything (1 John 4:1), which means through science, archeology, history, and so forth. Therefore, this is a voluntary choice to interpret data that fits a belief that has been scrutinized. That belief is that God exist, and thus morality is absolute. For this reason, one makes a voluntary choice to interpret the observable evidence so that it aligns with allowing one to live with the absolute morality of the Bible. The root is a conscious choice to interpret data to align with the Bible and give God the honor due Him.

Subsequently, both sides attain general conclusions from a conscious choice of whether the Bible is true as it is plainly written or it contains errors. This choice results in a subjective bias that favors their already preconceived notions. This is a voluntary choice to form conclusions from viewing the physical evidence that fits what one wants to believe is the truth. It seems reasonable to draw conclusions based on what is seen and observed to determine what occurred at some distant moment in the past. But no one was there when these major earth-changing events occurred, except one: God (according to the Bible). Therefore, some form of faith-based decision making is required for both the evolutionist and creationist. Evolutionists and creationists observe the same evidence, but evolutionists interpret the observable so that the earth is billions of years old; thus, they align with the conclusion that the Bible has errors regarding the creation account. Therefore, they determine that the Bible was not supernaturally written, but written by humans alone. The problem is that evolutionists already come to the table with a notion that the Bible cannot be true and base their deductions on that foundation and form opinions to support their view. This is where the opinions of evolutionary scientists fill the textbooks. Creationists abide by the very same principle when viewing the same information as evolutionists but interpret the observable through the eyes of science and the Bible.

Both sides make the same conscious decision to validate their prior convictions. The evolutionist consciously wants to disprove the literal creation account in Genesis, while the creationist wants to validate the Bible. For this discussion, we'll use as example the validity of the CRD (Constant Rate of Decay) in the formula for radioactive dating, which is based on the Uniformitarian theory. Why do the evolutionists have a steadfast faith that the CRD has always been constant, when one can illustrate that the CRD is not constant? They voluntarily want conclusions that support an old earth and come up with techniques that suggests an old earth, which supports their already established faith that the Bible is unreliable. A methodology exist in evolutionary reasoning that suggests that if one is going to be a scientist or call oneself a scientist, he or she must limit the reasoning for explaining processes to "chance," random mutations, survival of the fittest, and deep time. This is a deep-rooted conscious decision (and this creates subjective discernment trumps objectivity) to interpret empirical data so that the Bible has some errors. Thus, they rely on their own wisdom to discern the evidence rather than the wisdom of God to determine the proper way to interpret the evidence. Evolutionary hypotheses require lots of time, so all interpretations are required to support this preconceived belief.

This voluntary aspect of discerning an old earth has an outward appearance of being based on objective findings. But is really only lip service to veil the subjective bias of the heart and mind. Evolutionists will tell you that they alone possess the objective mind to interpret evidence and that their data proves a very old universe.

What the evolutionists won't admit or cannot admit is that the evolutionary hypothesis has failed the observable and testable tenets of the scientific method and the existence of compelling evidence and science of a young earth. They won't acknowledge the plausible young earth explanations for all the old earth beliefs in evolution.

Believers who accept mankind's interpretation of evidence (i.e., evolution) versus accepting the Bible (tested and scrutinized) as the standard of truth for which all science is measured against are guilty of one or more of the following: not fully trusting God, putting some faith in man over God, acting on a selfish desire to avoid looking foolish, or not diligently reading the Bible. They also may be guilty of not sharing the Bible with others, even though it commands us to share the good news about the Bible. Well, if they believe that the Bible is not divinely inspired, no compulsion exist to read or risk embarrassment with sharing a man-made book. Also, they are free to do as they wish if they believe that the Bible is not written by God. In that case, God would not be monitoring mankind to check on the required obedience.

Review: A voluntary choice exist to interpret data to align with preconceived beliefs. For creationists, this is a conscious choice to honor God as creator, that His Word is true, and to follow His standard of absolute morality. For evolutionists, such as Darwin, his preconceived belief was racism. Through the sin of his superiority, he interpreted data to justify his sin. For you, it may be different, but for all evolutionists, the preconceived belief is that the Bible contains errors, and/or to reject God. This allows for relative morality, and self-glory as the pinnacle of evolutionary achievement. This denies God honor as creator. Why believers accept evolution: they have a lack of knowledge about the Bible, of knowledge about evolution, and of faith in God. They fear mankind and prefer self-preservation over honoring God at all cost.

The involuntary realm

For the evolutionist: This is drawing conclusions from the empirical data using their own desire as the standard or foundation on which to formulate such conclusions by unconscious drive. This is not a choice; this is from within and ingrained in the inner person, from the heart. This is addressed in Colossians 1:21: "And although you were formerly alienated and hostile in mind, engaged in evil deeds." it is the age-old discussion of Martin Luther and Jonathon Edwards about the free will to choose or not. The answer is that we have free will to choose evil or good, but once we choose evil upon reaching the age of accountability, we can only choose degrees of evil going forward until we are saved from sin. Those adults who are spiritually dead in sin, their choices will be to glorify themselves, satisfy the flesh, or test God. We have a free will to choose but because of sinning, we can only choose evil because we are alienated from God, we have a hostile mind toward God, and our actions are evil self-glory. To compound the problem, evolutionists do not accept the Genesis creation account because it is foolishness to them, and they cannot understand it because their spiritual nature is contrary to the spiritual nature of God. I Corinthians 2:14: "But a natural man (not saved) does not accept the things of the Spirit of God, for they are foolishness to him; and he cannot understand them, because they are spiritually appraised."

For the creationist: This is drawing conclusions from the empirical data using God as the standard or foundation on which to formulate such conclusions by unconscious drive. This is not a choice; this is innately ingrained in the inner person. This is addressed in the Scriptures with II Corinthians 5:14–18:

> For the Love of Christ controls us . . . we live for him who died and rose again . . . Therefore from now on we recognize no one according to the flesh . . . Therefore if anyone is in Christ, he is a new creature; the old things passed away; behold, new things have come. Now all these things are from God.

I Corinthians 2:7–16 says, "We speak God's wisdom . . . For to us God revealed them through the Spirit; For the Spirit searches all things, even the depths of God . . . We have the mind of Christ."

This is a spiritual motivation (our spirit), an inner drive that directs and battles the conscious mind (soul) for power/control. This is where the spirit influences the soul. A spirit that is alive will influence the soul to choose good, and a spirit that is dead in sin will influence the soul to choose evil. It is a preconceived paradigm that determines which lens we look through to interpret the observable. On the other hand, atheistic evolutionists reject God, thus allowing them to potentially fulfill any carnal desire they want. They have an involuntary urge to lean on their own understanding. The creationist does the same thing, but inversely, and suggests that God is real and therefore a judgment, thus allowing freedom from the sins of our carnal desire and instilling a desire to live according to the Bible's moral code. Creationists have an involuntary urge to lean not on their own understanding and in all their ways to acknowledge God.

This involuntary response has a spiritual motivation. We are either enemies of God or an ally. Jesus said that you are either for me or against me. No middle ground exist (Matthew 12:30). Therefore, one either acknowledges God in all their ways, or they do not. If you claim to be a believer, yet reject what God wrote as truth, this is a good time to do a self-evaluation.

Chapter Summary: An involuntary drive affects the decision-making process. This is the condition of the spirit that affects the desire, thoughts, and motivation of the soul, and this affects the actions of the body. This is why we do not wrestle with flesh and blood (soul), but with principalities of the spiritual realm (Ephesians 6:10–17). The spirit of a saved person will have the mind of Christ and have the Holy Spirit to guide him or her in interpreting data and understanding the Bible. The spirit of the unsaved person cannot understand the Bible because it is spiritually discerned only through the Holy Spirit, and thus he or she is left spiritually blind and cannot see the correct interpretation of the physical realm.

Section III
The Seven Days of Creation
Chapter 32
The First Day

Gen. 1:1 In the beginning God created the heavens and the earth. The earth was formless and void, and darkness was over the surface of the deep, and the Spirit of God was moving over the surface of the waters. Then God said, 'Let there be light'; and there was light. God saw that the light was good and God separated the light from the darkness. God called the light day, and the darkness He called night. And there was evening and there was morning, one day.

In the beginning God. What existed prior to creation? According to evolutionists, their belief is that prior to the Big Bang, all matter was squished down to the size of a dot and existed as energy. Something created that energy and caused it to be densely packed into a dot. Existing exclusively as energy and zero matter is highly ordered, so something had to organize everything into energy. Some force caused this energy to spin at a high velocity in a superheated state beyond comprehension. Something unknown caused the Big Bang, which set in motion all the laws of the universe we see today and initiated the processes for life to evolve. To have all that orderly compact energy, something intelligent had to organize all that energy to the size of a dot. All the matter in the universe came from the energy that exploded in the Big Bang, but no one knows where all that energy came from in the first place.

The Bible does not use the same nomenclature, but that does not mean they are as different as creationists contend or as similar as theistic evolutionists contend. The Bible records that "God stretched out the Heavens." This indicates that the Heavens were much smaller and closer together when God initially put form and life to the matter. So let us take a closer look and see how similar or dissimilar the Bible is compared to the Big Bang.

Only God (Father, Son, and Holy Spirit as one) existed prior to the first day of creation. The Bible records that God created everything in six days (Exodus 20 and 31), which means nothing eternally existed before the six days of creation. All matter, space, time, and life had a beginning, and their beginnings are found within the Genesis creation account.

In the beginning God created the heavens and the earth. It seems the theologians are split on how to interpret this verse between two options. Option 1 is that Gen. 1:1 is a summary of the entire creation account, and then Moses goes into the details of that general summary. Option 2 is that Gen. 1:1 is the creation of time, space (universe), energy, and matter, though they were without form and void of life and tightly compressed.

To properly chose which option, we must view it through the eyes of Scripture and science. For example, God twice verbally told Moses and twice wrote in stone that He created everything in six days (Exodus 20:11 and Exodus 31:17). God told Israel to observe the Sabbath and that they shall work six days and rest on the seventh day to remind them that it is God who makes them holy. Combining this with Numbers 12:3–8, God said that He does not speak to Moses in veiled dreams and visions: "I speak mouth to mouth, even openly, and not in dark saying and he beholds the form of the LORD." This means that when we read Moses' biography of God's account of creation, as God inspired Moses to write, it is clear, plain language, not mysterious veiled meanings. It is simple language as in blue means blue and one means one and one day means one day. Blue does not mean red, and one day does not mean thousands or billions of years.

Let us tackle both options, and you can decide for yourself, but remember with Scripture, only one correct interpretation exist.

Option 1: Summary of the entire creation account.

We need to lay a foundation about Moses' writing style that could give us a clue to interpret Gen. 1:1. Moses wrote Genesis but He was inspired by God to record what happened at the beginning. II Timothy 3:16 tells us that "All scripture is inspired by God." The word inspired in the Greek is _pneuma_, which means breathed, or moved. We use this word for pneumonia (a respiratory/breathing condition), and when you go to the drive-through at a bank, the transactions are done through a pneumatic system (air-breathed). Humans cannot speak unless air is moving through the larynx (vocal cords). In music, with wind instruments, it is the reed that initiates sounds. So when we speak, we breathe out words, and without breath, no words come forth.

Since the Bible has different writing styles yet with a harmonious theme, it tells us that the writers wrote with their own personalities as God gave them the laws, precepts, and truths to write about. In the creation account, it is possible that Moses started off with a general idea of what was created and then gave the specifics of the general idea. For example, Gen. 1:26–27 is the general creation account of Adam and Eve on the sixth day. While Gen. 2:7 is the detailed creation account of Adam, and Gen. 2:18–25 is the detailed creation account of Eve in sixth day.

Note that the general and detailed accounts are separated by the seventh day in Gen. 2:1–4. After Moses writes about the seventh day of creation, he goes back to give more details. The Apostle John used a similar literary style a couple of times when he penned the book of Revelation. John even went all the way back in time to discuss Satan deceiving a third of the angels.

With this hypothesis of utilizing Moses' writing style, suggests Gen. 1:1 could be the general creation account summary of all that was created. Then Moses gives a detailed creation account in Gen. 1:2–2:4. Is this the best option? No, that is why two options exist.

Review: Moses wrote a few general accounts of creation and then gave the specifics. Suggesting that Gen. 1:1 is a general summary, and the following verses provide the specifics.

Option 2: The opening verse of 1:1 is the creation of a small universe, densely packed with all the water, dirt, and the elements and brings into the physical realm all the laws of the universe and establishes the standard for which time will be set to on the fourth day of creation. This is summed up with God creating the standard for time, force, action, space, and matter.

Twice God spoke to Moses and wrote in stone that He created everything, the heavens, and the earth, the sea and all that is in them in six days and rested on the seventh. Gen. 1:2 alludes to a densely packed universe by saying, "The earth was formless and void, and darkness was over the surface of the deep, and the spirit of God was moving over the surface of the waters." The items that are listed in verse two, all matter, space, and time, were created at the beginning of the first day, and the first day was not finished until verse 5, so by default, all matter (waters, dirt, and the elements) were created at the beginning of the first day and set in motion prior to anything else being made. This is where I reside in interpreting Gen. 1:1. But we'll go further because more nuggets exist with option 2.

Created ex nihilo, or created out of nothing, means that everything was created without any starting material. This rules out a re-creation of any prior civilization of angels and dinosaurs because angels were created on the first day with the light and all land creatures were created on the sixth day.

The Hebrew word for earth is _erets_ (Strong's Conc. #776), which means to be firm (matter is tangible or has firmness, whereas the absence of matter is intangible or has no firmness), the earth (at large, or as land), common, country, field, ground, land, nations, wilderness, and world. In Gen. 1:1, most version translate that God created the earth, but we are not forced to view the Gen. 1:1 _erets_ as the Earth, as the Hebrew word that Moses used gives us room to use the physics term _matter. Matter_ refers to everything that has mass, such as water, dirt, gas, and the elements. If we use the term _matter_, it fits nicely with God just creating all matter. Then verse two reveals that this newly created matter is still formless of shape and still void of life.

It is interesting to note that God spoke everything into existence (Psalm 33:9 and Hebrews 11:3), and when He spoke everything into existence, it was with the Breath of Life. When the Spirit of

God was moving over the surface of the deep in verse 2, it was according to the will of the Father as He gave the words for God the Son to speak. Since all of creation came as a result of God speaking it into existence, the Holy Spirit moving over the surface of the waters and over the matter could very well represent that the Holy Spirit was moving because God just spoke Gen. 1:1 into existence, with the creation of all matter in a confined space at a defined moment in time, that is, at the beginning of the first day of creation. Thus, from verse one to verse five flows as one complete day.

Even though Moses wrote a general statement about the creation of Adam and Eve in Genesis 1:26–27, and then the details of their creation in chapter 2, this writing style does not permeate the first five books. It only appears in the creation account. Thus, option 1 does not negate option 2, which is that God created all matter in a confined space at a specific moment in time on the first day of creation.

Review: Option 2 is that the opening verse is the creation of all matter and space at a specific moment in time. With verse 2 as the continuation that refers to the newly created matter, space, and time, which was without finished form and was void of life.

Option 2 is the better option because verse 2 informs us that this newly created matter was still without its finished form and void of life. The matter will eventually be made into all the things we see today. The creation of all this matter is without any starting material and completely comes from the essence of God. The universe is dark at this moment and is densely packed. Immediately upon being created, matter starts to coalesce (merge) together. Since the end of the first day records that the burgeoning and eventual earth is already rotating, with the phrase, "there was evening and there was morning, first day," then all the eventual planets, moons, and stars were rotating and coalescing. A coalescing formless earth, looked like a hurricane. As a hurricane  coalesces moisture to increase in mass, so too did the coalescing Earth rotate and coalesce matter to increase mass. However, the core of a hurricane is empty, and a coalescing celestial body progressively gets denser approaching the core, with the core being the densest portion. This looks like matter spiraling radially inward and progressively increasing in temperature and rotational velocity as it gets closer to the core. As mass builds at the core, gravity proportionately increases, and this causes more matter to accelerate inward toward the core with a rotational angular acceleration. Now multiply the number of coalescing masses by all the planets, moons, and stars in the universe, and that is how many coalescing celestial bodies were rotating, coalescing and yet still formless on the first day of creation. In between each coalescing mass, was water. The universe was much smaller and densely packed. With each passing minute of the first day, matter coalesced together and each individual future planet, moon, and star increased in mass, density, heat, electromagnetism, and volume.

With matter combining together rapidly, this generated heat at the centers of eventual planets, stars, and moons. Though everything was close together and the universe was small and dark, heat increased. Although none of the planets, stars, and moons were located where they would eventually be completed on the fourth day, they were adjacent to the celestial bodies that they would eventually be adjacent to after creation was complete. *Photo credit: NASA.*

Now, since the galaxies vary in their rotations and shapes, additional information may be applied to this small universe to explain or account for the differences. When viewing the rotational difference from hurricanes and typhoons, meteorologists have discerned that all cyclones rotate according to their geographical location. They will rotate counter-clockwise in the northern hemisphere, and clockwise in the southern hemisphere. If we hypothesize that the entire universe is rotating, we would anticipate that every coalescing future galaxy in the southern hemisphere of the universe would rotate clockwise, and every coalescing future galaxy in the northern hemisphere of the universe would rotate counter-clockwise. If this is true, we would expect to observe the spinning planets, moons, stars, and solar systems will mirror the rotational direction of the galaxy they are in because of angular momentum. A law in physics regarding the conservation of spin, is summed up with; a smaller object that is spun off from a larger object because of the rotational velocity of the larger object, the smaller object conserves (spins in the same direction) the original spin of the larger object.

Let us look at the rotational direction of celestial bodies near us and determine if support exist for this hypothesis. We accept the axiom that because of the earth's rotation, the sun appears to rise in the east and set in the west. For this reason, if we view the earth from the North Pole, it would spin counterclockwise. In addition, the earth orbits the sun in the same counterclockwise rotation. The moon travels around the earth in a counterclockwise revolution and the moon rotates on its axis in a counterclockwise rotation (though at 1/24th of the rotational velocity of the earth, and that is why we always observe the same side of the moon). Cosmologists have determined that every planet in our solar system orbits around the sun counterclockwise when viewed from the Sun's north pole. Also, every planet in our solar system rotates on their axis in a counterclockwise fashion, except Venus and Uranus. Cosmologists hypothesize that Venus and Uranus were hit by large asteroids that altered their original counterclockwise rotation, so that Venus rotates clockwise (albeit very slow) and Uranus rotates on a horizontal axis. The remnant matter that did not coalesce into a planet, speaking of the asteroids and meteors in the Kuiper belt and asteroid belt, they also orbit the sun counterclockwise. In fact, we can now observe sun spots and determine that our sun is rotating counterclockwise.[171] This evidence suggests that our solar system is rotating counterclockwise in relation to the Milky Way Galaxy for which it resides in. This is true because of a principle in physics called angular momentum.

For this reason, we may infer that not only is our solar system rotating counterclockwise to explain why the matter contained within it is spinning counterclockwise, but also that our solar system is spinning counterclockwise because our Milky Way Galaxy is rotating counterclockwise. Since we observe that the direction of spinning coalescing cyclones, such as hurricanes, is determined by which hemisphere they reside in, we may deduce that our Milky Way Galaxy is rotating counterclockwise because it resides in the northern hemisphere of the rotating universe. This leads to the conclusion that if we were able to view the universe from its northern pole, we would observe that the entire universe is also rotating counterclockwise. Since cosmologists suggest a seemingly equal amount of galaxies in every direction from the Milky Way Galaxy, this suggests that our galaxy resides closer to the center of the universe, albeit in the northern hemisphere of a counterclockwise spinning universe.

Review: All the matter that would eventually form planets, star, and moons was densely packed and coalescing together; this generated hot spots at the centers of every eventual planet, star, and moon to keep water liquid in the darkness at the beginning of the first day. The observable evidence of cyclones, the direction of spin and orbit of the sun, moon, and planets of our solar system, suggests that our Milky Way Galaxy is spinning counterclockwise because it resides in the northern hemisphere of the universe that is also spinning counterclockwise.

The Gap theorist believe: *In the beginning God created the heavens and the earth* billions of years ago for the angels, then He destroyed the angelic realm and all the dinosaurs with it, forming all the fossils, and left *the earth formless and void.* The gap theory hypothesis is that the first verse in the Bible is a creative statement for angelic beings, and their world got destroyed by God because of Lucifer's fall. All the dinosaurs are from their time frame, and the Genesis creation account is a re-creation of everything that was destroyed. This theory suggests death occurred on earth before the fall of Adam and Eve, and this is not supported by Scripture. In fact, I Corinthians 15:21 and Romans 5:12 clearly state that sin and death came into the world through Adam's. Gen. 1:31: "God saw all that He had created, and behold it was very good." God would not look over all that He had created—and see the death of billions of dinosaurs and billions of pieces of vegetation, with demons going too and fro—and say, "Behold it was very good." To argue that God was only talking about what He had created in the six days and not what He had created in some past era is not supported in Scripture. What is

---

171 Http://scienceblogs.com/startswithabang/2010/10/07/counterclockwise-but-there-are/.

supported is that God made everything; let that sink in, He made everything in six days (Exodus 20 and 31). When God saw all that He had made, *all* means all, and it was very good, which eliminates the death of dinosaurs and the existence of demons and Satan and sin during the Genesis creation record.

When reading the Bible, do not get too caught up on periods and commas, for no punctuation existed in the original manuscripts; nor were their verse numbers. Get that out of your head. Because verse 1 is labeled by man as verse 1 does not mean that it is not associated with verse 2. That is an error in logic since there were no verse numbers in the original manuscripts.

Review: The "gap theory" is not a viable option.

In the beginning God created the heavens and the matter. Now that we have discussed the best option for understanding Gen. 1:1 is with a literal interpretation, how did God create all the matter in the universe at the beginning of the first day? Oddly enough, the answer may reside with those who adamantly oppose the Genesis creation account in the Bible. This may be the second greatest ironic moment in the history of mankind. The greatest irony is that what man meant for evil, by crucifying Jesus, the Father used for good to purchase every life (of those who accept this free gift) with the blood of Jesus (Acts 2:23–24). The law has always been a "life for a life." Since the life is in the blood and the wage of sin is death, then when sin entered the world, the requirement was blood to pay the cost of sin. Thus, Jesus' blood paid the cost of sin to all those who receive His free gift. And the second greatest irony in the history of mankind, may be with the endeavors of mankind to seemingly disprove God by finding the "God particle"—via the Large Hadron Collider—that actually forces the conclusion that God exist. See the chapter: The Big Bang Versus Physics. The *God particle* is what allows massless energy, photons, to obtain mass (matter). As energy collides into each other at the speed of light, they pass through a Higgs boson field, which allows energy to convert to matter. Thus, the term *God particle* because now God is allegedly not needed to explain how matter came about.

The amount of intelligence involved in converting energy to matter as with the Large Hadron Collider, suggest only an infinite amount of energy and infinite intelligence could create all the matter in the universe. The only conclusion is an all powerful God created of all that we see.

I am thankful that one of the defining terms of the Holy Spirit is even violent, anger, blast, tempest, and so forth, because if the Hadron Collider is any indication of the violence required to form miniscule amount of matter, the amount of violence required to account for all the matter in the universe is staggering. This event, the creation of energy and converting energy to matter, was the most violent event in the history of the universe.

Furthermore, the parameters that the Large Hadron Collider is set in, is based on all the laws and constants of the universe already established. Therefore, their test could suggest that all the laws and constants in the universe were created at an instance—such as creation—or eternally existed. This excludes that all the laws and constants in the universe evolved over time.

Review: Mankind has discovered, that with a great deal of intelligence, with precise design and measurements, and extreme amounts of energy and power, they can create mass from energy—albeit 1.0×10^{-19} times smaller than a grain of sand. The irony is mankind intended to prove that all matter occurred naturally and without a God. However, they have firmly established that only an all knowing and all powerful God could account for the immeasurable amount of matter we see in the universe.

Just as the Bible describes that God begot man and life begot life, life did not come from nonliving material. The same is true with energy and matter and all the laws of the universe. The logic from reading the verses is that "light begot light" and "energy begot energy." When God created all the laws of the universe and all matter and energy within the universe, He did so from Himself by speaking them into existence as the Holy Spirit moved violently. Therefore, just like man was created from God, so to was all matter and energy; all the laws of the universe were created from the essence of God. This is summed up in 1 Corinthians 11:12 "all things originate/are from God," and Colossians 1:16–17: "All things have been created through Him and for Him. He is before all things, and in Him all things hold together." All the laws in physics, chemistry, cosmology, biology, mathematics, and so forth were

254

brought forth on the first day from God and through God. Since these laws are based on God's knowledge, and since God does not increase in knowledge, it seems that all these laws have existed eternally because of God's omniscience. Therefore, He brought to our realm and our dimension all the laws and constants of the universe on the first day of creation.

The earth was formless, as in no designed shape, not that the earth was not existing. The earth was void, as in nothing (no life) was living on it. The Hebrew word for formless is *tohuw*, which means to lay waste, desolation (that is, a desert; figuratively, a worthless thing), and an empty place, without form, or nothing (Strong's Conc. #8414). God caused the earth to coalesce matter and finish forming by the third day with the words, "Let the waters below the heavens be gathered into one place, and let the dry land appear . . . God called the dry land earth and the gathering of the waters He called seas." The phrase, "let the dry land appear," means it was covered prior to that point, not that it was nonexistent. The phrase, *Let the waters be gathered* means that the already existing waters were brought together to take the form of seas, not that the waters were not existing. On the third day, God took the waters and dirt that were already created on the first day and finished making them to take their final shape and have a purpose; He did not create them again. The Hebrew word for void is *bohuw*, which means to be empty, emptiness, or a void (Strong's Conc. #922).

After God created all the matter in the universe, and since it was formless or without form, what did it look like? The future Earth couldn't be a sphere or other shapes we use in geometry (pyramid, cube, trapezoid, etc) because that would indicate form. Since the expansion of the universe did not occur until the second day of creation, we may infer that the matter was in close proximity in a small universe. What is the shape of an asteroid, or the oil floating up and down in a lava lamp? Those both seem shapeless, without finished form, something random and without design. The formlessness of an asteroid seems to suggest it was leftover matter that did not coalesce into a planet, moon, or star while they were forming, and the asteroids stayed in their original formless state and cooled to a solid. This information suggests that the shape of all the matter was that of the formlessness of asteroids, but hot, malleable, and "sticky." Nearly all the matter coalesced together to form stars, planets, and moons, but a few were not close enough to a rotating core and remained separate as asteroids, meteors, and comets.

Therefore, at the beginning of the first day (in verse 1), the best view of what the universe looked like, was that of ~100 billion hot coalescing hurricane-like storms of matter—galaxies, that were slowly rotating in close proximity with each other, with water filling the gaps in between each galaxy, and the entire universe was tightly sealed with a shell of thousands of miles of solid ice. Within each coalescing future galaxy, there were ~100 billion hot coalescing hurricane-like storms of matter—solar systems, that were rotating faster in close proximity with each other, with water filling the gaps in between each solar system. Within each coalescing future solar system, existed hundreds of hot coalescing hurricane-like storms of matter that would become the future stars, planets, and moons, that were quickly rotating (fastest) in close proximity with each other, with water filling the tight spaces in between each rotating body. The center core of each coalescing celestial body was gaining in mass, density, gravity, electromagnetism, and heat with each passing minute of the first day. This suggests that not only was the earth formless and forming into a sphere, but so too was all matter (dirt) coalescing into a planet, star, or moon. Therefore, at the beginning of the first day, Mars was formless, Jupiter was formless, Saturn was formless, and so on. All matter was created at the beginning, but not finished forming into planets, moons, or stars, hence *formless* at the beginning of the first day of creation. All matter was void of life. Not even a single-celled prokaryote was alive. Darkness was everywhere for half of the first day.

The concept of time as we are able to perceive it was not made clear until the fourth day, so how long was this formless and lifeless dirt existing? Remember that in Numbers 12, God used plain simple language, not veiled meanings when He spoke to Moses face to face and since Moses wrote God's words, we may deduce that the same plain simple language applies. Always, when the Bible uses a number in front of the word "day," it indicates one rotation of the earth. Therefore, each day was one

255

rotation of the earth, even the first day. Both creationists and evolutionary cosmologists accept the concept of how all the planets, moons, and stars coalesced mass—by a hurricane-like storm of matter. It is a valid argument that the core spun many times during this first day. Thus, if a creationist stipulated that this one day had ~10–100 core rotations, this is an acceptable concept in a six day creation, and here is why; utilizing the same model to support a faster spinning core—hurricane-like storm of matter—then the angular acceleration decreases as the radius from the core increases. Meaning that the slowest rotational velocity of matter is on the outer edge of the storm, and the fastest rotational velocity of matter is at the core, with incremental changes in rotational velocity at varying radii. For this reason, although the core was spinning much faster, and the distal radius of the coalescing Earth was spinning slower, the distal radius from the core that would eventually be the surface of the earth, was rotating around 1,600 mph, which is about 17 hours to complete one rotation. This concept explains the formation of each celestial body's electromagnet field. Since the narrative of the creation account is from the perspective of Earth's surface, the quantity of core rotations during each day is inconsequential, and it is imperative that our interpretation of *one day* is from the quantity of rotations of the eventual surface of the earth.

Review: Gen. 1:1 is the actual creation of all matter, energy, laws of the universe, and space at a defined time. All this was before the midpoint of the first day of creation. All matter (dirt, water, and the elements) existed in the small universe with trillions of formless, hurricane-like rotations that coalesced matter, and darkness prevailed over all the universe.

A lot of times we get caught up in the physical realm because that's all we see, but a spiritual realm is potentially more vast, more glorious, and more fulfilling for our senses than the physical realm. When Paul was sent up to heaven, he said that he heard words so glorious that they were "inexpressible words, which a man is not permitted to speak" (2 Cor 12:4). The Bible tells us frequently to be mindful of the spiritual realm and to store up treasures in heaven where moths, rust, and thieves cannot touch them (Matt 6:19–21), but because of sin, we are unaware of this spiritual realm. However Ephesians 6:12 tells us that we battle forces of evil from this spiritual realm daily.

What are some of the things that were brought forth on the first day of creation that are usually overlooked because they are from the spiritual realm? One clue is revealed in Proverbs 8:1–36. in verses 1–3, King Solomon is the narrator talking about wisdom; Solomon says that wisdom calls for us, and Solomon calls her *she*. She calls from everywhere, and she cries aloud from everywhere for all to listen. Verse 4 changes from Solomon narrating to wisdom speaking in first person, using the personal pronouns "I" and "my." Wisdom is calling all to listen and seek her as one seeks treasure. In verses 6–21, Wisdom testifies about how worthy and valuable her sayings are for humans. In verse 22, Wisdom talks in first person still and reflects back to the beginning of time, to creation, and it is here that we learn some of the spiritual things that were brought forth from the spiritual realm into our realm:

> The LORD possessed me at the beginning of His way, before His works of old. From everlasting I was established [This is God's testimony that wisdom was eternally established and has always existed.], from the beginning, from the earliest times of the earth. When there were no depths I was brought forth . . . before water . . . before the mountains . . . before hills . . . while He had not yet made the earth and the fields, Nor the first dust of the world.

Wisdom was brought forth from the spiritual realm to the physical realm before the first dust of the world. On the first day of creation, the very first thing that was brought forth, before the creation of matter at the beginning of creation, was wisdom. Wisdom, which has eternally existed, was brought into our physical realm. When Wisdom was brought forth, so too were prudence, knowledge, and discretion; so says Proverbs 8:12. It is not that wisdom, prudence knowledge, and discretion are eternally existent on their own, but because they are from God's nature and of God's mind, so it is God's Wisdom, God's prudence, God's knowledge, and God's discretion that have eternally existed and that were brought forth into the physical realm for mankind. Beyond this, God brought all that is good, everything that is pure, all truth, perfect law, a sure testimony, right precepts, pure commandments, enduring loving awe and reference, and true judgments (Psalm 19:7–9).

Review: God brought forth wisdom, prudence, knowledge, and discretion into our realm on the first day of creation before any matter was formed, yet they eternally existed because they are from God.

Now, let us go back to the physical, tangible aspect of creation. One aspect of the matter created on the first half of the first day was water. Gen. 1:2: "Darkness was over the surface of the deep, and the spirit of God was moving over the surface of the waters." Vast amounts of water existed throughout the universe, not just what we see on earth today, but enough water to fill many galaxies' worth throughout the small universe. It is no wonder that many planets and moons have erosion patterns on them. Since the earth was made from water, this suggest that so too were all the other planets throughout the solar system and galaxies. Once our technology improves, every planet may show that water was there. Water was everywhere, but not 100% like in a pool. It was more commingled with soil, with many surfaces, and many faces. Water abundantly existed in solid, liquid, gaseous, and plasma forms. This helps to explain why waters was plural.

In a universe with no stars, the water farthest away from the coalescing masses would not have enough heat to remain liquid. Thus, the entire outer shell of the small universe was solid ice. The thickness was enough to allow pressure to build, but not too thick as to prevent the expansion on the second day. Without this external shell of ice to keep the universe compact during these critical beginnings of the universe, matter loses its proximity to each other and does not coalesce into the celestial bodies we see today. Also, the water that was closer to a coalescing future star, planet, or moon had enough heat and pressure to remain in liquid form. The water that was too close to coalescing stars vaporized to gas and plasma. This sealed system, with immovable shell of solid ice, was a recipe for immense pressure and heat.

Review: The proximity of waters to the heat source of a coalescing mass determined the state of water. *Waters* is in plural form to represent vast quantities and different forms: solid, liquid, gas, and plasma. Water was one aspect of the parts of matter that was created at the beginning of the first day of creation.

Another important aspect is the volume/area of all this water, minerals, and dirt. Over what area was all this matter and water spread out? Isaiah 48:13b gives us some insight in the creation of the universe: "My right hand spread out the heavens." Therefore, before being spread out, the heavens (filled with forming galaxies, stars, planets, moons, etc.) were close together. The Isaiah verse is also in harmony with cosmology, which suggests that all the galaxies are moving away from each other from a time when the universe was much smaller. Since the sun and stars ignited on the fourth day of creation, then from the first day to the fourth day, they were ever growing in mass and heat. After the first Big Bang—the creation of everything, the universe was densely compact. We may deduce this by the existence of water during the first day of creation before a star formed to warm it.

God violently expanded, by natural processes (the second Big Bang), the universe, galaxies, solar systems, and atmospheres of every celestial body on the second day. Before they were violently expanded, they were closer, but not too close to prevent water from existing on the first day. The Bible clearly says that waters existed, so the Bible is saying that before God stretched out the universe, it was small enough and dense enough to generate heat, and the weight of the universe generated pressure that prevented water from completely freezing or from completely vaporizing.

When God created the elements and matter, He also brought through Himself all the laws pertaining to those elements and matter. For example, God brought forth the nuclear charge for the atoms to attract electrons. Too little charge, and the nucleus could not have held onto an electron, and no life could have been sustained. Too much charge, and the electrons would have collapsed onto the nucleus, and no life could have been sustained. All the fine-tuning of the universe came from God's knowledge that has eternally existed. Therefore, it is consistent to say that all the laws of the universe were brought forth into our realm, not created, on the first day. They eternally existed because they are from an eternal God that does not increase or decrease in knowledge.

Review: When God created all matter on the first day before the light, it was densely packed. Before the first day of creation, nothing existed in our realm, or in our dimension. All water and dirt were created in a densely packed universe with many surfaces; it was void of life, intermingled, and formless. *Waters* is plural because the water was in a solid, liquid, gas, and plasma form, with vast quantities. God brought all the laws of the universe into our realm through Himself on the first day. There were countless focal points of spinning hot spots of mass.

I was taught growing up that the first and only thing created on the first day was light. But this does not add up logically from a Biblical perspective, and let me show you why. We know from Scripture that God made all things in six days. With that foundation, let us pretend we were creating the universe, and since the first half of the day starts with darkness, why would we wait for half the day to expire before we created light? Since the day starts with evening and finishes with morning, the creation of light represents the midpoint of the first day, so why would we wait to do this, if indeed this was the first thing we created. The point is that it is incorrect that the first thing God created was light, and all the waters and dirt were already there. This is incongruous with Scripture and science. God created all things in six days, and matter is a thing. Therefore, God created all matter and space on the first day with countless regions of coalescing, and rotating regions. This would look like trillions of coalescing hurricanes of matter, but instead of gathering moisture, they were gathering matter. Some to become stars, others to become planets and moons.

Let us go deeper into the author's (Moses) perspective of life. For the earliest Hebrews on earth, the day started at sunset, and the first light was the middle of the day. Where did this cultural perception come from? It came from the Genesis creation account. The initial second of the first day of creation began in total darkness and continued in darkness for half the day; then God created the light at the midpoint of the first day. For the first portion of the day, God created the dirt, minerals, the elements, and water, yet they were formless and void of life. Then the second half of the day was light. All the matter that would eventually become the earth, moon, sun, stars, planets, and galaxies was already rotating and coalescing matter together from God's work on the first half of the day.

Therefore, rotation (of what would eventually become earth, stars, planets, moons, and galaxies) was another thing created on the first half of the first day. This is why each day of creation starts with evening and ends with morning.

Review: God did not sit around doing nothing for half of the first day until He created light. God was busy creating matter and causing the matter to have countless rotating focal points of coalescing hot spots at the beginning of the first day. Then, as the countless spinning hot spots coalesced enough matter, they glowed hot from liquid magma; thus, God created light at the midpoint of the first day. God created space and matter at a specific moment at the beginning of the first day. The matter that was going to become planets, stars, and galaxies began rotating, coalescing, and generating heat from the very beginning it existed. Therefore, the Bible explains that God created light at the middle of day one. Jewish tradition follows this same pattern, with the day beginning with evening.

Another thing or place that was created on the first day of the Genesis creation account is the throne of God, Heaven. The Hebrew word for heaven is *shamayim*. It is used for all three heavens, which is why "heavens" is plural in Gen. 1:1, representing the throne of God and a small universe. Shamayim means to be lofty and refers to the sky where clouds move and higher where the celestial (planets/stars/moon/etc.) bodies revolve and heaven (the Throne of God)(Strong's Conc.: *shamayim*, #8064). John MacArthur summarizes the three heavens as atmospheric heaven, planetary heaven, and divine heaven.[172] The first heaven is the atmosphere (created on the second day; Gen. 1:6–8), the second heaven is the universe, where all the planets/stars/moons exist—initially created as a small universe (commenced expansion on the second day and ignited the stars on the fourth day; Gen. 1:14–

---

172 John MacArthur, "Heaven", pg. 14.

19), and the third heaven is the Throne of God. The Genesis creation account does not specifically mention this third heaven being created, so how do we know it exists? In 2 Corinthians 12:2–4, it says, "I know a man (Paul is talking about himself) . . . whether in the body I do not know, or out of the body I do not know, God knows (physically or spiritually taken to heaven), such a man was caught up to the **third heaven** . . . was caught up into paradise and heard inexpressible words." Therefore, this third heaven could be a distance beyond the universe or in a dimension beyond our perception. We live in the third dimension and cannot perceive higher dimensions. Considering Isaiah 40:22, "It is He who sits above the circle of the earth," and God sits on a throne, it is conceivable that heaven could be close in distance, such as everywhere, but dimensionally beyond our perception. We know this is a literal, physical place because a real tangible New Jerusalem descends out of heaven in Revelation 21:2: "I saw the holy city, new Jerusalem, coming down out of heaven from God . . . Behold, the tabernacle of God is among men, and He (Son) will dwell among them." Since Jesus created all things, and the third heaven, or the Throne of God, is a thing, it is a created thing. It was probably created on the first day before the light in the opening first line of Gen. 1:1.

How do we know whether the Throne of God, eternally existed or was created? Colossians 1:16: "For by Him all things were created, both <u>in the heavens</u> and on earth." The clue is "in the heavens." The verse goes on: "visible and <u>invisible, whether thrones</u> . . . all things have been created through Him and for Him." The conclusion is that Throne of God was created at the beginning of the first day with the very first verse in the Bible: "In the beginning God created the heavens."

<u>**Review:**</u> <u>The third heaven, the Throne of God, was created on the first day of creation. It is probably near Earth just beyond our dimensional perception.</u>

Was there anything that existed prior to the first day of creation? God did. Deut. 33:27 "The eternal God is." The Hebrew word God is Elohiym (Strong's Concordance #430, which means the plural form of the one true God). We cannot be more clear than that. But let us try. Christians believe in three personages of God, called the Trinity, which is one God with three personalities. If one argues that Deuteronomy is only referring to God the Father, what about the Holy Spirit and the Son, Jesus? Well for the Holy Spirit, this is easy. Hebrews 9:14 calls the Holy Spirit an "eternal Spirit," and in Gen. 1:2, we already have "the Spirit of God moving over the surface of the waters." So the Father and the Holy Spirit are eternal. What about the Son, Jesus? Did He begin at His physical birth in a manger some 2,000+ years ago? Or was Jesus created on the first day with the angels and promoted as a glorified angel? This is the great mystery in the Bible—who is Jesus really? The Apostle Paul wrote about a great mystery that has been hidden and now has been revealed. In Colossians 1:25b–27, Paul says that he serves God "so that I might fully carry out the preaching of the word of God, that is, the <u>mystery</u> which has been hidden from the past ages and generations, but has now been manifested to His saints, to whom God willed to make known what is the riches of the glory of this mystery." What is this mystery? Apostle Paul further wrote in Colossians 2:2b–3 that he wants us to attain "all the wealth that comes from the full assurance of understanding, resulting in a true knowledge of God's <u>mystery</u>, that is, Christ Himself, in whom are hidden all the treasures of wisdom and knowledge." The first mystery was that Jesus is the Messiah, and the Messiah does not just save us from our sins, but dwells in us (Colossians 1:27: "which is Christ in you"). The second mystery is that all wisdom and all knowledge is held by Jesus, and He blesses whom He wishes with it. This is linking Jesus to being deity, as only God gives wisdom and knowledge to people. James 1:5: "If any of you lacks wisdom, let him ask of God, who gives to all generously." And Proverbs 1:7: "The fear of the LORD is the beginning of knowledge." Proverbs 9:10 says, "The fear of the LORD is the beginning of wisdom." Also, in Genesis, the Hebrew word for God is *Elohiym*, which is in the plural form.[173] In Colossians 1:16, Paul gives clarity for what Jesus has done: "For by Him all things were created, both in the heavens and on earth, visible and invisible, whether thrones or dominions or rulers or authorities, all things have been

---

173 Strong's Conc. # 430 *elohiym: (plural)* Gods in the ordinary sense; specifically of the supreme God. Root word is #433 *eloahh:* a deity or God. Root word is #410 *El:* (singular) Deity—God.

created through Him and for Him." Since we know angels are all created beings, and Jesus created all angels (thrones, dominions, rulers, and authorities are terms for angels), Jesus therefore, CANNOT be an angel; nor can He be the half brother of Lucifer. Lucifer is a fallen angel. The Apostle John (1:1–14) affirms that Jesus was at the beginning in Gen. 1:1 as God the creator: "In the beginning was the Word [Jesus], and the Word was with God, and the Word was God. He was in the beginning with God. All things came into being through Him, and apart from Him nothing came into being that has come into being . . . the Word became flesh, and dwelt among us, and we saw His glory as of the only begotten from the Father." Alright, so on face value, Jesus was part of the Elohiym "God" who was doing the creating in Gen. 1:1.

But how do we know that Jesus was not a created being before the first day of creation in some past era? This is the theme of the entire Bible. You find the answer to this, and a whole new world of mystery will be revealed to you. Let us lay a foundation to build up to the answer: All theologians agree that the Bible clearly says that humans should not worship anything created or man-made, but should worship God alone. The Ten Commandments make this abundantly clear (Exodus 20:3–4): "You shall have no other gods before Me. You shall not make for yourself an idol or any likeness of what is in heaven above or on the earth beneath or in the water under the earth. You shall not worship them." And Paul warns about worshiping angels in Colossians 2:18: "Let no one keep defrauding you of your prize . . . by the worship of the angels." Therefore, it is a sin to worship angels, and by default, it is a sin for angels to accept and command humans to worship them. An angel that accepted or commanded humans to worship them would instantly become a fallen angel. Fallen angels are known as demons. But the Bible gives no evidence that angels are still falling and becoming demons. In fact, the Bible gives evidence that the sum of angels that fell and became demons occurred at one specific point in history. Revelation 12:3–4–9 and Luke 10:18 talk about when Satan and a third of the demons were cast out of heaven to earth like lightning. Also, when angels are bowed down to by humans in an act of worship, the angels tell the humans to get up. For example, the Apostle John began to worship an angel after receiving a revelation from the angel. Read how the angel responded in Revelation 19:10: "Then I fell at his feet to worship him. But he said to me, 'Do not do that; I am a fellow servant of yours and your brethren who hold the testimony of Jesus; worship God.'"

Review: Angels will not accept worship. If you see something angelic and worship it, an angel will tell you to get up and stop. A demon, disguised as an angel, will accept your worship.

The other foundational point is that no one has seen God the Father at any time. This is critical to know. Consider the following verses: **Exodus 33:20**: "He (God) said, 'You cannot see My face, for no man can see Me and live!'" **John 1:18**: "No one has seen God at any time." **Colossians 1:15**: "He (Jesus) is the image of the invisible God." I John 4:12: "No one has seen God at any time." **John 6:46**: "Not that anyone has seen the Father, except the One who is from God; He has seen the Father" (Only Jesus has seen God the Father). **I Timothy 6:15–16**: "He who is the blessed and only Sovereign, the King of kings and Lord of lords, who alone possesses immortality and dwells in unapproachable light, whom no man has seen or can see. To Him be honor and eternal dominion! Amen." **Colossians 2:9**: "For in Him (Jesus) all the fullness of Deity dwells in bodily form."

Review: No one has seen God the Father at any time, and God the Father is invisible. Jesus is the physical image of God the Father, has all the fullness of deity dwells in the bodily form in Jesus. Jesus is the physical representation of God the Father to mankind.

Considering these verses that suggest that no one has seen God the Father and that God the Father is invisible and angels will not accept worship, then who was it that frequently appeared in the Old Testament accepting worship from the likes of Abraham, Isaac, Jacob, Moses, and Joshua, and they called Him Lord? Let us find out.

A man appeared in Joshua 5:13 that gives us a clue: "Now it came about when Joshua was by Jericho, that he lifted up his eyes and looked, and behold, a man was standing opposite him with his sword drawn in his hand" (*Behold* suggests a bit of shock and awe, so this man miraculously appeared, as in "poof"). Clearly, this is more than a human. Most pastors proclaim this to be an angel. Let us continue with the verse to find out if this is an angel: "And Joshua went to him and said to him, 'Are you for us or for our adversaries?' He said, 'No; rather I indeed come now as captain of the host of the LORD." This being, in the form of a man who miraculously appeared, declares to be the captain of God's angelic army and says He has brought His own army of angels. The word "host" is often associated with an army of angels, (i.e., Heavenly Host). At this point, we do not know if this being is an angel or someone greater. What was Joshua's response to this being that appeared as a man? "And Joshua fell on his face to the earth, and bowed down, and said to him, 'What has my Lord to say to his servant?'" Now if this was an angel, the angel would tell Joshua to not do that, to get up, and that he was a fellow servant of God as well. But what does this being do when Joshua falls down in worship? "The captain of the LORD'S host said to Joshua, '**Remove your sandals from your feet, for the place where you are standing is holy**.'" Oh my, this being not only accepts Joshua's worship but tells Joshua that his worship was inadequate and that Joshua needs to remove his sandals because the ground was holy. This is crucial! Where Joshua and this being were standing was outside of the promised land, just east of the Jordan river. It was not where they were that made the ground holy, it was who was there making the ground holy. This being accepts worship and commands further worship, so this cannot be an angel. Did you catch the part about "Remove your sandals from your feet for the place where you are standing is holy"? Does that sound familiar?

That phrase was previously spoken in Exodus 3, written by Moses. Since Moses was already dead by the time Joshua 5 occurs, that means that Joshua was fully aware of what Moses had written. Let us set the scene: Moses sees a bush burning and decides to go look. Exodus 3:4:

> When the LORD saw that he (Moses) turned aside to look, God called to him from the midst of the bush and said, "Moses, Moses!" And he said, "Here I am." Then He said, "Do not come near here; remove your sandals from your feet, for the place on which you are standing is holy ground."

Holy cow! it is the same phrase. With only five holy books having been written at the time of Joshua 5, Joshua, a Godly man, would have been familiar with the words being spoken by God in Exodus 3 and this being who appeared as a man. The only conclusion about this being that appears to Joshua in the form of a man, accepting worship and commanding further worship, is that this was God in the flesh, God in human form. Moses asks God, "What shall I say your name is to the Israel?" God declares His name to be "I AM" (Exodus 3:13–14). The Hebrew word for "I AM" is *Yahweh*, meaning eternal. "This name for God points to His self-existence and eternality."[174] This means that God exists at any point on the space-time continuum.

So what, what does "I AM"/JAHWEH have to do with Jesus? In John 8:56–58, Jesus proclaimed to not only walk and talk with Abraham (defying mortality, and being Melchizedek; Gen. 14–17), but to be the great I AM (Yahweh or eternally existing), for which the Pharisees picked up stones to stone Him, but He disappeared from their midst. Jesus also said "You search the Scriptures because you think that in them you have eternal life; it is these that testify about Me" *(John 5:39).* Jesus was referring to the Old Testament, since the New Testament had not been written yet. Is the Old Testament testifying about Jesus? Where do you find His name? He is hidden in the Old Testament. He is the mystery revealed. In fact, Jesus gives us a clue to how hidden He was in the Old Testament, when He said, "If you believe Moses, you would believe Me, for he wrote about Me" (John 5:46). Moses wrote about Jesus? Yes. Moses wrote the first five books of the Old Testament. But where is the name Jesus? It is not there; it is hidden, a mystery to be revealed. Since no one has seen God the Father at any time, since God the Father is invisible, and since angels do not accept worship, then **ALL** physical appearances of God in the Old and New Testament are not the Father, but the Son, Jesus.

---

174 MacArthur Study Bible quote of John MacArthur pg. 96.

God walked and talked with Adam and Eve in Gen. 3:7–21. God appeared to Abram in Genesis chapters 15–17. God declared that He appeared to Abraham, Isaac, and Jacob as God Almighty in Exodus 6:2–3. God spoke that He appeared to Moses face to face in Numbers 12:6–8. Jacob declared he saw God face to face after wrestling with Him in Gen. 32:24–30. These are all appearances of Jesus before He was revealed to be God in the flesh.

When will all the hidden mysteries of Jesus be revealed to all? The book of Revelation is all about revealing who Jesus was, is, and will be. Revelation 22:13 Jesus says, "I am the Alpha and the Omega, the first and the last, the beginning and the end." Philippians 2:10 says, "The name of Jesus Every knee will bow, of those who are in heaven and on earth and under the earth, and that every tongue will confess that Jesus Christ is Lord, to the glory of God the Father." Therefore, the reason the Jews in the Old Testament were saved by faith is because they were worshiping the Father through the Son, but did not know His name was Jesus. The Jews once worshiped Him through the millennia, from Adam to Malachi, from the book of Genesis to the Book of Malachi—the one they crucified—they will once again worship Him. They will once again worship God the Father through the name of Jesus, His Son. For Jesus is the same yesterday, today, and forever (Hebrews 13:8), the I AM, and God in the flesh.

Review: God the Father, the Holy Spirit, and God the Son are all three personages of one God. They are all eternal and not created.

In the beginning God created the heavens and the earth. The earth was formless and void, and darkness was over the surface of the deep, and the Spirit of God was moving over the surface of the waters. After God created all the water and dirt in a tightly compact universe, there was *darkness over the surface of the deep.* This is from the perspective of Earth. Since God is light physically and spiritually, John 1:4 says, "In Him was life, and the life was the light of men. The light shines in the darkness" (figuratively or spiritually in man's dark heart, God brings the light). And God is light, literally and physically, as it says in Matthew 17:1: "Jesus took with Him Peter and James and John his brother, and led them up on a high mountain by themselves. And He was transfigured before them; and His face shone like the sun, and His garments became as white as light." Jesus literally changes from mortal human flesh to light, though still in the form of a human. It is like Jesus peeled away His humanity, His mortality, and revealed the I AM in the flesh. As Revelation 21:2–23 says:

> I saw the holy city, new Jerusalem, coming down out of heaven from God . . . I saw no temple in it, for the Lord God the Almighty and the Lamb are its temple. And the city has no need of the sun or of the moon to shine on it, for the glory of God has illumined it, and its lamp is the Lamb . . . There will no longer be any night; and they will not have need of the light of the lamp nor the light of the sun, because the Lord God will illumine them.

In context, the Lamb is Jesus. Considering both verses about God being light spiritually and physically, it seems logical that heaven, where the throne of God is, is brilliantly lit up because of the Glory of God. It is either too far away for us to detect or in a different dimension beyond our mortal capabilities. Either way, there seems to be strong evidence that the Throne of God, heaven, is very bright. After all, "Jesus is the same yesterday, today and forever" (Hebrews 13:8), so since God will be lighting up the New Jerusalem, God is currently lighting up heaven.

Review: Darkness is over the surface of the waters, but heaven (the Throne of God) is brilliantly lit up with the Glory of God.

You may be thinking: "Without a heat source, how is water remaining in liquid form?" We already discussed this in detail in the chapter *The Canopy,* but here is a brief review; A small universe increases pressure and increases heat, which alters the freezing point of water. Salt and other elements reduce the freezing point as well.

One of the basic laws of physics, the first law of thermodynamics, states that the sum of matter and energy cannot be added to or taken away from. When matter is increased, energy must decrease.

And when matter decreases, energy increases. Also, matter is not destroyed; it just changes form. For example, wood has a certain amount of matter. If we burn the wood, the matter reduces down to ash, and a subsequent rise in energy (heat) occurs, but the sum of matter and energy remains the same. When the Hadron Collider collides massless particles to form miniscule amounts of mass, a lot of energy is consumed. Why are we talking about the first law of thermodynamics? Because one of the problems our scientists have with the Bible is that some theologians use the Latin phrase **ex nihilo** (out of nothing) when referring to creation. Some Bible scholars say that God created the universe ex nihilo, which means God created something out of nothing. From a theological point of view, this is correct, but from a physics point of view, this needs further explaining to avoid any hint of violating a foundational law of physics. The theologians that are using ex nihilo and saying that God created everything out of nothing are simply affirming that God started from nothing, from scratch, and from a vacuum. But let us provide a little more clarity for the words. Just as the Bible explains that God begot man from Himself and that life begot life, so it is with energy and matter. When God created all the laws, matter, and energy within the universe, He did so from Himself by speaking them into existence as the Holy Spirit moved violently. Therefore, just as man was created from the essence of God, all matter, all energy, and all the laws of the universe were created from the essence of God. This is summed up in Colossians 1:17: "All things have been created through Him." Therefore, it is not wrong to say that God created everything ex nihilo because it emphasizes the point that God did not need help or start with any material—there was nothing there but God, and He brought forth all matter, energy, and the laws of the universe from Himself, through Himself, as part of His eternal essence literally became matter and energy in our physical realm, by speaking them into existence. But let us help the brilliant minds of physics wrap their thoughts around this concept. The basis is the concept in physics of the conservation of energy, that the amount of energy cannot be increased or decreased. Now, this gets a little tricky because of matter, but remember that matter (soil, water, and so forth—all that we can feel and see) is energy albeit in a different form. Energy may be converted to kinetic energy (such as motion), thermal energy (heat), or potential energy (such as matter). This is known as the law of conservation of mechanical energy. The first law of thermodynamics is a generalization of the conservation of mechanical energy, that if one form of energy decreases, another form of energy must increase. Thus, the total sum of energy must remain constant, neither increasing or decreasing.

For the purposes of our discussion, since God exists in both our physical realm and the spiritual realm, we'll consider our universe both a closed system with God existing in our universe and an open system with God as the outside system that applied force to create energy and matter to the universe. This duality is allowed in physics because God exists in both our physical realm and outside our realm in the spiritual realm. How did God create all the matter (potential energy) in the universe, all the heat (thermal energy) in the universe, and all the kinetic energy in the universe without violating the conservation of energy of the first law of thermodynamics? Well, is God infinite? Does God eternally exist? Yes, His name is "I AM," which is Yahweh in Hebrew and means eternal, forever, and infinite (Exodus 3:14).

Colossians 1:16 answers the question: "For by Him all things were created, both in the heavens and on earth, visible and invisible . . . all things have been created through Him and for Him." Since energy and matter (water, the elements, dirt, etc.) are all things, they are created things, not eternally existing. In other words, water and dirt had a beginning too, just like everything else that was created. Let us focus on "by Him and through Him all things were created." Since physics, biology, and chemistry teach us that nothing comes from nothing, and the first law of thermodynamics says that the net sum of matter and energy in the universe cannot be added to or taken away from, then with God being the all-powerful, limitless source of power, science is not violated with the notion of an all-powerful God creating everything from Himself and through Himself. This is one explanation for why Jesus said, "I AM the light." Light is energy, and Jesus, as the co-creator, was saying that He was the source of light, the source of all energy, and since energy and matter are essentially the same thing, then

Jesus is the source of all things. The source of all matter and energy came from the Godhead and are sustained by the Godhead (Colossians 1:17).

Therefore, no thing came from nothing, but all things came about through an infinite God, and from an all-powerful God. Atheists contend that all matter came from energy and all energy came from—well, it just existed as a singularity, and they are still working on the origin of energy.

If something came from nothing, that would be a violation of physics. This is curious because Big Bang theorists start their concept with the preexistence of all matter as energy and all energy already created and bound up into a dot. Where did all the energy come from? And what caused everything to be so tightly packed. Even more bizarre is that some evolutionary cosmologists believe that before the Big Bang, nothing existed, and nothing exploded, and all matter and energy evolved out of the nothingness. Some cosmologists hypothesize that energy was squished into a dot, and matter evolved from the energy of the Big Bang.

This is why the physics community is so excited about the C.E.R.N. Large Hadron Collider and the recent discovery that colliding two particles (protons) that have zero mass at nearly the speed of light creates a muon, which has trace amount of mass. Therefore, the implication is that this explains the origin of mass. From the energy of the Big Bang, massless particles picked up mass as they passed through the Higgs boson field. But this still does not address the origin of the energy and the amount of mass formed from the collision, which does not match the amount of matter required to form a solar system, let alone a galaxy or universe. There would be too much energy consumed to form enough matter to fill a solar system under this hypothesis.

Back to our discussion: all matter and all energy are part and parcel from God's essence. It would be like saying a volcano came from the earth, through the earth, and because of the earth. The volcano did not come from nothing; it came from the earth. It is the same with creation; nothing came from nothing, but everything came from an infinite God. Therefore, the total sum of matter and sum of energy did not increase at any point in the creation account of Genesis because all matter and all energy are from God's existence, from God's essence. That's why John 1:1 writes, "All things came into being through Him, and apart from Him nothing came into being that has come into being." That is why Paul wrote in Romans 11:26: "For from Him and through Him and to Him are all things." All things are part of His essence, all things are from Him, and all things are created through Him. Although, everything came from God and through God, none of the things God created are to be worshiped as God because they are not God. Just like a human's skin cells that settle to the ground as dust, though they came from you and through you, they are not you. By including an infinite and all-powerful God to the equation, the total sum did not increase with creation because infinity cannot be increased, and no decrease in an infinite God upon the creation of all matter and all energy from Him because infinity cannot be decreased. Therefore, physics is in harmony with the Genesis account of creation.

Review of the first half of the first day: Water, dirt, energy, and the heavens (the Throne of God and the small universe) were created on the first day by eternal Elohiym (God: the Father, the Son, and the Holy Spirit). The size of the universe was relatively very small and sealed with an outer shell of solid ice that prevented any relieving of pressure with expansion, and this allowed heat and pressure. All the matter that would eventually become the stars, planets, and moons were each coalescing matter and gaining in density, mass, gravity, electromagnetism, and heat. The heat and pressure from the small universe and coalescing celestial bodies allowed water to exist in four forms (solid, liquid, gas, and plasma) depending on proximity to a heat source. Since all things came literally from God's essence, the total sum of everything, even after the creation of matter and energy, did not change. Also, with no decrease of an infinite God giving of His own essence to create everything. Darkness dominated our dimension, but brilliant light existed in heaven. God brought forth wisdom, prudence, knowledge, all the laws and constants of the universe, truth, and all that is good from His realm to the physical realm.

The Middle of the First Day: The traditional beginning of the first day is the creation of light, but those who start here have missed so much about what was created in verses 1 and 2.

Gen. 1:3: *Then God said, "let there be light"; and there was light. God saw that the light was good; and God separated the light from the darkness. God called the light day, and the darkness He called night. And there was evening and there was morning, the first day. NIV.*

Then God said, "let there be light"; and there was light. What is the light that was created here? This cannot be the sun, moon, and stars, as they are not finished forming until the fourth day. Is this energy then? Since energy includes light, and light includes radio waves, microwaves, infrared, <u>visible light</u>, X-rays, gamma rays, and cosmic rays, then an argument could be made that at least a portion of energy or light was created here. But a simpler answer fits via a natural process that caused the glow of hot liquid matter from future stars. When the future stars coalesced enough matter to generate enough heat, density, and gravity then matter liquefied at the core and glowed hot like magma. Scientists hypothesize that when the planets and stars initially began to form (14.6 billion years ago) that when they coalesced enough mass that they glowed from liquid magma. As those burgeoning bodies rotated, they collected nearby mass and coalesced into ever larger planets/stars. Creationists accept this hypothesis, but differ on when this event occurred and how long it took for this event to finalize. A creationist hypothesizes that when God created all the matter in the universe in the first verse of the Bible (Gen. 1:1),<u> the universe was tightly packed, and for this reason, the proximity of all the matter in a small universe greatly reduce the amount of time required for a burgeoning star to coalesce enough mass to glow hot as light by the middle of the first day.</u> Within this tightly packed small universe, the individual rotating masses that would eventually become the trillions of stars started to glow hot at the mid-point of the first day when God said, "Let there be light." This does not mean that they were stars or planets yet; it means that there were focal points of heat that glowed like lava glows, and these celestial bodies coalesced into larger and larger bodies.

The above hypothesis would also explain how water could exist in the universe in Gen. 1:2 in liquid form because the universe was tightly packed with trillions of focal points of hot mass. This also indicates that each planet, star, and moon had water surrounding it at its origin. In fact, scientists have found tremendous amounts of water stored, in mineral form, under the crust in the mantle of the earth.[175] This corroborates the Genesis creation of Earth from water. 2 Peter 3:5 makes it quit clear that at this time during the earth's formation, "the earth was formed out of water and by water," indicating that although the earth was very warm as it coalesced matter, and hot enough to vaporize water, there was too much pressure from the weight of the densely packed universe to allow water to vaporize around Earth. This information will become critical for us to discern how God made our atmosphere. In addition, physics explains that with high pressure, water can be super heated beyond its normal boiling temperature and remain in liquid form. For this reason, and the observable evidence of seeing many planets with ice rings surrounding them, I surmise that most forming planets and moons at this time during creation, also had water surrounding them, and they too were also hot enough to vaporize the water, but because of the weight of the densely packed universe, this kept super heated water in a liquid state.

In a densely packed universe that has trillions of coalescing (hurricane-like storms of matter) celestial bodies, with liquid metal and liquid soil centralized at the core of all the future planets, moons, and stars, this would cause electrons to flow on a cosmic scale. And while all these rotating metal cores were causing electrons to flow like trillions of electric generators, charge was building up, magnetism was building up, gravity was increasing, and so forth. All the while, any water that was too close to a future star was vaporized that added to the pressure in the universe. To make matters worse, the outer shell of the universe was too far from heat and water froze as a shell that sealed in the pressure of the universe. Each minute that passed, pressure mounted, electromagnetism within each celestial body grew, and electrical charge around each celestial body grew, and gravitational forces grew. This was an unsustainable formula.

---

175 http://news.discovery.com/earth/oceans/oceans-of-water-found-locked-deep-inside-earth-140612.htm.

Also, associated with the creation of this light is the creation of angels. Colossians 1:16 says, "For by Him all things were created, both in the heavens and on earth, visible and invisible, whether thrones or dominions or rulers or authorities." The "thrones or dominions or rulers or authorities" are used to indicate angels.[176] Angels were created before God lays the foundation of Earth on the third day. How do we know this? Job 38:4–7 says, "Where were you when I laid the foundation of the earth? . . . When the morning stars sang together and all the sons of God shouted for joy?" *The morning stars* (Isaiah 14:12) and the *sons of God* both represent angels (Gen. 6:2, Job 1:6; 2:1). The definition of the Hebrew word for *morning* includes dawn the first light,[177] and the Hebrew word for *stars* includes princes.[178] Therefore, the verse can read, "Where were you when I laid the foundation of the earth? . . . When the dawn princes sang together and all the sons of God shouted for joy?" Since the first light is the first dawn and the first dawn came with the creation of angelic princes, the dawn princes are angels. Now, since angels are created beings, and they already existed on the third day, that leaves the first day or the second day as their day of creation. So why is there a distinction between *princes of the dawn/morning stars* and *Sons of God*? It may be because angels have ranks, and the morning stars are the brightest and highest ranked angels. Now, the reason the angels were named *morning stars* and *sons of God* is because they were formed in the image of the true bright morning star (Revelation 22:16) and the true Son of God (I John 4:15)—Jesus.

Since the earth was formed on the third day of creation, then angels were included in the light created on day one. Angels often appear with a bright light shining around them; in Acts 12:7 for example: "An Angel of the Lord suddenly appeared and a light shone in the cell" and in 2 Corinthians 11:14: "For even Satan disguises himself as an angel of light." Therefore, deduction gives us only one conclusion: all Angels (and angels that later became demons) were created on the first day and referred to as the "light." Jesus is also referred to as the light, but since He is co-creator of everything (John 1:1 and Colossians 1:15–17), then He is the source of light. That's why the gospels repeatedly tell of Jesus being the light. For example, the Israelites were required to light a lamp every evening and keep it lit until morning (Lev. 24:1–3). Why? It was a reminder to the Jews that God was always with them and a reminder that God led them out of Egypt with a fire (light) by night. Well, fast-forward 1,500 years to John 8:1: "Jesus went to the Mount of Olives, Early dawn in the morning He came again into the temple." Since it was early in the morning, Jesus had entered the temple just as a priest was extinguishing the light from a lamp. Jesus says to the priest, (John 8:12), "I am the Light of the world; he who follows Me will not walk in the darkness, but will have the Light of life." Why is this significant? Jesus is claiming to be the pillar of fire (the light) that led the Jews out of Egypt. This is corroborated in Revelation 21:22: "I saw no temple in it, for the Lord God the Almighty and the Lamb are its temple. And the city has no need of the sun or of the moon to shine on it, for the glory of God has illumined it, and its lamp is the Lamb. The nations will walk by its light."

Review: When God created the "light," this seems to be both visible from glowing magma of forming celestial bodies, and angels. This is not the finished sun, moon, and stars.

Since the burgeoning future stars emit light, it is not a problem with calling the lit side of the eventual earth "day" from the perspective of Earth or with calling the dark side of the would-be Earth "Night," which cannot view the sun's glowing liquid magma.

Since *evening* is mentioned first before *morning*, then no light existed in the solar system before the angels were created. The angels were created in the middle of the first day, and the first morning was as the angels were created. This probably explains why God calls Lucifer the "son of the dawn" in Isaiah 14:12 because the first dawn occurred at his creation. This is in harmony with the phrase "darkness was over the surface of the deep, " which was written before the angels were created in Gen.

---

176 Other references conferring angels as thrones/dominions/rulers/authorities: Romans 3:38, Ephesians 1:21 and 3:10 and 6:12, 1 Peter 3:22, and Jude 6.

177 Strong's Conc. #1242 *boqer*: dawn (break of day); morning, early.

178 Strong's Conc. #3556 *kowkab*: a star (as round or shining), a prince.

1:2. It should be noted that evening is mentioned before morning for each day of creation. This is why Israel, in the Old Testament, before the split of the kingdom into two portions, started the day at sunset in the evening and ended the day at sunset.

Review: Angels, even those that would fall shortly after creation, were created in the middle of the first day.

Angels cannot physically die, they are immortal. However, they can spiritually die, but not cease to exist. When God does His final judgment on all the fallen angels, we get clarity in terms of whether angels can or cannot die. Revelation 20:10: "And the devil who deceived them was thrown into the lake of fire and brimstone, where the beast and the false prophet are also; and they will be tormented day and night forever and ever." God himself does not kill them. No, the fallen angels are bound physically alive for eternity in a lake of fire. To be more clear, Luke 20:36 comes right out and says, "those who are considered worthy to attain to that age and the resurrection from the dead . . . they cannot even die anymore, because they are like angels, and are sons of God." Why are angels physically immortal?

Is it that time was created on the fourth day of creation and angels were created on the first day, that could explain why they are not mortally bound by time with a mortal body? No. Time was created at the beginning of the first day, it was the perception (sun, moon, and stars were finished forming) of time that was created for humans on the fourth day. Is it that angels are the only living thing created without the breath of life? No. The Breath of Life is another name for the Holy Spirit (Gen. 2:7), and like God, angels do not require oxygen to live, and they do not breathe to live, yet they use breath to speak on Earth. This suggests that angels were created closer to the image of God than humans. Is it that immortal beings do not eat and therefore are not subject to the decay associated with biodegradable food? No. Angels eat, in Psalm 78:25, it talks about when the Israelites wandered the wilderness for 40 years, they ate "the bread of angels." Also, when Jesus rose from the grave, He had His immortal body and still ate fish (Luke 24:41), and when Jesus walked and talked with Abraham, He ate curds and milk and meat (Gen. 18:1–8). Clearly immortal beings may eat, but it is not required to sustain their immortal body. This also indicates that angels were created closer to the image of God than humans. Is it that immortal being (angels) are not flesh and blood? Yes (I Corinthians 15:50), but the simple answer is that God is the God of the living, not the dead. Angels were created already worthy of attaining being called sons of God (Luke 20:34–38). A title of immortality not achievable with our flesh and blood. Likewise, when adults confess Jesus as Lord and savior, their spirit and soul instantly convert from being dead in their sin to being alive as a son of God (Galatians 3:26), to live forever with God. When their mortal body dies, they await the resurrection of the dead mortal body and receive an immortal body (I Corinthians 15:50–54). Thus, the angels were created as sons of God, bypassing the need for the physical resurrection from the dead that mortals with flesh and blood go through to attain their immortal body (without flesh and blood) and be called sons of God. An immortal body may be energy (including light, Matt 17:2) that is able to morph from massless to tangible matter—since matter is energy in a modified form. This explains how angels are able to move as fast as light, and appear and disappear, and defy gravity.

Review: Angels are immortal because God created them as already attaining the title of sons of God. God is the God of the living.

God separated the light from the darkness. God called the light day, and the darkness He called night. In the physical realm, this is a description of the rotation of the soon-to-be Earth with half of the earth lit from the hot glow of the liquid magma of the future sun. For if there were no rotation, then there would not be a side that was in the light and a side that was in darkness for each day. There needs to be rotation for evening and morning to exist for each day. It was not that the light source was blinking on and off. This is strong evidence of a literal seven-day creation account.

The Hebrew word for light on the first day is *owr*, which means illumination or luminary (in every sense, including lightning, happiness, etc.), bright, clear, day, light (-ning), morning, and sun

267

(Strong's Conc. # 216 *owr*), but this is not the finished product of the sun and stars that we see today, as they were not finished forming until the fourth day. The Hebrew word for light on the fourth day is different, it is *maor*, which means bright, light, luminary, or luminous body (Strong's Conc. # 3974). This definition of *owr/light/luminous* is broader than anticipated. It is closely associated with joy. Let us journey further into this light that was created on the first day, and let us see what else we may find besides the glowing magma of future stars and angels being created with this light.

In Matthew 5:14, Jesus is talking to believers: "You (believers) are the light of the world . . . Let your light shine before men in such a way that they may see your good works and glorify your Father who is in heaven." In one sense, we are representatives of the source/co-creator of light, Jesus, to the world. Our origin is light. Luke 11:35 says, "Then watch out that the light in you is not darkness. If therefore your whole body is full of light, with no dark part in it, it will be wholly illumined, as when the lamp illumines you with its rays." In a spiritual sense, being of the light equals being saved and being of the darkness equals being lost. In a physical sense, our spiritual condition of being in the light/day or being in the dark/night is revealed by our actions. We are either of light or of darkness in both the physical realm and in the spiritual realm. Consider 1 Thessalonians 5:2–5, in which Paul writes, "You know . . . the day of the Lord will come just like a thief in the night . . . But you, brethren, are not in darkness, that the day [judgment: "Day of the Lord"] would overtake you like a thief; for **you are all sons of light** and **sons of day. We are not of night nor of darkness.**" A clear picture is emerging that the spirits of all of humanity that enter each human at conception from the beginning of time to the end of the age were created on the first day with the phrase *let there be light*. Matthew 13:41–43:

> The Son of Man will send forth His angels and they will gather out of His kingdom all stumbling blocks, and those who commit lawlessness, and will throw them into the furnace of fire; in that place there will be weeping and gnashing of teeth. Then **the righteous will shine forth as the sun** in the kingdom of their Father.

Daniel 12:3: "Those who have insight **will shine brightly like the brightness of the expanse of heaven**, and those who lead the many to righteousness, **like the stars forever** and ever." This illustrates the point; therefore, our spirits were created on the first day as part of the light because the body and soul of Adam was not fashioned and made until the sixth day.

Review: The spirits of all that will have the breath of life had their spirits created on the first day.

This seems like a double meaning, does the Bible allow for double meanings? It is true that only one correct interpretation exist for each verse, yet sometimes, albeit infrequently, two meanings for the same passage of Scripture is an appropriate interpretation. For example, Isaiah 14 makes a reference to the King of Babylon in Isaiah's day and a reference to the fallen angel Lucifer, when he fell some 3,000 years before Isaiah's day. Also, Ezekiel 28 makes a reference to the King of Tyre in Ezekiel's day and a reference to why and how Lucifer fell and became the devil and then tempted Adam and Eve. Jeremiah 31:15 talks about the weeping Israeli children as the Babylonians are slaughtering them, yet Matthew 2:18 quotes the same Jeremiah verse for when King Herod was slaughtering Jewish children in attempts to kill baby Jesus some 700 years later. One verse has two correct applications that do not contradict the other.

And God separated the light from the darkness. God called the light day, and the darkness He called night? How do we handle the second half of the verse? We already discussed the physical realm, how it is simply the burgeoning earth rotating with one side lit by the glowing magma of the future sun and the other side dark. But this phrase has more to it. Since God knows all things (Psalm 139), then God knew who would love Him and who would reject Him. No one can come to Jesus unless the Father who sent Jesus draws him (John 6:44), so when did God determine who He would draw to Himself, and when did He predestine salvation to those He knew would love Him? Ephesians 1:4 says it is "just as He chose us in Him before the foundation of the world." The foundation of the world was on the third day of creation, so the only verbiage of the creation account that fits when God created our spirits and predetermined us to heaven, based on His all knowing ability to know whether we would love Him or reject Him, is right here on the first day with the phrase in Gen. 1:3: "Then God said, 'let there be light'; and there was light. God saw that the light was good; and God separated the light from the darkness. God called the light day, and the darkness He called night." Did God predetermine or predestine those who would find Him? Yes, He knows which path people choose, and they have 100% free will and are 100% responsible for their choices. We either store up wrath based on our actions or store up blessings. Ephesians 1:5: "He predestined us to adoption as sons through Jesus Christ to Himself." In Gen. 1:3, when God separated the light from the darkness, this is the exact moment in time when God predetermined—based on His full foreknowledge and predetermining abilities of knowing who would reject Him and who would Love Him—and God judged who would be saved and who would not be saved. This does not mean that any of the spirits predestined for hell were sinful at this time; they were perfect, sinless spirits. This does not mean that those spirits separated to darkness had no choice, they had 100% choice. God looked forward in time at each persons life and based on their fully informed choice of whether to accept or reject God, He separated them unto light or darkness. Based on the individual choice that God sees in the future, He determined who He would draw to Himself based on His foreknowledge of their actions, of who would love or reject Him. This does not mean that at this moment some spirits were evil or sinful. The spirits that would eventually go into hell had not entered the body and joined with the soul to sin and need a savior. This demonstrates the mercy of God to take to heaven stillbirths, infant deaths, and young children that die before the age of accountability for their sins. All the iniquities committed by children are on the head of the household until the child becomes responsible for their own sin, which is at the age of accountability, roughly at age thirteen. Every time you hear of a child that dies prematurely, this may have been the mercy of God to take a spirit that was on the path for hell based on their future sins, but God gave full mercy and grace. It is doctrinally incorrect to say that God predetermined someone to go to hell because we are fully responsible and without excuse for rejecting God (Romans 1:20). We earn our wage for our sin—death and hell (Romans 6:23). Sin is never inherited (Ezekiel 18:20,30). As a murderer cannot blame the judge for the verdict and sentence, God is not credited for anyone going to hell, but God gets all the credit for someone going to heaven because we all deserve hell. It is only by God's mercy and grace that anyone goes to heaven.

If it is true that we were predetermined to be adopted as sons through Jesus Christ before time began, then Jesus had to be predetermined to die on the cross before the foundation of the world as well. That is stated in Acts 2:23: "This Man, delivered over by the predetermined plan and foreknowledge of God, you nailed to a cross by the hands of godless men and put Him to death." Also, 2 Thessalonians 2:13 says that we are "chosen from the beginning for salvation." The beginning was the first day.

Do we have free will? Yes, according to Psalm 119:108: "O accept the freewill offerings of my mouth, O LORD." Romans 10:9 says, "If you confess with your mouth Jesus as Lord, and believe in your heart that God raised Him from the dead, you will be saved."

This is not a cruel gesture on God's part to seemingly choose some and reject most; no, quite the contrary, He died on the cross for the world—for all (John 3:16), not for a few. However, most reject His free gift of a pardon from our crimes against Him. God knows our actions, our free will. God knows who will reject Him and who will love Him; He sends His missionaries for others to hear the gospel message, so they are without excuse, and even those who never hear of the gospel message still have creation to look at to know God and to worship Him. So they too are without excuse. Now someone may say, "I thought someone can only be saved through Jesus." That is correct, and since Jesus created everything, then even though someone hasn't heard of Jesus' Gospel message, they can still worship the Father through the creator, namely Jesus. By worshiping the creator of everything, they are worshiping Jesus. This is also in harmony with how the Jews were saved before Jesus died on the cross. When they worshiped the God they saw, they were inadvertently worshiping Jesus because no one has seen God the Father at any time and Jesus is the physical image of the Father.

Review: God predestined and predetermined by foreknowledge, who was going to reject Him and who was going to Love Him on the first day of creation. God selected those spirits for either eternal heaven or eternal hell. God already knew about those who would reject Him in the future, not because the spirit had any sin in it at the time of creation.

This is not to say that the spirits that were not selected for salvation were not good and therefore creation had sinful spirits before the fall. Their future body had not been born yet, and they had not sinned yet. The omniscience of God knew who was going to seek Him and who was going to knock on the door for Him. God, in His sovereignty, chose that spirit so that when the spirit would unite with the body and soul at conception, God would be in a relationship with them until they sinned, then God would draw that person to Himself, and God would change that person's heart at the appropriate time for salvation. Therefore, God gets the credit for choosing us and being the source of our salvation. We are responsible to seek Him, to knock for Him, and He will open the door to salvation, and we are without excuse if we reject Him. Therein lies the harmony between free will and predestination because we have a choice and because sovereign God chose us before time began based on our choice.

God repeats the same phrase in Genesis when He created the sun, moon, and stars in verse 14, *to separate the day from the night,* and in verse 18, *to separate the light from the darkness.* Since this is clearly the physical separation of the day from the night by a fully formed sun and moon, this adds further evidence of the dual application of *God separated the light from the darkness* on the first day. One physical meaning is the simple deduction that the light emitted off hot magma of the coalescing future sun (and all the future stars too) shone on a burgeoning, rotating Earth. A spiritual meaning is the light from the spirits of all future life forms, God separated those of the light and those of the darkness. This could be the very moment of predestination, of God choosing based on His foreknowledge of our actions, of God separating those who would love Him and those that would hate Him.

How do we know that God is still not creating spirits for humans with each birth? Several verses give us clues that our spirit is not created at our birth, but on the first day of creation and then placed into our forming body at conception. God finished creating all things in the seven days of creation. This is clarified in John 1:1–3: "In the beginning . . . All things came into being through Him, and apart from Him nothing came into being that has come into being." This means that all things were created in the beginning. Also, Colossians 1:16 says, "For by Him all things were created . . . all things have been created . . . in Him all things hold together." Notice the past tense. God is still working, and births seem like a new creation to us, but God is sustaining His creation, causing His creation to endure and to hold together. That is what each birth represents, an enduring genetic copy of Adam and Eve created in the image of God.

Our bodies are shells for the spirit, and the body is just a temporary shell. It is not a new creation, but a continuation of our parents' genetic makeup going all the way back to Adam and Eve. Each parent passes on chromosomes to form a continuation of their bodies via the fertilization process, and a portion of each parent is passed on to form another generation to house the spirit.

On a side note, I believe animals have a spirit as well. We do read about animals in heaven in Revelation, so this would also be the creation of all the animal spirits as well.

Review: The countless, hot rotating and coalescing future stars, generated enough gravity and heat to glow from liquid magma. In addition to light and angels being created at the middle of the first day with the creation of light, so too were all the spirits of all of life forms from the beginning of time to the end of time. God separated the light from the darkness and predestined believers to adoption as sons of God through Jesus Christ.

All the matter in the universe initially had no form and darkness prevailed everywhere, but now, all the future planets, moons, and stars have been rotating and coalescing matter and gaining in density, mass, gravity, electromagnetism, pressure, and heat to the point that all the future stars glowed hot from liquid matter. Trillions of hurricane-like rotations in close proximity with water filling the gaps and edges in between them. Since the universe was tightly packed together, and since the future sun coalesced 99% of the mass of our solar system, the sun must have been gigantic from Earth's perspective. With such close proximity, quite possibly the burgeoning sun was as close to Earth as the moon is now, and took up almost all the view from the coalescing Earth. But not just the sun, every planet in our solar system was very close. The moon was so close that potentially the outer rotation of matter coalescing toward the moon, was intermingling with the outer edge of the matter that was coalescing toward the earth. As a result of this close proximity of celestial bodies, the amount of weight pressing down on Earth's soil was staggering, and this shaped the formation of the Earth's inner and outer core, mantle, and crust with high heat. The bedrock of the crust—the granite rock, was formed during this intense weight, pressure, and heat, yet it will remain liquid until the weight and pressure from the compact universe is alleviated. But the earth's surface was not magma as some claim, it was hot on the surface and beyond the normal boiling point of water, yet because of the pressure liquid water covered the surface of the earth.

The first complete rotation of the soon-to-be earth, though forming and void of life, was completed here at the end of the first day. Since evening precedes morning, it is logical that the rotation of the matter began rotating at the start of the day in darkness, prior to the creation of light, immediately upon the creation of all matter.

The soon-to-be earth was rotating at a slightly faster pace than today. How do we know this? The moon's gravitational force causes our ocean tides, and the ocean tides slow the earth's spin by taking energy away from the spin of the earth. That energy is used up to push the moon away from the earth 3.8 cm per year at its current pace. Going back in time to about 6,000 years ago, the moon was potentially moving 30 meters per year away from the earth in the beginning, and the duration of one rotation of the earth was approximately 17 hours.

Review: The evening and morning represent the rotation of the soon-to-be earth.
When the word *day* is used in the Bible and it does not have a number in front of it, it can mean any amount of time, such as eons, millennia, ages, or epochs. It is not specific. For example, Isaiah 13:6 has no number in front of "day" when it says, "Wail, for the day of the Lord is near." But when a number is in front of it, the day literally and always refers to one complete rotation of the earth on its axis.

This is a critical verse that lays the foundation of the rest of the Bible for all readers for all generations. Imagine trying to witness to someone and telling them about God and how powerful He is, and the person asks you, "I heard there were errors in the Bible, and the Genesis creation account is false and cannot be taken literally; is that true?" Now if the one sharing the message of God says "yes," then the conversation is over. For who in there right mind would follow a God that claims His Word is true, yet is not able to write a truthful Bible that is filled with scientific errors. Rarely does this scenario happen because the ones who believe that errors exist in the Bible and that the Genesis account violates science, are less likely to share God's Word with others because they have a weak view of Scripture, and subsequently they become less useful for God. Deep down, they doubt God. The people who doubt the authenticity of divine Scripture are less inclined to read the Bible—why read words that are merely man-made? When those people do read the Scriptures, by what arbitrary means do they start taking the Bible literally? The fact of the matter is that when people believe that the Bible has errors of science in it and is inaccurate and should not be taken literally, they do not spend a lot of time reading the Scriptures to equip themselves for every good work.

The creation account of Genesis is all one needs to read to know whether to take the Genesis creation account literally as seven rotations of the earth or figuratively as ages for each rotation of the earth. But let the following verses help you to overcome humanity screaming that the Bible is unclear, filled with errors and weird veiled language. In Numbers 12:6–8, God says that He speaks to Moses clearly, face to face as a friend to a friend, not in veiled dreams or visions. The Genesis creation account is in plane, clear language. Also, in Exodus 20:11 and Exodus 31:17, God twice said and wrote in stone: "For in six days the Lord made the heavens and the earth, the sea and all that is in them, and rested on the seventh day." That is clear as day. Lastly, Jesus quotes Gen. 1:27 and 2:24 and says that God made man male and female from the beginning. We can infer that Jesus affirms the creation account, and not an evolutionary process, and since Jesus takes Genesis literally, so too should we.

Review: The matter that would eventually become the earth, though initially formless and void of life, was immediately rotating and coalescing matter at the start of the first day when the matter was formed, and this first complete rotation of the earth's matter took one day.

God did not create evil. It is our free will that brought evil into God's creation, and the wages of sin is death. Thus, we have earned eternal death. For example, honey is sweet and tasty, but if I eat too much of it and get sick. Am I now entitled to blame the bee for creating the honey as though it was evil? No. Also, water is good, but if one drowns in water, does their relatives now blame the clouds for creating evil? No. Thus, we cannot blame God for something He did not create, which is the evil actions of mankind.

Now, a logical interpretation is that hell is at the center of the earth. When someone reaches that location, it is a bottomless pit—an abyss, with no floor. When God formed the earth, no evil existed, in fact God declared all was very good. But upon mankind sinning, God declared that He would put those evil doers that reject His free grace at the center of the earth—the abyss. Therefore, it is the plight of the evil doers' final destination that is hell for the unsaved, not an evil structure that God created. For example, if I build a perfect submarine, and as a result of piloting errors the submarine sinks killing its crew. The submarine becomes a permanent tomb for their bodies. But, I did not create the tomb, their actions created their own tomb. I just called it their tomb. Likewise, God created the earth that happens to have a center, now when men die having rejected God's atonement for their sin, their souls and spirits are sent to the center of the earth, which God calls their plight hell. God did not create Hell. Similarly, the premise with the Great White Judgment, when all evil doers receive their immortal bodies, and are cast into the Lake of Fire, which could be our sun. It is not that the sun was created by God as evil, it is just a location that God sends these people and their plight is eternal hell in the Lake of Fire. Thus, it is not that the Lake of Fire is evil, it is that the plight of those sent there is hell.

The Bible does not say that God created hell. It exists because of man's sin and that God prepared hell for them (Matt. 25:41). "Prepared" means to get ready from what exists, not create as in from nothing. Like a chef prepares a salad. The foundation for this is that God did not create anything bad or evil.

Chapter Summary: At the beginning of the first Day there was darkness, God brought forth wisdom, knowledge, discretion, and everything that is good as He created matter through Himself. Within this small universe, the formless earth, waters, and all the matter that would eventually be the stars, planets, solar systems, and galaxies were rotating and coalescing. The countless future stars, coalesced enough matter and density, to generate enough gravity, to produce enough heat, to liquefy matter and glow hot as God said, "Let there be light." Also angels and all the spirits of all life were created at the midpoint of the first day; this becomes the first morning. This is also the first complete rotation of the forming Earth and waters. The predetermination of believers to be sons of God through Jesus occurred on the first day.

Chapter 33
The Second Day

Gen. 1:6: *Then God said, 'Let there be an expanse in the midst of the waters, and let it separate the waters from the waters,' God made the expanse, and separated the waters which were below the expanse from the waters which were above the expanse; and it was so. God called the expanse heaven. And there was evening and there was morning a second day.*

Then God said. The word "*said*" is *amar* in Hebrew. *Amar* means to say, or to speak. God literally spoke the words out loud. God did not just think the words. This is important because words have power. Even our words, as insignificant as we may feel at times, are still created in the image of God. This is why we should guard the words we speak. The words that we speak and the power from our words can condemn us (James 3:5[179]) or result in eternal life (Romans 10:9).

Jesus is called the Word because He made all things (John 1:1 and Colossians 1:16). Our words reveal the condition of our heart (Proverbs 4:23 and Matthew 15:18[180]). Satan's primary mission and first act on earth was to deceive Adam and Eve about the Words of God. This is why Proverbs 18:21 says, "Death and life are in the power of the tongue." Through God's Word, He created all life, and with our words, we confess God unto salvation, only through Jesus do we get to the Father, and that is either by hearing the Word or seeing Jesus by His creation. This is why Ezekiel 3:16–21 says that when God puts someone in our path and we do not tell them of the Gospel message and they perish in their darkness, their blood is on our hands because the law requires life for life (Exodus 21:23). Words are powerful, we can wound someone with our words and crush their spirit, or we can edify one with our words and heal them or lead them to eternal life. Choose your words wisely. When in doubt, do not say anything. Even a fool, when silent, appears prudent and discerning (Proverbs 17:28).

Review: God's Word has power to create. Since we are made in His image and in His likeness, our words have power too. They have the power to condemn us or for salvation, for blessings, or for curses. How we wield this power reveals the condition of our heart.

As we have discussed, the Hebrew word for expanse is *raqiya*, which means extended surface (solid), expanse, firmament, or visible arch of the sky (vault of heaven supporting waters above) (Strong's Conc. #7549). The root word of raqiya is raqa, which means to pound the earth (as a sign of passion) to expand (by hammering), by implied to overlay (with thin sheets of metal), beat, make, make broad, spread abroad, stamp, or stretch (Strong's Conc. #7554 *raqa)*. Most translations use the word *expanse* and others use *firmament,* they are synonyms. Notice that the definitions indicate that this was a very violent process, similar to a blacksmith that hammers glowing hot metal, with sparks flying, violent force, and steaming water.

Most Christians read the words for the second day and only interpret one expanse. However, I contend that two actions are mentioned, and therefore, two expanses made on the second day. We can have confidence that God made two expanses because on the fourth day of creation, God finishes making the sun, moon, and stars in an already existing other expanse we call the universe. God said on the third day, "Let the waters below the **heavens** be gathered into one place and let the dry land appear." Then on the fourth day of creation God said, "Let there be lights **in the expanse** of the heavens." Since *heavens* is already plural at the beginning of the third day of creation, and no additional command to create the expanse/universe for the sun, moon, and stars on the fourth day, and God places the sun, moon, and stars in this second expanse that is already existing, then this is strong evidence that the universe that was created on the first day of creation, though densely packed and

---

179 James 3:5-6 "The tongue is a small part of the body, and yet it boasts of great things. See how great a forest is set aflame by such a small fire! And the tongue is a fire, the very world of iniquity; the tongue is set among our members as the which defiles the entire body, and sets on fire the course of our life."

180 Proverbs 4:23: "Watch over your heart with all diligence, For from it flow the springs of life."
 Matthew 15:18: "The things that proceed out of the mouth come from the heart, and those defile the man."

small, was stretched and expanded on the second day of creation to cause the stretching/expanding of the atmosphere.

Let there be an expanse in the midst of the waters, and let it separate the waters from the waters. Two actions occur in this verse. *Let there be an expanse,* this is the first action. Remember, the hypothesis is that all the galaxies, solar systems, suns, moons, and planets were near in proximity on the first day, and they were all connected by water. Also, the water surrounding the universe, since it did not have a heat source, was a frozen shell. Thus, when God declared, '*Let there be an expanse in the midst of the waters,* this was the stretching of the universe, galaxies, and solar systems by expanding the waters in the middle of them.

And let it separate the waters from the waters. This is the second action. The *it* is referring back to the previous action. The *and* is indicating that the *it* will cause another action that will *separate waters from the waters.* The specific *waters from the waters* is in reference to the narrator's perspective, and that is from the perspective of Earth. This harmonizes with 2 Peter 3:5 that explains, "The earth was formed out of water and by water." Thus, this action is the formation of our atmosphere, with water above and water below. The water above became the canopy and the water below became the seas. Since every celestial body had water around it, this is also the making of various atmospheres around every celestial body, albeit however brief because of harsh environmental conditions.

Therefore, two actions occur on this day, and the first action caused the second action. The first action was the expansion of the universe, by the expansion of space in between galaxies, solar systems, planets, moons, and stars, and the second action was the expansion of the atmospheres of all the planets, moons, and stars surrounded by water. But for this discussion, it was specifically the atmosphere around Earth.

Now, Moses gives us a review of what just happened. Moses tells us what God said in the prior verse, and then he explains the results with the following: *God made the expanse, and separated the waters which were below the expanse from the waters which were above the expanse.* The two actions are mentioned here by Moses. The first is that *God made the expanse,* referencing the expansion of the universe, and the second is result of the first action that another expanse was made that *separated the waters* to be both below and above the expanse. Since water existed as a shell around the universe and water existed in between each galaxy, solar system, and celestial body, then this latter explanation by Moses is revealing that the expansion of the universe separated waters around every star, moon, planet, solar system, galaxy, and the entire universe, and this action caused atmospheres around all celestial bodies.

We know that not every celestial body has an atmosphere today, but that does not negate that they had one at their origin. In fact, most celestial bodies that cosmologist study, show signs of remnant water on their surface, which indicates that an atmosphere was present at one time to allow water on the surface in the first place. Even today, many planets still have rings of ice orbiting them, this indicates that water was above their atmosphere at one time. Thus, the observable evidence allows for the hypothesis that every celestial body had an atmosphere with water above and water below. The harsh environmental conditions of the universe destroyed nearly all atmospheres, along with the waters above and below.

God stretching out the universe and the atmosphere on the second day of creation explains why the expanse in verse 8 is pluralized as *heavens* one verse later in verse 9. This is strong evidence that God stretched out the universe on the second day and this caused the expansion of the atmosphere. Someone may argue that since the verse contains this phrase: *God called the expanse heaven,* then this represents that only one expanse was formed on this day. However, since both the universe and the atmosphere are called heaven, then God is not referencing the quantity here with that phrase, He is only telling us what the general name of each expanse is called—heaven. Throughout the Bible, both expanses will be referenced as heaven by God through His scribes. This is illustrated with God forming the stars in the expanse of the heavens—the universe, galaxies, and solar systems—on the fourth day, and forming the birds to fly above the earth in the open expanse of the heavens—atmosphere—on the fifth day. Also, the apostle Paul was caught up to the third heaven—throne of God (2 Cor. 12:2). Therefore, the three expanses are each called heaven.

Review: The root word for expanse and the Holy Spirit, indicate that this was a violent day. Two actions occurred on this day, the stretching of the heavens that contain the stars and this expansion caused the separation of waters that surrounded every celestial body, but specifically the earth.

This is the day that God stretched out the waters and made openings in between the waters. One of the expanses is Earth's atmosphere. Some principles in physics help to explain how God created our atmosphere. The Bible teaches that our faith comes from Jesus, the author and perfecter of our faith (Hebrews 12:1–2), and since faith is increased by studying the Scriptures (Romans 10:17), then as we study and grow in the knowledge of the truth and science, it becomes easier to faithfully accept the Scriptures. Let us set the scene from the first day to understand the forces involved for the second day.

The universe was small and densely packed on the first day. It was filled with countless hurricane-like storms of coalescing matter, with liquid magma at the cores, and soil and water rotating around each core. The following are the four states of water: An extensive thick layer of **ice** acting as a shell that prevented the tightly packed universe from expanding to alleviate the pressure. Water closer to hot forming planets and moons, was hot enough to vaporize, but the pressure from the weight of the universe was too intense, and the water remained in **liquid** form (pressure alters the boiling point of liquids). Water too close to forming stars **vapor**ized, as the temperatures of burgeoning stars exceeded the pressure that tended to keep water liquefied This increased the internal pressure of the universe. Lastly, the waters involved with each star's formation had so much energy from the heat, pressure, and electromagnetism that it turned to **plasma**. With the rotation of liquid metal of each coalescing star, electrons flowed (a similar process to how a generator creates electricity) and huge quantities of electrical charge and magnetism built up. Although at varying quantities and rates, with each passing minute, heat, density, mass, gravity, and electromagnetism increased with every coalescing future planet, moon, and star. The increased gravity of each planet, moon, and star in close proximity was a strong force that wanted to collapse the universe onto itself. But the repulsion force of electromagnetism, and the expansion force from the heat and vaporized water, and the centripetal force generated from a spinning universe, galaxies, solar systems, planets, moons, and stars that counteracted gravity, each force prevented the universe from collapsing onto itself from the gravitational force. The forming Earth, although warm enough to vaporize water, was surrounded by water (2 Peter 3:5) because the weight of the universe created too much pressure, and this prevented water from boiling and generating gas. That is the image of the first day of creation. An environment with conditions that were hot, hostile, unstable, and unsustainable.

On the second day, the centripetal force, heat, pressure, and electromagnetism inside the small universe was growing at an accelerated rate and neared the tensile strength of the external shell of ice. With the stars, planets, and moons being in close proximity, strong electromagnetism applied a repulsive force that wanted to push every celestial body away from each other. The spinning universe, galaxies, and solar systems generated centripetal force that wanted to push every celestial body away from each other. Even the intense heat generated within the universe wanted to expand the universe. With trillions of growing stars spinning a core of liquid metal, this built up an unstable amount of electrical charge of positive electrons, that grew to unsustainable levels. This resulted in electrical discharge—lightning on a cosmic scale that instantly vaporized all water along its path. This was the final straw of too many internal forces, that exceeded the force of gravity and the strength of the external shell of ice, which both kept the universe small and dense. *And God said, 'Let there be an expanse,' God made the expanse.* Thus, from a creationist point of view, countless internal Big Bangs from each expanding galaxy and solar system would have generated the rapid expansion that cosmologists call the Big Bang. The universe expanded exceedingly fast, and most cosmologist hypothesize that the small universe expanded faster than the speed of light (called universal inflation).

This rapid expansion caused a sudden reduction of pressure surrounding every celestial body. With the monumental weight of the universe now removed from every star, planet, and moon this quickly reduced the pressure surrounding every celestial body. *And God said, '. . . let it separate the waters from the waters,' God . . . separated the waters which were below the expanse from the waters which were above the expanse.* So that this resulted in immediate cavitation—the conversion of water instantly to gas—around every celestial body surrounded by liquid. Therefore, creating an atmosphere surrounding each planet and moon.

When God separated the waters from the waters, the waters above became the canopy of salt water that surrounded the atmosphere and led to the global flood, and the waters below became the seas. The water, forming Earth, and the atmosphere were already spinning on an axis. This spinning of water, dirt, and atmosphere on an axis generated a centripetal force, which helped keep the atmosphere expanded and prevent the canopy from crashing down onto the forming earth. Also, when the universe expanded and cavitation formed air in the middle of the waters surrounding Earth, the atmosphere pushed the canopy up and away from the Earth, until an equilibrium occurred where the weight of the canopy equaled the buoyant force of the atmosphere that pushed the canopy up. Then, with the universe expanded, the space in between celestial bodies, solar systems, and galaxies quickly lost heat. This caused the canopy, spherically surrounding the atmosphere, to freeze in place with an arch support that prevented collapse. With each orbit of the moon and spin of the earth, the canopy morphed over time from spherical to a bulge, then to disk-like with a visible arch in the sky. This is in harmony with the definition of the Hebrew word expanse. This canopy enabled life on earth to live 900+ years by shielding life from harmful cosmic energy, gamma rays, UV rays, and x-rays, and created temperate global temperatures, and reduced the effect of Earth's gravity by its buoyancy force. Until the advent of the Flood when the canopy came down to Earth as rain for 40 days.

The method that God used to stretch out the universe is that He spoke it so, and the Holy Spirit moved violently as a passionate breath of life. This Biblical language of the passion and violence for which the Holy Spirit is defined by is expressed in cosmology as the Big Bang. The second day of creation was the second most violent day in the universe (the most violent day was the conversion of energy to matter on the first day). The universal expansion on the second day appeared as one external Big Bang, but was initiated by trillions upon trillions of internal Big Bangs from each galaxy, solar system, and star. Once the internal forces exceeded the external shell of the universe and the force of gravity, a violent large explosion and subsequent expansion occurred. Such as when Icelandic volcanoes internal pressures exceed gravity and the shell of soil covering and a violent explosion occurs. A small model that is a close representation (albeit a much smaller scale) of the dynamics of water pressure on the small universe, is a kernel of corn that pops. This presents a similar setup to the early small universe with a shell that resists the vapor pressure internally. When the pressure inside exceeds the integrity of the shell from heat and vaporized water, the result is a popped kernel. The shell of the universe was thick ice, and the heat source was all the countless eventual stars and galaxies gathering mass, density, and heat. One set of ingredients for the countless Big Bangs were magma, pressure, charge, and water. This resulted in immeasurable explosions and quick expansion, just like a kernel that pops relative to its size.

The effects on pressurized fluids that undergo a sudden release of pressure, will have a dramatic affect on those fluids. For example, take a deep water scuba diver that comes up too quickly to the surface, the sudden reduction of pressure on their vascular system results in their blood literally boiling. This is not because of heat, but merely the sudden change in pressure. This is called the bends, or decompression sickness. This condition is from dissolved gases coming out of solution as bubbles.[181] In physics, this process is called cavitation, and it is the same definition, gases coming out of solution as bubbles because of a rapid reduction in pressure.[182] For this reason, when the pressure in the universe

181 Http://en.m.wikipedia.org/wiki/Decompression_sickness.
182 Http://en.m.wikipedia.org/wiki/Cavitation.

was suddenly and drastically released, this instantly caused air bubbles to form in the middle of the waters, and thus the expanse had water above and water below. On the first day of creation, the universe had immense pressure from its weight and density, and this pressure increased with each passing minute on the first day. Until suddenly the weight was removed as each solar system and galaxy expanded, this resulted in rapid reduction in pressure around every celestial body. This process is elucidated every time someone opens a new, pressurized soda bottle. The formation of the bubbles from soda bottles opening and releasing the pressure, mimics how the atmosphere was formed as a result of the rapid reduction in pressure from the rapid expansion of the universe. This expansion of the universe rapidly reduced pressure of the water that surrounded every celestial body, thus, air bubbles were released from solution to form various atmospheres with water above and water below on every planet, star, and moon. As a result of the varying conditions, no two celestial bodies are the same. As a result of the intense heat near burgeoning stars, all their water converted to either vapor or plasma, depending on proximity, to form gaseous giants.

Another profound effect the expansion of the universe had on the earth was with the granite rock. Toward the end of the first day, granite rock was formed as the foundation of the crust, yet because of the weight of the universe and pressure and subsequent heat, the granite was liquid. With the expansion of the universe and complete removal of the weight, and severe reduction of the pressure and subsequent reduction in temperature, the granite rock solidified almost instantly. Dr. Robert Gentry has found irrefutable evidence that the granite rock of the earth cooled quickly from a liquid state to a solid state almost instantly, and debunks that the granite cooled over millions of years as others claim. He has found granite rock to contain primordial polonium halos without an ancestral halos from heavier elements, indicating that (a) the granite rock had a quick creative moment, and (b) that the granite rock cooled quickly to capture these radioactive halos that are fleeting like effervescent bubbles.[183]

God established an expanse throughout the universe and this expanse separated the waters from the waters of every celestial body. This is why remnant signs of water exist throughout the universe. At the end of the second day, the universe was stretched out and rapidly expanding, with the force of pressure removed, and centripetal force no longer forcing the galaxies apart, and the electrical charge dissipated, then gravity slowed the rate of expansion of the galaxies. At this moment in creation, the coalescing of matter that would eventually become the stars, planets, and moons were nearing completion; they were still hot spinning masses that were coalescing matter and gaining in density, mass, and heat; though the stars glowed from the magma, they did not ignite yet as starlight. God often uses natural means to accomplish His supernatural commands.

One may argue that the universe was stretched out on the fourth day after the formation of the earth. Isaiah 48:13: "Surely My hand founded the earth, and My right hand spread out the heavens." This verse seems to explain the order in which God did things. But hold on a minute; Isaiah 44:24 reverses the order and says, "I, the LORD, am the maker of all things, Stretching out the heavens by Myself and spreading out the earth all alone." Isaiah isn't focusing on order, just that God created these things. We are back to relying on the fact that *heavens* is plural on the third day because God stretched out both the atmosphere and the universe on the second day and God finished forming the sun, moon, and stars on the fourth day in an already-stretched-out universe. The phrase *Let there be lights in the expanse of the heavens* indicates that the universe had already been expanded on the second day of creation.

We can be assured of two expanses/firmaments, as the sun, moon, and stars were created in one expanse called heaven on the fourth day. And the birds were created to fly in another expanse called heaven on the fifth day. Therefore, both expanses were created on the second day of creation because we cannot have birds flying in the same expanse as the sun, moon, and stars. They are clearly distinct openings and separate heavens. This explains why *heavens* is plural in verses (Gen. 1: 9,14,15,17) following the second day.

---

183 Halos.com by Dr. Robert Gentry.

One of the major benefits and harmonies maintained by having the universe initiating its expansion at the beginning of the second day is that it keeps in place a canopy of salt water surrounding the earth. If only one expanse/firmament existed, and the sun, moon, and stars were created in the same expanse as the birds, then you could not have a canopy of salt water surrounding the earth. The water that is above the expanse would have been pushed to the edges of the universe instead of to the edge of the atmosphere. A two expanse/firmament/heaven view created on the second day of creation, where the first expanse causes the second expanse is the better view because it does not violate Scripture, or science, or present interpretive challenges. It also allows for an explanation of where all the water came from for the Flood.

The simplest argument for the universe commencing with expansion on the second day is that it would have been a slow productive day otherwise. The first day has many things created and lots of action, from the creation of all matter, energy, laws, light, and focal points of spinning matter that would eventually be the celestial bodies. The second day has only one thing created? The third day has the earth taking shape and function, with seas and fresh water and grass, plants, and trees. The fourth day has the sun, moon, and all the stars and galaxies finishing their form and the stars ignite and the perception of time formed. Are you seeing the picture? Each day has many things being created and taking form and function, lots of stuff going on, but only one thing occurs on the second day? This does not fit. What does fit is to including another major significant action to harmonize with the wording of the second day. This keeps creative acts for each day in order of most things created to least quantity created, and is in harmony with Gen. 1:9 having *heavens* as plural at the start of the third day.

The atmosphere being stretched out because the universe stretched out allows the spherical waters above the atmosphere to be in contact with the coldness of space, which instantly freezes an external archway and an inner support structure on the canopy of water to hold it in place. However, since every coalescing mass, including the universe, galaxies, solar systems, planets, moons, and stars were already spinning from the first day of creation, this canopy of water would be spinning and thus morphing from a spherical shape at its origin toward an equatorial bulge and eventual disc-like shape. This frozen arch structure of support may be why the Hebrew word for "firmament/expanse" means a visible arch in the sky.[184] It would become gradually thinner at the poles and thicker at the equator as time passed. If the Flood had not occurred, the canopy would have eventually become rings like those of Saturn. But Earth's gravity and conditions meant ring formations were not to be. Considering the above discussion, a plausible version of the second day could be written:

> *Then God said, 'Let there be an expansion in the middle of the waters of the universe, and let that expanse separate the waters from the waters surrounding the earth,' God stretched out the universe, which separated the waters which were below the atmosphere from the waters which were above the atmosphere; and it was so. God called the expanse heaven. And there was evening and there was morning a second day.*

Review: God stretched out both the universe and atmosphere on the second day of creation. The expansion of the universe started at the beginning of the second day and caused a sudden release of pressure throughout the universe, which caused all celestial bodies with water surrounding them to form atmospheres by the process called cavitation. The forming of the atmospheres probably commenced at the middle of the second day.

And it was so. This did not take billions of years. God said *let there be*—and it was so by the end of the second day. God did not say, *let there eventually be,* and it eventually became so, a second billion years.

God called the expanse heaven. All three expanses are called heaven. In relation to the proximity of Earth, not in order of creation. The atmosphere would be the first heaven or first expanse.

---

184 Strong's Conc. # 7549 *raqiya*: expanse, firmament, or (apparently) visible arch of the sky.

The second heaven or second expanse is the universe. The third heaven or third expanse, where the Throne of God is in relation to earth, was created on the first day of creation.

And there was evening and there was morning, a second day. This is one single rotation of the forming Earth and atmosphere, which we call a single day. Time, from our perspective and for our perspective, was manifested on the fourth day to match what was already occurring on days one through three. Why? When God finished forming the sun, moon, and stars to enable us to determine the days and years on the fourth day of creation, it was based on what God had already established as the standard, which was how long it took for one complete revolution of the waters and formless earth on the first day. God did not alter the velocity of the rotation to fit our perception of time. In others words, since God caused the revolution of the waters and formless earth first and then created the manifestation of time four days later, the perception of time was subjected and created to fit what was already established by God *in the beginning*. Why is this important? Because God is not subject and subservient to time, God set in motion and established exactly what He wanted on the first day, second day, and third day; God did not need to change anything to fit the manifestation or perception of time. God created time to fit with what He had already established. Because if a revolution of the earth were billions of years for one complete revolution, God would have had to accelerate the rotational velocity to fit the time created on the fourth day, and then God would have had to do a correction to the rotational velocity because it was not correct the first time. This is opposite of science because we observe and test that the earth's rotational velocity is continuously slowing from its initial state. More importantly, the Genesis account of creation would then be in violation with Exodus 20 and Exodus 31, where God explicitly says He created everything in six days. Therefore, the only acceptable interpretation is that each revolution of the matter that would eventually become the earth was relatively consistent with what we see today, and the perception of time was manifested as subservient and obedient to what God had already established. Even though the ability to perceive time began on the fourth day, what occurred on the third day was only ~17 hours (one full revolution) earlier, not billions of years earlier. What occurred on the second day was another ~17 hours (one full revolution) earlier, not billions of years earlier. What occurred on the first day was another ~17 hours (one full revolution) earlier, not billions of years earlier. Nothing changed for time; everything submits to God, including time, because God is the author of time.

Chapter Summary: God also stretched out the densely packed universe. This resulted in cavitation in the middle of the waters surrounding Earth. There were waters above (outside/canopy of salt water) and below (inside/the seas) the atmosphere. The waters above became the canopy of salt water that protected life from the sun's harmful rays and enhanced life on earth until Noah's Flood (Gen. 7). The waters below the atmosphere became the seas (on the third day) and were stored in deep caverns in the earth (Gen. 7).

Chapter 34
<u>The Third Day</u>

Gen. 1:9–13: *Then God said, "Let the waters below the heavens be gathered into one place, and let the dry land appear"; and it was so. God called the dry land earth, and the gathering of the waters He called seas; and God saw that it was good. Then God said, "Let the earth sprout vegetation, plants yielding seed, and fruit trees on the earth bearing fruit after their kind with seed in them";and it was so. The earth brought forth vegetation, plants yielding seed after their kind, and trees bearing fruit with seed in them, after their kind; and God saw that it was good. There was evening and there was morning, a third day.*

Then God said, "Let the . . . and it was so." Words have power. When a coach tells the players what to do, they do it. When an employer makes a request, the employee performs the job. When a judge speaks an order, it is carried out. When a general gives the word, his soldiers do it. When a king speaks, people take heed. And when God speaks, *it was so*. Doctrinally speaking and to split the details, it can be argued that the one who spoke when it says, *Then God said*, or *Let Us make man in Our image, according to Our likeness,* or when God said, *"Let the . . . it was so,"* was Jesus. How can this be known? Colossians 1:15–17:

> He is the image of the invisible God, the firstborn of all creation, For by Him all things were created, both in the heavens and on earth, visible and invisible, whether thrones or dominions or rulers or authorities—all things have been created through Him and for Him.

This passage states that Jesus made all things. It is interesting to point out who the Father declared is the embodiment and fulfillment of His Word. Jesus is the "Word." John 1:1–3, 14:

> In the beginning was the Word, and the word was with God, and the Word was God. He was in the beginning with God. All things came into being through Him, and apart from Him nothing came into being that has come into being . . . the Word became flesh, and dwelt among us, and we saw His glory, glory as of the only begotten from the Father.

Therefore, of the Trinity, God the Son was the one doing the speaking. So does this mean that God the Father did not create/speak anything in the Genesis creation account? No. God the Father equally created everything. In John 12:48–50, Jesus is talking:

> He who rejects Me and does not receive My sayings, has one who judges him; the Word I spoke is what will judge him at the last day. <u>For I did not speak on My own initiative, but the Father Himself who sent Me has given Me a commandment as to what to say and what to speak.</u> I know that His commandment is eternal life; therefore <u>the things I speak, I speak just as the Father has told Me.</u>

Therefore, the Word that Jesus spoke at creation was the very Word of God the Father. Now we have more clarity. Jesus spoke the Word in the Genesis account of creation, and every Word He spoke, was the very Word of God the Father.

What about the Holy Spirit? Did God the Holy Spirit create anything? Yes. God the Holy Spirit equally created everything. See 2 Peter 1:21: "No prophecy was ever made by an act of human will, but men <u>moved by the Holy Spirit spoke from God</u>." Therefore, when the Son speaks the Father's words, the Holy Spirit moves Their words into action. Also consider John 6:63: "It is the <u>Spirit who gives life</u>; the flesh profits nothing; the words that I have spoken to you are Spirit and are life." In other words, Jesus spoke the Word that the Father gave Him at creation, and the Spirit gave life to the Words spoken. This is why the "Breath of Life" (Holy Spirit) breathed into the nostrils and gave life to mankind and beasts. Life begot life. This is why after God creates the universe and the matter, the Holy Spirit is moving over the waters.

Putting the pieces together, we get an image of what occurred at creation. God the Father, Son, and Holy Spirit, each equally created all. They are all co-creators and equal personages with different roles, yet as one God. This is why Moses used Elohiym, the plural form of God to describe God. The Godhead is personified in life. The body (Son), the soul/mind (Father)(voluntary thought and desires), and the Spirit (Holy Spirit) (involuntary thought and desires). They act as one, yet they are individual components of a person. As Jesus is the physical image of the invisible God,[185] so too is the body the physical image of the invisible voluntary thought and desire. Jesus does the will of the Father,[186] as the body does the will of the mind. Yet they are equal,[187] one and divisible; when you see Jesus, you see the physical representative of the invisible Father,[188] and likewise, when you see the body, you see the physical representative of the invisible mind. The spirit influences the soul's decisions.

Then God said, "Let the waters below the heavens." Heavens is plural here because God had already created the three heavens—the Throne of God, universe, and atmosphere.

Heaven, where the Throne of God exists, is the third heaven from the perspective of mankind, since it is far away from mankind dimensionally. Luke 16:19–31 tells a parable of a man in hell talking to Abraham in heaven; the man in hell wants Lazarus to dip his finger in water and touch his tongue because he was in agony in the flames of hell, but Abraham says, "Between us and you there is a great chasm/gulf fixed, so that those who wish to come over from here to you will not be able, and none may cross over from there to us." This is a parable, so we cannot take details from it, but it is a general overview. Since the man in hell was communicating with Abraham in heaven, the gap/chasm/gulf, must not be physical distance, but a dimensional paradigm. We cannot say definitively.

Review: The creation of Heavens by distance from earth versus by chronology created:

Heavens by distance from earth:	Heavens by Chronology created:
1. Atmosphere	Day 1: Throne of God and small universe
2. Galaxies	Day 2: Universal expansion and atmosphere
3. Throne of God (Heaven)	

Let the waters below the heavens be gathered into one place, and let the dry land appear. The third day starts off in the evening; it is dark because the forming earth is rotating while the glowing magma of the sun (though not ignited yet) emits light. The light emitted from the angels and spirits of all the creatures (that will eventually live on the earth) is lighting up the spiritual realm as they glorify God. This day God puts form and purpose to the water and dirt, and He starts with gathering the waters below the atmosphere into one place. Notice that the waters are being moved around, not created. The waters have already been in existence from the beginning of the first day.

How did God move the waters and dirt? God moved the waters and dirt through natural processes from a spinning earth and the violent expansion of the universe on the second day. During the trillions of violent Big Bangs on the second day, this caused vibrations to the matter on a global scale. The vibrations reduced the **friction coefficient** of matter, which helps hold matter together, and allowed the separation of water and dirt to be easier and quicker leading up to the third day. Friction is the resistance of movement between objects in contact. The more soil vibrates, the more it acts like a liquid than a solid. This process is called **liquefaction** in physics.

Another factor in moving the soil and water on the earth, was the change in distance from the earth to the moon, sun, and all the other planets. On the first day of creation, the weight of the nearby celestial bodies dramatically increased the pressure on the soil. With the expansion on the second day and subsequent complete removal of the weight of the sun, moon, and planets pressing down on the

---

185 Colossians 1:15: "Jesus is the image of the invisible God."
186 Luke 22:42: "Father, if You are willing, remove this cup from Me; yet not My will, but Yours be done."
187 John 10:30: "I and the Father are one."
188 John 14:9: "He who has seen Me has seen the Father."

soil, this allowed the soil to expand, which caused changes in topography (elevations) on Earth. As a result of land expanding as Pangaea, water simply flowed down to lower elevations because of the earth's gravitational force, and made the land appear. We actually see this process with the melting of glaciers and the removal of weight on the soil beneath, which causes soil to rise/expand. This process is called **Post-glacial rebound**. Since no scientist has coined a name for the soil rebounding resulting from the expansion of the universe and removal of a enormous amount of weight, let us call it Post-expanse rebound.

Let the waters below the heavens be gathered into one place . . . the gathering of the waters He called seas. Where did God move the waters to? God moved most of the waters into deep caverns in the earth and used some waters to form seas, lakes, and rivers. At the beginning of the third day, a thin layer of water covered the earth. How do we know that most of the waters went into deep caverns inside the earth and for what purpose?

For one thing, God formed "seas," not oceans. What is the difference? Seas are vastly smaller in volume than oceans. Oceans did not exist until the Flood. The clue comes from oxygen bubbles in glacial core samples and air bubbles in amber; both reveal that oxygen was 50%–55% higher in the past. The logic being that to have more oxygen, requires more vegetation, and to have more vegetation, we cannot have oceans, as oceans physically limit vegetation growth and subsequently limit oxygen production. Thus, Pangaea was potentially ~70%–80% of the earth's surface, with many seas, lakes, and rivers covering ~20%–30% of the surface. Today, with the vastness of the oceans, phytoplankton mitigates against the severe loss of oxygen production because they produce O_2.

The Bible records that water was stored below the surface in deep caverns in Gen. 7:10–11: "Water of the flood came upon the earth . . . on the same day <u>all the fountains of the great deep burst open</u>, and the floodgates of the sky were opened. The rain fell upon the earth for forty days and forty nights." This verse reveals that tremendous amounts of water was stored below the surface in deep caverns that violently burst forth for 40 days and helped form the Flood and the oceans.

To solidify the notion that God stored water under the crust of the earth, consider Psalm 24:1–2: "The world . . . He has founded it upon the seas and established it upon the rivers." Psalm 33:7: "He gathered the waters of the sea together as an heap; he lays up the depth in storehouses." The plural "storehouses" and "lays up the depth" indicate that God placed what would eventually become the ocean waters, the depths, in storehouses. Now, laying them up could indicate the canopy of water or both the canopy and the fountains of the deep. Lastly, Psalm 136:6 says, "To Him who spread out the earth above the waters."

To further establish that God did not form oceans during the third day, oceans are referred to as the *deep*, while smaller seas are referred to as *seas*. Consider Job 28:14, "The deep . . . and the sea." Elucidating the point that the larger *deep/ocean* is a different body of water than the smaller *sea*. Also Psalm 33:6–7, it says, "By the Word of the LORD the heavens were made, and by the breath of His mouth all their host. He gathers the waters of the sea together as a heap; He lays up the deeps in storehouses." This clearly indicates that smaller seas were formed during the third day of creation, and the storehouses of the deep were not released until the Flood—which formed the oceans.

Review: <u>Smaller seas were fashioned from the water, and vast amounts of fresh water were stored below the surface. Oceans did not exist until the Flood.</u>

On the third day, God placed substantial amounts of waters in many deep caverns under the crust of the earth to be released for judgment with the global flood. You mean to say that God knew He was going to destroy the earth before even creating it? Yes. Nothing is a surprise to God, He does not increase in knowledge because He is all knowing. God is so sovereign, He is in such control, that Proverbs 16:33 states, "The lot is cast into the lap, but its every decision is from the LORD." In our vernacular, this means that "chance" does not exist. Even the outcome of an insignificant game of dice is determined by God. This may explain why most believers rarely win at gambling, the lottery, and so forth. God does not want us to be tempted to rely on wealth, or love money. God is so sovereign that

He predetermined the event of crucifying Jesus (the co-creator of the universe) before the first day of creation. Acts 2:23: "This Man, delivered over by the predetermined plan and foreknowledge of God, you nailed to the cross." God did not react to Adam and Eve's fall and say, "Well, now I will go to plan B to correct that mess." God the Father had already determined before the first day of creation began that His Son would be put on the cross because of Adam's free will and knowing Adam would choose to sin. God never gets the credit for us choosing sin, just like a judge never is credited for a criminal's crime. And God never gets the credit for sending someone to hell, just like a judge is never at fault for sentencing a criminal to prison. God gets all the credit for offering a full pardon to all that are guilty, just as a judge gets the credit for offering a pardon to the guilty. To demonstrate the love of God, He offers a full pardon to all guilty and convicted criminals, and to all those who accept His free offer, He then adopts as His children. No judge has ever offered a free pardon to the guilty and then adopted them as their child. The only catch is that this offer is a time sensitive gift, once the sentence has been carried out—death, there is no appeal with God because He uses absolute truth, absolute morality, and therefore, His judgments are absolute. However, once a sentence has been carried out—prison, with our court system, we may appeal verdicts and have them overturned. This is because the courts use relative truth, relative morality, and therefore, human judgments are not absolute but subject to change as the perception of truth and morality change.

How do we know there were more than one deep cavern of water? Well, the word deep is both singular and plural, but *fountains* is plural. It seems that the fountains of the deep were stored in hundreds of locations, with Pangaea resting on top of them, and when Pangaea broke apart, that "great deep" had many openings, fault lines, with fountains of water bursting out. The freshwater underground reservoirs we see today are possible remnants of that water, with the existing tectonic plate fault lines as the remnant openings of where the water burst violently out from. The mantle still has much water in it. This suggests that potentially volcanoes were part and parcel to the *fountains*.

Review: God predetermined with foreknowledge where to store the water and for what purpose, even before the fall of mankind.

Let the waters below the heavens be gathered into one place . . . the gathering of the waters He called seas. How do we reconcile the waters being gathered into <u>one</u> place, with seemingly two locations, one being the great deep reservoirs of water under the soil that burst open during the Flood and the other being seas, lakes, and rivers on top of the soil like we see today? Is this another one of those faith only premises? Some principles in science allow us to understand how God separated the waters into freshwater and saltwater, how God formed huge deep pure salt deposits, how God stored freshwater as the great deep, and by increasing our knowledge it becomes easier to accept by faith exactly what the Word of God records.

The Hebrew word for "one" is *echad* (Strong's Conc. #259): a numeral, **united, one**, first, a, **alike**, alone, altogether, and any (-thing), apiece, a certain, or together. This word stems from the root word *achad* (Strong's Conc. #258), which means to <u>unify, collect (one's thoughts)</u>—go one way or other. The Hebrew word for "place" is *meqomah* (Strong's Conc. #4725): a standing, a spot, but used widely of a locality (general or specific) as country, home, open, place, room, or space.

The Hebrew word for *place* seems self-explanatory and does not seem hard to break down and understand. However, the broad definition of the word *one*, is a challenge to break down. Does this mean that all the waters were in one location as one body of water, and freshwater lakes and rivers occurred over time via the natural process of evaporation from the salt water? Or does this mean that the waters were gathered alike together in place so that the freshwater was gathered together to make lakes and streams, the salt water was gathered together to make seas, and the great deep caverns of water were gathered together and stored under the surface to be released later for the Flood? Additionally, were the deep caverns of water fresh water or salt water? Let us tackle these questions.

With the vibrations that just occurred from the expansion of the universe and the instant removal of the immeasurable weight of the neighboring celestial bodies, not only did this change things in space surrounding the earth by forming our atmosphere, but within and below the crust some rapid changes occurred as well. The amount of weight caused by the proximity of all the celestial bodies in a dense universe was enough to form liquid granite by the end of the first day of creation. The sudden removal of that much weight and sudden reduction of pressure converted liquid water to gas and formed the atmosphere with saltiest water above and least saline water below. In addition, this instantly converted liquid granite to solid granite that became the bedrock to the crust.

During this time, one hypothesis is that the freshwater and saltwater was separated from each other during the first and second days of creation. More on this hypothesis later. Another hypothesis is that the entire crust of the earth expanded from the mantle and drew up freshwater from the mantle and drew in freshwater from the crust by the change in weight, pressure, and temperature of the universe expanding. The water filled vast caverns below the crust, and trapped and sealed it under the crust until it was forced out during the Gen. 7 catastrophic global flood as *the fountains of the deep*. A hypothesis about the plate movements during the Flood is that they hydroplaned on the fountains of the deep to reduce the drag/friction coefficient. Whether the hydroplaning of the tectonic plates was on literal water or on highly viscous liquid lava is immaterial because scientists have discovered that volcanic eruptions emit a large quantity of water. When volcanoes erupt, they do appear as fountains from the deep, within the earth. Since volcanoes often contain large quantities of water, it is possible that the fountains of the deep mentioned in the Flood saga were high viscous volcanoes containing water and/or literal liquid water bursting out of the earth. I suspect a little of both, but the point is that water was stored below the surface of the crust. This coincides with an Earth made from water, with water surrounding it as it coalesced matter, and this explains that it should contain water.

Utilizing the other Hebrew definitions for the word *one*, then all the waters were *unified* into place, such as the waters were gathered <u>alike</u> in place. This is to say that the fresh water was gathered together and made lakes, rivers, streams, and the deep caverns of water stored for the Flood, and the salt water was gathered <u>together </u>to form seas.

Since freshwater rivers flowed out of the Garden of Eden (Gen. 2) and split into four rivers, and since the water did not flow from melted snowpack up in the mountains as we see occurring today because the mountains were not nearly as tall as today, the water that poured out of the Garden of Eden came up from deep caverns within the earth and from a mist that rose from the ground. This also means that the water stored in the deep caverns was fresh water. This is similarly seen today around the globe, for instance in Israel, freshwater springs come out of the ground underground reservoirs. So the freshwater underground caverns we see today are potentially remnants of the "Great Deep."

Review: <u>The waters were created on the first day and separated by an expanse called the atmosphere on the second day, with waters above and below the atmosphere. The waters below the atmosphere were organized and called seas and gathered alike into place. This means that salt water was gather with its like kind and fresh water was gathered together with its like kind.</u>

How did God separate freshwater from saltwater? The waters and dirt created on the first day were not stagnant. Things were moving and shifting because of countless coalescing storms of matter rotating and thermal updrafts called convection. This means that soil and water were jostling for position. A plausible hypothesis explaining how God fashioned freshwater closer to the earth, with progressively saltier water farther away from the earth, was by **convection** and **distillation processes** during the first and second days of creation. Due to the thermal energy of the earth heating up the water that surrounded it, water would mimic a circulatory motion with hotter water rising away from Earth and cooler water sinking closer toward Earth. Since the earth was hot enough to liquefy granite rock, it was certainly hot enough to evaporate some water nearest the high heat. This is where the hypothesis resides, the saltwater nearest the high heat of the earth received enough heat to overcome the intense weight and pressure of the close celestial bodies, and evaporated. This separated freshwater from the salt via a distillation process. This means that with each passing minute, more and more freshwater built up closest to the earth, huge pure **salt deposits** grew, and the highly concentrated saltwater remained furthest away from the earth. This process repeated during the first day so that the waters were segregated, with pure freshwater being closest to the earth and the saltiest water being furthest away from the earth. Then, when the universe expanded on the second day and caused cavitation that formed our atmosphere and separated the saltiest waters above (as the canopy) from the freshest waters below. This explains why the canopy spherically surrounded the atmosphere was saltwater, and freshwater was trapped in the deep caverns below the crust, and suggests that the salinity of the seas from creation to the Flood were at a lower concentration than today. Potentially, the seas at creation were only 1% salt as compared to 3% for oceans today.

The salinity of an ocean is not uniform, take for example the Atlantic ocean, the central portion of the Atlantic ocean has a higher salinity than the coastal regions. This is because of freshwater that flows in from rivers, this is mentioned to illustrate that just because there was one body of water that surrounded the earth, does not negate the premise that there was freshwater closest to the high heat and highest salinity concentration furthest away from Earth. To elucidate the point, consider the fastest way to separate the two main components of saltwater (salt and freshwater), and that is through evaporation. The high heat generated from the earth caused significant amount of steam, this left behind granule salt in solid form and evaporated freshwater as steam. This process explains some of the larger and deeper salt deposits around the globe. The other way to separate the two components of saltwater is through freezing. The freshwater comes out of solution as ice, leaving behind granule salt in solid form. This process occurred toward the end of the Flood saga, and explains the rest of the salt deposits around the globe that have a shallower deposit. Thus, God potentially used both methods of separating salt from water, high heat during first days of creation and cold during the latter days of the Flood, both are efficient methods of separating the two components of saltwater, and producing pure salt granules in solid form and freshwater.

On the third day of creation, God separated the dirt from the waters, and it collected together to form seas, deep freshwater reservoirs, rivers, and lakes, and He made the dry land appear. One whole system of water was connected together via evaporation that formed into a mist and fed the lakes, rivers, and the deep caverns. The rivers then drained back into the seas to complete the cycle. We have a similar setup today. The waters comprise one system, separated from the land. Today, the waters are one because fresh water evaporates out of the oceans and forms clouds, and the clouds release fresh water that falls on the land and eventually drains back into the ocean. Therefore, just like today, the waters are all connected, yet we have freshwater lakes, rivers, and seas.

Since all living organisms were herbivores (Genesis 1:30–31), it was sufficient to have a smaller quantity of marine life in the seas than the vast quantity of marine life in the oceans today. Most of the water gathered together on the third day would be in the "great deep" underground. With this much water below the surface and a lot more water hovering above the atmosphere in the canopy of water, ~70%–80% of the earth was usable land for vegetation growth. That much vegetation would cause oxygen levels to rise to a concentration that caused life to thrive before the global flood.

The deep caverns of water below the surface would have fed the ground with freshwater for vegetation growth. If the great deep were salt water, there would have been no filtration process to get the salt out of the water. With the water table being so high, the land would have been inundated with salt, and that would have hindered vegetation growth. Therefore, the great deep caverns would have been filled with fresh water.

Although we are able to understand the natural processes that God used to form the waters into a particular location, concentration, and so forth, all of these natural processes are based on God's knowledge, and only because He commanded it, it was so. In other words, it is God that sustains His creation through His natural processes. It is not, by natural processes—which evolved out of nothing—that believers use to form their make believe god. God is to get all the glory due Him from His creation. Any view short of giving all credit to God alone is blasphemy.

Review: The waters below the atmosphere were gathered into one place, as in together in like kind, but connected as one. This was a combination of the deep underground caverns of freshwater, seas (salinity of ~1%), freshwater lakes, and rivers that drained water back into the seas. They were all connected together as one system; evaporation caused a mist that watered the ground. The deep caverns stored water for the Genesis flood. The distillation process of the first day, formed deep pure salt deposits around the globe, formed freshwater closest to the heat of the earth, and left highly concentrated saltwater (~3.5% salinity) to become the canopy that was formed on the second day of creation. Most of the water was stored below the surface in the great deep caverns and the canopy above the atmosphere, with potentially 70%–80% of earth's surface ready to be covered in vegetation, which would produce abundant amounts of oxygen for life to thrive.

And let the dry land appear. God called the dry land earth. When God gathered the waters into one place, this revealed land. Notice that the dry land appeared from the waters being moved around. The dirt was not created on this day; it was created on the first day. The earth was formless in the beginning, then it was forming during first, second and beginning of the third day. The shape of the earth morphed from formless to a hurricane-like storm of matter, to a sphere by the end of the second day. As God commanded, the dry land appeared and took form. Evolutionary scientists tell us that the earth was superheated liquid magma that slowly cooled over billions of years. Although, the earth was hot enough to liquefy granite, which means the earth was much hotter during creation than today, it was still covered with water. Therefore, the evolutionary model of a molten surface does not match with the Bible's description in the beginning. Other planets and moons could have had origins that included hot magma on their surface as evolutionists theorize, and that is acceptable, but not the earth—at least not near the crust where the water was hovering.

Review: The process of moving the waters to make the land appear, was the result of the change in distance from the earth to neighboring celestial bodies on the second day of creation. On the first day of creation, the dense universe and nearby celestial bodies, put a lot of weight and pressure on the soil. With the expansion of the universe (galaxies and solar systems) on the second day, and subsequent complete removal of all their weight and pressure on the soil, this allowed the soil to expand, which caused changes in topography (elevations) on Earth. As a result of land expanding to cause hills, elevations, small mountains, and so forth, the water simply flowed down to lower elevations because of the earth's gravitational force. This simple process made the land appear. A similar process is repeated today with the melting of glaciers, and the subsequent removal of weight on the soil beneath, which causes soil to rise/expand. This process is called Post-glacial rebound.

And God saw that it was good. All was good, and nothing bad existed. Such as, no death, no sin, no evil, no dead creatures from a prior era, no fossils, no oil, no coal, no petrified trees, and so forth. This seems like a transitional phrase between creative moments. The earth had rotated halfway from completing the third day, and morning was dawning on a newly formed sphere of seas and land, called Earth. This must have been such an epic, monumental moment in the realm of the Heavenly Host. Being human, I imagine the theme song from *2001: A Space Odyssey* (originally by Richard Strauss) playing as the brand new earth is revolving with form for the first time. Even though this sounds awesome in my imagination, I think it would pale in comparison to what the angels and spirits were doing when God was laying the foundation of the earth. Let us go back in time and hear from God in His own words. God was talking to Job and posed a few rhetorical questions to Job (Job 38:4–11):

> Where were you when I laid the foundation of the earth? Tell Me, if you have understanding, Who set its measurements? Since you know. Or who stretched the line on it? On what were its bases sunk? Or who laid its cornerstone, When the morning stars **sang** together and all the son of God **shouted for Joy**.

The angels sang together and shouted for joy when God was forming the earth. I grew up thinking that angels did not sing and that they only shouted. I heard this from a beloved pastor. I'm here to tell you that the Christmas carol "Hark the Herald Angels Sing" has been correct all along. Angels do sing. This

286

is overwhelming to think about the angels and the spirits singing to God as He formed the earth. Imagine the dawn of morning, as the newly formed earth rotated on the third day for the first time, with the earth illuminated by the glory of the Lord, angels, the spirits of all creatures that will ever live, and the future sun glowing red hot from magma (just one day before it ignites as a yellow sun). The Hymnal "How Great Thou Art" comes to mind:

> O Lord my God! When I in awesome wonder consider all the worlds Thy hands have made, I see the stars, I hear the rolling thunder, Thy power throughout the universe displayed. Then sings my soul, My Savior God, to Thee; How great Thou art, How great Thou Art!

The newly formed and newly designed earth, was still void of life. Not even a single one-celled organism existed—no bacteria, no fungi, not even a virus. So let us venture into the second half of the third day, which was morning, and see what else was fashioned.

Then God said, "Let the earth sprout vegetation, plants yielding seed, and fruit trees on the earth bearing fruit after their kind with seed in them'; and it was so. The earth brought forth vegetation, plants yielding seed after their kind, and trees bearing fruit with seed in them, after their kind; and God saw that it was good."

In the narrative of the creation, this was probably the middle of the day around 6 a.m. at dawn. God spoke again and created all plant life. This begins the second half of the third day. The Hebrew word for vegetation is *deshe*, which means a sprout, grass (tender), green, (tender) or herb (Strong's Conc. #1877 *deshe*). The Hebrew word for plants is *eseb*, which means an unused root, to glisten (or be green), grass (or tender shoot), or herb (Strong's Conc. #6212 *eseb*). The Hebrew word for fruit is *periy* (Strong's Conc. #6529 *periy*), which means fruit (literally or figuratively), bough, first fruit, fruitful, or reward. Coupling the Hebrew definitions together, the three things created on the third day are vegetation (grass), plants (herbs), and fruit trees.

God produced fruit trees? On first reading, one might think that fruit is merely a term for seed. Surely, trees exist today that do not produce fruit. But some evidence is given in verse 12: "trees bearing fruit with seed in them." The word *fruit* is different than the word *seed*. In Hebrew, "seed" is *zera* (Strong's Conc. # 2233), which is from the root word *zara*, which is to sow, disseminate, plant, or seed. And *zera* means seed, fruit, plant, or sowing time. Some overlap exist in the definitions, but since God combined the words "fruit with seed in them" for trees, it makes one wonder if every tree produced edible fruit with seeds in it before the fall of man. The simplest answer is that every tree produced a fruit with seed, meaning that some trees produced nuts as the fruit that were also the seed, and some trees produced fruit with seed inside of it.

Combining this with the curse at the fall in Gen. 3, mankind would have to toil to eat through tasks such as laying seed for plants, harvesting the seed of the plant, and working the seed for food, the ease of getting fruit off the trees would become more difficult. Prior to the fall, Adam walked up to any tree and grabbed a fruit (either edible seed as in the nut or edible fruit with a seed inside). If this strains your faith, consider Revelation 22:2. Life and the environment returns to a pre-fallen condition, and "The tree of life, bearing twelve kinds of fruit, yielding its fruit every month; and the leaves of the tree were for the healing of the nations." This is not what we see today, so it is tough to comprehend, but the evidence suggests that all the trees created on the third day produced fruit (either a nut or fruit), and the tree of life produced a different fruit each month. Are you thinking, "Yes, God is awesome and this is the majesty of God," or are you thinking, "Whatever—this is not possible." In the physical realm we only have partial knowledge, "we know in part" (I Corinthians 13:9), so for some things we may have to rely on faith alone, but let this ease your doubt: mankind used to doubt the ability of the virgin birth, until science caught up and discovered artificial insemination. Mankind used to mock the wisdom of circumcision on the eight day, until medical science caught up and learned that this reduces cervical cancer with the wife, reduces infections with the male, the eight day is the quickest blood clotting time versus any other day of his life, and the required cutting tool, the flint rock, the process of sharpening it by breaking off edges exposes sealed inner rock surfaces that are sterile. Therefore, just because science has not caught up to God, does not negate what God did. I agree an element of faith required, but more faith is required with evolution. Either have faith in God's Word or have faith in evolution; either way, you have to have a measure of faith.

Since the definition for *seed* (Hebrew: *zera*) means both seed and fruit, the plants yielded an edible fruit as well. Also, note that no tree at the time of creation had tree rings. They were created fully grown, just like Adam and Eve did not have a belly button.

God created the vegetation out of the ground just like He fashioned all other living things. He utilized His DNA (intelligence) so that grass, plants, and trees know how to grow, reproduce, heal, and benefit creation with food and oxygen and nutrients to the soil. Some similarities in the DNA exist with every thing on Earth because we were all initially fashioned from the dirt and made with a portion of God's essence, His DNA. As God spoke the botanical life into existence, the Holy Spirit moved and made it so. As mankind's knowledge grows, soon mankind will discover how God fashioned the vegetation from the soil and gave some of His DNA for life. After all, we just discovered that living things have DNA just recently and now we can splice genes and remove mutated DNA to help life thrive, and clone.

When scientists look for intelligent life in space, they look for patterns. The most rudimentary signs that indicate intelligent life exists in the unknown are straight lines and geometric shapes, as they indicate some type of designed order or intelligence and not randomness of chance. God created the atmosphere, land, and waters as one set of three. Then He filled them with grasses, plants, and trees as another set of three. Then He created birds of the air, fishes of the waters, and creatures of the land as another set of three. Three heavens were created, the Throne of God, the universe, and the atmosphere. Then He created mankind in His image with body, soul (thought and desire), and spirit. Also, the one God has three aspects, the Father, Son, and Holy Spirit. This is good evidence of a pattern and order and that intelligent life created all this, not chance.

This is why Romans 1:18–32 renders all life on earth without excuse for rejecting God. It says, "That which is known about God is evident within them; for God made it evident to them. For since the creation of the world His invisible attributes, His eternal power and divine nature, have been clearly seen, being understood through what has been made, so that they are without excuse."

When people are embarrassed and ashamed to accept and proclaim God's Word because of man's evolutionary tale, so that they reject a major portion of God's Word—creation, Jesus says this: "Whoever is ashamed of Me and My words, the Son of Man will be ashamed of him when He comes in His glory, and of the Father and of the holy angels."

Review: God created grass, plants that yielded a seed/fruit, and fruit trees that yielded fruit with seeds in them. God created everything with a design, and this design is self-evidence of God. Human beings who reject creation are rejecting the Word of God—Jesus (John 1:1–14).

After their kind. This phrase is repeated twice on this day, and repeated frequently on days five and six as well. The number of types (species) of each kind of the three categories is unknown. Mankind is still discovering new plants and trees today, so it is safe to say that there were thousands of different types of each kind of vegetation. We can also say the same about the birds, fish, and animals created on the fifth day. With the diversity of the shapes and sizes of the different moons, planets, and stars that were formed, it is safe to say that the three botanical categories of each kind had a myriad of variations (species).

This is the first mention of this important word, **kind**, in the Bible. The Hebrew word for *kind* is *miyn*, and the definition is to portion out, a sort, or a kind. The root word is *min*, which means part of, from, out of, or after. Thousands of species of dog exist, yet they are the same kind of creature. From the wolf to the Maltese pup, from the Great Dane to the poodle, though they are different species, they are the same kind. Do not let the word *species* throw you for a loop, as it is a classification word invented by man to categorize creatures. Yet, scientists do not know where to put every creature; the categories overlap with many shades of gray when defining which creatures go into which species. To help wrap your mind around the word *kind*, look at humanity. We reproduce after our own kind, just like every creature and every botanical life form reproduces after their kind. Mankind was created in the image and likeness of God. This means in the physical shape/form of God, internally and externally and in personality, characteristics of mind, and thought. One way to categorize animals by kind would be based on their physical features (internal and external) and their behaviors, thoughts, and social characteristics.

This word *kind* is a deal breaker that should prevent people from believing in evolution. Once someone reads the Genesis account of creation and gets to this word, *kind*, one cannot get around the idea that this word nullifies evolution. The Bible explicitly says that each thing on earth will produce after its kind. Biology and medical science confirms that no crossbreeding of kinds and no changing of kinds occur, ever. Though evolutionary biologists and evolutionary medical scientists will faithfully tell you that millions of years ago, such and such evolved into such and such. To still reject this line drawn in the sand by God and still say, "well, given enough time, life evolves into different kinds of creatures," is to be intellectually dishonest. One is fooling themselves thinking they are loving God and being obedient to God and saying to God, "Your Word is in error; changes exist of kind given enough time." Do not confuse the broader God-given term of *kind*, with the narrower man-made term *species*.

It is an axiom that vegetation cannot read, so it is logical that God put the phrase, *Then God said, "Let the earth sprout vegetation, plants yielding seed, and fruit trees on the earth bearing fruit after their kind,"* not for vegetation to read or hear, but for mankind. Since God does not increase in knowledge, you know God knew that mankind would believe in evolution. This is why God put these specific words in the Genesis account to make each person that chooses to believe in evolution to be without excuse. It should be noted that Darwinian evolution was not the first time mankind deviated away from God's account of creation. Jeremiah 2:27–28 says,"Who say to a tree, 'You are my father', and to a stone, 'You gave me birth.' For they have turned their back to Me and not their face." When tracing back all life on earth through the lens of evolution, it starts off with water raining on the rocks and a complex chemical mixture of amino acids from the rocks eventually evolving into the first self-replicating single-cell organism. Therefore, the forefather of life with evolution are the rocks and dirt. The Israelites believed that they were children of God and some added to that doctrine by believing they were the offspring of rocks and trees. Look at how God viewed their beliefs: "They have turned their back to Me and not their face." God declares that they fully rejected God. Look what happens later on in the verse: "In the time of their trouble they will say, 'Arise and save us.', and God says, "But where are your gods which you made for yourself? Let them arise, if they can save you in the time of your trouble." They were worshiping God in error, which is equal to worshiping a false god. Their judgment came swift and fierce by the mighty hand of God through the Babylonian empire. Do not hold onto evolution and repeat the same fate.

The seeds produced from each kind is to produce more of the same kind. This is embedded in the DNA code, and the type of kind embedded in the DNA code is never altered. Even with artificial selection of a horticulturist growing multiple species of roses and cross-pollinating of species, the results may be different colored roses, with different petals, or different growing patterns, but the end result is always roses. This is because the *kind* in the DNA never changes. Do not confuse adaptation (changes within a kind), which is the epigenome turning DNA switches on or off, with evolution (changes to form different kinds).

Even when a farmer uses the grafting technique, which is to take a foreign vine/branch and graft that foreign vine/branch into a different "kind" of plant/tree, the wild branch will still remain the same "kind," even though it is drawing nutrients from an entirely different "kind" of plant/tree. That is because the DNA will always provide the information for only the same "kind."

Review: *After their kind* is a defining phrase. Here, God draws the line in the sand and says, "There is no crossbreeding of kinds, and each kind will remain the same kind forever." To reject God's

Word and still hold the opinion that *kinds* evolve to other *kinds,* given enough time, you have turned your back on God, and the same fate awaits you as those of Jeremiah 2:27–28.

Even today, after many millennia, only three kinds of botanical life exist: grasses, plants, and trees. Even after millennia of changes in the environment, diseases, insects, floods, droughts, earthquakes, cosmic rays hurricanes, tornadoes, lightning, fire, and so forth, only three categories exist today as in Genesis. There may be different species (types within the same kind) of grasses, plants, and trees, but they are still the same kinds. Again, the Bible is in direct conflict with the theories of man. God inspired Moses to describe three kinds of botanical life from the beginning, and it is still this way today.

It has always been true that a certain kind of plant will only produce seeds for the same kind of plant. Trees will only produce seeds that grow into the same kind of tree. Grass will only produce seeds or grow offshoots that are always the same kind of grass. Though thousands of kinds of plants exist, with each kind having thousands of variations (species), they all only produce seeds that grow into the same ancestral kind of plant. The same with the grass and trees. Although changes occur within the variations (species), absolutely zero changes occur in the kind or crossbreeding into different kinds. Strawberries will always produce strawberries, pine trees will always produce pine cones that grow into pine trees, and so on. Mankind can selectively breed watermelons to eventually produce seedless watermelons, but that only proves intelligent design—it took intelligence to do that, and the ability of the fruit to adapt was already encoded in the DNA.

Evolutionists suggest that all botanical life came from a single-cell organism and evolved to the complexities of today. The Bible says that God created all vegetation on the third day. Both cannot be right. Yet we see today that grasses, plants and trees are able to adapt to changes. Isn't this proof of evolution? No. Why? Because limits exist to their ability to adapt that are set by the DNA code. When they do adapt, it is because they already have the DNA code that gives them the ability to adapt, and the adaptation occurs in the epigenome. Though they adapt and mankind can call them a different species, they are still the same kind. The word *kind* is set by God. He set boundaries on botanical life's ability to adapt and how far it can change by information already in the DNA code. Plants have to remain the same kind; it is impossible to change kind because it is not in the DNA code to do so—the receptor sites for fertilization are kind specific. For example, we will never observe an oak tree naturally produce strawberries from an adapted or evolved DNA. This is observable evidence that kinds always remain the same. Why cannot an oak tree produce strawberries? Because that would violate God's decree, *bearing fruit after their kind*. This decree by God is sealed in the DNA code. Even the botanical kingdom is obedient to God's Word. We will never see in the fossil records any plant in transition to become anything other than the same kind. Why? Because God's decree, *bearing fruit after their kind*, is unchangeable. God's decree is sealed in the DNA code so that each kind will remain the same kind.

Evolutionists argue that you're not going to see any transitional kinds today because those transitional kinds occurred hundreds of millions of years ago. However, since evolution is based on random, unguided changes to the DNA code, there would have to be millions of transitional kinds still ongoing—not 100% of grass being 100% grass, and 100% plants being 100% plants, and 100% humans being 100% humans, and so forth. Furthermore, since evolutionists theorize that creatures and botanical life evolved from the same self-replicating organism, we would expect to see some creatures currently using photosynthesis, which is the conversion of the sun's light into energy. After all, that is an efficient way to get fuel to function. To allegedly lose that ability is a loss of information, not a gain. No observable evidence exist of mutations adding information to the DNA code for a new function or new kind or enhancing the DNA code for new function or new kind; mutations always degrade the DNA code, not enhance.

All the examples that evolutionists use to support evolution, such as new bacterial species, new finch species, or different cat species, are flawed. When it is all said and done, bacteria are still bacteria, dogs are still dogs, and cats are still cats. The ability to adapt and modify external features is based on DNA code that already exists within them and occurs as a result of the epigenome. Mutations of DNA code do not cause adaptation, new functions, or new kinds of creatures, it degrades code.

Review: All botanical life forms reproduce after their kind. This in obedience to God's Word. It is observable all around the world every day as a testimony that when God said, "bearing fruit after their kind," it is law. Believing that life can evolve into different kinds, given enough time, is going against the law of God.

Not only was mankind cursed from sin, but so too was all of creation. Romans 8:20:

> For the creation was subjected to futility, not willingly, but because of Him who subjected it, in hope that the creation itself also will be set free from its slavery to corruption into the freedom of the glory of the children of God. For we know that the whole creation groans and suffers the pains of childbirth together until now.

From the curse of Gen. 3, the whole of creation was subjected to the curse of sin, which is death. From the Flood of Noah's time, we have the resultant four seasons that represent this groaning for the coming of the Lord to restore creation back to the Garden of Eden status. The groaning is death (fall), burial (winter), resurrection/birth (spring), and life (summer).

God will restore all of creation to a pre-fallen state. Some vegetation today is not edible, but were all things edible at the time of Adam and Eve? We learned that at the fall of mankind in Gen. 3, which is the origin of thistle, thorns, weeds, and the like, the ground becomes cursed. Mankind is to toil, through sorrow and hard work, to eat of the land. By the sweat of your face you will eat bread (Gen. 3:17–18). This means that prior to the fall, no thistles, thorns, weeds, and the like existed, and it was easy for mankind to find food—as if the land was on autopilot, and food was everywhere. But back to the question—were grasses, plants with seeds, and fruit from trees all edible for humans? Remember the scene in the movie *Willie Wonka and the Chocolate Factory*, when the contestants entered a room where everything was edible? Is that what Adam and Eve had? No, but let us turn to Scripture for clarification. Gen. 1:29–30: "Then God said, (to Adam and Eve), Behold, I have given you every plant yielding seed that is on the surface of all the earth, and every tree which has fruit yielding seed; it shall be food for you." Two out of the three categories were edible. The seeds from plants and the fruit from trees were edible, but not the grass. Continuing on with the verse, we learn something else: "And to every beast of the earth and to every bird of the sky and to every thing that moves on the earth which has life, I have given every green plant for food." However, no restriction existed for birds and everything that moves on the earth in terms of what they may eat. For they may eat any of the three categories: grass, plant-yielding seeds, and/or fruit trees. All three categories were summed up with *every green plant*.

At this point, no sin and no death exist in creation. This means that mankind, birds, and everything that moved on the earth could not eat other life forms. Before the fall of mankind, no carnivores (meat eaters) and no omnivores (meat and vegetation eaters) existed; only herbivores. That means that even mighty T. rex, one of the fiercest creatures on the planet, was an herbivore before the fall.

Review: Mankind was allowed to eat the seeds and fruit of plants and trees. All other creatures were allowed to eat any vegetation. All creation became cursed from the fall of Adam.

Is there a contradiction in the Bible because death did not occur prior to the sin of Adam and Eve, yet all animals, fish, birds, and humans ate vegetation? No. Vegetation does not have the breath of life in it. They do not have the blood that carries life (oxygen). Lev. 17:11: "For the life of the flesh is in the blood." By the way, the Bible has zero contradiction. If you think there might be one, it is because the interpretation is off. I have had many fun debates with atheists through the decades, and I always ask them to give me their best evidence of a contradiction in the Bible, and always their best allegation turned out to be amazing evidence of the divine nature of the Bible.

Was food plentiful enough that mankind did not have to work hard to find food? Yes and No.

Plenty of food existed, but humans still worked. How do we know this? Gen. 2:7–15:

> Then the LORD God formed man of dust from the ground, and breathed into his nostrils the breath of life; and man became a living being. The LORD God planted a garden toward the east, in Eden; and there He placed the man whom He had formed. Out of the ground the LORD God caused to grow <u>every tree that is pleasing to the sight and good for food</u> . . . Then the LORD God took the man and put him into the garden of Eden <u>to cultivate it and keep it.</u>

The phrase *to cultivate it and keep it* suggests work. Also, 2 Thessalonians 3:6–15 makes it clear that "if anyone is not willing to work, then he is not to eat, either." Paul explains that someone who has idle hands and is unwilling to work is sinning.

So how do we harmonize the notions that food was everywhere, with each tree producing tons of fruit, and yet man had to cultivate it and keep it? Well, this is hard to imagine because we only know our world with sin, thistles, weeds, disease, and so on. Maybe the cultivation involved pruning unwanted growth to encourage the growth desired. For example, an arborist/horticulturist cuts the lower branches of a tree to allow walkways and pleasant views through the tree lines, and they chop down trees that they do not want growing in their garden to allow the desired trees to flourish. Also, if the brush is not cultivated or cut, then land becomes impassable, so I'm sure Adam had to trim a lot of brush to allow walkways to and fro. Also, one would pick up the fallen fruit from a tree to prevent hordes of ants from invading their garden. Enough cultivating work was required for Adam and Eve to keep them busy in the Garden of Eden.

Review: <u>Vegetation was abundantly plentiful and good, and yes Adam and Eve had to cultivate and keep the Garden of Eden.</u>

How much vegetation did God produce on the third day? Well, since oceans, deserts, and polar ice caps did not exist until the Flood. Then vast amounts of land was usable for vegetation growth.

Today the surface of the earth is made up of 70% water, 10% deserts and ice, and 20% usable land. At the time of the Garden of Eden and up until the Flood, the surface of the earth was probably 20%–30% water, and the remaining 70%–80% was usable land covered with vegetation that produced vast amounts of oxygen. With that much vegetation, oxygen concentration was ~55% higher, which is corroborated with glacial core samples and amber samples. The increased oxygen would have caused living beings to live longer with accelerated growth and healing. See the chapters: Oxygen Concentration and Land Was More Plentiful in the Past.

Note that while the Genesis creation narrative explains from the perspective of Earth, God was also separating the waters into one place from the dirt of all the other celestial bodies that had water encompassing them. The same natural processes that shaped Earth were shaping each planet and moon.

There was evening and there was morning, a third day. The Holy Spirit moves on Moses to write this repetitive phrase to drive home the point—this is one rotation of the earth.

Chapter Summary: On the third day, God finished shaping the earth and gathered the waters together to form saltwater seas, freshwater lakes and rivers, and deep underground caverns of freshwater and made the land appear. A mist rose from the ground to water the whole Earth. Probably 70%–80% of the earth's surface was usable land. Then God created grasses, plants that yielded seeds, and fruit trees to cover the land. So plentiful was the vegetation that oxygen levels were 50% higher than today's levels.

Chapter 35
The Fourth Day

Gen. 1:14–19: *Then God said, 'Let there be lights in the expanse of the heavens to separate the day from the night, and let them be for signs and for seasons and for days and years . . . and let them be for lights in the expanse of the heavens to give light on the earth'; and it was so. God made the two great lights, the greater light to govern the day, and the lesser light to govern the night; He made the stars also. God placed them in the expanse of the heavens to give light on the earth, and to govern the day and the night, and to separate the light from the darkness; and God saw that it was good. There was evening and there was morning, a fourth day.*

Then God said, "Let there be lights in the expanse of the heavens." The Hebrew word for "lights" is different than the "light" used on the first day of creation. The Hebrew word for "light" (as on the first day of creation) is *ore* and means illumination, luminary, or luminous (Strong's Conc. #216 *ore*). The Hebrew word for "lights" (as on the fourth day of creation) is *maw-ore* and means luminous <u>body</u> (Strong's Conc. #3974 *maw-ore*). Indicating that the light on the first day was different than the luminous bodies on the fourth day. The light from the first day was from the angels, the spirits of all future living mortals, and the hot glow from liquid metals, magma and plasma of burgeoning stars. The light from the fourth day was from ignited stars, and from planets and moons that reflect starlight.

The definite article in *let there be lights in **the** expanse* reveals that the universe was already there, already stretched out, already waiting to have the sun, moon, and stars finish forming.

It seems that God timed the creation of the stars to coincide with them having coalesced enough mass to ignite during the first half of the fourth day. Also, a similar notion with the planets during the fourth day. However, it seems fair that the stars and planets still coalesced additional mass during their first initial years, as they absorbed other wandering asteroids. Scientists call this period the late heavy bombardment. The creation of the sun and moon was at the middle of the fourth day. But it is not an important point as to the exact hour each was formed.

<u>**Review:** The creation of celestial bodies occurred on the fourth day of creation in the already-existing, expanded, and expanding universe. The lights on the fourth day are from stars coalescing enough matter, density, and gravity to ignite as stars. The light on the first day are from burgeoning future galaxies and stars that had coalesced enough matter to glow hot.</u>

To separate the day from the night. This seems straightforward. The sun, moon, and stars give distinction to the day and night and thereby separate the day from the night.

*Let them be for **signs** and for seasons and for days and years.* The overall theme is the manifestation of time, that was created on the first day, to all future living creatures. But let us work on the word *signs* first for more clarity.

The Hebrew word for signs is *owth* (Strong's Conc. #226), which means in the sense of appearing, a signal as a flag, beacon, monument, omen, or evidence. So *signs* is acting as a signal for coming prophetic events, as in signs in the heavens. But it also can be seen as a beacon for navigation and as a monument to the glory of God by His creative majesty. God is saying let them (planets, moons, and stars) be beacons for navigation, an omen of prophetic events, a flag for direction, and a monument dedicated to honor, worship, and glorify God. Psalm 19:1–4 sums up this notion:

> The heavens are telling of the glory of God; and their expanse is declaring the work of His hands. Day to day pours forth speech, and night to night reveals knowledge. There is no speech, nor are there words; their voice is not heard. Their line has gone out through all the earth, and their utterances to the end of the world.

The sun, moon, and stars cry out every second, "Glory to God," and everyone metaphorically hears their speech. When people reject God, they are without excuse from His judgment. His invisible attributes, His eternal power and divine nature are clearly seen by all every day (Romans 1:18–20).

Matthew 2 records the wise men from the East saw His star and knew that the Messiah was born. Since the wise men of God were Magi (astronomers from Babylon), they would have read the prophecy of Daniel 9:25, which foretold that the Messiah would come 476 years from the decree to rebuild the temple and the wall. The decree to rebuild the temple and the wall in Nehemiah's day (Nehemiah 2:1-8) from King Artaxerxes was fulfilled exactly to the day when Jesus rode into Jerusalem on a donkey that had never been ridden. The Magi would have studied the Biblical law that said that the high priest started their ministry at the age of 30 (Numbers 4:3); thus, by combining this information and studying the heavens, they discerned the date when the time was near for the Messiah to be born. They were looking up to the heavens for the "signs" and saw it with a comet/star. Many theologians interpret today's current events as new signs that the Messiah is coming soon—such as four sequential blood moons (Joel 2:31) on spring Passover 2014, fall Feast of Trumpets 2014, spring Passover 2015, and fall Feast of Trumpets 2015, with a solar eclipse in the middle. Also, within the lifetime of one generation (Matthew 24:34) many fulfilled prophesies pertain to the second coming of the Messiah, such as Israel becoming a nation (1948), Israel capturing Jerusalem (1967) (Joel 3:1), Jews from around the world gathering back into Israel (Joel 3:2), Israel again flowing with milk and honey (Exodus 3:8)[189], Turkey building damns on the Tigris and Euphrates rivers (Turkey will be able to stop water from flowing and dry up both rivers) (Rev. 16:12), China boasting that they have a 200-million-man army at the ready that potentially could fulfill Revelation 9:16, knowledge increasing (Dan12:9), and so forth. Christ said that when you start to see these signs, know that the time is near, and that generation in which these signs start won't pass till you see the Messiah. A generation is not only from a parent to a child, but also the length of life for a group of people born during a specific time. We call those people the baby boomers. They may be the ones to see the coming of the Messiah.

Review: *Sign can mean a beacon for navigation, an omen of prophetic events, a flag for direction, and a monument dedicated to honor, worship, and glorify God.*

*Let them be for signs and for **seasons** and for days and years.* The Hebrew word for *seasons* is *mowadah* (Strong's Conc. #4150), which means appointment, festival, or assembly for a feast or synagogue. This is not spring/summer/fall/winter as we know seasons today. The first mention of winter was not until after the Flood in Gen. 8:22. Before the Flood, the four seasons did not exist. What? Let us look at Romans 8:18:

> For I consider that the sufferings of this present time are not worthy to be compared with the glory that is to be revealed to us. For the anxious longing of the creation waits eagerly for the revealing of the sons of God. For the creation was subjected to futility, not willingly, but because of Him who subjected it, in hope that the creation itself also will be set free from its slavery to corruption into the freedom of the glory of the children of God. For we know that the whole creation groans and suffers the pains of childbirth together until now.

How and Why is there suffering, groaning and pain? Because of Sin and the result of sin on creation—death. All of creation goes through a symbolic death (fall), burial (winter), resurrection (spring), and life (summer) each year. Before mankind sinned, death, autumn, or winter did not exist. The fall came with the first sin of Adam, and the consequences of sin were not fully manifested until the advent of the global flood. Physically, what changed to initiate the four seasons was the loss of the canopy of water that surrounded the atmosphere, and multiple asteroids impacting the Earth to initiate the Flood, which altered the Earth's tilt. Before that, it was spring all the time. After the canopy was lost to cause the Flood, the four seasons commenced.

Since *Seasons* means appointment, festival, or assembly for a feast or synagogue. Then, the sun and moon are for telling humans the appropriate time for festivals, the appointed time for assembling

---

189 Israeli cows are the world leaders of dairy production per cow. algemeiner.com/2014/03/11/the-land-of-milk-israels-super-cows-are-the-worlds-most-productive-video/.

for a feast, and the appointed time for humans to worship God and give glory to God. The Jewish feasts are all symbols that point to Jesus the Christ, the Son of God, and God also establishes the means of worshiping God the Father, and that is through God the Son, through Jesus the Christ, the Messiah, who is God in the flesh. It is amazing how the means and mode of salvation have never changed from the first day of creation to today. The New Testament does not usher in a new or different method of salvation; on the contrary, the New Testament affirms the Old Testament and gives more details to the Old Testament. That's why gentile believers that only read the New Testament are getting half of the information, and Jews that only read the Old Testament are only getting half of the information. Jesus summed up the necessity to read all the Bible when He said, "I AM the beginning and the end, the first and the last." Jesus is in the first verse of Genesis, Jesus is in the last verse in Malachi, Jesus is in the first verse of Matthew, and Jesus is in the last verse of Revelation.

Sabbath: An appointed time set as a holy convocation (ceremonial assembly). Six days work may be done, but the seventh day is the sabbath, a day of complete rest (Lev. 23:1–3). It is a sabbath to the LORD; Exodus 31:12 says "that you may know that I AM the LORD who sanctifies you." Having a day that solely honors the LORD with all one's actions, thoughts, and intentions separates one from the lust of the world. This is called Sanctification, and it represents separation for the service of God. Hebrew 10:10–14 clarifies that we have been separated from the sin of the world "by this [Christ's sacrifice] will we have been sanctified through the offering of the body of Jesus Christ once for all . . . For by one offering He has perfected for all time those who are sanctified." Therefore, as the Sabbath is to sanctify the Jews, it is a symbol pointing to Christ's perfect work on the cross. The Sabbath is to honor Christ as the one who sanctifies us for the Father and to glorify Christ as co-creator. This is why it was not a violation for Jesus to heal on His Sabbath day; it is a day to honor Him and His creative work. What better way for Him to accept the glory of His Sabbath and honor His Father than to heal His inheritance (His people) and sanctify them with miracles of forgiveness and healing.

Do Christians celebrate the Sabbath? Exodus 31:16–17 says that "the sons of Israel shall observe the sabbath . . . throughout their generations as a perpetual covenant. It is a sign between Me and the sons of Israel forever." Romans 14:5–6: "One person regards one day above another, and another regards every day alike. Each person must be fully convinced in his own mind. He who observes the day, observes it for the Lord." Of the Ten Commandments, the one related to the Sabbath is the only one not affirmed and repeated in the New Testament. Christians celebrate the Lord's day on Sunday because Jesus rose from the grave on Sunday, but Jews should still observe the Sabbath because it is a permanent command for Israel. However, Jesus is the fulfillment of the Sabbath, as Christians are sanctified and set apart for God the Father to honor God through Jesus. In everything we do, even the basic things of life, such as eating and drinking, Christians are to do everything unto the Lord. As a result of Christ's work on the cross, believers have rest from sin eternally. Therefore, as the Sabbath is to remind Jews that "I AM the LORD who sanctifies you," Christians observe that Jesus is the *LORD who sanctifies them*. Therefore, Christians are daily observing the Sabbath; that is why each day can be holy for Christians.

Let us work on the Feasts: Passover, Unleavened Bread, First Fruits, Pentecost, Trumpets, Day of Atonement, and Booths (Tabernacles or Ingathering).

Passover: The full moon of Nisan 14, March to April (Exodus 12:1–4). Passover reminds humans of God's deliverance of the Jews out of bondage of slavery to Egyptians by killing all the first born of all that lived that did not have the blood of the lamb. Jesus, with title of the first born[190] of God (Colossians 1:15), is the sacrificial lamb that delivers all of humanity out of bondage of sin (Rev 5:12).

So why do not Christians celebrate the Passover on Nisan 14? Christians do celebrate Passover; it is called "Good Friday," the day Jesus was the sacrificial blameless lamb and died on the cross.

---

190 This is not physically born, for Adam is the first human begotten by God (Luke 3:38). The title refers to the rightful heir, just like Kind David was the eighth born of Jesse, but held the title of "First born" (Psalm 89:27). Similarly, Jesus, born of Mary, was not the first begotten from the Father, holds the rightful title of "First Born" of the Father.

Unfortunately, Christians no longer go by the solar-lunar calendar; thus, they set themselves up to miss some of the significance of the signs. It would be more meaningful if Christians remembered Jesus' crucifixion as the complete and final sacrificial lamb on Nisan 14, on the same day as Israel remembers Passover.

Unleavened Bread: The week of the full moon of Nisan 15–21, March–April (Exodus 12:15–20). For one week, the Jews ate unleavened bread as a memorial of the blameless blood of the lamb that saved them from death and a symbol of separating from sin. Jesus is the bread of life (John 6:35) that was without sin (2 Corinthians 5:21), and He said while breaking the unleavened bread on the Passover, "Take, eat; this is My body" (Matthew 26:26). The symbol of the unleavened bread points to Jesus.

First Fruits: The first fruits of the harvest from Passover start on Nisan 16, March/April (Lev 23:9–14). The Jews gave their first fruits of the harvest as an offering to God to symbolize that their thoughts and actions were first toward God. Likewise, for Christians, "We ourselves, having the first fruits of the Spirit" (Rom 8:23) "will practice . . . the fruit of the Spirit is love, joy, peace, patience, kindness, goodness faithfulness, gentleness, self-control" (Gal 5:22). For this reason, Christ is the embodiment and fulfillment of all those fruits, and "Christ has been raised form the dead, the first fruits of those who are asleep." The feast of First Fruits points to Jesus the Christ, the Son of God, who is the physical image of the invisible God the Father. Christians celebrate First Fruits with Christ's resurrection (Easter). Unfortunately, the ubiquitous word Easter is a pagan word that stems back to the days of original Babylon, with Queen Semiramis, the wife of King Nimrod, who was the grandson of Noah. Queen Semiramis declared herself to be the god of fertility and rebirth and the queen of heaven (Jeremiah 44:17); her worshipers passed eggs and called them Semiramis eggs, but her Hebrew name was Ishtar (pronounced Easter), so the Jews passed around Ishtar eggs. Through dialect changes, Ishtar eggs became Easter eggs.[191] Unfortunately, churches use *Easter* in error; it is not in the Bible to denote celebrating the holiest day of the year with her name. It should be called Passover (I Cor. 5:7), the day Jesus rose from the grave.

Pentecost: Fifty days after Passover, God requires a gathering of the people to observe the feast of the harvest of the first fruits of their labors (Ex. 23:16). Ex. 34:22 says that "you shall celebrate the feast of weeks, that is, the first fruits of the wheat harvest." This is one reason a dual term exist for this feast, and it comes from honoring God for the first fruits of the wheat harvest from Deut. 16:9–12: "Count seven weeks . . . then celebrate the feast of weeks . . . remember that you were a slave in Egypt." After seven weeks (49 days), the celebration of the first fruits is held on the 50th day (in Latin, p*enta* means 50). Jesus died on Passover, and was in the abyss for three days (Matthew 12:40, Ephesians 4:9–10, and 1 Peter 3:19). After His resurrection, He remained on the earth for forty days (Acts 1:3), then seven days later, for a total of fifty days after Passover, we read in Acts 2:1: "When the day of Pentecost had come, they were all together in one place and suddenly there came from heaven a noise like a violent rushing wind . . . and they were filled with the Holy Spirit." This is why this feast is called the Feast of Weeks, Feast of Harvest, and Pentecost. This also commemorated the exodus from Egyptian slavery and gratitude for God's provision. This feast was also a symbol of the spiritual fruits from the Holy Spirit.

Trumpets (Rosh Hashanah): Another feast occurs on the first day of the seventh month of the year, upon the full moon, "a holy convocation, no labor, a day of blowing trumpets . . . an offering of fire to the LORD" (Numbers 29:1–6 and Lev. 23:23–25). The keys are the seventh month, blowing trumpets, and fire. In Numbers 10:9, Israel is told to blow trumpets "when you go to war . . . against the adversary who attacks you, then you shall sound an alarm with the trumpets, that you may be remembered before the LORD your God, and be saved from your enemies." The first battle of capturing the promised land involved Jericho, when the ram horn was blown (Joshua 6:2–6). This is why Israel today has a Shofar (ram horn to blow trumpets) with the high priest. Well, for Christians

---

191 Christiananswere.net/ "Where-did-Easter-get-its-name?"

today, 1 Corinthians 15:52 says that "in the twinkling of an eye, at the last trumpet; for the trumpet will sound, and the dead will be raised imperishable and we will be changed. For this perishable must put on the imperishable, and this mortal must put on immortality." Also, the seven trumpets of Revelation point to judgment by fire. This points to the triumphant return of Christ and judgment by the fire of Revelation. This leads me to think that the start and end of Revelation's seals, trumpets, and bowls will be at the full moon of the seventh month of the Hebrew lunar calendar. The trumpets in the Old Testament point to Jesus physically leading His host of angels (Joshua 5:13–15 and Joshua 24 give a summary) and leading Israel to the promised land, and the trumpets in the New Testament point to Jesus physically leading His host of angels and leading believers to the promise land, some to heaven and some to the new Jerusalem. Both the Old and New Testament trumpets point to Jesus.

Day of Atonement (Yom Kippur): On the tenth day of the seventh month is a day of atonement and holy convocation (ceremonial assembly) for humbling your soul and presenting an offering by fire to the LORD (Lev. 23:27). This is recognition to God for forgiving and cleansing of sin, specifically for priests and then the nation and tabernacle (Lev. 16:1–34). The system of a sinful priest making sacrifices on behalf of the people bordered on hypocrisy; therefore, the priests had to be cleansed of sin and have the penalty of their sins paid for as well. A bull was sacrificed on the Day of Atonement to symbolize a payment for the sins of the priest. This is where Christ comes in, as He was/is the only high priest that was/is sinless and did not need a bull to be sacrificed on His behalf to pay for His sins. This is why Jesus was/is described as being in the order of Melchizedek (means Righteous King), the high priest of Salem (mean Jerusalem)(Genesis14:18–20), a sinless priest who did not need a sacrifice for His sins and a priest forever. He was not in the order of Aaron or Levite priests who were sinful and required a bull sacrifice to pay for their sins (Psalm 110:4 and Hebrews 7:17–24). Melchizedek is another name for Jesus, as suggested in Hebrews 7:1–3:

> For this Melchizedek, king of Salem [Jerusalem], Priest of the Most High God, who met Abraham as he was returning from the slaughter of the kings and blessed him, to whom also Abraham apportioned a tenth part of all, was first of all, by the translation of his name, King of Righteousness, and then also King of Salem, which is King of Peace. Without father, without mother, without genealogy, having neither beginning of days nor end of life [meaning Melchizedek is eternal], but made like the Son of God, He remains a priest perpetually.

Look at all the titles of Jesus in those verses. The feast of Atonement may be looked at as the feast of being "At-One" with God, which is synonymous with reconciled. Colossians 2:21–22: "Although you were formerly alienated and hostile in mind, in evil deeds, yet He has now reconciled you in His fleshly body through death [cross], to present you before Him holy and blameless and beyond reproach." This reveals that the Feast of Atonement points to Jesus. It is Jesus' death on the cross that reconciles us to God the Father through Jesus and atones for our sins. Look at 2 Corinthians 5:18–20:

> Now all things are from God, who reconciled us to Himself through Christ and gave us the ministry of reconciliation . . . Therefore, we are ambassadors for Christ, as though God were making an appeal through us.

Believers are the physical representatives of Jesus and the message of reconciliation, of being "At One with God" or atonement. Believers are the priests, the ambassadors to share the Word of reconciliation, which is the message of how to restore the relationship between God and man. Therefore, the Feast of Atonement points to Jesus, as the blood shed on this day of the feast is a symbol of Jesus' blood that was shed on the cross and that atones for the sins of the world.

Booths (Tabernacles or Ingathering) (Nehemiah 8:1–9:38): On the first day of the seventh month and for seven days, all Israel gathered together and lived in individual family (hastily built) huts to remember the 40 years of sojourning in the desert after their exodus from Egypt. During the seven days, the high priest reads and explains (Neh 8:7) the law for six hours, and the people respond with confession, mourning, and worship for six hours (Neh 9:3). Later, after Israel resided in the promised land, the name was more associated with the fall harvest and was called the Feast of Ingathering. During this feast, though the people tend to mourn from conviction from the reading of the Law, they celebrate God's provision (Deut 16:14 and Neh 8:9). The keys to this feast are what God provided during the 40 years, manna from heaven, water to quench their thirst in the desert, and the light of fire by night that guided them. The symbol of the law being read for six hours with Christ hanging six hours on the cross, and potentially the people mourning for six hours after the reading being associated with six thousand years of mourning that sin reigns on earth, and Jesus is the fulfillment of the Law (Matthew 5:17), the Word of God (John 1:1–14).

Jesus declared that the manna that came down from heaven to feed the Jews for 40 years was a symbol of Him in John 6:51: "I AM the living bread that came down out of heaven; if anyone eats of this bread, he will live forever; and the bread also which I will give for the life of the world is My flesh." The manna from heaven was a symbol pointing to Jesus. Also, to remind Israel of the Light of God that lead them out of Egypt with a pillar of fire, they were to light a Menorah every evening till morning to remind them of God (Lev. 24:1–4). In the early dawn of the morning (John 8:1), while the priests were extinguishing the light from the Menorah in the Temple, Jesus said (John 8:12), "I AM the Light of the world, he who follows Me will not walk in the darkness, but will have the Light of life." The pillar of fire by night was a manifestation of Jesus, but only a foreshadowing of what Jesus is. When the Father and Lamb dwell in Jerusalem, Revelation 21:22–25 says, "The city has no need of the sun or of the moon to shine on it, for the glory of God has illumined it, and its lamp is the Lamb. The nations will walk by its light." As Israel walked by the Light of Jesus via a pillar of fire, the nations will walk by the Light of Jesus at the end of days.

As much as the Feast of Booths/Tabernacle/Ingathering point to Jesus, they are all part and parcel to the final harvest, the final Ingathering for His second coming.

Horoscopes, sorcery, mediums, fortunetellers, seances, and palm readers: Deut. 18:10–14 says:

You shall not imitate the detestable things of those nations. There shall not be found among you anyone who makes his son or his daughter pass though the fire, one who uses divination, one who practices witchcraft, or one who interprets omens, or a sorcerer, or one who casts a spell, or a medium or a spiritist or one who calls up the dead. For whoever does these things is detestable to the LORD.

Do NOT communicate with the dead or with spirits or sacrifice your baby (abortion) to any god, even to a god of freedom. Do NOT look to the arbitrary alignment of the stars at your birth as a source of information for your life, or how to conduct your life, or that defines you. All of them are detestable to the LORD.

To sum up that the Old Testament ceremonial laws were symbols pointing to Jesus, turn to Colossians 2:16–17: "Therefore no one is to act as your judge in regard to food or drink or in respect to a festival or new moon or a Sabbath day—things which are a mere shadow of what is to come; but the substance belongs to Christ." Jesus is the manifestation of the ceremonial laws, and He is the fulfillment of those laws. Thus, Christians that obey Jesus are in compliance with the ceremonial laws.

Review: The sun, moon, and stars are for seasons (feasts) to notify humanity of their appointed time to assemble to honor God with feasts. The feasts are symbolic occasions that direct humanity to glorify the Father through the Saving Son, Jesus Christ.

Days and years. The Hebrew word for days is *yowm* (Strong's Conc. #3117), which means to be hot or a day (as in the warm hours), whether literally (from sunrise to sunset, or from one sunset to the next sunset), or figuratively (a space of time defined by an associated term). In other words, the associated term determines if *day* is literal or figurative. The term *days* has no associated terms, so it means any or every day of mankind. Two associated terms occur for each day of creation that clarify whether to define *day* as literal or figurative. One is that numbers exist immediately in front of "day," for example, first day, second day, and so on. Therefore, the associated term requires a literal definition of the word *day*. Ergo, the "day" in Genesis is not eons, ages, or some unknown amount of time, so it is not figurative. The second associated term that indicates whether to interpret *day* as literal or figurative is the phrase before each number of the day: *and there was evening and there was morning of 'x' day."* Both associated terms require and only allow for a literal day, a single rotation of the earth.

Some examples where the word *day* can mean eons or ages or an unspecified day are when you read phrases such as "in the day of our Lord" or "in that day" or "the day is coming when."

A little footnote that a Bible student may want to know to better understand the dates in the Bible. Gentiles have made alterations in times (potentially fulfilling Daniel 7:25, as to when to observe a festival) with the introduction of the Roman (Julian) calendar and then Catholic Pope Gregory made a minor adjustment and introduced the Gregorian calendar. But this change of the calendar is slightly different than the solar-lunar calendar of our solar system and the Bible. Consequently, this is why differing dates occur when comparing a Biblical solar-lunar calendar with the Roman/Gregorian calendar. The Bible explains that Passover is on Nissan 14, which is always the spring full moon, and that Jesus was crucified on Passover (Nissan 14). But the equivalent day with the Roman Gregorian calendar can range from March 15 to April 8. This is why the Jewish people celebrate Passover on the correct day, the same full moon every year, and Christians celebrate Jesus' crucifixion (the Holy Passover) rarely on the full moon of Nissan 14. Therefore, Christians celebrate Jesus' crucifixion on the wrong date, and compound their error by calling the most holy event in the Bible by a blasphemous pagan name—Ishtar (Easter). This is an indictment on the corruption within the church.

Review: The formation of time was made to reflect and mirror an already-established parameter for time. The associated terms that are used with *day* determine whether it is taken literally or figuratively. The phrase *and there was evening and there was morning* requires a literal day interpretation, and each day has a number in front of it, which requires a literal day interpretation.

Then God said, "let there be lights in the expanse of the heavens to separate the day from the night, and let them be for signs and for seasons and for days and years . . . and it was so. There was evening and there was morning, a fourth day." Simply put, this is the manifestation of time as we know it. From the first day, though the earth was formless and void of life, it started rotating. Hence the phrase *there was evening and there was morning, 'x' day* was used for each day. Therefore, one reading the Scriptures cannot say that the first, second, and third days were billions of years or even thousands of years because our perception of time did not start until the fourth day. That would violate several passages of Scriptures, including Exodus 20 and 31, which both say that God created everything in six days and rested on the seventh day. Another way of looking at this is that God did not speed up the rotation of the earth from the first through the third days to match "time" that was manifested on the fourth day. That is incongruous with God's Word, logic, and science. Even science discerns the earth's rotational velocity is slowing over time.

Review: God manifests for us the perception of time on the fourth day, and it is based on what was already established by God's standard, as the rotation of the earth was already set in motion on the first day with the phrase *there was evening and there was morning, first day.*

And let them be for lights in the expanse of the heavens to give light on the earth. This portion of the fourth day seems like a repeat phrase, but more clarity is given here. God is commanding the stars and other celestial planetary bodies to be physical lights (to ignite through fusion as in stars, or to be reflective of light, as in planets and moons) in the expanse of the heaven**s**. *Heavens* is plural representing the universe and atmosphere. God commands that there be light on Earth, indicating the translucency of space, our atmosphere, and the canopy surrounding the atmosphere. Remember that this is different than the light created on the first day; this light is literally the stars coalescing enough matter to ignite, through hydrogen fusion, as the stars we see today. The light created on the first day represents the glowing hot magma of future stars, and the angels, spirits of all life to come.

The Bible does not violate any law of physics or science, and the creation of light from the sun, moon, and stars is in harmony just like everything else. Even evolutionary cosmologists suggest that as burgeoning bodies of matter coalesced into larger masses, their density, pressure, and subsequent heat increased. When enough matter coalesced together, scientists suggest that the stars were able to collide hydrogen into each other at the speed of light and cause starlight. Creationists and evolutionary cosmologists are saying the same thing; they just disagree on the amount of time it took for burgeoning unlit stars to glow hot from magma and ultimately ignite as starlight, and when this event occurred.

How did God ignite the stars on the fourth day of creation? Some simple principles of chemistry provide knowledge to make it easier to accept God's testimony. Let us go back to the first day of creation to set the foundation. When God created the matter that would eventually become the sun, though darkness existed everywhere, it was rotating as a hurricane-like storm of matter. Scientists have termed this action as coalescing matter. The Bible affirms this with the phrase regarding the forming Earth, *there was evening and there was morning, "x" day.* Since the sun's matter was also created on the same day, in the same way, from the same creator, and was formed by the same process the earth was formed, albeit at a much greater rate, this indicates that each celestial body was rotating. Fast forward to today, telescopes affirm the sun is rotating. Now, as the sun was rotating and increasing in matter, density, heat, gravity, magnetism, and so forth there was another critical process occurring, and that was the generation of electricity.

How did each star generate electricity? Well, scientists appropriately combine the term electricity with magnetism and call it **electromagnetism** because the two processes are linked together by the spinning material of the core. But let us break it down and explain how every forming star generated electricity. Each forming star gained enough mass—on average a million plus more mass than the earth—to form liquid metal at its core. With the core spinning fast (much faster than its surface), it generated a flow of electrons that stored up electricity. This electricity was instrumental in producing huge amounts of lightning that vaporized some water that aided the expansion of the universe, galaxies, and solar systems during the second day of creation. However, an even more important function occurred with this electrical charge.

Cosmologists, physicists, and heliologists (one who studies the sun/star) do a great job of explaining how the sun works, of how the sun performs fusion to generate heat, light, and a helium byproduct from hydrogen fusion. But no scientist has discerned where the sun got hydrogen in the first place. Scientists understand some of the processes occurring today on the sun, but they lack the understanding of the processes that formed the hydrogen in the beginning. They proclaim hydrogen formed from the Big Bang, but a simpler and superior hypothesis exist. The reason they miss this is because they start with the wrong hypothesis, and every premise built from that error is usually in error. The correct starting point of where H2 came from is contained in the Bible. 2 Peter 3:5 explains that "the heavens existed long ago and the earth was formed out of the water and by water." Also, Gen. 1:2 explains that waters existed before any celestial body was formed and water was abundant in the universe that God just created. Thus, every celestial body was formed out of the water and by water, even the stars, just like Earth. Since evolutionary heliologists do not start with the sun forming out of water and by water just like Earth, they are missing the critical ingredient God used to form all the hydrogen gas for each star—water. With this premise, and that every forming star had a rotating core of liquid metal (just like Earth's, but a ~hundreds of times larger), this caused electrons to flow and built up electricity around every celestial body. Then a simple principle of chemistry solves how God formed hydrogen gas for each star. Chemists have discerned that when electricity is applied to water with a cathode and anode, that the H2O is separated and forms diatomic atoms H2 and O2, through a process called **electrolysis**.[192] The process of electrolysis is accelerated with salt added to the water, and guess what? That is exactly the type of water that was in between and surrounding every celestial body— saltwater. This is seen in our own oceans, that came from the saltwater that once hovered around the

192 Http://www.youtube.com/watch?v=OTEX38bQ-2w&feature=youtube_gdata_player.

atmosphere as the canopy, and now resides as the oceans because of the Flood.

As the sun's core of liquid metal spun coalescing soil and water, during the initial days of creation, this generated electrical charge with a cathode (positive charge) and an anode (negative charge), that separated water into its base elements. The cathode collected the lighter hydrogen at a distal radii (outer mantle) to the core, and the anode collected the heavier oxygen at a proximal radii (inner mantle) to the core. Since the sun's mass is so large and generates huge amounts of heat, electromagnetism, and pressure the gases exist in an altered state of higher ionized energy called **plasma**.[193] Ionized gas, means an electron that normally circles an atom, is forced off its orbit by high energy (heat and/or electrical charge), and essentially floats freely, creating plasma.[194] A simple explanation of plasma is, that it is just a higher energy state beyond gas. For example, with water, when very little energy is applied to water, it freezes at low temperatures. When more energy is applied to ice water, it becomes a liquid. When more energy is applied to liquid water, it becomes a gas (H2 and O2). When even more energy is applied to the gas of H2 and O2, they go into the next phase called plasma.

As the sun continued to gain in mass, density, electromagnetism, and hydrogen by the fourth day of creation, enough build up of forces occurred to force hydrogen protons to collide into each other at the speed of light, and create nuclear fusion. The sun is fusing hydrogen protons well below the surface but just distal to the O2 plasma layer, and each H to H fusion releases a trace amount of mass and a tremendous amount of energy and the left over is helium plasma. Multiply this by the countless nuclear hydrogen fusions, and the total amount of mass being lost by the sun every second is 4.3×10^{12} g.[195] As hydrogen fusion occurs, this results in a gradual reduction of hydrogen plasma and an increase in the quantity of helium plasma. The heavier helium sinks below the hydrogen layer, but is not heavier than the oxygen layer. Regarding the O2, it is probably existing as a dense plasma layer deep within the sun because of the intense heat, electromagnetism, and pressure. The sun isn't large enough or dense enough to collide O2 atoms together at the speed of light and produce fusion from oxygen.

Scientists estimate that hydrogen fusion must occur at the core because of the density, heat, and pressure of the core, and then that energy takes millions of years to travel from the core to the surface, which we see eight minutes later. However, this hypothesis is based on the premise that the sun was initially made up of 98% hydrogen. And through 4 billion years of nuclear fusion, the sun now consists of 73% hydrogen, 25% helium, and 2% oxygen, carbon, iron, and other elements. With this premise, the conclusion is that fusion can only occur near the core.[196] However, starting with a premise that the formation of the stars were surrounded by water, and coalesced matter just like the earth and all the other planets and moons coalesced matter, then the sun is denser and hydrogen fusion does not have to occur at the core. With this hypothesis, one would expect to find many signs of water on all the celestial bodies. Cosmologists find ample signs that water was ubiquitous throughout the solar system. Whether it is actual ice, erosion marks, an atmosphere, or rings, signs exist that water was abundant in the universe. Therefore, this aids the hypothesize that at creation, the sun was made up of 25% core (similar material as the earth), 24% oxygen, 3% other elements and 48% hydrogen. This is based on the 2:1 ratio of H2O. Remember, O2 is 16x greater molecular mass than H2. This would make the sun denser, and allow hydrogen fusion at a more distal radii than the core. Thus, it would not take that nuclear energy as long to reach Earth.

It seems plausible that every celestial body was formed in the same manner as the earth, from the same type of material (though at varying percentages), and with waters surrounding them, but because of the rate of coalescing matter varied with each celestial body, and because there were differences in pressure, mass, volume, density, heat, neighboring celestial bodies, rotational velocity, and so forth, then no two celestial bodies are alike. Some formed into stars, some formed into moons,

193 Http://www.youtube.com/watch?v=2osF616-zWg&feature=youtube_gdata_player.
194 Http://en.m.wikipedia.org/wiki/Plasma_%28physics%29.
195 Http://solar-center.stanford.edu/FAQ/Qshrink.html.
196 Http://solarcellcentral.com/sun_page.html.

and some formed into planets, and some material never coalesced into a celestial body and we call them asteroids, meteors, and comets. We see a similar premise in the formation of snowflakes. All snowflakes are formed from water, but because of variations of pressure, altitude, temperature, and so forth when they are forming, then no two snowflakes are alike.

Review: This light represents stars gathering enough mass to ignite through nuclear fusion of hydrogen atoms. The two key ingredients to a star's formation during creation were vast quantities of water and matter, that had a spinning liquid metal core. During the initial days of creation, the spinning metal generated electricity, which caused electrolysis of the H_2O that surrounded every celestial body. The positive and negative charges separated the hydrogen and oxygen. Thus, forming hydrogen plasma in a 2:1 abundant ratio, with the heavier O_2 being deeper in the sun, and the lighter H_2 forming from the surface toward the middle of the sun. The intense mass and gravity of the sun collides hydrogen protons into each other at the speed of light to form lots of energy with the byproduct of helium.

And it was so. God's command did not gradually come about over billions of years. God spoke the command, and it was so. End of discussion. The ultimate power in the universe, the only power in the universe, the source of all power in the universe, God, does not have to wait for His orders to be carried out. God is not at the mercy of time. Numbers 12:1–16 tells us that when Miriam and Aaron spoke against Moses and questioned the words Moses had received from God, "The anger of the LORD burned against them and He departed. But when the cloud had withdrawn from over the tent, behold, Miriam was leprous, as snow . . . for seven days." Do not doubt the clear, plain, lucid, concise Word of God through Moses as Miriam did. Do not test God or to test the words Moses wrote through God's inspiration.

God made the two great lights, the greater light to govern the day, and the lesser light to govern the night; He made the stars also. God placed them in the expanse of the heavens to give light on the earth, and to govern the day and the night, and to separate the light from the darkness. The word *Great* is relative to the narrators perspective, and that is from Earth. Also, this shows distinction from the light created on the first day. The greater light is the sun, the lesser light is the moon, and the stars make up the rest of the celestial bodies in the universe.

The moon has an oxygen isotope concentration that is similar to Earth's, which suggests that the planet and its moon formed at an equal distance from the sun and at the time. This evidence is in harmony with Scripture. Cosmologists differ from the Bible in terms of how the moon began to orbit the earth. The current belief by evolutionary cosmologists is that some 4.4 billion years ago, when the earth was in its infancy as molten magma at only 50 million years old, a nearby small planetary body collided with Earth, which was not a solid structure as we know it. This super impact destroyed the small planet and vaporized the crust of the earth, ejecting material into space that orbited the earth. From the impact, the material eventually coalesced over time, and the debris formed the moon. This is a leap of faith for evolutionary cosmologists, when the evidence for this hypothesis is only the similar oxygen isotopes. Evolutionary cosmologists need an impact theory to solve the moon dilemma because the earth needs a moon to stabilize its rotation on an axis for life to be sustained. Since the moon is receding away from earth at a known rate, the moon cannot be old enough to match the billions of years required for evolution.

One of the problems with the impact belief is that the density of the moon is roughly 60% of earth's density, yet the planetary body that existed before it impacted earth and coalesced into the moon would have had to have an iron core center to form into a planet in the first place. If a super impact occurred and the debris from both celestial bodies were intermingled, the compositions of both would be similar and the densities would be close. Think about this. The smaller planet that collided with earth would also have had to have a denser core to cause enough attraction of debris to form into a planet, just as the earth had a dense core to attract debris in its embryonic stages, allegedly 50 million years before the giant impact. Cosmologists solve this with the hypothesis that the original impacting planet's dense core was absorbed into the center of earth, and the moon formed without a dense (potentially iron) core. That sounds plausible, as some items will stick together in space without an iron core if a charge exist with the matter. But how much things collect in space is limited without a dense core to attract. Once the charge is satisfied or balanced, the attraction is gone to draw more matter together. An example of this is Saturn's rings. They are not coalescing into a small moon. This impact hypothesis is just that, a hypothesis. The simplest answer is that the earth and moon formed from similar material, at similar times, and at a similar distance to the sun, as the Bible explains in clear language, and this explains why similar isotopes exist.

Another problem with the impact theory is that the Roche limit states that a distance exist at which the moon cannot be any closer to the earth, or else the moon will disintegrate. That distance is 11,500 miles. After this alleged super impact, the debris had to form beyond the Roche limit, or else the moon would have never formed. However, a progressive rate of recession further back in time puts the impact to occur about 305 million years ago, but not 4.45 billion years ago as cosmologists allege. The probability that a planetary body collided with earth at the correct angle to cause earth to spin at just the right amount is more faith based than science.

Look, we are discussing the fourth day of creation, and this next fact should reveal to you the supernatural work of making the sun, moon, and stars and the fact that they did not evolve by chance over 14–20 billion years. The narrative of creation is told from the perspective of Earth, and one of the solar system's greatest testimonies on behalf of the creator is that the sun and moon have the same apparent diameter (by 0.5 degree) as viewed from Earth. The sun is 400 times the size of the moon but is 400 times farther away from earth.[197] This allows for both solar and lunar eclipses. Only a precise size-to-distance, with the same diameter from that ratio, and that the moon crosses in front of the sun, allows for this cosmic phenomenon. The sun and moon were finished forming on the fourth day. To a believer, this is reason for reverence for an all-powerful God. To a nonbeliever, this is merely coincidence. Now every time you see the sun and moon, you will understand why the Psalmist wrote in verses 19:1–3: "The heavens are telling of the glory of God." How rare is this creation? With 176 moons orbiting the planets of the solar system, only the sun, moon, and earth have both solar and lunar eclipses.

An estimated two trillion stars exist for every human that has walked on the face of the earth. Atheistic evolutionists declare the wonders of the Big Bang; creationists declare the wonders of God.

Review: On the fourth day of creation, God set the sun 400 times farther away from Earth than the moon and made the sun 400 times larger than the moon. He gave both the same diameter as viewed from Earth and made both bodies in a spherical shape. A precise combination of all these factors and only a precise combination created solar and lunar eclipses.

On the fourth day of creation, the making of the sun, moon, and stars is the start of photosynthesis for all the grasses, plants, and trees that were created the prior day. This is a defining moment. Since God knows all things, why did God create the sun, moon, and stars after He created the grasses, plants, and trees? Why not create the sun first and then create the vegetation? I contend that God in His sovereignty, with predetermined foreknowledge, was making it crystal clear that there could not have been thousands of years between the third day of vegetation being fashioned and the fourth day of the sun being made for photosynthesis. In fact, there could not have been one month between all green plants being formed on the third day and the sun, moon, and stars being made on the fourth day. Only one single rotation of the earth is the only acceptable, logical option for each day of creation. Otherwise, all vegetation that was formed on the third day would die without the sun for photosynthesis. The same argument can be made for the insects that were not formed until the sixth day. How long does a theistic evolutionist want to go in time before plants are pollinated? A million years, or a thousand years, or one year? The answer is so obvious, plants require bees to live, produce fruit, flowers, and seeds.

It is sad to observe believers who want to be accepted by atheists so much that they will believe

197 Http://spaceplace.nasa.gov/review/dr-marc-earth/moon-general.html.

that the Bible is not that far off from evolutionary constructs and say, "believe in God because there are millions to billions of years between each day of creation; the Genesis story is made up by man to give us an idea, not to be taken literally." Their proof text is a half-twisted quote in 2 Peter 3:8. They say, "with God, a day is 1,000 years." Oh really? First off, the verse is not talking about creation; it is saying that God is not slow to judge, but He is patient in his judgments to give all an opportunity for salvation:

> But by His word the present heavens and earth are being reserved for fire, kept for the <u>day of judgment</u> and destruction of ungodly men. But do not let this one fact escape your notice, beloved, that with the Lord one day is **like** a thousand years, and a thousand years **like** one day. The Lord is not slow about His promise, as some count slowness, but is patient toward you, not wishing for any to perish but for all to come to repentance.

This verse is not saying that one day is 1,000 years; it is saying that God is not bound by time. That is it —no more, no less. Christians should stop twisting this verse into the Genesis creation account so that they look acceptable to atheists. No matter what, believers are foolish in the eyes of atheists; we gain no ground by giving up a holy, inerrant Bible to please atheists. Think about it. Suppose one says to an atheist, "Hey, the Genesis account has errors in it, so I believe in evolution and in God." Would you like to believe in a god that wrote a book with errors? This is laughable, but this is the view of some believers, and the end result is that they have effectively weakened their ability to be used by God. The atheists still think them to be foolish for believing in God, so zero ground is gained.

Only God can change the heart of an atheist, so do not come up with a clever scheme to force God to do His part on your timetable. Just be a faithful witness and proclaim the truth, and let God be God. The Bible is a roaring lion; it is best to read it to others and get out of the way and let God roar.

I attended a sermon of a prominent pastor, that was a YEC that switched to an old Earth believer. His sermon was about the Genesis creation account, and he proclaimed that the earth was billions of years old, and that the Genesis creation was figurative language. During a brief interlude, I got to briefly speak with him. I asked him what made him change his mind? He explained that the Genesis creation account is figurative. I asked, "What is your best argument for that?" He explained that, "there are so many scientists that teach this, and on the fourth day of creation, God made two lights, a greater light and a lesser light. But the moon does not produce any light. Therefore, this proves the Genesis creation account is figurative." At that moment the music started, and he said, "excuse me," and went back up stage. I did not get the opportunity to inform him that the moon does reflect light, and that light is actually photons from the sun bouncing off the moon and hitting the retina of the eye. Therefore, indeed the moon may be expressed as a lesser light. For it is diminutive in size as compared to the sun, and though it does not generate its own light, it does reflect photons that are 100% light. This always bothered me that a prominent pastor, shepherding 10,000 souls each week, would be so reckless with his interpretation that is relying on a lack of knowledge of science, and to switch his view based on faith in fallible mortals that call themselves scientists, and turn his back to the Word.

And God saw that it was good. This indicates a completed work, not a slow process over thousands of years. *There was evening and there was morning, a fourth day.* This indicates the brevity of time, in one rotation of the earth.

Chapter Summary: God finished making the sun, moon, and stars in the second expanse/heaven called the universe. God stretched out the universe on the second day and placed the sun, moon, and stars in the universe on the fourth day. God manifested the perception of time according to the rotational spin velocities of matter already established and determined on the first day. Therefore, even time is subject to God. The sun, moon, and stars were created for us to determine days, years, signs in the heavens, and covenant festivals. The sun (along with photosynthesis) was created only one day after the vegetation was fashioned on the third day, not a day longer.

Chapter 36
The Fifth Day

Gen. 1:20–23: *Then God said, "Let the waters teem with swarms of living creatures, and let birds fly above the earth in the open expanse of the heavens." God created the great sea monsters and every living creature that moves, with which the waters swarmed after their kind, and every winged bird after its kind; and God saw that it was good. God blessed them, saying, "Be fruitful and multiply, and fill the waters in the seas, and let birds multiply on the earth." There was evening and there was morning, a fifth Day.*

Let the waters teem with swarms of living creatures. This is the creation of all life in salt and fresh waters. *Teem* is used to express the abundance and diversity of life. *With swarms* is used to express movement and the abundant number of like kinds cohabiting with like kinds. This refers to God creating great numbers of fish, specifically aquatic life that swarms in schools, such as dolphins, salmon, sardines, tuna, krill, and so on, including saltwater and freshwater marine animals. This is the creation of the first life forms that have the breath of life in them. Did God create life from dirt as evolutionists have been proclaiming? Did life spontaneously come from dirt?

Scripture is clear: "For by Him all things were created, in the heavens and on earth, visible and invisible . . . all things have been created **through** Him" (Colossians 1:16). Therefore, the Bible is in harmony with biology, which says that life cannot come from nonliving material. The Father gave the Son the command to speak, the Son spoke what the Father commanded Him, and the Holy Spirit moved as the "Breath of Life" to give life to the dirt that was shaped into thousands of kinds of fish. When the Holy Spirit moved through the fish, they became life.

Every living thing on earth, whether from botanical, fish life, bird, beast, or human, was made from the ground and shaped into their form; then the Breath of Life (Holy Spirit) moved through them. Life begot life. For those that have blood and the breath of life, God breathed the Breath of Life into their nostrils/face and they became life. This comes from Gen. 2:7: "The LORD God formed man of dust from the ground, and breathed into his nostrils the Breath of Life; and man became life." Both words for "life" are *chay* in Hebrew, which means life, living, living being, or living soul—thus, life begot life. Gen. 2:9 says, "Out of the ground the LORD God caused to grow every tree," and Gen. 2:19 says, "Out of the ground the LORD God formed every beast of the field and every bird of the sky." Do not be alarmed when an evolutionist says, "Hey, the Bible says we came from dirt." We both say life came from dirt. The big difference, which is too large a gap to close, is abiogenesis—creating life from nonliving material has been proven impossible. Therefore, the evolutionary model has been proven wrong by Pasteur, and the Biblical model of life begetting life has been proven correct by every birth.

And let birds fly above the earth in the open expanse of the heavens. This is a blanket statement that covers all bird life in the atmosphere, from the tiny hummingbird to the great flying dinosaur pterodactyl; all bird life was created here. How? Does God give us any indication of how He did this? Gen. 2:19 says, "Out of the ground the Lord God formed . . . every bird of the sky." God forms birds out of the ground in the same fashion that He formed man, beast, and vegetation from the dust of the ground. The Hebrew word for dust includes clay in the definition.[198] This is illustrated best as with a potter's hands that forms clay. So too did God form and fashion all life out of the clay of the ground (Jeremiah 18:1–6) and the Holy Spirit moved to combine the spirit created on the first day, with the formed being and make it a living soul. Birds also have the breath of life in them, as do land animals, aquatic life, and humans.

Because of weaker gravity before the Flood, it is plausible that some birds that are grounded these days may have flown in the past. The ostrich may have flown short distances like chickens, and the roadrunner may have flown longer distances. Even though these birds are grounded today (or

---

198 Strong's Conc. #6083: *aphar:* dust (as powder or gray); hence clay, earth, mud, ashes, ground, mortar.

mostly grounded), they most likely took flight before the Flood.

God created the great sea monsters and every living creature that moves, with which the waters swarmed after their kind. Here, God gives us a little more details of the aquatic life He created. The word used for "great" is gadowl,[199] which indicates a range from large or great in size, number, or importance. The Hebrew word for "sea monsters" is *tanniyn*,[200] which ranges from a marine or land monster, sea serpent, jackal, dragon (dinosaur), serpent, sea monster (dinosaur), or whale. The King James Bible uses "great whales," but that falls short of the leviathan. The wording of the definition indicates that God created the great creatures in the waters, even the fire-breathing dragons and dinosaurs. When using the Bible to define itself, we can get better clarity of what the features of this great creature are.

The description of the leviathan in Job 41, is that it is fierce and powerful and that it literally breathes fire. Earlier in the book, we talked about taking this as a literal fire-breathing dragon, and science supports a chemical fire in water. One verse mentions that he makes the sea like a jar of ointment; perhaps this is in reference to the oily chemical that remains in the waters after he passes by. The language for Job 41 is too great to leave out since it nicely ties in with this creative moment of God creating a sea monster or sea dragon. God is talking to Job and intending to make Job realize how puny he is to the Creator, who can make a creature so magnificent as the leviathan (Job 41:1–34):

> Can you draw out **Leviathan** with a fishhook? . . . Can you put a rope in his nose or pierce his jaw with a hook? Will he make supplications to you, Or will he speak to you soft words? . . . will you bind him for your maidens? Will the traders bargain over him? Will they divide him among the merchants? Can you fill his skin with harpoons, or his head with fishing spears? Lay your hand on him, remember the battle, you will not do it again! Behold, your expectation is false, will you be laid low even at the sight of him? No one is so fierce that he dares to arouse him; Who then is he that can stand before me? . . . I will not keep silence concerning his limbs, Or his mighty strength, or his orderly frame. Who can strip off his outer armor? Who can come within his double bridle? Who can open the doors of his face? Around his teeth there is terror. His strong scales are his pride, shut up a tight seal. One is so near to another that no air can come between them . . . His sneezes flash forth light, And his eyes are like the eyelids of the morning. Out of his nostrils smoke goes forth as a boiling pot and rushes. His breath kindles coals, and a flame goes forth from his mouth. In his neck lodges strength, and dismay leaps before him. The folds of his flesh are joined together, firm on him and immovable. His heart is as hard as a stone, even as hard as a lower millstone. When he raises himself up, the mighty fear; Because of the crashing they are bewildered. The sword that reaches him cannot avail, nor the spear, the dart or the javelin. He regards iron as straw, Bronze as rotten wood. The arrow cannot make him flee; Slingstones are turned into stubble for him. Clubs are regarded as stubble. He laughs at the rattling of the javelin. His underparts are sharp potsherds; He spreads out a threshing sledge on the mire. He makes the depths boil like a pot, he makes the sea like a jar of ointment. Behind him he makes a wake to shine; One would think the deep to be gray-haired. Nothing on earth is like him, one made without fear. He looks on everything that is high; He is king over all the sons of pride.

This truly was a remarkable fire-breathing dragon to behold. As we have discussed, not all dinosaurs are extinct, but this dinosaur is extinct, since nothing today fits this description. This creature and all the other fierce sea creatures were created on the fifth day. Gen. 1:21: "God created the great sea-Dragon" gives clarity that this creation moment is describing an aquatic dinosaur. It was not just any

---

199 Strong's Conc. #1419: *gadowl*: Large (in magnitude and extent), in number, in intensity, in importance (great, distinguished).

200 Strong's Conc. #8577: *tanniyn*: a marine or land monster, i.e., sea serpent or jackal, dragon, serpent, sea monster (dinosaur), whale.

dinosaur, but a fire-breathing dragon. It makes sense that almost every culture on earth has a fire-breathing dragon legend and drawings because ancient people potentially saw this dragon before it became extinct.

Review: God created aquatic dinosaurs and dragons on the fifth day of creation.

Creatures and insects only ate vegetation (herbivores) from creation till the fall of Adam. Then life changed, and all of creation was cursed. Therefore, when God was describing the leviathan to Job, that creature may have been a carnivore; however, at the time of creation and up to the fall of Adam and Eve, all creatures were herbivores. A clue about the savage nature of the beasts before the Flood is in Gen. 6:5 and 7:

> Then the LORD saw that the wickedness of man was great on the earth, and that every intent of the thoughts of his heart was only evil continually . . . The LORD said, "I will blot out man whom I have created from the face of the land, from man to animals to creeping things and to birds of the sky; for I am sorry that I have made them."

God was sorry that He made man, animals, creeping things, and birds. Nearly all had evil intent in their heart. What would that look like? Well, they were commanded to eat only grass, plants, and trees (Gen. 1:30–31). All the animals and birds were obedient by only eating vegetation, but after sin entered the world and all of creation became cursed, many became carnivores and being greedy. What? They were being greedy? Yes. That is self-love; according to Colossians 3:5, it is *greed which amounts to idolatry.* We can see this today when dogs fight over the same bone instead of sharing. Do not laugh too hard at this topic. Additional evidence that the intent of the carnivores was evil after the fall of man is in Isaiah 65:25: "The wolf and the lamb will graze together, and the lion will eat straw like the ox . . . *They will do no evil or harm* in all My holy mountain." This verse is pointing to a future time after sin is removed from Earth; the notion that *they will do no evil or harm* means that some animals are committing evil acts and doing harm before the restoration of creation. I contend that this refers to carnivores. Do not get me wrong. I enjoy a steak, and it is not a sin to eat meat, but after all of creation is restored to a pre-fallen condition, all life will return to being herbivores again. Animals are given the breath of life too, and some animal-like creatures exist in heaven (Revelation 4:6–9). The snake in the Garden of Eden was corrupt in his heart to allow Satan to possess him and deceive Eve. Therefore, animals can choose to be obedient to God or do evil and harm.

But the hope is that all carnivores will become herbivores again (Isaiah 65:25). Even more information is given about this in Isaiah 11:6–10:

> The wolf will dwell with the lamb, and the leopard will lie down with the young goat, and the calf and the young lion and the fatling together; and a little boy will lead them. Also the cow and the bear will graze, their young will lie down together, and the lion will eat straw like the ox. The nursing child will play by the hole of the cobra, and the weaned child will put his hand on the viper's den. They will not hurt or destroy in all My holy mountain, For the earth will be full of the knowledge of the LORD as waters cover the sea.

When will this be? Isaiah 11:10: "In that day the nations will resort to the root of Jesse,[201] Who will stand as a signal/standard for the peoples; And His resting place will be glorious." This is when the kingdom of heaven comes down to earth, as foretold in Revelation 21:1–6 "He will dwell among them, and they shall be His people, and God Himself will be among them, and He will wipe away every tear from their eyes; and there will no longer be any death; there will no longer by any mourning, or crying or pain; the first things have passed away."

Review: Aquatic dinosaurs were created on the fifth day. The great fire-breathing dragon, the

---

201 The "*root of Jesse,*" King David was begotten of Jesse, and Jesus is the heir of King David. Therefore, Jesus is the root of Jesse. The genealogies are in Matthew 1:1-17 [Joseph's royal legal line] and Luke 3:23-38 [Mary's blood line].

leviathan, was created on the fifth day. It was an herbivore until the fall of Adam and Eve.

And every winged bird. This seems redundant, but the "winged" portion that gives us a clue. Everything winged like a bird is in the bird category, even the winged birds that cannot fly today because gravity is too strong for them. If animals have similar shapes and similar characteristics, then most likely they are of the same kind though they may have many species within the kind.

*God created the great sea monsters and every living creature that moves, with which the waters swarmed after their **kind**, and every winged bird after its **kind**.* This is an important phrase that draws a line in the sand against evolution and divides creation from evolution and should draw the attention of all theistic evolutionists. Birds only reproduce with birds of their same kind, and though adaptations occur for micro-changes (different species of the same kind), they always remain the same kind. Macro-changes (changes of kind) do not exist, only micro-changes (changes within a kind) exist.

A kind is a living thing that is grouped based on having similar physical features (internal and external) and similar characteristics of thought, mind, behavior, and so on. Each kind of living thing will only and exclusively produce the same kind. Creatures will only reproduce with those that have the same internal systems because hormone production is receptor specific. If they have a different birthing process, nursing process, mode of transportation, external structures, or reproductive equipment, then no reproduction occurs.

For example, the stamen of a plant will never get a female dog pregnant. Though adaptations occur resulting in minor variations, such as slight changes in beak or color or height, size, eye color, and so on, they will remain the same kind. To help with what constitutes a *kind*, here is a simple explanation: if it has the same image (shape, features, etc.) and has the same likeness (character, behavior, etc.), it is the same kind. That was the criteria by God when He created man in Gen. 1:26. Humans come in many shapes, sizes, hair colors, eye colors, voice sounds, nose shapes, gaits, levels of strength, mental acumen, blood type, eyebrow thickness, and so forth, but we know a human when we see one; they have the same image and the same likeness. All humans are the same kind, with many species of humans.

The bottom line is that the information within the DNA code exclusively allows only reproduction within the same kind and always prevents reproduction with an outside of kind. This is why all kinds today are 100% of their kind—100% of humans are 100% humans, 100% of dogs are 100% dogs, and so forth. This is why transitional fossils do not exist. God sealed each kind within the DNA code, and this exclusivity is His signature saying that He designed creation to be this way. Just like artists sign their work, writers copyright their work, and inventors patent their work, God signed His work with a DNA seal of exclusivity. That is why some overlaps occur in the DNA code because (a) we came from the same creator, from His essence, and (b) some of our proteins do the same job, such as enameled teeth. That does not mean we evolved from them; it means we were created by the same creator.

God does not increase in knowledge, and birds and marine life cannot read the Bible. Then why mention that marine life *swarmed after their kind, and every winged bird flew after its kind*? God knew mankind would drift away from the truth, and "not endure sound doctrine; but to have their ears tickled, they will accumulate for themselves teachers in accordance to their own desires, and will turn away their ears from the truth and will turn aside to myths" (2 Tim. 4:3–4). God knew that mankind would turn to the myth of evolution and would use the Uniformitarian theory to do so, which is a theory that "All things continue just as it was from the beginning of creation." God knew that mankind would use the Uniformitarian theory to mock believers, who adhere to the Word of God, with their mocking, saying, "All things continue just as it was from the beginning of creation" (2 Pet. 3:4). For this reason, since birds and marine life do not read the Bible, then God put the phrase, *God created the great sea monsters and every living creature that moves, with which the waters swarmed after their kind, and every winged bird after its kind,* not for them to know and understand, but for humans to know and understand. The phrase is an indictment on all those who believe in the evolutionary model and all those who buy into the atheistic timeline that is designed to support evolution.

The word *kind* is such a deal breaker that God declared that anyone who says they eventually came from a rock or tree or that a rock or tree is their ancestor, is guilty of idolatry. Evolution says that rain fell on rocks and produced complex chemicals, and eventually a single cell evolved over time, and through genetic mutations, more complex organisms evolved. Listen to Jeremiah 2:27:

> Who say to a tree, "You are my father" and to a stone, "You gave me birth." For they have turned their back to Me and not their face; But in the time of their trouble they will say, "Arise and save us" But where are your gods which you made for yourself? Let them arise, if they can save you.

When a theist evolutionist claims to love God, yet says we evolved and the Bible has errors in it, this is idolatry. Worse yet, theist evolutionists often teach others to do the same and use academia to teach children about evolution and consequently push them away from the truth.

Satan's first act and first approach in deceiving is always to peddle doubt of the Bible, to keep people away from the Word of God, and to question the Word of God, and that is exactly what evolution does. So stop in your tracks, stop persecuting God and doing the work of Satan.

Review: The term *kind* is a deal breaker for remaining in acceptance with the Bible or rejecting the creation account and accepting the hypothesis of evolution. *Kind* is God's seal that there never has been and never will be crossbreeding of kinds. If you find yourself on the wrong side of the Bible, that means you are on Satan's side—no middle ground exist in the war on truth.

And God saw that it was good. All that God created was void of sin—all birds and fish were living in the will of God and according to the commandments of God that He placed in their hearts' desire. All creatures were obedient to God's will. They were sinless. It is hard to think of creatures as having sinned, but that is what happened. Take the serpent in the Garden of Eden for example, a literal snake with a corrupt heart that allowed Lucifer to possess it. The snake was more deceitful than any other creature (Gen. 3:1);[202] therefore, all their kind were cursed more than any other creature (Gen. 3:14).[203]

We often read about creation being obedient to God in terms of judgment, such as when God appoints a creature, a volcano, hailstorm, or other natural phenomenon to carry out His judgment. We read about the locusts in the Exodus from Egyptian slavery and in Revelation, the lions in the den with Daniel, the great fish with Jonah, or the bears that slaughtered those youths that mocked Elijah. This is even seen with nonliving aspects of creation, such as darkness lasting three days (most likely a haboob; a type of intense dust storm that can cover a large city) during the ten plagues of the Egypt exodus and three hours (perhaps another haboob) while Jesus hung on the cross. Therefore, when God saw that what He had created was good, it also represents that what He created was obedient to Him. Obedience to God shows our love for Him. We also see creatures and natural things obeying God, such as with the bountiful fish that were caught in the apostle nets when Jesus told them to cast the nets on the other side of the boat. The fish were obedient to the Word of God. Also, when the winds were disobedient and disrupted the seas when God was resting on a boat, He awoke to the pleas of the disciples to rebuke the wind and seas—and at the Word of God, they obeyed. It may seem trite to say that creatures and the wind, earth, sun, moon, stars, asteroids, and so on are obedient to God, but it is true. Even creation groans to be free from the curse of sin and continues bold obedience to God. Romans 8:18–25 reveals that all of "creation groans and suffers . . . to be set free from slavery to corruption (sin)."

God saw that it was good. This phrase demonstrates that what God commanded to occur happened at His command immediately. This is to say that God did not say, "It will eventually be good." God did not command it to be so and then wait for evolution to carry out His command four

---

202 Gen. 3:1-"Now the serpent was more deceitful than any beast of the field which the lord God had made."

203 Gen. 3:14 "Because you have done this, Cursed are you more than all cattle, and more than every beast of the field; On your belly you will go, and dust you will eat all the days of your life."

billion years later. A clue is the past tense of the verse with *was*. With one swift simple decree of the King, God debunks the "gap theory," in which angels allegedly reigned for billions of years and then some rebelled, so God destroyed everything. Proponents believe that Genesis verses 1–2 are about the re-creation. *It was good* rules out theories of fallen angels roaming the earth as demons during creation. Gap theorists also believe that all the dinosaurs lived and died between verses 1 and 2 of chapter one. The only reason the gap theory evolved was because people questioned the Word of God and accepted mankind's version that the earth is billions of years old. People who wanted to believe in God and still look good to atheists accepted evolutionary theory over accepting the literal interpretation of the Word of God.

Usually, the simple, clear interpretation is the correct one; God saw that it was good because all was good, which means no demons, no dead dinosaurs, no dead vegetation, no death, no sin, and no past before the start of creation.

Review: *God saw that is was good* is a past tense statement of the command given by God, not an evolutionary slow fulfillment over billions of years. All that God created was complete and lovingly obedient to the Word of God.

God blessed them, saying, "Be fruitful and multiply, and fill the waters in the seas, and let birds multiply on the earth." This is the first recorded blessing in the Bible, and it means that God delighted in them and approved of them. He devoted them to the solemn purpose of carrying out God's designed purpose. Why does God say "Be fruitful <u>and</u> multiply"? Why not just say, "Multiply"? The word *multiply* is to increase in number and quantity and is straightforward. The Hebrew word for "fruitful" is *parah*, which means to bear fruit (literally or figuratively), bring forth fruit, be, cause to be, or make fruitful, grow, or increase (Strong's Conc. #6509: *parah*). The obvious answer is to be diligent and productive; birds build nest, beavers build damns, worms work the soil, bees pollinate vegetation, which produces oxygen for life to thrive, and so on. The ecosystem stays in balance and in harmony because each thing that makes up the whole does its equal share and contributes to the efficiency of the ecosystem. If one level of the ecosystem is not diligent, not fruitful, this would throw the whole of creation out of balance. The Bible clearly says to be diligent and to work and that the lazy will come to poverty (Prov. 6:6–11) and hunger. It also says that if a lazy body does not work, then it should not eat (2 Thess. 3:6–14). God sets the supreme example for diligent work by sustaining His creation and causing all things to hold together and endure (Col. 1:17). Therefore, God obviously commanded all of creation to be diligent, to work, and to be fruitful. This is regarding deeds, actions, and the physical body. Being fruitful also includes our thoughts, desire, and mind.

God commands believers to be fruitful. Those fruits are love, joy, peace, patience, kindness, goodness, faithfulness, gentleness, and self-control (Gal 5:22). When the curse on creation is finally done away with at the second coming of the Messiah, then all of creation will be set free from the bondage of sin and will no longer groan and suffer and will return to being herbivores and a life of peace, joy, kindness, goodness, faithfulness, gentleness, self-control, and love (Isaiah 11:6–9).

Since God is talking to fish and birds and not plants here, we can rule out "fruitful" as in edible fruit from plants and trees, but fruits of the spirit as in obedience to the Word of God. Should this surprise us since all life forms were herbivores until the fall of Adam and Eve as God decreed in Gen. 1:30? This sheds light on the ability of fish, birds, and animals to be obedient to God and that they have free will as humans do, and possess souls and spirits.

Since God spoke to them, it implicitly says they can hear, understand, and communicate back. In the chapter, Life in the Beginning Before Sin, the notion of the lost ability of animals to communicate with humans as a result of the fall is addressed. Balaam's donkey in Numbers 22:22–33 and Eve talking with a snake in Gen. 3 exemplify that all creatures were subsequently cursed, even though only the snake did the deceiving. The hypothesis is that creatures lost the ability to communicate with humans because they, through the cunning snake, used that ability to deceive Adam and Eve.

Review: God blessed the fish and birds, gave them a solemn purpose and design, and told them to increase in numbers with physical offspring (multiply). And God commanded them to be fruitful: to be diligent, to work, and to bear fruits of the Spirit. He commanded them to be kind, gentle, peaceful, joyful, and good, practice self-control, be faithful to God, and love each other.

There was evening and there was morning, a fifth day. This is a repeated phrase for each day, indicating that the earth was rotating one revolution with each day. When an author wants to drive home the point, they will repeat a specific point that is important. Here, God could have had Moses write, "for each day there was evening and there was morning," but God goes out of His way to drive home the point. It seems that with God's foreknowledge of knowing that the most devastating false doctrine ever formulated by demons, that leads people into idolatry, is evolution.

Remember, the word *day* can be figurative in the Bible or literal in the Bible. The way one determines whether the days of the Genesis creation account are literal or figurative is by the associated term(s). The first is the phrase *and there was evening and there was morning*; the other is the number in front of *day*. Always, whenever a number is directly in front of the word *day*, it is always a single rotation of the earth, one literal rotation of the earth. This is without exception. For our time, a day is about 23 hours, 56 minutes, and 4.1 seconds, but for Adam and Eve it was roughly ~17 hours. With no associated term, then *day* could be eons, ages, or thousands of years.

The Genesis creation account is a record of seven literal days. This is crystal clear and leaves zero room for one who loves God and submits to the Word of God to wiggle out of, unless one loves evolution more than they love God and His Word, or one trust atheistic timeline more than they trust God.

Chapter Summary: On the fifth day, God made the birds, from gigantic pterodactyls to tiny hummingbirds and all aquatic life forms, from fire-breathing dinosaurs to clown fish. And God commanded them to be fruitful and multiply after their kind. God spoke to them and blessed them with a purpose and commanded them to practice self-control and to be kind, loving, peaceful, gentle, humble, good, and faithful.

Chapter 37

The Sixth Day

Gen. 1:24–31: *Then God said, "Let the earth bring forth living creatures after their kind: cattle and creeping things and beasts of the earth after their kind"; and it was so. God made the beast of the earth after their kind, and the cattle after their kind and everything that creeps on the earth after its kind; and God saw that it was good. Then God said, "Let Us make man in Our image, according to Our likeness; and let them rule over the fish of the sea and over the birds of the sky and over the cattle and over all the earth, and over every creeping thing that creeps on the earth." God created man in His own image, in the image of God He created him; male and female He created them. God blessed them; and God said to them, "Be fruitful and multiply and fill the earth, and subdue it; and rule over the fish of the sea and over the birds of the sky and over every living thing that moves on the earth." Then God said, "Behold, I have given you every plant yielding seed that is on the surface of all the earth, and every tree which has fruit yielding seed; it shall be food for you; and to every beast of the earth and to every bird of the sky and to every thing that moves on the earth which has life, I have given every green plant for food;"' and it was so. God saw all that He had made, and behold, it was very good. And there was evening and there was morning, the sixth day.*

*Then God said, "Let the <u>**earth**</u> bring forth living creatures after their kind: cattle and creeping things and beast <u>**of the earth**</u> after their kind"; and it was so. God made the beasts <u>**of the earth**</u> after their kind, and the cattle after their kind and everything that creeps on the <u>**earth**</u> after its kind; and God saw that it was good.* This is the sixth day of creation, the final day of God's creative work. As the earth rotates and the sun sets from the fifth day, we enter the creation narrative in the evening of the sixth day. The earth is filled with lush vegetation, grass covering the prairies, fragrant flowers, and juicy fruit on plants, with some trees that tower ~500 feet tall and fruit trees so abundant that the branches bend toward the ground. The saltwater seas and freshwater lakes are filled with life forms enjoying the riches of abundant edible sea plants and algae and the freedom from predators and death; life is full and clean, and no death or fossils exist. The birds soar high and free, romantically singing to honor and worship the Lord. The stars, sun, and moon declare the glory of the Lord, and the atmosphere is clean with a frozen canopy of water above. Oxygen levels are high, net gravity is weaker, and the length of a day may be 17 hours long. All is good.

In the beginning of the sixth day, in the darkness of evening, with the moon's light in the background, God begins fashioning the land creatures. Just as God made Adam from the ground, so too were all things made from the dirt, clay, and earth. Everything was fashioned from the dirt of the earth, from Adam and Eve, to fish, birds, beast, cattle, insects, grass, plants, and trees. All life that breathes oxygen and has blood came to be a living life by God speaking their existence and breathing into them the Breath of Life of the Holy Spirit, just like Adam. God fashioned him out of clay and spoke him into existence, and the moving of the Holy Spirit, the Breath of Life was breathed into his nostrils, and Adam became alive. All creatures were created the same way. This is found in Gen. 2:18–19 as God reflects back on creating all the birds, fish, and land animals and says, "<u>Out of the ground the LORD God formed every beast of the field and every bird of the sky</u>." Everything was made from the ground, even vegetation, according to Gen. 1:12: "The <u>earth brought forth</u> grass, plants yielding seed after their kind and trees bearing fruit with seed in them after their kind." Gen. 2:7: "Then the LORD God formed man of dust from the ground." Lastly, Ecclesiastes 3:19–29: "For the fate of the sons of men and the fate of beasts is the same. As one dies so dies the other; indeed, they all have the same breath . . . All go to the same place. <u>All came from the dust and all return to the dust</u>."

All creatures have a soul as humans do. This is corroborated in Genesis 9:1–8:

Every moving thing . . . <u>with its life, its blood. Surely I will require your life-blood</u>; from every beast I will require it. And from man, from every man's brother I will require the life of man. "Whoever sheds man's blood, by man his blood shall be shed."

The blood transfers the breath of life throughout the body, and each animal that breathes in oxygen and transfers that oxygen via the blood has the breath of life in them and is a child of God's kingdom. This is why we are to be respectful of the animal kingdom. Look at it this way; many of you have pets, and you love those pets as part of your family and care for them daily, and as much as you love them, you love your physical children all that much more. We get this characteristic from God. God lovingly takes care of all life on earth as part of His family. How much more does He take care of us because we are His direct offspring? This is summed up with Matthew 10:29–32: "Are not two sparrows sold for a cent? And not one of them will fall to the ground apart from your Father . . . But the very hairs of your head are all numbered. So do not fear; you are more valuable than many sparrow." Since one sparrow does not escape God and we are more valuable to God than many sparrows.

Review: Everything came from the dust of the earth. All that breathe oxygen and have blood became alive by The Word of the Son speaking them into existence; the Son spoke as He was commanded by the Father, and the Holy Spirit moved those Words into action by being the Breath of Life. Life begot life. Evolutionists believe that all life came from nonliving material from the dirt and that nonliving material begot life. This is idolatry.

Let the earth bring forth living creatures after their kind: ***cattle and creeping things and beast*** *of the earth after their kind'; and it was so. God made the* ***beast*** *of the earth after their kind, and the* ***cattle*** *after their kind and* ***everything that creeps on the earth*** *after its kind.*

Everyone understands the *creeping things* to be all the insects, all the micro-life that lives and is an integral part of the ecosystem. This is another reason that a believer in God should reject the notion that each day of the Genesis creation account stands for eons, billions of years, or thousands of years because all plants were created on the third day of creation, and plants cannot survive without insects for pollination. Ask yourself, "How long could plants go if they were created on the third day and had no sun for photosynthesis until the fourth day and no insects for fertilization until the sixth day?" Now if the Word of God is dearest to you, you will pause here and say, "that is a problem." But if evolution is dearest to you, you will not pause, but merely say that the Bible is written by humans and prone to have some errors and mistakes, or justify with some figurative, arbitrary language. However, Jesus held to a literal Genesis account by quoting verses in chapter 1 and 2 of Genesis, saying, "Have you not read that He who created from the beginning made them male and female" (Matthew 19:4).

The word "beasts and cattle" seem to require more explanation. *Beast* in Hebrew is *Chay* (#2416): alive, flesh, strong; life, creature, quick, raw, running, springing, or troop. This is the same word used in Gen. 2:6–7 when the Breath of Life, or the Breath of Chay, was breathed into the nostril of man and he became a chay, a life, or a living soul. Here, God is creating beasts via the same means by breathing the Breath of Life into their nostrils; then they became life. Life begot life for the animal kingdom as well.

Cattle in Hebrew is *behemah* (#929): a simple beast, quiet, especially any large quadropod or animal, beast, or cattle. This is the root word for *behemowth* for which we get "Behemoth" in Job 40. Let us turn to Job 40:15–24 to get a description of this beast from Genesis that was living in Job's day some 2,000 years after creation. God is talking to Job and telling Job how insignificant Job is and how great God is by illustrating how great the behemoth is that God created:

Behold now, Behemoth, which I made as well as you; He eats grass like an ox. Behold now, his strength in his loins And his power in the muscles of his belly. "He bends his tail like a cedar; The sinews of his thighs are knit together. His bones are tubes of bronze; His limbs are like bars of iron. He is the first of the ways of God; Let his maker bring near his sword. Surely, the mountains bring him food, And all the beasts of the field play there. Under the lotus plants he lies down, In the cover of the reeds and the marsh. The lotus plants cover him with shade; The willows of the brook surround him. If a river rages, he is not alarmed; He is confident, though the Jordan rushes to his mouth. Can anyone capture him when he is on watch, With barbs can anyone pierce his nose?

This great behemoth is one of the descendants of the very great creatures created on the sixth day of creation as the great cattle, or *behemah*. The phrase *He bends his tail like a Cedar* is telling because cedar trees in the Mesopotamian region grew as tall as 130 feet.[204] This no doubt fits only one type of creature, the dinosaur (such as brontosaurus or Argentinosaurus), and rules out the hippopotamus and the elephant because they both have tiny tails.

There seems to be an overlap of the two words *chay* for beast and *behemah* for cattle. Even *behemah*/cattle includes the word *beast* as one of the defining terms, so it seems that *beast/chay* are those creatures that are at the top of the food chain and are more aggressive. The *cattle/behemah* seem to be the simpler grazers that are less aggressive.

Some possible examples of *beast/chay* include T. rex, lion, tiger, gorilla, grizzly bear, fox, and wolf, the ones that are clever, higher intelligence, problem solvers, and became the hunters upon the fall of man. These are some of the creatures that resemble the defining terms for *chay*: alive, flesh, strong, life, creature, quick, raw, running, springing, and troop.

Some possible examples of *cattle/behemah* include brontosaurus, elephant, cow, deer, stegosaurus, koala, kangaroo, moose, and woolly mammoth, the grazers of vegetation. These are some of the creatures that resemble the defining terms for *behemah*: cattle, beast, a simple beast, or quiet, especially any large quadropod or animal.

Review: The beast-like creatures, the cattle-like creatures, and insects were created on the sixth day.

Let the earth bring forth living creatures <u>*after their kind:*</u> *cattle and creeping things and beast of the earth* <u>*after their kind';*</u> *and it was so. God made the beast of the earth* <u>*after their kind,*</u> *and the cattle* <u>*after their kind*</u> *and everything that creeps on the earth* <u>*after its kind.*</u>

After their kind is a repeated theme in the Genesis creation account, and it is because God knows all things, He knew evolution would rule the day toward the end of days. Upon the soon coming of the Lord, mankind will fall away from God and His Word and believe in fables. Romans 1:21–22: "For even though they knew God, they did not honor Him as God or give thanks, but they became futile in their speculations, and their foolish heart was darkened. Professing to be wise, they became fools." Also, 2 Timothy 4:3–4: "For the times will come when they will not endure sound doctrine; but to have their ears tickled, they will accumulate for themselves teachers in accordance to their own desires and will turn away their ears from the truth and will turn aside to myths." The Bible draws a line in the sand and says each thing, whether it be grass, plant, tree, fish, bird, beast, cattle, or insect, will always, 100% of the time, produce after their own kind.

A) It is a law in the Scriptures.

B) It is a law in the DNA code,

C) We can observe all creatures producing after their kind.

D) Even with artificial and natural selection, creatures produce after their kind.

E) The DNA code, specifically the epigenome is what governs and allows artificial and natural selection, not vice versa.

F) The DNA code governs and allows adaptation for minor variations, yet creatures alway remain the same kind (e.g., wolf to poodle).

G) Evolution suggests that natural selection and random, unguided mutations in genes produce new information, new functions, or new kinds. Clearly, this is at odds with Scripture.

Since animals cannot read, then God did not put the phrase *After their kind* in His Word for animals, but for corrupt man.

---

204 Http://en.wikipedia.org/wiki/Cedrus_libani.

Review: *After their kind* is an important concept that stands against evolution and supports life being created by God.

And God saw that it was good. Let us keep this simple, God saw that it was *good*, as in nothing bad or no sin existed. God *saw* that it *was* good, as in the commands of His Words *Let there be . . . and God saw that it was good* being completed. God speaks in the present tense (*let there be*) for the action and in the past tense (*God saw that it was good*) for the result. This stands against the slow evolutionary process that says that the earth waited billions of years to evolve the first self-replicating cell and then waited another billion years to evolve the diversity and complexities of beasts, cattle, and insects.

Review: God said "Let there be . . . and God saw that it was good." This means that His work was complete and did not require billions of years.

Then God said, "Let Us make man in Our image, according to Our likeness; and let them rule over the fish of the sea and over the birds of the sky and over the cattle and over all the earth, and over every creeping thing that creeps on the earth." God created man in His own image, in the image of God He created him; male and female He created them. God blessed them; and God said to them.

This is the fashioning and making of Adam and Eve. The violent days of creation have progressively become less with each day. The first set of three days violently gave shape to the celestial bodies (planets, moons, and stars), the second set of three days filled the earth with life. With each day of creating life, there seemed to be more detail, and a closer representation of God's DNA, until God crescendos with Adam (the Hebrew word for man is *Adam*[205]), the image and likeness of God. God is the alpha and the omega, He created angels in His image and likeness with the first dawn of creation, and finished creating with making Adam and Eve at the last dawn of the six days of creating.

Notice the equality of man and woman to both rule, and both originated from God. However, and this is important to prevent chaos—divorce, since there cannot be two heads to one body, then to be doctrinally specific, Adam was made in the image of God, and woman was made in the image of the man (1 Corinthians 11:7–12). In the sinful world, and the fight for the top and self promotion, this sounds demeaning. But to demonstrate in a sinless creation, or in a loving relation, this is not demeaning, the harmony of this relationship is personified by the image of God. The one God, the Father, Son, and Holy Spirit, though each are equal personages of God, the Son submits to the will of the Father with the union of the Holy Spirit. Likewise, though both Adam and Eve ruled over all the earth as one, Adam was head over Eve. This is clarified with, everyone is to "be subject to one another in the fear of Christ. Wives, to your own husbands, as to the Lord" (whether the husband is deserving or not is immaterial, for the desire to submit is for the Lord, in honoring the Lord, in obedience to the Lord and in worship to the Lord). Also, "For the husband is the head of the wife, as Christ also is the head of the church, He Himself the Savior of the body. But as the church is subject to Christ, so also the wives to their husbands in everything" (Ephesian 5:21–24).

God spoke directly and clearly. He did not say "man will eventually be in My image." God said, *Let us make man in our image . . . God creat**ed** mankind in His own image, in the image of God He creat**ed** them; male and female He creat**ed** them . . . And it **was** so . . . God **saw** all that He **had made**, and behold, it **was very good**.* Before the sixth day was over, God instructs Adam and Eve to be fruitful and multiply, He calls them by name. He does not command amino acids to evolve and multiply into different kinds. If one still doubts God's Word, then consider the words that the Holy Spirit inspired Paul to write in Acts 17:24–26 "The God who made the world and all things in it . . . He made from one man every nation of mankind to live on all the face of the earth." This should bring all theistic evolutionists back to the Word of creation and reject evolution.

Jesus quotes Gen. 1:27, 5:2, and 2:24. Matthew 19:4–5: "Have you not read that He who created them from the beginning made them male and female, and said, 'For this reason a man shall leave his father and mother and be joined to his wife, and the two shall become one flesh?" God in the

---

205 Strong's Conc.: # 120 *Adam*: A human being. The name of the first man.

flesh, confirms a literal rendering of the Genesis creation account. Do not fool yourself in thinking that you can reject the first five days of creation as being figurative and then by some arbitrary means jump into believing that the Genesis creation account is literal from Adam and Eve on. You do not get that right or privilege, as God declared in the Ten Commandments that He created everything in six days and rested on the seventh (Exodus 20:11) and then repeated Himself (Ex. 31:17).

In Our image, according to Our likeness. The word *image* is *Tselem*[206]. It means "resemblance" as representative of a figure, as in an idol or doll image of something else. This seems to suggest the physical image of God. We are literally the form of God. This is clarified with Jesus creating all things (John 1 and Col 1:16–17) and "Jesus is the physical image of the invisible God" (Col 1:15). Humans were literally made from God as a copy of God. The first copy is always closest to the original, so the angels are the closest copy of God, then Adam and Eve were the next purest copies of the original, and each generation of people are copies of copies, genetically speaking.

The word *likeness* is *Demuth*[207]. It means "resemblance," as in a model, shape, fashion, like, mannerisms, or similitude (similar). This seems more like the characteristics (mind, thoughts, emotions, etc) of God. The soul of a human is their thoughts, emotions, desires, and voluntary thoughts —the real you. In Hebrew, this is called the *Nephesh*. Both creatures and humans are said to have a Nephesh, or a soul.[208] This is the life of every living thing (Job 12:7–10). The soul is said to connect the body to the spirit, and the spirit connects the body and soul to God. Both Hebrew words for image and likeness have overlapping definitions, but everything in the Bible has a reason for it being there.

The creation account repeats that God made all plants, fish, birds, land animals, and insects after their kind, so evolutionists always want creationists to define *kind*. Using the terms *image* and *likeness* sums it up nicely. Things of the same *kind* will manifest similar physical images and similar characteristics of mind, emotions, and behavior. God created each *kind* with DNA information to have the ability to adapt to external stimuli and to produce slight adjustments, yet remain the same *kind*. Mankind labels these subtle changes with the term *species*. That is fine, but the ability to adapt is based on information already encoded in the DNA code; it is not new information within the DNA code that produces the ability to adapt.

<u>**Review:** God created us in His image, which is the physical appearance (body), and in His likeness, which are the thoughts, desires, and mind of a person (soul). God created His offspring after His kind, named Adam and Eve. The "image" is the hardware, and "likeness" is the software.</u>

When God appeared physically in Gen. 3, He was walking about on two feet and talked with Adam and Eve. The Bible establishes early that mankind was not a group of tree-swinging apes that evolved into humans over millions of years. The Bible is clear from the start that man was created in the image and likeness of God. Therefore, man did not evolve from any primate to become human. Even when God appeared in the flesh, He always appeared as a human male, never as a monkey.

Then God said, "Let Us make man in Our image, according to Our likeness; and let them rule over the fish of the sea and over the birds of the sky and over the cattle and over all the earth, and over every creeping thing that creeps on the earth." God created man in His own image, in the image of God He created him; male and female He created them.

God has just finished created the animals and insects in the darkness of evening at the beginning of the sixth day, and as the sun rises over the Garden of Eden, at the break of day (the midpoint of the day), the Lord speaks Adam into existence from the voice of God, the Holy spirit moved as the Breath of Life and entered the nostrils of man, and Adam became life. Life begot life.

God has created Adam and Eve, and some of us may be wanting a little more detail as to how God made Adam and Eve. Fortunately for you, God inspired Moses to write additional information. In Gen. 1:26–27, we get the general creative moment, and in Gen. 2:7–25, we get more details of the

---

206 Strong's Conc.: # 6754: *tselem*: resemblance, representative figure, an idol- image.
207 Strong's Conc.: # 1823 demuth: resemblance, model, shape; like:-fashion, like (as, -ness) manner, similitude.
208 Http://en.wikipedia.org/wiki/Nephesh

creative moment on the sixth day of creation.

One lie pops up from deceivers that deals with Eve and terms such as *female*, *woman*, *she*, and *her*. Nowhere does the name Lilith appear in the Bible; this is a false doctrine. Gen. 2:7–25 adds additional details about the sixth day of creation, not the creation of a second wife for Adam. Men were only allowed to have one wife, so if Adam had divorced Lilith, then there would be sin occurring before the fall of Gen. 3. Lilith is not Biblical; it is satanic doctrine. So let us take a look at the details of the sixth day of creation provided in Gen. 2:7–25: "Then the LORD God formed man of dust from the ground, and breathed into his nostrils the Breath of Life; and man became life [a living being]." Remember that in Hebrew, it is written the Breath of *Chay* is breathed into his nostrils, and man became *chay*. Life begot life. Verse 8:

> The LORD God planted a garden toward the east, in Eden; and there He placed the man whom He had formed. Out of the ground the LORD God caused to grow every tree that is pleasing to the sight and good for food; the tree of life also in the midst of the garden, and the tree of knowledge of good and evil.

Here we have God reflecting back on the third day of creation when He created all the grass, plants, and trees, and God says that out of the ground the LORD God caused to grow every tree, and then God places Adam, who He created on the sixth day, in this garden that was created on the third day.

In verse 15, *Then the LORD God took the man,* man is singular, and the Hebrew word is *Adam*. God did not create a single-celled self-replicating prokaryote, and God did not create more than one male.

In verse 18, God said, "It is not good for the man to be alone; I will make him a helper suitable for him." God had already created all the land animals at the beginning of the sixth day, and each one of them had a suitable mate for reproduction. God commanded the birds and fish to be fruitful and multiply in Gen. 1:22, and God commanded Adam to be fruitful by diligently working the Garden of Eden, but Adam could not multiply because he had no mate. Now this is an important point. God had formed every creature from the ground just like He had formed Adam, but the animals were not suitable for Adam because bestiality is forbidden. Look at the following from verse 18:

> Then the LORD God said, "It is not good for the man to be alone; I will make him a helper suitable for him." And out of the ground the LORD God formed every beast of the field and every bird of the sky, and brought to the man to see what he would call them; and whatever the man called a living creature, that was its name. The man gave names to all the cattle and to the birds of the sky, and to every beast of the field, <u>but for Adam there was not found a helper suitable for him.</u>

The whole purpose of this exercise was for God to demonstrate to Adam that he was not to try and mate with any creature on earth and that there was none suitable for him to reproduce with. This is in harmony with verse 15, where God commands Adam to be fruitful by telling him to cultivate the garden and keep it, but God does not command Adam to multiply because no mate existed for Adam.

No contradiction exist here with God revealing to Adam that though He created all the fish, birds, and land animals from the same ground that Adam came from, they were not suitable for him. God reflects back through the days of creation, this is not a reversal of order of creation; birds were created on the fifth day, and animals were created on the sixth day before Adam and Eve. God is not saying that He created Adam, then created the Garden of Eden, and then placed Adam there, God is saying He created Adam and placed Adam in the Garden that He had created. The same language and format is used with God discussing a suitable helpmate for Adam to multiply.

It would be logistically impossible to bring every species of animal and bird to the Garden of Eden; the abundance of life forms would not have fit into the Garden of Eden.

However long it took God to bring one of each kind of animal to Adam and have Adam name them, it would have been toward the end of the sixth day. Therefore, God created Eve toward the evening, or just prior to the evening, and hence named her Eve. Eve was created just before the sunset and the start of the evening of the seventh day. The whole point of the verse is summed up with this: "It is not good for the man to be alone, <u>I will make him a helper suitable</u> for him." Notice that *I will make* is future tense. God shows Adam all the different kinds of birds and animals:

> <u>But</u> for Adam <u>there was not found a helper suitable</u> for him. So the LORD God caused a deep sleep to fall upon the man, and he slept; then He took one of the his ribs and closed up the flesh at that place. The LORD God fashioned into a woman the rib which He and taken from the man, and <u>brought her to the man.</u>

God brought one of each kind of bird and animal to Adam to see what he would call them, but there was not found a helper suitable for him, so God creates Eve from the ground out of the same DNA of Adam (from the rib) and brings her to Adam to show him a suitable helper. This is all about fulfilling the second command given to each living thing—multiply. Every living creature is given the command to be fruitful and multiply. This means to be diligent with work and fruits of the Spirit and to produce offspring. God had already commanded Adam to be fruitful, to tend and cultivate the Garden of Eden, but God had not commanded him to multiply yet, not until Eve was created. Then the command was given to be fruitful <u>and</u> multiply. So the whole point of Gen. 2:7–25 is not about the creative order—it is solely about Adam being able to multiply.

Adam was not insufficient in his ability to fully obey God or to be fruitful. Adam was not lacking anything of himself; however, Adam could not reproduce. Likewise, Jesus was not insufficient or lacking anything, and Jesus remained unmarried. Also, Paul was not insufficient or lacking anything (2 Tim 3:16–17), and Paul remained unmarried (1 Cor. 7:7), so too was Adam. Yet, for reproduction, for a helpmate, Eve was created for Adam. For this reason, man is the glory of God, as God always appears in masculine form, and woman is the glory of man yet in the image of God because the attributes of God are in feminine form. Man does not originate from woman, but woman from man; indeed, man was not created for the woman's sake, but woman for the man's sake. Christ is the head of every man, and the man is the head of a woman, and God is the head of Christ—each in their image (I Cor. 11:11–12). Christ is the image of the Father (Col 1:15), man is the image of Christ (Gen. 1:26), and woman is the image of man (Gen. 2:21–25). This is not an insult; this designates roles for harmony. There cannot be two leaders of one flesh, so as the man and wife become *one flesh* (Gen 2:23–24), their is equality as being one, as Jesus is one with the Father and co-creator, yet He submits to the Father. It is a matter of preventing chaos. 1 Corinthians 11:11–12:

> The Father is the head of Christ and Christ is the head of man and man is the head of woman. However, in the Lord, neither is woman independent of man, nor is man independent of woman. For as the woman originates from the man, so also he has his birth through the woman; and all things originate from God.

Additionally, everyone is to "be subject to one another in the fear of Christ" (Eph. 5:21). Taking all this in perspective, the account of creation given in Gen. 2:7–25 provides details of the creation of Adam and Eve and a demonstration to Adam that the birds and land animals were not suitable for him to mate with; it is not a discussion about the order of creation. Therefore, Gen. 2:7–25 fits in the middle of Gen. 1:26: *Then God said, "Let us make man in Our image, according to Our likeness* **[Gen. 2:7–25 fits here]** *and let them rule over . . . over all the earth." God created man in His own image, in the image of God He created him; male and female He created them.*

As a side note on the supernatural aspect of the Bible, the number of completion is seven in the Bible. God created everything in six days and rested on the seventh when *it is complete*. God did His saving work on the cross in six hours and said *it is finished.* Then He rested entering the seventh hour. After sustaining His creation for roughly 6,000 years, and upon entering the 7,000th year, judgment occurs. The judgment is laid out with seals, trumpets, and bowls. Each has six events of action/work, with the seventh entering into the next. For example, six seals do work, and the seventh seal is the entering into the seven trumpets. Six trumpets do work, and the seventh trumpet is the entering into the seven bowls. Six bowls do work, and the seventh bowl is the final one, where *it is done* is said and Christ comes. This list can just keep going of the sevens that represent completion. You may be asking yourself, "What in the world does this have to do with Adam and Eve?" Well it turns out that 77 generations occurred from Adam to Jesus (Luke 3:1–38)—the complete Adam (I Corinthians 15:45).

Review: Gen. 2:7–25 is a detailed account of the creation of Adam and Eve and fits in the middle of Gen. 1:26. It is also a record of God illustrating to Adam that no creature was suitable for him to mate with for the purpose of multiplying before the creation of Eve.

"And let them <u>rule over</u> the <u>fish</u> of the sea and over the <u>birds</u> of the sky and over the <u>cattle</u> and over <u>all the earth</u>, and over <u>every creeping thing</u> that creeps on the earth." God created man in His own image, in the image of God He created him; male and female He created them. God blessed them; and God said to them, "Be fruitful and multiply and fill the earth, and <u>subdue it; and rule</u> over the fish of the sea and over the birds of the sky and over every living thing that moves on the earth."

Do you ever wonder why animals are innately skittish of humans? God gave the rule over all of creation to mankind. Why? Because mankind was created in the image of God. Also, Gen. 9:2 says, "The fear of you and the terror of you will be on every beast of the earth and on every bird of the sky; with everything that creeps on the ground, and all the fish of the sea, into your hand they are given." God gave Adam and Eve (i.e., humanity) authority to rule over fish, birds, cattle, insects, and all the earth. Men and women have equal abilities to equally love God and to be equally useful to God, though in different capacities and different roles. The Bible is clear that it is an abomination for a man to act like a woman and a woman to act like a man (Deut. 22:5); they are complete as they are and not to become something they are not. This crown of glory given to the human race to rule all on earth was a title of ownership, a title deed.

Do you ever wonder what prompted Satan to turn against God after creation was done, and since God is all powerful and omnipresent, what on earth prompted one-third of the angels (Rev. 12:4) to also get upset enough to follow Satan? Gen. 1:26b–27 may have the answer, and we can turn to Isaiah and Ezekiel to paint a clearer picture. Lucifer was created as a sinless angel on the first day of creation, sealed with perfection, full of wisdom, and perfect in beauty. Lucifer saw Adam and Eve being created on the sixth day and dwelling in the Garden of Eden, the place of God's holy mountain. Lucifer was a blameless, beautiful, high-ranking anointed cherub, and hearing that God bestowed this crown jewel of being ruler of all of earth to Adam and Eve, and also knowing that humans would one day out rank angels in the future, Lucifer envied and coveted their crown. The title was not his, and unrighteousness was found in him (Ezekiel 28:11b–17a) after creation. Lucifer revolted against God's will, and Lucifer said, "I will ascend to heaven, I will raise my throne above the stars of God, I will sit on the mount of assembly, I will ascend above the heights of the clouds, I will make a name for myself like God," and Lucifer fell (Isaiah 14:12–15) and became Satan. Lucifer, wanting to become God, fell and became the father of all death and all lies (John 8:44). Satan revolted against God's rule over all and God's decree to give rule of the earth to mankind. The other angels—seeing that Lucifer seemingly had a just claim to revolt against God giving the earth to puny mortal humans instead of giving the earth to powerful immortal angels—they revolted as well, and one-third of the angels followed Satan and became demons. The reason that we know that Satan wanted to be God is found in Isaiah, but potentially the reason that we know Satan wanted the title of "Ruler of Earth" is because he is called that in many places in the New Testament (John 12:31). Therefore, Lucifer wanted it all—he wanted God's title and humanity's title. This may solve what prompted 1/3 of the angels to follow Lucifer. In the same manner that Satan offered Jesus the title of Ruler of Earth, in Matthew 4:8–9, Satan most likely presented the angels with the same offer; "Follow me and I will give you the title of *Ruler of Earth*." Satan is always offering something that seems to have value, but he does not have anything good to offer.

In what manner, and how long did it take Satan to fall from the heights of heaven to Earth? Is this an opportunity to establish millions of years for Satan to reach Earth? In Jesus' words "I beheld Satan as Lightning fall from heaven/the heights" (Luke 10:18). Since Jesus spoke Hebrew, then let us focus on the Hebrew words that Jesus would have said. The Hebrew word for *lightning* is *Baraq* (Strong's Conc. #1300), which means a flashing, lightning. Thus, Jesus would have said, "I beheld Satan as *Baraq*." The Greek word translated as Heaven has two options *bamah or shamayim.*, Since the Greek word translated as Heaven includes *heights* in its definition, it is acceptable to use *bamah*, instead of shamayim (Strong's Conc. #8064: lofty, the sky aloft, visible arch where clouds move, as well as higher—heaven). The Hebrew word for heights is *Bamah* (Strong's Conc. #1116: an elevation, height, high place). Also, since Jesus is describing Satan's fall, it is fitting to use Satan's own choice word to describe the heights he was going to ascend, as the heights Satan came from—*bamah*. This event occurs only one time in the Bible, in Isaiah 14:14, where it describes Satan saying he will ascend above the *heights/bamah*. Therefore, it is fitting to use *bamah* to understand Luke 10:18. Thus, Jesus would have said, "I beheld Satan as *Baraq Bamah*. Two combine two words together, an "O" is used.

Therefore, Satan came from the heights of heaven to Earth in a twinkling of an eye, with the speed of lightning. This closes the door on any long period of time between Satan's fall and reaching the earth. I doubt Satan went straight to Adam and Eve directly to deceive them; he is more cunning than that. He does not show up with a pitchfork and horns; he always appears as an angel of light to deceive. Satan's first order of business was to recruit other creatures to abandon God as well. Satan built up recruits for his coup attempt. Most notably was a serpent located near the proximity of Eve. Satan eventually found a willing corrupt soul and convinced the serpent to disobey God, and Satan entered the snake. The snake was then possessed with the spirit of Satan and deceived Adam and Eve (Gen. 3). Lucifer's fall and humanity's fall most likely occurred many decades after creation.

As a result of sin, mankind has forfeited its authority to be rulers of the earth, and Satan has claimed the throne. Satan is the ruler of this world for a time. Satan even had his throne located in Pergamum (Rev. 2:13), which was in Babylon (modern day Turkey), but this throne, the Altar of Zeus, was moved in full to Berlin in the early 20th century,[209] just in time for Satan's all-out blitz in WW1 and WW2.

All will be restored when Christ comes again and He reigns from His throne on the holy mount as the true rightful heir as Lord of Lords and King of Kings (Rev. 22:1–5). Combining that with Jesus was/is the King and High priest Melchizedek (means Righteous King) of Salem (Jerusalem)(Genesis 14:18–20). This leads to the deduction that since the location of God's throne will be Jerusalem, it has always been that same location from the beginning. This leads to the notion that the perspective of the Genesis creation narrative was also from Jerusalem.

Do you ever wonder how long Adam and Eve lived after creation until they sinned? I hypothesize that the answer is implied in the Scriptures. Consider the descriptions of the curses applied to all the players involved in the crime. This list of players involved were Satan, the serpent (snake), Adam, Eve, all the creatures, and all of creation.

All of creation groans to be free from the bondage of sin (Romans 8:22), and symbolizes its struggle with sin, by the four seasons; fall (death), winter (burial), spring (birth), and summer (life). All of creation understood the magnitude of sin by knowing the pre-fallen state without the season of fall (death) and no winters (burial). Even the lion laid down next to the calf, and the wolf grazed with the lamb (Isaiah 11:6 speaks of the restoration of what was—creation). Therefore, creation knew the difference between the sinless creation and post-fallen conditions resulting from sin.

All the creatures were cursed as well (Gen. 3:14), though not as severely as the serpent. One

---

209 Http://en.m.wikipedia.org/wiki/Pergamon_Altar.

curse was that some became disobedient to God and became carnivores. I contend that another curse, was that they lost the ability to communicate with humans because they allowed their voice to be used to deceive. Thus, God closed this ability, to only be opened during special occasions (Numbers 22:28) and in heaven (Rev. 4:7, 5:8). Therefore, all the creatures were aware of the difference between sinless creation and the fallen state.

The serpent's (snake) curse is such that it also understood the magnitude of its sin. The serpent used to be able to walk on all four legs, but after the sin, it was reduced to slither on its belly (Gen. 3:14). Snakes today, still have a remnant claw that they used to use for walking, and can only use it for reproduction. Therefore, the serpent was fully aware of the difference between sinless creation and post-fallen state.

The Devil also understood the difference between sinless creation and his post-fallen state. Ezekiel 28:11–17 explains the beauty, adornment, wisdom, high rank, and that he dwelt with God, but he was cast down because of his corruption. Therefore, Satan also knew the magnitude of sin, and observed his pre-fallen environment and his post-fallen state.

Even Adam, he too understood the magnitude of sin. Adam fully knew the difference between his sinless state and his fallen state. Prior to his fall, he did not have to sweat to get food, there were no thorns, or thistles, or weeds. After his fall, Adam had to sweat to get food for his family, he would prick his finger on the thorns and thistles (Gen. 3:17–18). Therefore, Adam fully knew the difference from the sinless creation and the post-fallen condition.

So far we have discussed that every player (All of creation, all the creatures, the serpent, Satan, and Adam) involved in the fall of creation, had intimate first hand information of knowing the magnitude of sin, of knowing the difference between the sinless creation versus the post-fallen condition. Now we come to Eve, Gen. 3:16 records her curse, that God "will greatly multiply your pain in childbirth, in pain you will bring forth children." Do you ever wonder what Eve was thinking or what she asked God? Do you think she said, "uh, God, what is childbirth? Also, what are children? And after explaining those two things, please tell me the reference point of the multiplying my pain, in other words, you are going to multiply my pain in childbirth from what?" Are we to believe that everyone knew their sinless condition and the magnitude of their sin by comparing it with the post-fallen condition, except Eve? Is she the only one that did not understand what God was talking about? The answer may already appear obvious to you because God is consistent. I contend the preponderance of evidence suggests that Eve, just like the others, fully understood the difference between the sinless creation and the post-fallen condition. I contend that Eve had many children before the fall, only then could she understand what God was talking about.

Someone may argue, that Eve knew the difference between delivering a child in a sinless creation, versus a cursed environment, not because she gave birth prior to the fall, but because she ate from the tree of knowledge, and this magical fruit gave her the information. Let us look briefly at this tree and discern if that premise is valid. Gen. 3:3 "God has said, 'You shall not eat from it or touch it, or you will die.'" This statement is the truth, that "she will die." Now Satan, possessing the serpent, deceives Eve with half-truths and lies, "The serpent said to the woman, 'You surely will not die! For God knows that in the day you eat from it your eyes will be opened, and you will be like God, knowing good and evil.'" Did Satan speak the truth? Partially, but his information was from a deceitful perspective. Satan was referring only to the physical body not immediately dying, and he omitted the immediate death of their spirit, and death of their reign over all of creation, and the death of their ability to dwell in the presence of the LORD in the Garden of Eden. Then Eve and Adam ate the fruit from the forbidden tree, and "then the eyes of both of them were opened, and they knew that they were naked." Then God in the flesh atones for their death of sin, by killing a blameless animal, and clothed them. Thus, fulfilling the requirement of the law, "a life for a life," though not yet penned (code of Hammurabi and Mosaic law). "Then the LORD God said, 'Behold, the man has become like one of Us, knowing good and evil (Gen. 3:21–22). Thus, Adam and Eve did not eat from the tree of all knowledge, they ate from the tree that opened their eyes to the physical realm of knowing the difference between good and evil (by direct means, or first hand), and closed their vision of the spiritual realm. Adam and Eve already knew of the good, but now they knew both good and evil because of their direct evil actions. Whereas, God knows good and evil by indirect association. For example, an oncologist (a doctor that treats cancer patients) knows good health directly, and cancerous health indirectly, by their knowledge of the subject. Whereas, a cancer patient knows good health versus cancerous health, by direct first hand knowledge. In this illustration, God is the doctor, and Adam and Eve are the cancerous patients. Adam and Eve once only knew good health, but then they sinned and made themselves cancerous, then they knew both good health and cancerous health. Likewise, Adam and Eve knew good, but then they sinned and made themselves evil, and then they knew both good and evil.

For this reason, by Eve eating the fruit of the forbidden tree, it was not that there was special knowledge hidden in the fruit, and all of a sudden she had knowledge of everything like God. She was not given special knowledge of what it was like to give birth before the fall of mankind, even though she hadn't given birth yet. That is purely speculative and not congruous with the text. The knowledge of good was already in Eve prior to, but now after she sinned, she knew what it was like to disobey God, what it was like to think and commit evil. Therefore, she knew evil as well as already knowing good. Therefore, when God announced the curses on Eve, she knew what God was talking about, as far as what children were, what childbirth was, and what it was like to deliver with little discomfort because she had multiple children before sinning—not because of a magical fruit she ate.

If you are not convinced by now, consider the words of God and Adam. Let us set the scene. God has just created Adam in the image and likeness of God. Adam is at the pillar of health and vitality and at the peak of hormone production. We may infer the peak levels because everything was perfect and at their best—this was creation after all. Now, God creates Eve just before sunset, and guess who Adam sees walking toward him? None other than the Father of the bride—God in the flesh, and His daughter—Eve. Gen. 2:22 "The LORD God . . . brought her to the man/Adam." If you are not sure what is going on, this is the beginning of the first wedding ceremony, when the Father of the bride gives His daughter to Adam. Then God (potentially Melchizedek of Salem—Jesus of Jerusalem) performs the High Priestly duties during the wedding, Gen. 1:27–28: "male and female He created them. God blessed them; and God said to them, 'Be fruitful and multiply, and fill the earth.'" They are officially married, and have the blessing, and have been commanded to multiply. Now ask yourself, how long do you think Adam and Eve waited to be obedient to God's command to multiply? After all, both were at the peak of hormone production, health, vitality, and fitness, and since Mosaic law declared a woman unclean during her cycle, then you know that Eve was not unclean or in her cycle as the sun was setting on the sixth day of creation. In fact, it could be argued that the discomfort associated with the menstrual cycle, as an unfertilized egg and endometrium die and get sloughed off, was not part of the sinless Garden of Eden, but was part of the curse because this process is part of childbirth. This further adds evidence that Eve did not have a menstrual cycle in the Garden of Eden because she immediately became pregnant. Let us go back to the discussion of the first sunset of Adam and Eve.

The answer to how long they waited is politely written in the Scripture in Genesis 2:23. "The man said, 'This is now bone of my bones, and flesh of my flesh; She shall be called Woman, because she was taken out of Man.'" This sounds like Adam has just "known" his wife Eve for the first time. Can you hear the exuberance? Then God inspires Moses to write this immediately following: "<u>For this reason</u> [what reason? For what just happened] a man shall leave his father and his mother, and be <u>joined to his wife</u>, and they shall <u>become one flesh</u>. And the <u>man and his wife were both naked and were not ashamed (Gen. 2:24–25)</u>." There you have it: they are now husband and wife. The marriage had been consummated on the sixth day as the sun was setting, and further evidence of this is in the discrete Word of God saying that Adam was joined to his wife, they became one flesh, and they were naked and not ashamed of joining together as one flesh. These are discrete terms that do not need to be grossly broken down. Now, since all children are a gift from God (Psalm 127:3), we may infer that God gifted their first act of obedience, to the command to multiply, with conception (pregnancy).

The first mention of children by Adam and Eve is not until Cain and Abel, but this does not negate that they had many children before then who aren't specifically named because they did not commit any atrocities worth mentioning. Genesis 4:1 states that Adam and Eve had relations (plural). But let us focus on Cain and Abel because the definitions of their names are interesting. **Cain**'s name (Strong's Conc. #7014 and 7013) includes the defining terms of a lance (as striking fast), or a spear. That seems to indicate that his birth was associated with a quick delivery, something non-troubling, a birth that was brief and satisfactory. Now compare that with **Abel**'s name (Strong's Conc. #1893 and 1892), which includes defining terms such as, something transitory and unsatisfactory, or vain. Potentially, the vain definition may be pointing to the fact that Abel was murdered and/or that the delivery process involved hopelessly tough labor, with pointless attempts of pushing and contractions. Abel's name (including the meaning of unsatisfactory) points to the difficult labor. The two different definitions of their names suggests a change in the process of delivery, potentially because of the curse applied because of sin.

To elucidate the point that Adam and Eve had hundreds of children, consider that when their son Cain killed Abel, Cain had to flee the presence of the LORD. He settled in the land of Nod, east of Eden, where he found a wife (Gen. 4:16). Therefore, Cain settled where other children of Adam and Eve were already dwelling. Additionally, by the time we get to Gen. 5, Adam is 130 years of age when he begets Seth. This illustrates that Moses only wrote about the prominent names in the genealogical record.

Putting the evidence together, I contend it supports that Eve had many children before their fall. Thus, after Adam's sin, and the curse applied, then Eve understood how much God increased her pain in delivering children and her discomfort during her menstrual cycle.

Review: I hypothesize that Adam and Eve were married, consummated the marriage, and Eve was pregnant by the end of the sixth day, with Eve giving birth 9 months later. Potentially, Eve did not have a menstrual cycle because she kept becoming pregnant after delivering a child, and thus, was never unclean while living in the presence of the LORD, in the Garden of Eden. Potentially, the fall of mankind came between the births of Cain and Abel many children later, with Cain being a quick delivery, like a strike of a lance, and Abel being a difficult painful delivery, that was unsatisfactory and vain.

Then God said, "Behold, I have given you every plant yielding seed that is on the surface of all the earth, and every tree which has fruit yielding seed; it shall be food for you; and to every beast of the earth and to every bird of the sky and to every thing that moves on the earth which has life, I have given every green plant for food'; and it was so. God saw all that He had made, and behold, it was very good. And there was evening and there was morning, the sixth day.

The animals that existed on earth were herbivores before the fall, even the great predators, such as lions, bears, great white sharks, killer whales, T. rex, and so forth. They were all vegetation eaters. Only after the sin of Gen. 3 did predators become disobedient to the will of God and sin alongside mankind, until evil was so rampant that God caused the global catastrophic flood. After the Flood, God allowed carnivores with these words in Gen. 9:3:

> Every moving thing that is alive shall be food for you; I give all to you, as I gave the green plant. Only you shall not eat flesh with its life, its blood. Surely I will require your life-blood; from every beast I will require it and from every man.

Before the fall, mankind and all life forms only ate the fruits of plants and trees and grass; now mankind and predators could add meat if properly prepared.

Was Adam an ape or tree-swinging monkey? No. The oldest artifact of writings is a code of laws written about 1772 BC before Moses wrote the first five books of Old Testament. The code of

Hammurabi is from ancient Mesopotamia and describes around 282 laws for mankind, establishing standards for wages for certain jobs, how to handle disputes, "eye for an eye, tooth for a tooth, and life for a life," and the issue of slavery. From the beginning, man is described as man, not any form of ape. The first humans on earth were just like humans today, except they were taller and had no diseases and no imperfections. We are copies of copies from Adam.

Did Adam and Eve know about fire or how to make bread? One of Adam's curses was, "By the sweat of your face you will eat bread." Adam and Eve were highly intelligent humans and were able to make fires, build a kiln, and bake ground wheat and nuts to make bread. Zero evidence exist of man ever evolving from any ape. One of the best pieces of evidence that evolutionists have is that humans and apes have similar DNA codes, but humans have similar DNA codes to everything, and many creatures have similarities with the human DNA code. This does not mean we evolved from them; this means we have the same creator, who made everything from and through Himself. We all have a part of the essence of God, so of course there will be some DNA similarities. Of course there will be similarities in the DNA code that produce proteins that carry out similar specific functions. For example, all animals that have enamel have the same genetic code to produce the same protein to carry out the same function. Specific proteins are needed for all functions of a life form.

And it was so. God saw all that He had made, and behold, it was very good. And there was evening and there was morning, the sixth day. God belabors the point that what He commanded was so, complete, totally finished, and lacking nothing. This is a line drawn in the sand by God against all those who believe in man's version of events. If the phrase *and it was so* was not clear enough for you, and it should be since God keeps repeating Himself for our thick heads, then God adds additional clarity with the words: "God saw all that He had made, and behold, it was very good." Everything is past tense—God did not see that it will be good; it is already complete, finished, and very good.

Let me focus your thoughts on the word *all*. God saw *all*. *God saw all that He had made, and behold it was very good.* What did God see? He did not see death, sin, fallen angels, a prior history of war, or a prior history of God killing all the dinosaurs and destroying all of heaven and earth and rebuilding everything through these six days. The fossils are NOT the remains of death and destruction of a pre-Adamic world that existed for angels. At the end of the six days, nothing evil, no sin, no death, or anything bad existed. *All* that God saw (and God sees everything) and *all* that He had made (and God made everything in the six days of creation, Exodus 20:11) was very good.

And there was evening and there was morning, the sixth day. Again, the proper way to define *day* is by the associated terms. And they are *evening, morning, and sixth.* They provide crystal clear clarity that *day* is one earth rotation. If there was no number in front of *day,* then an argument could be made for ages, eons. If you still question God's Word, turn to the end of the Book of Job for counsel on questioning God's Word. I keep saying God's **W**ord instead of God's **w**ord to draw your attention to the fact that Jesus is the Word that became flesh and died on the cross, so when one rejects a portion of the **W**ord, they are rejecting a portion of Jesus (John 1:1–14). This means that if one loves Jesus, he or she Loves His Word, but to call some of Jesus' Word inaccurate is to lose usefulness and effectiveness for sharing the gospel. Some are guilty of annulling a portion of Scripture and teaching others to do the same, and this leads to being least in the Kingdom of Heaven (Matt. 5:19). This does not mean you lose your salvation, as one cannot lose salvation, but you lose usefulness and lose effectiveness for God.

Chapter Summary: God created the animals and insects during the evening of the beginning of the sixth day. Then, when the sun rose over Jerusalem, the mount of God, and the Garden of Eden, God fashioned Adam by speaking him into existence, and the Holy Spirit moved as the Breath of Life into the nostrils of man, and he became life. Adam named the animals and birds during most of the daylight, and then before the sun set, God caused Adam to sleep, took a rib for DNA, and formed Eve out of the ground. Then Eve's Father brought her to Adam, they were joined as man and wife, with Eve plausibly conceiving just before the sun set on the sixth day.

Chapter 38
The Seventh Day

Gen. 2:1–4: *Thus the heavens and the earth were completed, and all their hosts. By the seventh day God completed His work which He had done, and He rested on the seventh day from all His work which He had done (had made). Then God blessed the seventh day and sanctified it, because in it He rested from all His work which God had created and made. This is the account of the heavens and the earth when they were created, in the day that the LORD God made earth heaven.*

The Hebrew word for "complete and finished and ended*"* is *kalah* (#3615). In the context of creation, it means to end, to cease, be finished, to complete, accomplished, finished, fulfilled, or brought to pass. The King James uses "finished" and "ended," and the New American Standard Bible uses "completed." Both convey the same concept. Creation has finished, has been completed, and has ended. It is to say that all of creation is perfect, whole, complete, and lacking nothing—all of which contradicts evolution. Evolutionists believe life is evolving toward more complexities, less entropy. The Bible is clear that all things were perfectly completed at creation and everything tends toward entropy; all things wear out: "The sky will vanish like smoke, and the earth will wear out like a garment and its inhabitants will die in like manner" (Isaiah 51:6). Also, Psalm 102:26: "And of old you founded the earth, and the heavens are the work of Your hands. Even they will perish, but you endure; and all of them will wear out like a garment." Also, 2 Cor. 4:16: "our outer man is decaying, yet our inner man is being renewed day by day."

It is important to note how many times the words or concepts of "completed/finished/ended" and "had done/had made" are used on the seventh day.

1. *Thus the heavens were **completed/finished**.* Grammatically, because of the word *and*, we can break up the phrase for clarity and still have the same meaning.

2. *And the earth was **completed/finished**.*

3. *And all their hosts were **completed/finished**.* Notice that it does not say that God paused from all His work or that He is completing or still to complete.

4. *By the seventh day God **completed/finished** His work.*

5. *Which He **had done/had made**,* another past tense phrase of completion.

6. *And He rested on the seventh day from <u>all</u> His work which He **had done/had made**."*

7. *He rested from <u>all</u> His work which God **had created and made**.*

Theistic evolutionists have another set of verses here to distort to make themselves tolerable to atheists, but they gain no ground. No atheist would ever say, "Since they believe in evolution, I'm going to believe in their god." The way to reach an atheist is through the science that supports the Genesis creation and exposes evolution and deep time as false.

The first ancestor of every kind of life form, whether that kind be grass, plant, tree, fish, bird, beast, land animal, insect, or human, was completed and fully created in the six days of creation, and God rested on the seventh day of creation. This is summed up with Jesus saying, "Have you not read that He who created from the beginning made them male and female, and said 'for this reason a man shall leave his father and mother and be joined to his wife'" (Matt 19:4–5). No where in the Bible does it ever hint that God made single-celled organisms that evolved into more complex life and that eventually primitive man was a tree-swinging monkey. Quite the contrary, Jesus said from the beginning that humans were in the form of man and wife. From the beginning of time, humans were already complete and had the shape, image, and characteristics of God.

Review: <u>The Bible directly records that creation was complete, finished, and ended and that God then rested from all the creative work that He had done. Everything was done and referred to in past tense. This excludes and contradicts the ongoing hypothesis of evolution.</u>

Now this "*work*" that was completed on the seventh day of creation refers to the creation of everything, the creation of all things, including the heavens, the earth and seas, and all things visible and invisible. This includes angels: "For by Him all things were created, in the heavens and on earth, visible and invisible, whether <u>thrones or dominions or rulers or authorities—all</u> things have been created through Him and for Him" (Col 1:1–17). This elucidates that angels are created beings. Since all things were created in the six days, that includes angels by default, and it excludes a pre-Adamic era before the six days of creation. Also consider Ezekiel 28:13: "On the day that you were <u>created</u>." God is talking to Lucifer, the one who fell after creation and became Satan. This clarifies that angels are created beings. Also, the phrase "the day," dispels the notion of an evolutionary process for angels.

Thus the heavens and the earth were completed (finished), and all their hosts. The *work* that is finished is the creation that occurred from *In the beginning . . .* to *sixth day.* This is clarified by the word *thus,* which is saying that as a result of everything mentioned earlier, then *"the heavens and the earth were completed and all their hosts."* Again, this rules out the slow process of evolution. After each thing that God creates, He says that it was so and that it was good, and after creating everything in six days, *God saw all that He had made, and behold, it was very good.* This negates the notion that God looked out over creation and saw death, decay, demons, evolution, and fallen angels.

The Exodus 20:11 and 31:17 verses are clear that God made everything, or *all* things, in six days. Gap theorists (including theistic evolutionists) have to alter Scripture and annul Scripture to deal with fossils, coal, oil reservoirs, and so on. The gap theory hypothesis violates Exodus' claim that *all* things were created in six days of creation and that God rested on the seventh day. Gap theorists must call God's testimony in Exodus 20 and 31 erroneous; by the way, it is part of the Ten Commandments and written in stone. Gap theorists claim that billions of creatures and billions of botanical life forms lived and died before the creation of Adam and Eve. The Bible records that when Adam and Eve sinned, then death entered the world. Romans 5:12–14: "Therefore, just as through one man sin entered into the world, and death through sin, and so death spread to all men, because all sinned, for until the Law sin was in the world . . . death reigned from Adam." The clear inference is that before Adam and Eve sinned, sin and death did not exist. This excludes death being in the world before the fall of Adam and Eve, which concretely excludes the gap theory hypothesis that all the fossils (life turned to stone), coal deposits (botanical life turn to fossil fuel), oil reserves (life turned to fossil fuel), salt deposits, layers of the crust, and so on occurred billions of years in some angelic era before Adam was created.

Since angels are part of the *all* that was created in the six days of creation, and since all dinosaurs and all soil and all water, and so forth are part of the *all,* then when God created everything in Genesis. This debunks the hypothesis of a gap in time between verse 1 and 2.

The writer of Hebrews 4:3–4 talks about the completed work as well: "His works were finished from the foundation of the world . . . And God rested on the seventh day from all his works." This contradicts the notion that life has been evolving ever since the first replicating single-celled organism. The Bible is quite clear that God finished His work and rested on the seventh day. God is sustaining His creation now, not still creating new kinds of life, new dirt, and other things. John 1:3: "All things came into being through Him, and apart from Him nothing came into being that has come into being." Also, Colossians 1:16 says, "For by Him all things **were created**, both in the heavens and on earth, visible and invisible . . . all things **have been created** through Him and for Him. He is before all things, and in Him all things hold together." Essentially, God created all things in the past through His essence, so each thing of earth and on earth and of heaven and in heaven has a piece of God in them, and this is why similarities exist in DNA with life on earth. Additionally, Colossians 1:17 talks about God sustaining His creation, making His creation endure, and holding it together. This gives great insight as to the type of work God is still performing. He is not continuing to create as He did in the Genesis creation account.

Review: *All* means all, *everything* means everything, *completed* means completed, *and finished* means finished.

How long did it take God to create all things that are referenced in the past tense, and when did He create all things? Exodus clearly states twice that God created everything in the heavens and on earth and in the seas and all that is contained in them in six days and rested on the seventh (Ex 20:11 and 31:17). From a Biblical perspective, one cannot hold Scripture to be true and without error and still believe in an evolutionary process or a gap theory. For God's own **W**ord declares that all things were created in the past tense.

Review: The Bible records creation as complete; all references to the Genesis creation are in the past tense, and all was created in six days. The Bible implicitly declares that evolution and the gap theory are false. The Bible directly says that God created everything in six days, and He made them male and female from the beginning.

Well, then if creation is done, then what in the world do we call all the babies that were born after Adam and Eve? And what about all the seeds that germinated from grass, plants, and tress? Are they not a new creation?

From a biological view, reproduction is a continuation of life that already exists, not a new creation from nothing. It is a continuation of ancestral life via combining two sets of chromosomes, the blueprints to generate a continuation of life with a combination of both parental genes. The act of reproduction is to produce another power source or temporary housing for the spirit, and since all spirits were created on the first day of creation, then spirits are not created either. Sure, a regeneration of the spirit occurs to make it clean or righteous or sanctified, but not in the since of Genesis creation. Each baby conceived is a continuation of the energy-generating force of their parents and not a new body from nothing.

From a scriptural perspective, all verses reference the Genesis creation in the past tense. Sure, David sand "create in me a clean heart," and a regenerated person is a "new creature" upon being saved. But no verse refers to the Genesis creation account in the present tense in terms of new kinds of life. Let us dig deeper for more clarity. The Hebrew word is _bara_ (#1254 Strong's Conc.), and it means to create (qualified), cut down (as in wood), select, feed (as a formative processes: choose, create (creator), dispatch, do, or make.

One verse needs attention regarding the definition of _bara_, and it deals with whether God is still creating. Psalm 102:18: "This will be written for the generation to come, that a people yet to be "bara"/created will praise the LORD." When taking the verse in context with the proceeding verses and following verses, it becomes very clear that the _people yet to be created_ is the birth of the nation of Israel, as the verses prior to are all about God restoring/building up Zion/Israel. Psalm 102:13–20:

> Compassion on <u>Zion</u>, for it is time to be gracious to <u>her</u>, for the appointed time has come . . . find pleasure in <u>her</u> stone . . . for <u>her</u> dust . . . for the LORD has built up <u>Zion</u> . . . This will be written for the generation to come, that a <u>people</u> [Zionists] yet to be created (_bara_) may praise the LORD. For He looked down from His holy height . . . to hear the groaning of the prisoner, to set free those who were doomed to death, that men may tell of the name of the LORD in <u>Zion</u> and His praise in <u>Jerusalem</u>, when the <u>peoples are gathered together</u> [as a nation is created], and the kingdoms to serve the LORD."

God is talking about the state of Zion that is created, and not talking about creating humans. Therefore, God made everything, visible and invisible, in heaven and on earth: "All things have been created."

Review: Creation as explained in Gen. 1 and 2 has ceased. The creating that God did later was gathering the people together to create Zion. Also, God created a clean heart in us and spiritually created us to be new creatures upon receiving salvation and that sort of thing. Other than that, God has completed all His creation and is done creating and is sustaining His creation, working to hold His creation together and to cause His creation to endure until judgment.

This means that at conception, when the spirit (created on the first day of creation) enters the fertilized egg, it becomes a living soul, a human life. The Bible declares that all who have the blood in them are living beings, and a fertilized egg has the DNA, which came from God (Luke 3:38), and it has been passed down all the way from Adam and Eve. Therefore, all fertilized eggs have the DNA of God in them, and it is the image and likeness in its base form. At conception, the image and likeness of God are residing in a fertilized egg as DNA, and mankind is not to murder any man, or else God will require their life (Gen. 9:4). The fertilized egg settles on the uterus, into the endometrium, and receives nutrients from the mother's blood supply and thus has the blood of life in it from the mother's blood. Around this moment, their spirit that was created on the first day is joined with a fertilized egg at conception, and the human becomes a living soul. Likewise, this goes for all creatures that have the breath of life in them and that had their spirits created on the first day of creation, including the fish of the seas, birds of the air, and land animals.

Spirits and souls eternally exist, but the body is currently mortal and short term. Since the spirit does not exist in the female ovum or the male spermatozoa, the spirit was a created entity, and since John 1:3, Colossians 1:16, and Genesis clearly state that God created all things at creation, the spirit was created on the first day with the "light." The body is not a new creation, but a continuation of both the lives of the mother and father and their DNA. Therefore, this maintains harmony that all things were created in six days of creation, and God sustains His creation through parents reproducing a continuation of life from their cells and DNA.

Other works of God are ongoing, but they do not have anything to do with the six days of creation, as far as creating something from formlessness and void of life. For example, God works to sustain His creation (Colossians 1:17) and to answer our prayers. We know that Jesus worked with His hands as a carpenter (Mark 6:3), and we can read about the works of Christ and His miracles (Matthew 11:2). God, who began a good work in us, will perfect it (Philippians 1:6). God works wonders for Israel (Psalm 66:5), for the church (Romans 8:28), and for the fulfillment of prophecy (Revelation 15:3). We are God's fellow workers (1 Corinthians 3:9), and Christ worked on the cross.

Those who believe that God created everything but through an evolutionary process, have to allegorize the entire Genesis creation account. Again, this is contrary to what God testified and how He clearly communicated to Moses—face to face, mouth to mouth, and not in veiled dreams and veiled visions (Num. 12:6–9).

Review: "Thus the heavens and the earth were completed, and all their hosts. By the seventh day God completed His work which He had done, and He rested on the seventh day from all His work which He had done . . . He rested from all His work which God had created and made."

A supernatural harmony exist in the Bible through the phrase: "It is complete," it is done, it is finished." God declares in His creation account that it is complete. In the entire Genesis account of creation, when the word *God* is *Elohiym,* which is the plural form of the one true God. This is because God consists of Father, Son, and Holy Spirit. When Jesus the Christ, the Son of God, was hanging on the cross, His last words before He yielded up His spirit were: "It is finished!" (John 19:30). God, in human flesh, finished His work on the cross in six hours and then rested. Elohiym (God) finished His work of creation in six days and then rested.

Fast forward to the end of times, when the workings of the son of Perdition, the beast, the bearer of 666, is finished at the hand of God, and God the Son declares, "It is done." Revelation 21:1–6:

> Then I saw a new heaven and a new earth . . . And He who sits on the throne said, "Behold, I am making all things new." And He said, "Write, for these words are faithful and true." Then He said to me, "**It is done.** I am the Alpha and the Omega, the beginning and the end."

This will potentially occur 6,000 years after creation (Revelation 21:6), and then entering into the 7,000th year of rest of the millennial kingdom.

Review: After six hours on the cross and entering the seventh hour, the Son of God declared, "It is finished." After six days of creation, on the seventh day, Elohiym declared, "It is done . . . it is complete." After 6,000 years of sustaining His creation, the Son of God will declare, "It is done" and there will be rest on Earth as He reigns in Jerusalem in the seventh millennium.

If God is finished creating, how do we handle "Then I saw a new heaven and a new earth; for the first heaven and the first earth passed away"? Matthew 5:17–19 helps to discern whether God violates His own Word by saying that He is done creating and then saying that He intends to create a new heaven and new earth. Let us look at these verses for help. Jesus said,

> Do not think that I came to abolish the Law or the Prophets; I did not come to abolish but to fulfill them. For truly I say to you, until heaven and earth pass away, not the smallest letter or stroke shall pass from the Law until all is accomplished.

God has finished creating and is sustaining His creation, causing His creation to endure until the judgment when heaven and earth will be severely damaged and what we knew the earth to be will pass away. Then all will be fulfilled, and God will restore creation to before the fall, and this will be a new heaven and new earth to us. As the law and the prophets have recorded, God has finished His creation and created everything; once all has been fulfilled from the law and the prophets, then God can and will create again and will be in harmony with His Word. It is not a brand new heaven and earth, it is a restoration of the earth through violent and catastrophic judgment via asteroid impacts splitting the earth asunder (Isaiah 24). Thus, restoring creation back to it was before the fall, which seems like a new heaven and new earth to us because the canopy will be restored. The stars will twinkle differently, the atmosphere will appear different, all mountains and islands are gone (Revelation 16).

    Review: God has finished creating, all creation is complete, and God is no longer creating, but is sustaining, causing His creation to endure (Col 1:17) until all is fulfilled regarding all that the law and the prophets testified to. Once all is fulfilled, then God will restore creation back to before the fall, and this will be a new heaven and new earth to us, as the first heaven and the first earth will have passed away with catastrophic events written in Revelation.

    God blessed the seventh day and sanctified it, because in it He rested from all His work which God had created and made. God did not rest because He was exhausted from His work. God is infinite, all-powerful, and eternal, He is not subject to entropy and decay. Why then did God rest? He did so to sanctify the day for mankind. Sanctified means to make holy, or to set apart. God set the seventh day apart from the other six days for mankind's benefit. Exodus chapters 20 and 31 provide the information to understand why God rested the seventh day. Let us set the scene. Moses is receiving the Ten Commandments from God; at the fourth commandment, we pick up Exodus 20:8–11:

> Remember the sabbath day, to keep it holy. Six days you shall labor and do all your work, but the seventh day is a sabbath of the LORD your God; in it you shall not do any work . . . For in six days the LORD made the heavens and the earth, the sea and all that is in them, and rested on the seventh day; therefore the LORD blessed the sabbath day and made it holy.

The sanctified seventh day was for the benefit of humans so that they would know who it is that makes them holy. It is not man that saves himself or makes himself holy; it is solely and exclusively God (Eph 2:8). Physically, humans needed to know that they require rest or will wear out. Humans need to rest to be refreshed. Spiritually, humans need to know who it is that gives them rest from their sin to be holy. Each day of rest reminds humans of what God has done for them. If this was not clear enough, let us consider Exodus 31:12–18. God repeats Himself to Moses to drive home the message:

> The LORD spoke to Moses, saying, "But as for you, speak to the sons of Israel, saying, You shall surely observe My sabbaths; for this is a sign between Me and you throughout your generations, that you may know that I am the LORD who sanctifies you. Therefore you are to observe the sabbath, for it is holy to you."

The whole point of God sanctifying the seventh day is for mankind to know that God is the one who sanctifies them and who makes them holy, pure, and clean. Israel needs to continue observing the Sabbath because it is written in verses 16–17: "Israel shall observe the sabbath, to celebrate the sabbath throughout their generations as a perpetual covenant. It is <u>a sign between Me and the sons of Israel forever.</u>" all the Ten Commandments are repeated in the New Testament for everyone to observe, except one, the Sabbath. Why? All the moral laws are unchanged and still observed, but the ceremonial laws are shadows and symbols that point to Jesus and are fulfilled in Jesus. Thus, Israel may be observant of the Sabbath by resting in Jesus. The church obeys each ceremonial law by default through obedience to Jesus. Colossians 2:16–17 sums up this point: "Therefore no one is to act as your judge in regard to food or drink or in respect to a festival or a new moon or a sabbath day—things which are a mere shadow of what is to come; but the substance belongs to Christ." This means that all the festivals and ceremonial laws in the Old Testament are pointing to God in the flesh, Jesus the Christ. That is one of the reasons why the Jews wanted to crucify Jesus because He healed on the Sabbath day. In their minds, Jesus violated the Sabbath and therefore deserved to die. However, the law of observing the Sabbath was to remind people that it is God who sanctifies, makes people holy, sets them apart, and cleanses them from sin. Jesus was fulfilling the Sabbath by cleansing the people of sin and its physical effects. No clearer picture of the fulfillment and embodiment of the Word made flesh and the Law fulfilled in Jesus than Him being God in the Flesh who sanctified the people with physical and spiritual healing on the Sabbath. The Word, or the Law of the Sabbath, is from the Father, spoken through and manifested through Jesus. Jesus is the one who sanctifies mankind to the Father by the washing away their sin, with His own personal shed blood representing the final complete and perfect sacrifice on our behalf. Jesus' death on the cross transcends time, meaning that those in the Old Testament were also saved by faith alone, and their sins were covered by Jesus' blood, even though they used a symbol that pointed to Jesus (the Passover lamb).

This is one of many illustrations of the harmony in the Bible from start to finish. Another is that salvation has always been through faith and grace alone, not of our works, so we should not boast. It is worthy to note that since God appeared to Abram, and no one has seen God the Father at anytime (John 1:18) and Jesus is the image of the invisible Father (Colossians 1:15), then Abram was saved through the Son of God. It was the Son of God who appeared to Abram, not the Father. Jesus said, "I AM the way, and the truth, and the life; no one comes to the Father but through Me" (John 14:6). The path of salvation, eternal life, has never changed from Adam and Eve to Abraham, to Moses, and through all the Old Testament and New Testament; the path of salvation has always been through the Son.

Review: <u>God sanctified the seventh and rested, not because God was fatigued or tired, but for man to learn how to be refreshed from six days of diligent work. God sanctified the seventh day for mankind, so people would know that it is God who makes them holy.</u>

All His work which God had <u>created and made</u>. Why does God distinguish between *created* and *made*? Everything in the Bible has a purpose, and God uses certain numbers and days and sayings for a reason. Things are not randomly put in the Bible, so when something as simple as two words that seem to be synonyms are put together, know that just because we may not fully understand why they are there, you should keep searching and praying to the Holy Spirit to reveal to you why they are there. The Holy Spirit will guide you on interpreting the Scripture correctly (1 Cor. 2:10–16). So let us look at the two words in their original Hebrew:

Made (Asah): made the firmament, made the sun and moon, made the stars, made the beast of the earth. *Asah* (# 6213)<u>: to do or make</u>, accomplish, become, bring forth, dress, execute, fashion, finish, fulfill, furnish, gather, be industrious, labor, procure, provide, or put in. Gen. 1:7: Made the expanse between the waters of the atmosphere and universe. Gen. 1:16: Made the sun, moon, and stars. Gen. 1:25: Made the beasts of the earth. Gen. 1:26: Let us make man in our image. Gen. 1:31 God saw everything that He had made. Gen. 2:3: All His work which God created and made.

Create (Bara): God created the heaven, God created great sea creatures, and God created man in his own image. *Bara* (#1254)<u>: to create</u>, select, feed, choose, create, creator, cut down, dispatch, do, and make (as in fat). Gen. 1:1: Created the heavens and earth. Gen. 1:21: Created the great sea monsters, fish, and birds. Gen. 1:27: Created man (Adam and Eve). Gen. 2:3: All His work which God created and made.

Some overlap of the two terms exist. How can God both create "ex nihilo" out of nothing and make that same thing? Both accounts of the creation of Adam and Eve use *bara* for "create" and *asah* for "made." Some say that these words are just synonyms and God was being thorough in describing His creation. When God uses *bara* and *asah*, it is for us to know more; they are not redundant words that are unnecessary. The Bible is supernaturally written. Oh, but we are not done, as another word needs to be added to the mix.

Formed *(Yatsar)*: This means formed or fashioned (Strong's Concordance # 3335). Gen. 2:7: "Then the LORD God <u>formed</u> man of the dust from the ground." We get some help in Isaiah 44: when God compares how He "formed you from the womb." Also, in regard to how mankind formed: "False idols mankind has <u>formed</u> (yatsar) out of a cast." Also, in verse 12: "Man <u>fashions</u> (*yatsar*) iron into a cutting tool and does his work over the coals, fashioning it with hammers and working it with his strong arm." This is an ongoing process of God sustaining His creation, not creating out of nothing, but the continuation of life.

To add another gear to this wheel of information, consider Isaiah 43:7: "Everyone who is called by My name, and whom I have **created**/*bara* for My Glory, Whom I have **formed**/*yatsar* , even whom I have **made**/*asah* ." Here we have all three: *bara, yatsar,* and *asah.*

When God uses *bara* to create something that it is ex nihilo (without starting material), it is to indicate something more supernatural that comes from God's essence, something more of a miracle. Even though we have discerned the means God used to create matter with the Large Hadron Collider, we cannot comprehend the power and intelligence of God to create all the matter that exists in the universe. Also, includes the creating the spirit of each person, all the matter, space, and time.

When God uses *yatsar:* to fashion or to form, it is to indicate a seemingly more natural or understandable process, such as God literally taking dirt and forming Adam by physically sculpting the clay to the image of God. Today this is every baby that is formed in the womb with the material of the parents. This is an ongoing process of God sustaining His creation.

When God uses *asah* to make something, this is God supernaturally making Adam to be a living being with the Breath of Life of the Holy Spirit breathed through Adam's nostrils—combining the spirit that was created via *bara* (on the first day) with the body formed via *yatsar.* Today, this is placing a fertilized egg onto the uterine wall for the blood of the mother and the spirit of that person that was created on the first day of creation joining the fetus to make (*asah*) a life that is born nine months later as a baby.

With this interpretation, all three Hebrew words have a specific meaning, and God is not being redundant by saying that He created man, formed man, and made man. God is still sustaining His creation with every birth that He forms in the womb (Isaiah 44:2).

And He rested. An all powerful God got tired? No, God did not get tired. Isaiah 40:28 "Do you not know? Have you not heard? The Everlasting God, the LORD, the Creator of the ends of the earth does not become weary or tired." This has to do with sanctification, not fatigue.

Chapter Summary: God has finished creating and will create again in the distant future (Rev. 22). Once all is fulfilled of what the Bible has foretold, then God will create a new heaven and a new earth. God sanctified the seventh day for the benefit of humanity, so mankind would know that it is the LORD God who makes man holy. God is sustaining His creation by forming babies in the womb. He joins their spirits to the fertilized egg—which is attached to the uterine wall that has the blood of life—to make a life (soul). Therefore, God is still forming a continuation of life in the womb, but He has ceased creating new kinds of life.

Chapter 39
Life in the Beginning Before Sin

Was life different in the beginning before sin entered the world? Yes. For one thing, death did not exist for life that had breath and blood. All life were herbivores. Gen. 1:29–30 says, "I have given you every plant yielding seed that is on the surface of all the earth, and every tree which has fruit yielding seed; it shall be food for you." Therefore, Adam and Eve did not eat meat. What about lions, tigers, and all the carnivores? Gen. 1:30: "To every beast of the earth and to every bird of the sky and to every thing that moves on the earth which has life, I have given every green plant for food." All beasts of the earth were herbivores. But that changed when Adam and Eve sinned. Then they ate meat, and some animals switched from being herbivores to carnivores.

It is important to know that death did not enter the world until Adam and Eve sinned. Some theistic evolutionists and gap theorists believe that billions of deaths occurred before Adam and Eve sinned. That view is based on the faith in the opinions of evolutionary scientists and a belief in the atheistic timeline—an old earth and is in contradiction with Scripture and science. Consider Romans 5:12–14: "Through one man sin entered into the world, and death through sin, and so death spread . . . death reigned from Adam on." This is one of several verses that talk about sin entering the world as a result of Adam and death subsequently entering the world. Immediately, one has to drop any notion that all the fossils and all the oil reserves are from a pre-Adamic era. One has to drop any belief that billions of deaths occurred in an evolutionary process to get to Adam and Eve; the Bible is clear—death did not occur until Adam sinned.

An even odder situation was that animals potentially talked before the fall, not just to their kind as we see today, but to Adam and Eve. Is there Biblical support for the notion that animals used to communicate with humans? Yes. First let us set the scene: Balaam was a prophet; he heard from God what to do and say and whom to bless and curse, but he had been disobedient to God, and God was angry with him. God dispatched a messenger of the Lord with a sword to judge Balaam for his wickedness. Balaam, unaware of his pending fate from the sword of judgment, arose in the morning, saddled his donkey, and went with the leaders to potentially curse Israel. Numbers 22:22–31:

> The angel of the LORD took his stand in the way as an adversary against him. Now Balaam was riding on his donkey and his two servants were with him. When the donkey saw the angel of the LORD standing in the way with his drawn sword in his hand, the donkey turned off from the way and went into the field; but Balaam struck the donkey to turn her back into the way. Then the angel of the LORD stood in a narrow path of the vineyards, with a wall on this side and a wall on that side. When the donkey saw the angel of the LORD, she pressed herself to the wall and pressed Balaam's foot against the wall, so he struck her again. The angel of the LORD went further, and stood in a narrow place where there was no way to turn to the right hand or the left. When the donkey saw the angel of the LORD, she lay down under Balaam, so Balaam was angry and struck the donkey with his stick. And the LORD **opened the mouth of the donkey, and she said to Balaam**, "What have I done to you, that you have struck me these three times?" Then Balaam said to the donkey, "Because you have made a mockery of me! If there had been a sword in my hand, I would have killed you by now." **The donkey said to Balaam**, "Am I not your donkey on which you have ridden all your life to this Day? Have I ever been accustomed to do so to you?" And he said, "No."

The LORD opened the mouth of the donkey and she spoke. I'm sure the donkeys in those days "hee-hawed" and made other sounds just like donkeys do today. The donkey was not a mute. That's not the point. The point is that the donkey and almost all creatures had their mouths closed (a portion of their communication abilities) at one time, and at this specific moment with Balaam and the donkey, God "opened" her mouth for a short period of time and <u>she</u> spoke. God did not put words in her mouth; the donkey spoke words from her own thoughts. It is as though the donkey and other animals were able to speak to humans at one time, but then had their mouths shut.

Review: <u>God opened what was previously shut, and for a brief moment in time, the donkey was able to speak to Balaam using her own words, and she spoke in Balaam's language. This ability was lost as a result of sin and was gifted back for a brief moment in time.</u>

How do we know that the donkey was not a mute, and then God allowed her to speak? If we continue on with the narrative, we see that God opens something for Balaam as well.

> Then **the LORD opened the eyes of Balaam, and he saw the angel of the LORD** standing in the way with his drawn sword in his hand; and he bowed all the way to the ground. The angel of the LORD said to him, "Why have you struck your donkey these three times? Behold, I have come out as an adversary, because your way was contrary to Me. But the donkey saw Me and turned aside from Me these three times. If she had not turned aside from Me, I would surely have killed you just now, and let her live." Balaam said to the angel of the LORD, "I have sinned, for I did not know that you were standing in the way against Me. Now then, If it is displeasing to you, I will turn back." But the angel of the LORD said to Balaam, "Go with the men, But you shall speak only the word which I tell you" (Numbers 22:31–35).

In the same manner that the donkey was not a mute, Balaam was not blind. Balaam could see in the third dimension just like any other human. But for a brief moment in time, God opened up Balaam's eyes to see in a spiritual realm in which humans have not been able to see since the fall of Adam and Eve. Just as the donkey was not a mute and God opened her mouth, and she spoke to Balaam using her own words, similarly, Balaam was not blind and God opened his eyes, and he saw the messenger of the Lord standing before him with a sword drawn.

Review: <u>For a brief moment in time, God opened what was previously shut, and Balaam was able to see in the spiritual realm. An ability that was lost as a result of sin was gifted back.</u>

A vital piece of doctrine is usually overlooked by many. Balaam, after seeing the Angel of the LORD, *bowed all the way to the ground*. This is an act of worship. The worship of angels is strictly forbidden. Colossians 2:18: "Let no one keep defrauding you of your prize by . . . the worship of the angels." Also, in Matthew 4:10, when Jesus was being tempted by a fallen angel, the devil tempted Jesus to worship him. And Jesus said, *"*It is written, 'You shall worship the LORD your God, and serve Him only.'*"* Also, twice in Revelation, John bowed down to worship an angel that delivered a message, and both times the angel replied, "Do not do that; I am a fellow servant of yours and your brethren who hold the testimony of Jesus; worship God" *(*Revelation 19:10 and 22:8–9). Therefore, when Balaam bowed all the way to the ground, if this was an angel, he would have said, "Do not do that. I am a fellow servant of yours and of your brethren the prophets. Worship God." Also, this Messenger of the LORD said,

> Behold, I have come out as an adversary, because your way was contrary to <u>Me.</u> But the donkey saw Me and turned aside from Me these three times. If she had not turned aside from Me, <u>I</u> would surely have killed you just now, and let her live.

This being is not only accepting worship, but is telling Balaam that He is judging Balaam's deeds because they were contrary to Him. The "angel" is rendering a verdict and enforcing the verdict. Only God is able to judge and to render a verdict of someone's deeds. An angel would have said, "Your way is contrary to God," not *contrary to Me*. Since this being accepts worship, judges, and enforces His rule, this can only be God in the flesh.

"Angel" is used for the Hebrew word *malak* (#4397), which means messenger, deputy, or messenger (specifically of God), that is, an angel, prophet, priest, teacher, ambassador, or king. Do not get too up in arms that the early patriarchs chose the word *angel* to represent *malak*. Several instances occur where the appropriate term *messenger of God is* used. Is not Jesus a messenger of His Father? Was not every Word that proceeded from Jesus' mouth a message from the Father as God commanded Him (John 12:44–50)? Since this messenger of the LORD (mentioned 10 times in this short record) accepts worship, decrees that Balaam violated His ways, and renders His judgment, then this was God.

Since no one has seen God the Father at any time,[210] and since God the Father is invisible,[211] this cannot be God the Father. This is Jesus, the Son of God. Jesus is the image of the invisible Father; Jesus is God in the flesh.[212] Therefore, this is Jesus talking to Balaam with His sword drawn—the same Jesus who appeared in Joshua 5, the same Jesus who was with the Father and Holy Spirit at Gen. 1:1, the same Jesus who hung on the cross, and the same Jesus who will come again in exaltation in Revelation with His sword drawn.

Review: Jesus is the messenger of the LORD talking to Balaam.

Were animals able to communicate to humans before sin occurred on earth? Let us take a look at the four living creatures in heaven, which is in a sinless environment, just like the earth prior to the fall of Adam and Eve, and these four living creatures are around the Throne of God. Revelation 4:6:

> Around the throne, four living creatures full of eyes in front and behind. The first creature, like a lion, and the second creature like a calf, and the third creature had a face like that of a man, and the fourth creature like a flying eagle. And the four living creatures, each one of them having six wings, are full of eyes around and within; and day and night they do not cease to say, "HOLY, HOLY, HOLY IS THE LORD GOD, THE ALMIGHTY, WHO WAS AND WHO IS AND WHO IS TO COME."

Most commentators agree that these four living creatures represent angels. Many of the commentators link this description in Revelation with Ezekiel 1:4–21. They may be correct, but some differences exist. Let us take a look at the differences:

Revelation creatures	Ezekiel creatures
Four living creatures	Four living creatures
Each had a different face:	Each had four faces of:
1. Like a lion	1. Face of a man (front)
2. Like a calf	2. Face of a lion (right)
3. Like a man	3. Face of a bull (left)
4. Like a flying eagle	4. Face of an eagle (rear)
Total of four faces, one for each.	Total of 16 faces, four for each.
They had six wings.	They had four wings.
Day and night they do not cease from saying:	These creatures ride to and fro on a wheel.
"HOLY, HOLY, HOLY IS THE LORD GOD, THE ALMIGHT, WHO WAS AND WHO IS AND WHO IS TO COME."	From an expanse above the creatures, God speaks to Ezekiel.

Review: The scholars could be correct that this is just the symbolic language of angels. But since the comparisons are slightly different, maybe these are really four living creatures that represent life on earth before sin. Perhaps, animals really will speak in heaven. After all, what is stranger—that animals could talk or that a wolf would lay down with a lamb in Isaiah 11:6-9 or that primates evolved to

---

210 John 1:18: "No one has seen God at any time."I John 4:12: "No one has seen God at any time." Exodus 33:20: "You cannot see My face, for no man can see Me and live!"

211 Colossians 1:15 "He [Jesus] is the image of the invisible God."

212 John 1:1–14: "In the beginning was the Word, and the Word was with God, and the Word was God. He was in the beginning with God. All things came into being through Him, and apart from Him nothing came into being that has come into being . . . And the Word became flesh, and dwelt among us, and we saw His glory."

humans?[213] Life was different before sin and will be different again after sin is removed completely from the earth.

Another point of evidence about animals speaking before sin occurred on earth involves finding a suitable mate for Adam. Let us go back in time to before Eve was created. Gen. 2:18–23:

> Then the LORD God said, "It is not good for the man to be alone; I will make him a helper suitable for him." Out of the ground the LORD God formed every beast of the field and every bird of the sky, and brought them to the man to see what he would call them; and whatever the man called a living creature, that was its name. The man gave names to all the cattle, and to the birds of the sky, and to every beast of the field, **but** for Adam there was not found a helper suitable for him."

First of all, God said, "It is not good for the man to be alone; I will make him a helper suitable for him." God is setting out to make man a suitable helper, so God shows Adam all the different kinds of beast and bird, that God formed out of the ground on the fifth and sixth days of creation, before He formed Adam. This is not a separate or new set of created creatures formed after God formed Adam. This is merely Moses reflecting back and reminding the reader that some similarities exist with how Adam and the creatures were formed. Such as both were formed from the ground, both have the breath of life, both originate from God, and so forth. Then God brought each kind of creature to Adam and tells Adam to name each kind. After Adam names each kind, it seems that Adam realizes that the similarities are not enough to consider any creature a suitable helpmate. It is like God wanted Adam to see and know that there was nothing suitable for a love connection between Adam and any of the animals. This is why the verse finishes with, ***but*** *for Adam there was not found a helper suitable for him.* As though this exercise was purposeful by God to establish to Adam that although he was able to communicate with the animal kingdom, no suitable helper existed for him in that realm, then God fashioned Eve from Adam. But why go through such a parade or displaying all the kinds before Adam?

Was it really God's intention to see if Adam would fall in love with one of the animals? No. God knows all things[214] and does not increase in knowledge. God did this for Adam's sake, to show Adam that none of the animals were an acceptable mate. God was not trying to find out the outcome, He knew the outcome. Since it was not God's intention to see if Adam would have a love connection with one of the animals, then why parade all the animals before Adam to see if a suitable helpmate existed? It seems too obvious that none of the animals are suitable mates today, but if animals spoke to us and could influence us, then because of the ability to communicate, it is possible for love to cultivate and grow. For the reason that God took an extra step to prove to Adam that none of the creatures were suitable for him, illustrates that something more persists to the animal's ability to connect with Adam than we observe today. Potentially because they were able to speak to Adam. Potentially, animals lost the ability to speak to humans because they used communication to deceive. Regardless, the evidence suggests that animals did indeed speak because a non-speaking animal would likely not have been paraded before Adam for him to determine if any of the animals could be a suitable mate. But a speaking animal—with the same blood and breath of life that was created from the same ground and on the same day—might. Granted, this is a tenuous argument.

Review: God brought all the animals before Adam, to establish to Adam that no creature was a suitable mate. Why did God go the extra step? Potentially because the creatures had an ability to connect with humans that does not exist today—speech. After all, verbal communication is a key to a successful relationship.

Whenever the Bible wants to indicate shock or surprise to the reader, the Bible uses words or

---

213 Isaiah 11:6–9: "The wolf will dwell with the lamb, and the leopard will lie down with the young goat, and the calf and the young lion and the fatling together. . . And the lion will eat straw like the ox . . . They will not hurt or destroy in all My Holy mountain, For the earth will be full of the knowledge of the LORD."

214 John 21:17: "Lord, You know all things." John 18:4 "Jesus, knowing all the tings that were coming upon Him."

phrases such as *behold, suddenly, they were afraid,* or *they fell to the ground as a dead man.* But none of those words or phrases or any other indication of shock is provided in the narrative of Eve speaking with a snake.

Now, I assure you that if an animal such as a horse, dog, snake, or cat started talking to us, we would be in shock, and we would be startled. One thing we would not do is carry on a conversation as though this was normal. Why? Because it is not normal to us. But that is exactly what Eve does. Let us turn to Gen. 3:1: "Now the serpent was more crafty than any beast of the field which the LORD God had made." This is interesting because snakes today have remnant paws/claws. The only purpose of these remnant paws is for mating. But we learn from one of the curses (Gen. 3:14) after the fall of Adam and Eve, that the snake is "cursed more than all cattle, and more than every beast of the field; On your belly you will go, and dust you will eat all the days of your life." Therefore, the snake used to be able to walk on four legs just like other beasts or cattle. Evolutionary scientists do not like to address the rudimentary paws because the evidence of the vestigial paws is evidence that snakes were cursed as the Bible declares.

We learn that the snake was working on behalf of the devil.[215] It is safe to say that Satan possessed the snake to do his bidding. The snake was willing to be filled with the spirit of Satan and not with the spirit of God. This explains why the snake was craftier than any beast of the field. The different versions of the Bible use different words to describe the snake's character:

King James uses *subtil.*
New King James uses *cunning.*
New American Standard uses *crafty.*
New International Version uses *crafty.*

They are saying the same thing. The snake was subtle, cunning, crafty, and deceitful (Strong's Concordance #6175: *aruwm*). It seems that not much has changed for the snake over the millennia. Is it possible for Satan/demons to possess animals? Yes. Jesus cast out of a man a ton of demons, called a "legion, for they were many" and into a herd of swine (Luke 8:26–33). Therefore, it is in harmony to say the snake was more deceitful and cunning than any other animal. That wicked heart of the snake allowed the devil to possess it and use its ability to communicate. Some pastors think that "Serpent" was just another name for Satan. They believe that Satan did not possess a snake, but it was Satan himself deceiving Eve. But that is not in harmony with the curse that followed after the fall. The snake was cursed more than all the other cattle and would be on its belly hence forth. That does not fit Satan at all, but it does fit snakes. Back to the narrative in Gen. 3:1–3:

> And he [the serpent] said to the woman, "Indeed, has God said, 'You shall not eat from any tree of the garden'?" The woman said to the serpent, "From the fruit of the trees of the garden we may eat; but from the fruit of the tree which is in the middle of the garden, God has said, 'You shall not eat from it or touch it, or you will die.

Do you hear any shock or surprise in what Eve says? NO! None of that occurred. Eve spoke with calmness and did not run away. This is evidence that it was normal for animals to talk before the fall. More dialogue occurs between the snake and Eve, but you get the gist.

Review: We have the same nature as Eve; if we heard a snake talking, we would be shocked and run away. Eve carried on a normal conversation with the snake for five verses, as though this was normal.

Some birds still speak, such as the parakeet. Maybe this is a reminder of what it was like before sin and a foreshadowing of what it will be like after sin is no more. Possibly, the curse given in Gen. 3:14 gives a clue. The snake was "cursed <u>more</u> than all cattle, and <u>more</u> than every beast of the field;

---

215 Revelation 12:9: "The great dragon was thrown down, the serpent of old who is called the devil and Satan, who deceives the whole world."

On your belly you will go, And dust you will eat all the days of your life." That portion and description of the curse does not fit Satan. Satan is not on his belly with dust in his mouth the rest of his life. For evidence that this is a description not for Satan but for the snakes, consider Job 1:6-7:

> Now there was a day when the sons of God came to present themselves before the LORD, and Satan also came among them. The LORD said to Satan, "From where do you come?" Then Satan answered the LORD and said, "From roaming about on the earth and walking around on it."

Therefore, Satan has the ability to enter heaven, roam about on the earth, and walk around the planet. Clearly, snakes cannot walk or enter heaven whenever they wish. Therefore, this portion of the curse is pertaining to snakes and to a lesser extent to cattle and beast.

Now let us focus on the word *more* in the curse because a greater curse was placed on snakes, and a lesser curse was placed on the rest of the animals. The snakes were cursed more than all the cattle and more than every beast of the field, and the explanation of that curse is that snakes have to be on their belly, eating dust as they slither. Then that would be the greater curse, which was that snakes could no longer walk, but had to slither. We see the result of this curse in the remnant claws of snakes that are no longer used for walking, but only for mating. But what was the lesser curse given to cattle and other beasts? Since snakes are cursed more, than that means cattle and beast are cursed less, but still cursed. So what is that lesser curse? It could be argued that it is death.[216] That argument is not wrong, but I think more exist to this because death seems like a greater curse, not a lesser curse. Coupling all the evidence together, I think one of the curses put on all cattle and every beast was the loss of the ability to speak to humans. This was because the snake allowed its voice to be used by Satan to deceive humans.

Review: The greater curse for the snake was the loss of walking, and the lesser curse that fell on all animals was potentially the loss of the ability to speak with humans.

An example of a similar speech curse being placed on humans occurs for using their common voice to do evil in the sight of the Lord. Let us set the scene: The Flood had occurred in Gen. 7. The verses are discussing Noah's great-grandson Nimrod. Gen. 11:1–:

> Now the whole earth used the same language and the same words . . . They said to one another, "Come, let us make bricks and burn them thoroughly." And they used brick for stone, and they used tar for mortar. They said, "Come, let us build for ourselves a city, and a tower whose top will reach into heaven, and let us make for ourselves a name, otherwise we will be scattered abroad, over the face of the whole earth." The LORD came down to see the city and the tower which the sons of men had built. The LORD said, "Behold, they are one people, and they all have the same language. And this is what they began to do, and now nothing which they purpose to do will be impossible for them. Come, let Us go down and there confuse their language, so that they will not understand one another's speech. So the LORD scattered them abroad from there over the face of the whole earth; and they stopped building the city. Therefore its name was called Babel, because there the Lord confused the language of the whole earth; and from there the LORD scattered them abroad over the face of the whole earth.

With their common language and same words, mankind desired to build for themselves a name and a tower to reach into heaven. Human beings wanted to be God, and mankind wanted the very same thing that Lucifer wanted in Isaiah 14, self-glorification—to replace God in their life with themselves. This is the sin of pride and idolatry. Humans were deceiving themselves, thinking they were more worthy than they were. How did God deal with people's craftiness? He cursed their speech by changing their words

---

216 Romans 8:19–22: "Creation was subjected to futility . . . in hope that the creation itself also will be set free from its slavery to corruption[sin] into the freedom [from sin]."

and language. Then for good measure, He scattered them around the world.

Review: <u>When humans acted deceitfully and craftily, God cursed their speech in a similar fashion as He did all the animals. A parallel exist with animals using their speech for evil, and their common language and ability to communicate with humans was suspended. Humans did the same thing with their common language and used it for evil, and subsequently their ability to communicate with every human was suspended as well.</u>

Speech has a lot of importance. Why? The words that come out of our mouth either save us or condemn us. If we confess Jesus as our Lord and savior from our sin, we shall be saved.[217] If we do not confess, then all of our words to save ourselves are filthy rags and full of evil intentions,[218] no matter how meritorious.[219] With words, God created the heavens and the earth and all that is contained in them.[220] With words, Jesus raised Lazarus from the grave.[221] Jesus is the fulfillment (Matt. 5:17) of the Word and is the Word (John 1:1–5, 14), which means that everything that is truthful, every wise saying, all knowledge, and all understanding are from the Lord Jesus Christ.[222] And as powerful as that sounds, every word that Jesus spoke was from the Father.[223] With speech being so powerful, it is no wonder that God removed the gift from animals to communicate with humans after the snake showed such abuse with it to deceive Eve. And no wonder God punished human beings by giving them different languages after they used their common language for evil.

Chapter Summary: The evidence suggests that in the sinless environment of heaven, four different creatures can talk. Balaam's donkey, after God temporarily opens her mouth, is able to speak to Balaam, which indicates that animals had their mouth shut at one time. That past event probably occurred with the curse in the Garden of Eden. And Eve has a calm conversation with the snake, which indicates that it was normal for animals to talk. And when man used their common speech for sin and tried to become god, God changed their speech and words. With all the evidence combined, it appears that living beings before the fall of mankind, including animals, consisted of open verbal communication and a common language.

---

217 Romans 10:9–10: "That if you confess with your mouth Jesus as Lord, and believe in your heart that God raised Him from the dead, you will be saved; for with the heart a person believes, resulting in righteousness, and with the mouth he confesses, resulting in salvation."

218 Colossians 1:21: "And although you were formerly alienated and hostile in mind, engaged in evil deeds."

219 Ephesians 2:8–9: "For by grace you have been saved through faith; and that not of yourselves, it is the gift of God; not as a result of works, so that no one may boast."

220 Gen. 1:1–3: "Then God said" This phrase is repeated each time and each day God creates.

221 John 11:43: "He cried out with a loud voice, 'Lazarus, come forth.' The man who had died came forth."

222 Colossians 1:3: "Christ Himself, in whom are hidden all the treasures of wisdom and knowledge."

223 John 12:48–49: "He who rejects Me and does not receive My sayings, has one who judges him; the word I spoke is what will judge him at the last day. For I did not speak on My own initiative, but the Father Himself who sent Me has given Me a commandment as to <u>what to say and what to speak</u>."

Chapter 40
<u>Seven-Day Creation Versus Seven-Eon Creation</u>

When Bible scholars argue about dates of origins, they focus on whether the "day" in the Genesis creation account are literal days or figurative days. In other words, does each day in the Genesis creation account represent one revolution of the earth or eons or ages?

The further one gets away from a literal Biblical interpretation, the more variances or the more errors occur in their doctrine. For example, when one takes a figurative approach to interpreting law books, scientific documents, academic papers, or Scripture, who is to say which view is correct or what standard will be applied? When does someone switch from a figurative interpretation to a literal interpretation? Some switch to a literal interpretation after the first verse, some switch to a literal interpretation on the sixth day with the creation of Adam and Eve, and some switch to a literal interpretation after the seventh day of creation. By what arbitrary method does someone say, "Well, now I will start to take the Bible literally." Since nothing in Genesis indicates to the reader to switch from figurative to literal. Then, what or whose standard determines when to switch from figurative to literal? What words are figurative and what words are literal? Once someone starts down this path, the door is open to interpret the entire Bible as figurative.

How does one start down this path of a figurative interpretation? Consider this phrase that we have all heard, "To the Lord, a day is a 1,000 years." Those who interpret Genesis creation as figurative lean on this phrase as evidence that the "days" in Genesis are a 1,000 years or greater. But that phrase does not appear in the Bible. I draw your attention to 2 Peter 3:3–10:

> 3 <u>In the last days</u> mockers will come with their mocking, following after their own lusts, 4 and saying, "Where is the promise of <u>His coming</u>? For ever since the fathers fell asleep, all continues just as it was from the beginning of creation." 5 For when they maintain this, it escapes their notice that by the word of God the heavens existed long ago and the earth was formed out of water and by water, 6 through which the world at that time was destroyed, being flooded with water. 7 But by His word the present heavens and earth are being <u>reserved for fire, kept for the day of judgment and destruction</u> of ungodly men. 8 But do not let this one fact escape your notice, beloved, that <u>with the Lord one day is **like** a thousand years, and a thousand years **like** one day</u>. 9 The Lord is not slow about His promise, as some count slowness, but is patient toward you, not wishing for any to perish but for all to come to repentance. 10 But <u>the day of the Lord</u> will come like a thief, in which the heavens will pass away with a roar and the elements will be destroyed with intense heat, and the earth and its works will be burned up.

First off, these verses are not about creation, but end time judgment and the second coming. Peter is not trying to clear up confusion about creation, he is clearing up confusion about the end times. Clearly, verse 8 is saying that one day is **like** a thousand years, and a thousand years is **like** one day to the Lord. This means that God is not bound by time. To switch this verse to mean that the Genesis creation account represents 7,000 years or greater is in error. It is a misinterpretation of 2 Peter 3:8 and an improper use of having Scripture interpret Scripture. The verse does not say a day is a thousand years. The verse in question is merely saying that God is not bound by time and is not slow about His promises to return and judge. To force the verse to say that a day is equal to 1,000 years is in error.

Those who switch 2 Peter 3:8 to force the Word to fit the atheistic timeline are guilty of annulling Scripture, and will be considered least in the Kingdom of heaven (Matt. 5:19). It is hypocritical that they take 2 Peter 3:8 literally by removing the figurative language of *like*, but do not take Genesis literally when it does not have the figurative language of *like*. Genesis says, "It was so." If the Genesis creation account said God created the sun, moon, and stars in *like* a day, or if God created simple life to eventually be *like* His image, then theistic evolutionists would have a case, but the word *like* does not appear in the Genesis creation account to describe a *day*. This self-serving means of interpretation they believe in the religion of billions of years for evolution versus the Bible.

Furthermore, this phrase in the verse, "in the last days mockers will come with their mocking, following after their own lusts, and saying, ". . . all continues just as it was from the beginning of creation." This is the evolutionary concept of Uniformitarian, which means that the rate of soil deposit today, is the rate it has always been. Thus, the layers of the crust prove an old Earth. The Bible indicts this belief as mockers fairy tales.

Theistic evolutionists gain no ground in the eyes of atheists, because once they use 2 Peter 3:8 to say a day is a thousand years, then their Genesis interpretation is only up to 7,000 years. This is still laughable in the eyes of atheists. Those that compromise the integrity of the Bible to look good in the eyes of atheists, undermine the Bible and still look foolish in the eyes of atheists.

Those that interpret a "day" in the Genesis creation account to mean a thousand years or greater also turn to Psalm 90:4 for support. Let us take a look at the verse: "For a thousand years in Your sight are **like** yesterday when it passes by, or as a watch in the night." Again, this verse is merely saying that God is not bound by time. The creator of time is sovereign over time, and a thousand years are remembered as though they were yesterday or like the four hours of a guardsman's watch. God remembers each second of every day for thousands of years as though they were yesterday.

What is the motivating factor to interpret the word "day" in Genesis to mean a thousand years or eons? It is to pacify the evolutionists that scream that the earth is 4.5 billion years old and that the universe is 14 billion years old. They think that if they can somehow get the Bible to say a day is literally a thousand years or figuratively billions of years, they'll be able to witness to evolutionists, or at least they won't look foolish to the evolutionists. Either way, that is a doomed philosophy. No clever speech or deceitful approach to witnessing ever converted anyone to believe in God. Our only job is to share the gospel message and speak truth.

Review: 2 Peter 3:8 talks about end time judgment, not creation, and clearly states that a day is *like* a thousand years and a thousand years is *like* a day. This means that God is not bound by time—it does not mean that the days in Genesis are actually a thousand years long. Psalm 90:4 does not say a day is a thousand years; it does say that God is all knowing and can remember everything that happened in a thousand years as though it was yesterday.

Now to someone who does not take the creation account literally, they are in conflict with the timeline in the creation narrative because of the following phrases in Gen. 1: (NIV and KJV)

There was evening and there was morning, the first day.
There was evening and there was morning, the second day.
There was evening and there was morning, the third day.
There was evening and there was morning, the fourth day.
There was evening and there was morning, the fifth day.
There was evening and there was morning, the sixth day.
By the seventh day.

Their solution is to discard these phrases as figurative for each day. Then, at some point, they have to change philosophies and start viewing Moses' writing as literal. At what point do they do that? This is an arbitrary juncture of judgment. Nothing in the text suggests that one should switch from a figurative interpretation to a literal interpretation.

Once someone starts down this interpretive path, a whole host of problems exist associated with this decision. For one, since the second half of the third day represents the creation of all grasses, plants, and trees, how do they survive for thousands of years without the sun for photosynthesis, as the sun was made on the fourth day? How do trees produce fruit without pollination, as insects (including bees) were not created until the sixth day?

Secondly, the one who discards the phrase *there was evening and there was morning, the "x" day* loses some effectiveness to witness to nonbelievers. A person who does not believe in the Bible will not accept hearing from a person who also does not fully believe in the Bible. That is illogical. Imagine going to someone who believes the Bible is hokum and saying to them, "You should believe in Jesus for He died on the cross for you. But do not worry about believing that Jesus' Word is accurate, as there are errors in the Bible." This is silly. No one will believe in something you do not believe in yourself. Pastors who doubt the literal Genesis creation account, will not dive deep in the Word because they are afraid of what other errors they may encounter. Thus, they starve their congregation from the Word, and give shallow feel good messages that do not equip their flock to handle the schemes of the devil. The Word is the only weapon we have to know what is of God and what is of the devil.

    <u>Review</u>: <u>With a figurative view, any and all interpretations hold consideration and can be considered. One could make the extremely figurative suggestion that Jesus did not literally rise from the grave, but His teachings symbolically rose from the grave instead. Genesis repeats the phrase *there was evening and there was morning, "x" day. Day* should be taken literally.</u>

    Here is the crux of the matter: Moses accepted a literal interpretation of the Genesis account of creation. How do we know what Moses believed as far as a literal or figurative interpretation of the word *day* of creation? After all, Moses lived some 3,500 years ago. If that isn't bold enough, God also accepts a literal interpretation of the Genesis account of creation. Does not that seem blasphemous to say what God thinks? It seems that I am proclaiming that "I know the mind of God." It is not blasphemous at all. The "Holy Spirit searches the depths of all things, even the depths of God . . . therefore we have the mind of Christ" (I Corinthians 2:10–16). Let us establish the evidence for how we know whether Moses and God used a literal interpretation of the Genesis account of creation. I turn your attention to the Ten Commandments in Exodus 20:8–11*:*

> Remember the sabbath day, to keep it holy. Six days you shall labor and do all your work, but the seventh day is a sabbath of the LORD your God; in it you shall not do any work, you or your son or your daughter, your male or your female servant or your cattle or your sojourner who stay with you. <u>For in six days the LORD made the heavens and the earth, the sea and all that is in them, and rested on the seventh day.</u>

How many days were we to work? Six. Why? Because the LORD made the heavens and the earth, the sea and all that is in them in six days. This is a one-to-one ratio. Which day were we to rest? The seventh. Why? Because God rested on the seventh. This too is a one-to-one ratio. By the way, the Ten Commandments were spoken by God and written in stone by God's own finger. If that was not enough, God repeated Himself a second time in Exodus 31:12–15:

> The LORD spoke to Moses, saying, "But as for you, speak to the sons of Israel, saying, 'You shall surely observe My sabbaths; for this is a sign between Me and you throughout your generations, that you may know that I am the LORD who sanctifies you . . . <u>For six days work may be done, but on the seventh day there is a sabbath of complete rest, holy to the LORD; for in six days the LORD made heaven and earth, but on the seventh day He ceased from labor, and was refreshed.</u>' When He had finished speaking with him upon Mount Sinai, He gave Moses the two tablets of the testimony, tablets of stone, written by the finger of God.

Twice God gave Moses His own testimony, both verbally and written in stone with His own finger. If God lied about what He saw and did, then His testimony is false, or if God is deceiving us about how long it took Him to create everything, then He is the Devil, but if God's eyewitness account of what He saw and did is truth, and "God cannot lie" (Titus 1:2), than we should accept it.

    Since Moses wrote the Genesis account of creation and wrote down what God had told him to write down twice on separate occasions, and since Moses listened to God explain how He created everything in six days and rested on the seventh, and since Moses read with his own eyes what God wrote down on the Ten Commandments in stone, twice, Moses views a literal seven days of creation too. The ages of the patriarchs, when they begot a son and when they died, in Genesis 5 and 11 is irrefutable evidence for a literal *day* in creation. In addition, Moses wrote, "the **day** that God crated man on the earth" (Deut. 4:32). If Moses is wrong, then God the Father is wrong. For Moses wrote down what God inspired him to write (II Timothy 3:16: "All scripture is inspired by God"). Furthermore, if Moses' account of creation is filled with errors, then God the Father should be discredited as a trustworthy testament of His eyewitness account of what He did. Also, if Moses is wrong about a literal account of creation, then God in the flesh, Jesus, is wrong. For Jesus authenticated a literal Genesis account of Adam and Eve. For Jesus (recorded in Matthew 19:4–6) says, "Have you not read that He who created them from the beginning." He then quotes Gen. 1:27 and Gen. 5:2 when He says God "made them male and female." Jesus also quotes Gen. 2:24: "For this reason a man shall leave his father and mother and be joined to his wife, and the two shall become one flesh" ("them" and "male and female" refer to Adam and Eve).

If the Genesis creation account has errors or is wrong, then three options exist. Since Jesus spoke literally about the creation account, either Jesus knew the Genesis account was in error and covered it up, and then Jesus would be the devil and not your savior. Or Jesus did not know about the errors in Genesis account of creation, and then Jesus was a fool and not the savior or God in the flesh. The third option is that Jesus spoke correctly as an eye witness because He was there at Creation as a co-creator when He created all things (John 1:2).

The writer of Acts, Luke, by the inspiration of the Holy Spirit, quotes the apostle Paul in Acts 17:24–26, "The God who made the world and all things in it . . . He made from one man every nation of mankind to live on all the face of the earth." Here we have both Luke and Paul, affirming the literal Genesis creation account of Adam. Now the theistic evolutionist must go against Jesus' teaching, Matthew's writings, Paul's teaching, Luke's writings, the heavenly Father, and the Holy Spirit.

If Moses was wrong, the Holy Spirit is wrong, as the Holy Spirit moved on Moses to write Genesis: "Know this first of all, that no prophecy of scripture is a matter of one's own interpretation, for no prophecy was never made by an act of human will, but men moved by the Holy Spirit spoke from God" (II Peter 1:20–21). Only one conclusion exist for those who believe in God: the Genesis account of creation is a literal record. It seems that the reputations of Matthew, Luke, Paul, God the Father, the Son, and the Holy Spirit hang in the balance, but the only thing hanging in the balance is our relationship with God and potentially our salvation. God remains God whether we are obedient to Him or not. How we view God's account of creation as literal truth or figurative sets the tone of how we view the whole of Scripture and potentially reveals our relationship with God. For when you love God, you trust Him, and when you trust Him, you trust His sayings as truth. Whether someone believes God's account of creation as truth or error is based on how much of God they actually know. Someone who knows God knows that He declared all His statements to be true. "The testimony of the LORD is sure, making wise the simple" (Psalm 19:7b).

If you are not convinced to take a literal interpretation of the word *day* in the Genesis account of creation, then consider that the Hebrew word for *day* is *yowm* (Strong's Concordance #3117*)*, which means a day, whether literally (from sunrise to sunset, or from one sunset to the next) or figuratively (a space of time), depending on the associated term that is used with it. The associated term(s) determines if *day* is to be interpreted literally or figuratively. When a number is used in front of *day*, and this is true 100% of the time in the entire Bible, a literal definition is required. The associated terms that clarify how to define *day* are numbers, that is, first day, second day, third day, fourth day, fifth day, sixth day, and seventh day. Thus, the *day* in Genesis is not eons, ages, or some unknown amount of time, and it is not figurative. The breakdown of the Hebrew word gives great clarity and ends the debate about a literal or figurative interpretation of the Genesis account of creation.

But consider God's consistency. Every time the word day has a number in front of it in the Bible, it literally means one rotation of the earth. For example, "It rained on the earth for 40 days and 40 nights." The creation account goes further to add clarity of one rotation of the earth with the phrase *there was evening and there was morning, a second day.* Conversely, when *day* is not proceeded with a number in front of it, it could mean eons, ages, or some time in the future. For example, "The day of the Lord" means an unspecified time in the future. Now you can clearly see that the associated term adjacent to *day* determines whether a literal or figurative interpretation is appropriate.

Review: Moses and God the Father, and the Son of God used *day* to mean a literal "day" when the term was preceded by a number, such as for creation. God's word commanded Israel's obedience with a literal "day" as an example. The Holy Spirit moved on the authors of the Bible to write about literal "days" in the Genesis account. The proper interpretation of the Genesis account is that God created everything in six literal days and rested on the seventh literal day.

Theistic evolutionists suggest that God used trial and error to create everything. But when God looked out over all that He had made, and said it was all very good, He excluded the trial and error theory of God using evolution. God did not see death, errant evolutionary steps, mutations, or weak mutated creatures eaten by predators. Everything was clean, pure, whole, complete, perfect, blameless, without flaw, without mutation, without weakness, without defect, and so on. God did not use misfits, blind chance, and mistakes to get it right. On the contrary, the very day things were created, they were perfect, and this is exemplified by the creation of the angel (Eze 28:12–15). Therefore, God did not use evolution because evolution violates the Word of God and calls the Word of God wrong and therefore calls God a liar. Since the Bible explicitly records that God made certain things on certain days and God did so in six days, then evolution and the Bible are adversarial to each other and enemies.

Never does the Bible ever hint toward an evolutionary process, but it explicitly says that God made Adam and Eve as male and female from the beginning (Matt 19:4–5). It explicitly says that God created all things in six days (Exodus 20:11). Never does the Bible hint of an eternal singularity of energy just prior to the Big Bang, but it explicitly records that in the beginning of creation, God created waters and dirt (Gen. 1:1–2) prior to the second expansion (Big Bangs on the second day of creation). This is contrary to a premise of the Big Bang because the Big Bang hypothesis suggests that a singularity of energy eternally existed.

Theistic evolutionists simply do not believe the Genesis creation account in the Bible, but believe atheists' timeline of the age of the heavens and earth. Therefore, theistic evolutionists either allegorize the Genesis creation account, or discard it as error, or reject it as a whimsical mythological tale and believe atheists' hypothesis of how matter and life began as the truth. For this reason, theistic evolutionists are left with marginalizing the authenticity of the Bible. But they gain zero ground by giving up the authenticity of the Bible to be accepted by atheists; in fact, they lose ground. Because Jesus said (Matt. 5:17–19) that if any believer annuls a jot or tittle of the Scriptures, they will be called least in the Kingdom of Heaven. Though theistic evolutionists can be saved by accepting Jesus as Lord and believing that He died on the cross and rose from the grave paying in full for all their sins, they lose a great deal of eternal blessings just to be minimally accepted by atheists for the brief years of their life on earth. One of the reasons they could be called least in the Kingdom of God, is because theistic evolutionists have an uphill battle in sharing Scripture with someone. This is because the desire to share the precepts in the Bible with another is significantly reduced when the one proclaiming lacks faith in the original manuscript's inerrancy and holy divine inspiration. Think about it, it is a tough sell to tell someone to believe in an all knowing God, that wrote errors at the very beginning of His book, and then He tried to cover up His errors by having His prophets further carry on the ruse, lies, or errors. Thus, they lose out on heavenly reward by not sharing the knowledge of God. The bottom line is that theistic evolutionists lack faith in the Word, and since faith comes from hearing the Word (Romans 10:17), then their faith grows slow and remains infantile (1 John 2:12). This is the other reason someone is called least in the kingdom, when they reject the inerrancy of the Scripture, the desire to read a book containing errors is significantly reduced. Thus, their knowledge, wisdom, understanding, faith, and maturity as a believer are kept rudimentary. Whereas, those who adhere to all of Scripture as the divine, inerrant, Words of God have a higher propensity to read, study, meditate in, share the gospel, are able to defend the Scriptures and overcome the evil one, and are more likely to produce fruit as fathers that lead others to become children born again to God (1 John 2:13–14). The ability to be obedient to the command by Christ to go and share the Word of God is proportionate to the amount of faith in the Word. If one doubts the inerrancy of the original manuscripts they will hold the Bible in low esteem, and God will hold them in low esteem. The one who trusts in the inerrancy of the Scriptures they will hold the Bible in high esteem, and God will hold them in high esteem (Matt. 5:19).

Another section of Scripture that theistic evolutionists have to reject is the global flood. Gen. 7:19–23 clearly states that every mountain under the heavens was covered by water. All flesh that moved on earth and every bird of the sky died by the floodwater. No ambiguity occurs as to whether the Bible records a global flood or a local regional flood; however, evolutionists have no choice but to reject the Bible as authentic and proclaim that their own version supersedes the Bible.

Some saved theistic evolutionists may exist, however it does pose a problem to have incorrect knowledge of God, His Word, and how He desires to be worshiped as creator. Examples of incorrect knowledge and the consequences may be studied with the Israelites in Exodus 32 that wanted to worship God, but did it incorrectly with a golden calf. Also, with Cain who offered an incorrect sacrifice to God that ultimately led to Cain murdering his brother. All incorrect worship of God is rejected by God. Therefore, presuming that theistic evolutionists have an incorrect knowledge of God's Word and His creation, this could have dire consequences. For those theistic evolutionists that are saved, their doctrine adversely affects their usefulness for God. One cannot lose their salvation, so this boils down to the effectiveness of a theistic evolutionist's ability to share the infallible Word to save souls. In addition, if one views the Bible to have errors, then one is less inclined to read it, and subsequently one is unaware how to obey God, how to properly worship God, and one has no sword of truth to combat Satan's temptations. They are unarmed in this war for truth and potentially defenseless against the evils of this world (Eph. 6:12–18). Here is a problem that only God can solve, since the Bible declares that salvation is from hearing the Word, and the Bible explicitly declares the Word of God to be without errors, perfect, true, clean, sure, and pure. Then only God knows the heart of a theistic evolutionist whether they are saved and just weak doctrinally, or are lost and merely fooling themselves.

Why give up so much reward and usefulness for God and be counted as least in the Kingdom of God, if saved at all, when the Genesis creation account is supported by true science? Although evolutionary scientists reject Genesis and their interpretations of the observable evidence is contrary to Genesis, many interpretations of the same observable evidence supports Genesis and are in harmony with science. The Bible is never in conflict with science, only with man's hypotheses. Do not accept a view that is intended to explain away God via natural processes, when the natural processes function based on a preexisting DNA code that God created and they conserve the original code, not enhance it.

Review: Theistic evolutionists reject the Genesis creation account and a portion of the Ten Commandments where God declares that He created everything in six days, and they reject the Genesis global flood. Instead, they say the Bible is wrong with its creation account and with its flood account. They say that Jesus was wrong for saying that the creator created Adam and Eve, male and female. The result of their beliefs is that the Bible must have errors and therefore must not be written by God as divine, but written by man alone. Though they believe in God and that Jesus died on the cross and rose from the grave and may be saved, they have reduced their ability to be useful in sharing the Scriptures to save others.

But God has a stern warning for theistic evolutionists. Since they believe that all life eventually evolved from rains on rocks that formed a primordial soup of complex chemicals that came from this planet or asteroids, then Jeremiah 2:27–28 specifically applies to them. God is talking to evolutionists:

Who say to a tree, "You are my father," and to a stone, "You gave me birth," for they have turned their back to Me, and not their face. But in the time of their trouble they will say, "arise and save us." But where are your gods which you made for yourself? Let them arise, if they can save you in the time of your trouble.

God drew the line in the sand and declared that those who claim they evolved from some nonliving material, such as from rock, or that proclaim they evolved from some living material, such as a tree or any other living thing, has turned their back to God. When times of trouble come, He will say, let the god that you constructed save you.

Any view outside of the Word, outside of saying God created everything, as is explained from the beginning as the Bible records, is a creation of a man-made god out of the constructs of thought and may be a doctrine of demons. In 1 Timothy 4:1, it says, "The Spirit explicitly says that in later times some will fall away from the faith, paying attention to deceitful spirits and doctrines of demons." We are in the later times, and many have fallen away from the faith today, so search your view. If it is not in the Bible, then by default, it is not from God and could be from a doctrine of demons. Additionally, God said through a letter Paul wrote in 2 Timothy 4:2–4:

Preach the word, be ready in season and out of season, reprove, rebuke, exhort, with great patience and instruction. For the time will come when they will not endure sound doctrine, but to have their ears tickled, they will accumulate for themselves teachers in accordance to their own desires, and will turn away their ears from the truth and will turn aside to myths.

Evolution is one of the myths, and mankind has accumulated teachers to teach it. Mankind has turned away from the Bible in all of academia. The time that will come is today, we are in the end times.

Mankind views idolatry as someone worshiping a golden calf, but the Bible declares that it is any error in worshiping God. Evolution is a doctrine that causes all who believe in it to commit idolatry. Yet, though this is a heinous crime against God, He will forgive. But be careful, the devil and his demons distort the truth and subtly push lies, and their goal is to get humans to doubt the Word of God. Why risk so much to believe in a doctrine that is a doctrine of demons to keep or push you away from reading the Bible and being fully useful to God?

Dr. Kent Hovind summarizes the differences between the Bible and Evolution:

Bible	Evolution
1. Earth formed before the sun.	Sun formed before the earth
2. Water on Earth's surface before land	Land before water
3. Plants first	Marine life first
4. Light before sun	Sun before light
5. Fish before insects	Insects before fish
6. Plants before the stars finished forming	Stars before plants
7. Birds before reptiles	Reptiles before birds
8. Atmosphere between water	Atmosphere above water
9. Man brought death into the world	Death brought man into the world
10. God created man	Man created God

Chapter Summary: Evolution is not in the Bible and is directly antagonistic and contrary to the Word; therefore, it is not from God. The Word is God manifested in the flesh, named Jesus. By calling a portion of the Word false, then you are calling Jesus, the one who saves, false. And since every Word that proceeded from Jesus came from the Father, then by default, you are calling God the Father false. And since all Scripture is of the inspiration of the Holy Spirit, by calling a portion of the Scriptures erroneous, you are calling the Holy Spirit's work false. This is blasphemy, so be careful. By taking away glory and the credit of truth from the Word and attributing that credit and glory to random, unguided chance and mutations is idolatrous.

Chapter 41
The "Gap" Theory Between Verse 1 and 2 of Gen. 1

The "gap" theory suggests a gap of time consisting of billions of years between Gen. 1:1 and Gen. 1:2. In this gap, another creation event occurred similar to the Genesis creation event, but this creation event was for angels, not humans. The angelic creation event in verse 1 had similar characteristics to the Adamic creation event from verse 2 to chapter 2, even down to a Garden of Eden for Lucifer (Ex 28:13). In that creation event for angels is where and when Lucifer supposedly fell from heaven and took a third of the angels with him. Then God destroyed that heaven and earth in between verses 1 and 2 and then performed the seven days of recreation for mankind in the rest of Gen. 1:2 and the ensuing verses.

What is the foundation for this idea? The foundation for this idea comes from the evolutionary suggestions that the earth is 4.6 billion years old and that the universe is 14.6 billion years old. The gap theory is an attempt to harmonize the Bible with the hypothesis that the universe is billions of years old and in accord with what evolutionists are proclaiming.

The problem for gap theorists and theistic evolutionists is that the Bible on face value supports a young earth and a young universe model and the tenet that everything was created in the six days of Genesis, suggesting that life on earth began 6,000 years ago, according to a literal interpretation of the word *son* in the genealogies of Genesis, to 10,000 years ago, according to a figurative interpretation of the genealogies in Genesis consisting of only the marquis names and *son* also meaning *grandson*. The gap theory is an attempt to reinterpret the Bible to fit preconceived doctrines so that Christians do not look foolish in the eyes of evolutionists. Gap theorists first believed that life began billions of years ago because that is what evolutionists told them, and they accepted the atheist version of time and rejected the Bible's version of time. Then they tried to fit the Bible to that belief system's time scale yet preserve as much as possible of the Bible because they still love God and love the Word and want to treat the Word as Holy, inerrant, and infallible but want to reconcile the Bible to man's version of time.

Review: Gap theorists believe that verse 1 was a creation event for angels and that verse 2 describes the destroyed earth. The ensuing verses describe a re-creation, not creation.

What is the motivation for this gap idea? First, gap theorists are afraid to look like fools and have become convinced about mankind's version of time. Second, they do not fully trust God and what He wrote and what He can do. I know some dear Christians that believe the gap theory, and I have no doubt I will see them in heaven, so this is not a question of their salvation; this is a question of whether one should be wise in man's eyes or a fool in man's eyes for Christ, and who will be least in the Kingdom of Heaven, and usefulness for God. Holding the Bible in low esteem, annulling some Scripture, and teaching others to do the same will not make one great in the Kingdom of Heaven (Matt 5:17–19). The desire to placate to powerful evolutionists reveals a belief in their doctrine of old life on earth, rather than the Bible, which foolishly shows that life began on earth 6,000 to 10,000 years ago.

Where does a gap theorist start? First, they start with what people tell them, specifically evolutionary scientists, who say the earth is billions of years old. Then they become convinced by man's doctrine and seek to morph Scripture to support what they believe to be true. Gap theorists also dwell on the word *was* in Gen. 1:2. Gap theorists want to change the word *was* to *became*. Let us take a closer look at this.

Gen. 1:1–2: *In the beginning God created the heavens and the earth. The earth **was** formless and void, and darkness **was** over the surface of the deep, and the Spirit of God **was** moving over the surface of the waters.*

The first **was** is the issue for the gap theorists. The other two usages of "*was*" is not a concern for them. They want the Bible to start off with: "In the beginning God created the heavens and the earth. The earth "*became*" formless and void." They do not want to change all three usages of "*was*" and have the verses read "In the beginning God created the heavens and the earth. The earth became formless and void and darkness <u>became</u> over the surface of the deep and the Spirit of God <u>became</u> moving over the surface of the waters." That would not suit their wants. They arbitrarily do not apply the same logic to the other two uses of *was*. They surmise that the word *was* should be changed to *became,* and this authenticates that Gen. 1:1 is an entire description of God's creation for angels, billions of years in the past and not the creation of matter in a defined small universe at a specific moment in time, though formless and void of life. Gap theorists believe that Gen. 1:1 describes a whole different and separate creation before the seven days of creation, and this first heaven and first earth were for angels, with verses 2 and following being the re-creation of the destroyed heaven and earth for humans. This different and prior heaven and earth is where Satan and his angels fell. Then God destroyed those heavens and earth and "the earth ***became*** formless and void, and darkness <u>was</u> over the surface of the deep, and the Spirit of God <u>was</u> moving over the surface of the waters."

The Hebrew word for *was* is *hayah*[224], which means to exist, that is, to be or become, or come to pass. Alright, now let us look at the Hebrew word for "became,": *hayah,*[225] which means to exist, that is, to be or become, or come to pass. Well that was not helpful—the Hebrew word *hayah* means both *was* and *became.* We are not any closer to discerning whether the word *hayah* should remain "was" or let the Gap theorists change it to "became." Therefore, we need to approach this from a different angle.

The entire Hebrew Old testament was translated by 70+ Jewish scholars into Greek, called Greek Septuagint. It is known by Roman numerals LXX (for 70 scholars). Let us see what word ancient Greek language had for *was* and *became*. The word for *became* is *ginomai*.[226] It has a bunch of meanings: to cause to be, to become, arise, be, be brought (to pass), continue, and so on [about 20 more definitions exist]. The Greek word for *was* is *ane*,[227] and it has a more narrow definition; it means was, be, was, were. The words are different. The third century BC Jewish scholars chose *ane* from the Greek language to appropriately represent Hebrew word *hayah* in verse 1. Seventy top Jewish scholars in the third century BC (Before Christ) translating Gen. 1:1–2, understood the word "hayah" in this context of Gen. 1:2 to mean *was*, as in "to exist" or *was*, and not *became*. By the way, Jesus would have had His hands on this text as well.

Review: <u>Third century BC Hebrew theologians interpret "hayah" to mean *was*. The Jewish scholars that translated the Hebrew Bible into Greek Septuagint and the early church interpreted "hayah" as *was* in Gen. 1:2 . Even Gap theorists interpret the second and third "hayah"(s) as *was*. That is strong evidence that "hayah" should remain as *was* and not be changed to *became*.</u>

God proclaims He was there and created everything. So His testimony should be the end all the discussion. For He and only He was there.

I turn your attention to the word of God: Colossians 1:16 explains that Jesus was there at creation and through Him and for Him <u>all things</u> were created. This passage specifically names heavens, all things on earth, and angelic hosts as things that Jesus created: *"For by Him all things were created, both in the heavens and on* **earth**, *visible and invisible, whether thrones or dominions or rulers or authorities—all things have been created through Him and for Him."* Notice that *earth* is singular. Since Christ created all things, that would include the earth that was created for the angels as well, according to gap theorists. Then earth should be plural in this passage. *Heavens* is plural to represent the atmosphere, galaxies, and the Throne of God. The verse shows that only one earth exist—not two earths. Gap theorists have a problem here because they consider our present earth to be the second earth, which means that Colossians 1:16 should read *earths.*

Not only is Colossians' *earth* singular, indicating only one earth, but every time that earth is referenced in the Bible, it is singular. Not one single time in the entire Bible is *earth* pluralized to help

---

224 Strong's concordance, #1961 *hayah*: to exist, i.e. be or become, come to pass. Be.
225 Strong's concordance, #1961 *hayah*; to exist, i.e. be or become, come to pass. Be.
226 Strong's concordance, #1096 *ginomai*; to cause to be, i.e. to become, used with great latitude (literally, figuratively.), arise, be, be brought (to pass), continue, be done, [there's about 20 more descriptions].
227 Strong's concordance, #2258 *ane*; was (wast or were), be, was, were.

out the gap theorists. They truly stand alone. Or are they alone? They do have backing and support, but not from God's Word. Oddly enough, their support comes from the evolutionists. Evolutionists love when the Bible is changed to fit their timeline.

If this one verse is wrong, the word of God hangs in the balance. Christ Himself said in Matthew 5:17–19:

> Do not think that I came to abolish the Law or the Prophets; I did not come to abolish but to fulfill. For truly I say to you, until heaven and earth pass away, not the smallest letter or stroke shall pass from the Law until all is accomplished. Whoever then annuls one of the least of these commandments, and teaches others to do the same, shall be called least in the kingdom of heaven; but whoever keeps and teaches them, he shall be called great in the kingdom of heaven.

Review: The word *earth* is written in the singular form. This contradicts the gap theory. The gap theorists must change many singular forms of *earth* to the plural form *earths* for their theory to have Biblical backing. God's Word, and therefore God Himself, is against the Gap theory.

Peter adds evidence that the gap theory is not Biblical even from a non–believers perspective. In 2 Peter 3:4, Peter uses what the unsaved will say when they mock believers in the last days (today), "For ever since the fathers fell asleep, all continues just as it was from the beginning of creation" (the Uniformitarian Theory). The beginning of creation is Gen. 1:1 where it says, *In the beginning*. The beginning of creation was not in verse 2 of Genesis. That excludes a gap theory hypothesis of a catastrophic event destroying heaven and earth between verses 1 and 2 that supposedly left behind billions of fossils from the destruction. In their view, demons were roaming around when God recreated heaven and earth and looked out over all the dead fossils and death and demons roaming and said "It is very good."   Let us continue with 2 Peter 3:5–7:

> For when they maintain this, it escapes their notice that by the Word of God heavens existed long ago and earth was formed out of water and by water [this is Gen. 1:1–10], through which the world at that time was destroyed, being flooded with water [this is Gen. 7:11–8:13]. But by His Word the present heavens and earth are being reserved for fire, kept for the day of judgment and destruction of ungodly men [the book of Rev.].

God rejects the gap theory by giving a history lesson about everything from *In the beginning* (Gen. 1:1), and regarding the destruction of the heavens and earth; God does not mention anything about this speculative angelic era that existed and that got destroyed before Adam and Eve. God does not mention the heavens being destroyed in the angelic era. No, God specifically mentions destroying the earth with a global flood, and then God specifically mentions that He will destroy the heavens and earth with fire. Zero is mentioned of destroying the alleged angelic heavens and angelic world, zero is mentioned of this re-creation of Genesis, and zero is mentioned of this alleged gap theory. This should be the end of the gap theory, but we are just getting started. The gap theory would provide a great opportunity for God to explain why He wiped out all the dinosaurs before creating Adam and Eve, but quite to the contrary, God says nothing of a pre-Adamic era. In fact, God explicitly declares that He wiped out all life during the Flood of Gen. 7 in verses 21–23. God explains that the Flood killed all life (except for those on the ark), and this is what led to fossils, not some illusive never-mentioned doctrine of a pre-Adamic era.

In addition, Peter makes it clear that when God created the heavens, "They were of old, or they were created long ago." In other words, God created the sun, moon, and stars in a mature and developed state, just like God made Adam and Eve in a mature and developed state. God did not make Adam and Eve as fetuses, He made Adam and Eve fully mature. God made a densely packed universe that coalesced matter together quickly on the first day to glow hot and continued to coalesce matter until the fourth day, when the stars ignited through fusion; thus, God made the sun and stars fully mature. This does not mean that God is the God of deception or illusions. God did not make Adam and Eve with navels as though they were born of a woman, and He did not make trees 1,000-feet-tall with tree rings, God did not make fake supernovas to suggest that a star exploded that was never there. Old looking supernovas are probably remnants of the second day of creation, the expansion of the universe, the second Big Bangs.

Peter makes it clear that *by the Word of God the heavens existed of old*. Exodus 20:11 clearly states that all things were created in the six days of creation, specifically listing heavens and earth and all that is in them. The evidence in the Bible suggests that the heavens were vast and mature when they were created, just as things were created on earth. The earth was created by the Word of God *out of water and by water (days 1, 2, and 3 of creation), then destroyed being flooded (Gen. 7) with water*. The Bible never hints at God creating some things before the Genesis creation, destroying them, and then re-creating everything. That doctrine is purely based on fitting into the evolutionary time scale.

Review: In 2 Peter 3:4–7 God gives us a history lesson of all things, explaining that He created everything from the beginning of creation. By the Word of God, the heavens were old and the earth was formed out of water and by water and later destroyed by the Flood, but the present heavens and earth are reserved for judgment by fire. God never mentions an angelic age or two destroyed earths (one of the angelic realm and one of Noah's day). God is mute on the subject of any angelic realm. This would have been a perfect time for God to mention one jot or one tittle of evidence to help them out, but no, He provides not one word that supports their hypothesis—not even for re-creation, not even by changing *was* to *became*. The reason God left out any mention of the gap theory is because it is a fabrication of man's schemes to force the Bible into the atheists' time scale.

Gap theorists look out at the vastness of space and see distant galaxies and doubt God's creative ability to create so much in such a young universe. Do not get too caught up on how many light-years a star must be from Earth for us to visualize the light. The term *light-years* is a measurement of distance and not a measurement of time, so to say that a star is x number of light-years away from earth represents a 1:1 relationship to time is a leap of faith. How God was able to get us to view stars that seem to be so far away may be solved with new discoveries as mentioned previously; for example, Dr. Lijun Wang, a particle physicists at the NEC Research Institute at Princeton, has accelerated a component of light 300 times faster than lights' accepted normal velocity. See the chapter *Light*.

Evolutionists accept the term *universal inflation* to explain an expansion faster than the speed of light. It is here that both creationists and evolutionist could unite, both accept some sort of universal inflation, but they disagree about how long the accelerated expansion lasted and when this event occurred. Thus, it is an acceptable hypothesize that the universe expanded very fast on the first and second days of creation. Evolutionists hypothesize that the universe expanded by a factor of 10^{90} in one billionth of a billionth of a billionth of a billionth of a second before gravitational forces slowed the expansion velocity, but they are guessing. Therefore, they cannot presume to say that the expansion on the second day of creation did not accelerate for hours or a day before gravitational forces slowed the inflation velocity. Creationists interpret the observable evidence through the lens of the Scriptures and suggest these many Big Bangs that caused the universal inflation occurred on both the first and second days of creation some 6,000 years ago. The first Big Bang as God created all the matter in the universe, but this remained a densely packed filled with water as trillions of burgeoning galaxies had trillions of burgeoning celestial bodies coalesce matter. The second Big Bang on the second day of creation as God expanded the densely packed universe and potentially lasted one day before gravitational forces slowed this rate.

Combining this information that light can be accelerated and universal inflation presents a plausible explanation of the vast distance of the stars with a young universe. In addition, the discovery that the universe is accelerating its expansion may help understand such a large universe in a short allotment of time. This expansion means the further back in time, the smaller the universe was and therefore the less distance light had to travel from point A to point B.

This suggests that when someone looks at the distance of stars from the earth today and divides the distance by the speed of light, a) they are assuming the speed of light has always been constant, which it hasn't, and b) they are not considering that items in the universe are accelerating away from each other, which they are, and c) they assume they know the duration and when the universal inflation occurred, which they do not. Since God was able to make man fully mature and did not have to wait for him to grow from being a neonate/baby to an adult, and since God created 1,000-foot-tall trees and did not wait for seeds to grow, and since God created matter from His essence with no starting material, why are some limiting God by saying that He could not have created stars with their influence of light and energy already traversing the distance between earth and the stars. It is possible that God could have performed another miracle, but I do not even think young universe creationists have to rely on that explanation; I think that the evidence of universal inflation and the expansion of the universe pushing galaxies away from each other at an accelerated rate shows that at the time of creation, the universe was much smaller and light did not have to travel as far as perceived. Since we can accelerate the speed of light from 186,000 miles per second to 300 times faster (55.8 million miles per second), it would mean that instead of the sun's light reaching Earth at the current time of eight minutes, it would reach Earth in 1.6 seconds.

Another star, called Betelgeuse, is 640 light-years away at the current speed of light; well, with an accelerated speed of light, it would only take two years for its light to reach Earth. This is not even factoring in that the universe was exponentially smaller at the time of creation. Think about this. If humans can accelerate light by 300 times, how much do you think God can accelerate light? In fact, Lawrence Krauss, an atheist cosmologist, said that the universe's rate of accelerated expansion means that at this pace, some five million years in the future, light leaving a galaxy traveling at the speed of light will not reach us because that galaxy is moving away faster than the speed of light.

Dr. Raymond Chiao, a professor of physics (University of California at Berkeley), reviewed Dr. Wang's work and conducted his own experiments that indicate simultaneous, multiple localities of light. Photons, the particles which constitute light, seem to apparently jump between two points separated by a barrier in what appears to be zero time. This is called "tunneling." Should we be shocked by this? Was it not God who caused Philip to appear in one city to share the gospel and then—poof—he was snatched away and appeared in another city (Acts 8:39–40). Was it not God who snatched Elijah away (1Kings 18:12) and Ezekiel (Ez 3:12,14, 8:3) and Paul (2 Cor. 12:1–6) to heaven and then back without time expiring from their life?

The farthest known galaxy is estimated to be 13.1 billion light-years from Earth, with a normal speed of light. However, with the speed of light accelerated to 300 times, it is 43 million years away. This still seems like a problem for YECs, right? Well, first off, when measuring the distance of stars to Earth, it is not an exact science, though we are getting closer and more precise measurements. When utilizing earth's orbit around the sun, we can use trigonometry with triangulation (called stellar parallax) to calculate the distance of stars up to 300–400 light–years away. Beyond that, we rely on star brightness to estimate the distance. Cosmologists do not know how far the farthest star is from Earth—they are approximating. They could be off by billions of years and the universe is vastly larger than ever perceived, such as 100's of billions-of-light years across. However, star distances are not a problem for YECs anymore than they are for evolutionists. Both utilize the universal inflation model to solve not having enough time for light to travel such vast distances to Earth. Creationists accept a recent Big Bangs event (the first and second day of creation) with a prolonged universal inflation. Evolutionists accept a distant Big Bang event with brief universal inflation. Both evolutionists and creationists seemingly do not have enough time from the Big Bangs to account for light reaching the earth from the vast distances of the universe, so the same argument that evolutionists use on creationists is a two-edged sword that equally cuts their timeline as well. They do not have enough time based on their argument to account for a universe that is 93 billion light–years across. However, when one considers the expanding universe at an ever-accelerated rate and universal inflation, both theories have enough time. Better yet, creationists accept a starting point of the universal expansion on the second day to be the volume of ~100–1,000 adjacent galaxies, which could provide the medium for light acceleration to be vastly increased. For that is how Dr. Lijun Wang successfully sped up light by using a medium for which light passed through. The same with Dr. Raymond Chiao's work, he too used a medium for light to pass through. Therefore, it is easier for creationists to explain how light has traveled such vast distances in such a short amount of time because they have a larger starting point of the universal volume filled with waters as the medium. Whereas, evolutionists start with the size of a dot as the initial volume of the universe and quickly move to empty space.

Cosmologists are discovering stars because of advances in technology, but we cannot discount the hypothesis that the stars being discovered is because their light is just reaching earth for the first time from the creation of Genesis.

How accurate are the cosmologists' measurements of distant stars? No one measuring technique can measure the distance to all the stars. One technique is used for closer planets, another for nearby stars, another for medium-ranged stars, and another for distant stars, and so on. Since each measuring technique is based on the previous one, then there could be compounded errors with each step of measuring along the way. Yet, I still think the distances of galaxies estimated by cosmologists is close enough to accept their measurements as solid scientific theory, which is just below fact. Mankind has just begun its discoveries of the cosmos. My perception of God is that the volume of the universe and the quantity of galaxies, is vastly underestimated.

Review: The measured distances of stars to earth are becoming more accurate as mankind advances with technology, and we are also finding the universe to be vastly larger than ever imagined with vastly more stars than ever comprehended. The speed of light can be accelerated, which shortens the time required for light to travel distances. The measurement unit of a light–year is not a time measurement, it is a distance measurement. One cannot say this is the distance divided by speed = the age of the universe because the distance is an estimate past 400 light-years (though a good one) and the speed of light can be accelerated by 300 times by scientists. At creation, God could have accelerated light via natural processes—just as mankind has been able to do—and more so since He is God.

When some scholars got together to translate the Hebrew text into Latin, they chose the word *ex nihilo* to define *created*, which is to say that creation is not a re-creation of prior existing stuff, but everything came out of nothing, that is, ex nihilo. This alone should be enough for gap theorists to pause and rethink their hypothesis. This means that God did not use any existing material to do a re-creation; everything came directly from Him and through Him. Several verses use "created" (ex nihilo):

Gen. 1:1–2: *In the beginning God **created** the heavens and the earth.*

Gen. 2:3: *God blessed the seventh day and sanctified it, because in it He rested from all His work which God had **created** and made. This is the account of the heavens and the earth when they were **created**, in the day the LORD God made earth and heavens.*

God is saying that He created the heavens and the earth with no starting material other than Himself, ex nihilo. When God formed the bodies of the great sea monsters, fish, birds, and Adam and Eve and joined their bodies with their spirits, God created life from no preexisting life other than His own Life that existed prior to the seven days of creation. Then God summarizes on the seventh day that He created the heavens and the earth ex nihilo, from no other starting material than Himself; it was not a re-creation, but a first, an initial creation from no starting material. In Hebrews 11:3 we read, "By faith we understand that the worlds/ages were prepared by the Word of God, so that what is seen was not made out of things which are visible." This explains that all we see today did not come as a re-creation from existing material left over from the destroyed angelic era. Instead, the verse explains that all we see came from God's essence which we cannot see.

Why does this exclude the gap theory? Because the gap theory is a re-creation from existing material. Its proponents believe that the heavens and earth were destroyed before Adam and Eve, and from that existing leftover material from God's wrath, He re-created everything but left the dinosaurs and fossils in the ground. So the destruction of the angelic world was not so devastating, and the recreation of the Adam and Eve world, was not so disruptive, as to disturb the fossils. That is illogical.

Review: The early scholars understood *created* to equate to *ex nihilo*, which means God did not use material from a destroyed angelic era. God created from no starting material other than His own essence, and this excludes the gap theory. The gap theory has God re-creating the universe from leftover material after the destruction of the angelic age.

The original Hebrew text is without punctuation at all. It would read: "In the beginning God created the heavens and the earth the earth was formless and void and darkness was over the surface of the deep and the Spirit of God was moving over the surface of the waters." I have been told by a few gap theorists that the period between verse 1 and 2 represents a stop in creation and a destruction of the pre-Adamic era of angels and that the period (the punctuation mark) between verse 1 and 2 is to let us know that verses 2 onward is a re-creation. No, punctuation does not exist between verse 1 and 2 in the original manuscripts. In fact, no punctuation marks exist in the original Genesis creation account. Also, spaces between words does not exist. Therefore, the gap theory is not based on the original text and has no Biblical support. The two verses are not separated; they flow together as one creation event, not two creation events.

Additionally, no verse numbers and no chapters exist in the original text, which means verse 1 and verse 2 do not exist; it is one flowing text. The verses were added later for convenience, not to build a hypothesis based on a punctuation mark.

Review: The Bible does not have verse numbers, punctuation marks, or even spaces between words in the original Hebrew text, so basing a hypothesis on any modern-day addition cannot be Biblically accurate.

Another misunderstanding involving the gap theory involves Revelation 21:1: "Then I saw a new heaven and a new earth; for the first heaven and the first earth passed away, and there is no longer any sea." This verse is describing a future time after the seven years of tribulation and after the 1,000-year kingdom on earth, when a new heaven and a new earth occur. The first heaven and first earth had passed away. I draw your attention to the word *first*. If the Genesis creation account had two earths and two creations of the heavens as gap theorists hypothesize, this Revelation verse would say, "The second heaven and the second earth passed away." Either God, who caused the Holy Spirit to move on John to pen those words, is all wrong, or the gap theory is wrong. Take your pick; either hold onto an atheist view and try to force the Bible to fit their timeline, or submit to the Word and accept the fact that John, the Holy Spirit, and the Father are all correct.

This clearly reveals that the creation account from Gen. 1:2 to Gen. 2 is not the details of a second earth or a re-creation of the first earth, which was allegedly created for angels. The Bible speaks clearly: the Genesis creation account is about the first earth and first heaven. In the future, God will create a new heaven and new earth after the *first* heaven and *first* earth have passed away.

Since God clarifies that He created a new heaven and a new earth, why did not he say the same thing in Gen. 1? God does not say in Genesis that He is re-creating or creating a new heaven and a new earth because the prior heaven and prior earth had passed away—quite the contrary, God declared that He created the heavens and the earth from nothing, with no starting material.

In addition, angels do not require an atmosphere; they are immortal beings that do not require oxygen to survive, so it is an error of thought to think that God made the heavens (plural, representing space and the atmosphere) for them. Angels would not need an atmosphere.

Review: Revelation 21:1 reveals that the Genesis creation account was about the first heaven and first earth, not the second heaven and the second earth as gap theorists contend just to appease evolutionists' old earth views.

Another problem for gap theorists is how to answer the question: "When did God create the angels?" If you ask a gap theorist when God created angels, they tell you that God created angels billions of years before the Genesis creation of Adam and Eve, and Gen. 1:1 is a brief description of the entire creation of the world for angels. Their premise for this is the alleged age of the earth. Again, they use evolutionary time scales as evidence for their belief. They are making a mistake by fitting the Bible to human wisdom, instead of fitting human wisdom to the Bible.

Colossians 1:16 specifically names heavenly hosts (angels) as one of Jesus' created things: "For by Him all things were created, both in the heavens and on earth, visible and invisible, whether thrones or dominions or rulers or authorities—all things have been created through Him and for Him." The terms *thrones*, *dominions*, *rulers*, and *authorities* are frequently used for angels. All four terms are used together here, and they are referring to angels as created beings. Since Exodus 20 and 31 explicitly explain that all was created in the six days of creation, the only option is that angels were created during the six days of creation. Not in some era before the six days of creation. As we discussed earlier, the only language fitting the creation of the angels is when God said, "Let there be light," in the middle of the first day of creation. As angels are manifestations of the light, they are representatives of the Light, they are messengers of the Light, they are even shown with the glory of the light, and Satan tries to appear as an angel of the Light. Who is the author and perfecter of the light? The one and only God —Elohiym (Father, Son, and Holy Spirit). Additionally, creation is written as a singularity. The creation of all things is <u>never</u> written as two distinct and separate events. For example, you will never find a verse in the Bible where God created something during the first creation and something else during the second creation of Genesis. It is always written as a singularity and as one seven-day event.

<u>Review:</u> <u>Angels were created at the middle of the first day, with *Let there be light*. This rules out that angels existed in Gen. 1:1 and debunks the gap theory.</u>

Another problem with the gap theory is that all people have sinned and fallen short of the glory of God.[228] The wages of sin is death,[229] and before the fall, all the lions, tigers, bears, cobras, eagles, sharks, and so on were herbivores, not carnivores.[230] After the fall of Adam and Eve, all were subjected to the futility of sin. When the Bible says, "Creation was subjected to the futility of sin," it means the earth, stars, creatures, and so forth.[231] The futility of sin is death. Before sin, death did not occur.[232] No life died that had the breath of life and the blood of life in them. After sin occurred, then some creatures ate other creatures, and death entered the world. Some herbivores were converted to carnivores, and the futility of creation to sin began.

This completely goes against the gap theory. Because according to the gap theory, there was already death before Adam and Eve sinned. The fossil records are proof positive against the gap theorists because they are a record of death. Gap theorists contend that the carnivore dinosaurs were already fossils before the fall. This is incongruous with the notion that all creatures were herbivores in Genesis 1:29. Gap theorists surmise that all dinosaurs and prehistoric fossil records are part of the first earth age that occurred millions or billions of years before Adam and Eve. But the Bible records that death did not occur before Adam and Eve sinned, and all things were created in the six days of creation (Ex. 20:11). That excludes preexisting fossils that represent death before the fall of Adam and Eve.

Gap theorists try to harmonize the Bible to fit what humans estimate to be the age of life on earth. How do young universe creationists, who hold the Bible as the standard and set all doctrine

---

228 Romans 3:23: "for all have sinned and fall short of the glory of God."

229 Romans 6:23: "For the wages of sin is Death."

230 Gen. 1:30: "And to every beast of the earth and to every bird of the sky and to every thing that moves on the earth which has life, I have given every green plant for food." Isaiah 11:6: "The wolf will dwell with the lamb, and the leopard will lie down with the young goat, and the calf and the young lion and the fatling together."

231 Romans 8:19–22: "For the anxious longing of the creation waits eagerly for the revealing of the sons of God. For the creation was subjected to futility, not willingly, but because of Him who subjected it, in hope that the creation itself also will be set free from its slavery of the children of God. For we know that the <u>whole</u> creation groans and suffers the pains of childbirth together until now."

232 Romans 5:12: "Therefore, just as through one man sin entered into the world, and death through sin, and so death spread to all men, because all sinned."

based on what the Bible says, harmonize the two different views? The Bible indicates that life began on earth some 6,000 years ago, while evolutionary scientists say that life began on earth billions of years ago. How do we harmonize the two? We do not, and we do not have to. The two doctrines are exclusively incompatible. The idea of the earth being billions of years old is a hypothesis, not fact as we are told by evolutionary scientists.

Review: Before Adam sinned, there was no death. This rules out the existence of demons, fossils, oil, and so forth prior to Adam's sin. The fossil records and oil reserves are a record of death. According to the Bible, death did not occur until after Adam and Eve sinned, not billions of years before Adam and Eve. Therefore, gap theorists proclaim that the death of animals occurred before Adam and Eve sinned, which is contrary to the Bible.

Now the question comes, did not Lucifer sin first before Adam and Eve? For was not it a fallen Lucifer in the name of Satan who tempted Eve? The answer is yes. John 8:44 says, "You are of your father the devil . . . He was a murderer from the beginning, and does not stand in the truth because there is no truth in him. Whenever he speaks a lie, he speaks from his own nature, for he is a liar and the father of lies." Gen. 3 reveals that Satan possessed a serpent and deceived Eve. Does that mean that the serpent spoke to Eve? Yes.

We need to get clarity on when Lucifer sinned and how much time occurred between Lucifer's sin and the temptation of Eve in the Garden of Eden. Since angels are immortal, even fallen angels (demons), then death still came through Adam and Eve's sin. God in the flesh (Jesus) was the first high priest to sacrifice an animal to pay for the sin of Adam and Eve (Gen. 3:21). Sin did not exist in the world prior to Adam and Eve sinning. This is why God repeats the phrase *God saw that it was good* many times during creation. God created the universe from the first day to the seventh day without any sin or death anywhere in all of creation, which rules out fossils existing before the six days of creation.

We discussed earlier that all angels were created on the first day of creation with the phrase *Let there be light,* now we need to determine when Satan fell from being an angel and took a third of the angels with him. At the moment that Lucifer fell and became Satan, he wasted no time combating against God. Satan's first action was to undermine the truth and God's Word. God spoke to Adam and Eve and commanded them that they could eat from every (could be tens-of-thousands) tree but not to eat of the tree of knowledge of good and evil (only one tree restricted). Satan's first recorded act on earth was to deceive Eve. Because of Satan's aggressive nature and lack of patience[233] (and knowing that patience is a gift of the Holy Spirit[234]), Satan would have wasted no time at all after his fall to deceive Eve. Since God continued repeating the phrase *God saw that it was good* seven times, the fall of Lucifer must have come after all of creation was complete.

The phrase *it was good* was said after the creation of light (angels, humanly spirits, and the glow of magma) (Gen. 1:4), the earth and seas (Gen. 1:10), grass, plants, and trees (Gen. 1:12), the sun, moon, and stars (Gen. 1:18), the birds and fish (Gen. 1:21), the beasts/cattle/insects (Gen. 1:25), and finally Adam and Eve (Gen. 1:31). After all things were created, Lucifer was still a glorified angel, serving God and worshiping God, until some time after God had finished creating everything. This is because God saw **_all_** that He had made (that includes angels) and said it was **_very good_**.

A salient point solidifying that Lucifer fell after creation, comes at the mention of his curse in Gen. 3:15. If Lucifer fell in Gen. 1:1 as gap theorists contend, then Lucifer's curse for falling would be spoken of and written near the time of his fall. But the curse spoken of and written for Satan was exactly the same time as the sin of Adam, Eve, the serpent, all the animals, all the land, and all of creation. Like a series of falling dominoes because all of their falls were during the same event. Probably, Lucifer's fall as Satan, was the very same day he possessed the snake and tempted Eve. Since

---

233 1 Peter 5:8: "Be alert and of sober mind. Your enemy the devil prowls around like a roaring lion looking for someone to devour."

234 Galatians 5:22: "the fruits of the Spirit are love, joy, peace, patience, kindness, goodness, faithfulness, gentleness and self-control."

Adam and Eve were the rulers of all the earth (Gen. 1:28), then it was only upon the fall of the head of the earthly kingdom, did God announce the curses on all of creation. Indicating the brevity of time between Lucifer's fall, becoming Satan, and him tempting Eve.

Jesus reveals that when Lucifer sinned, and instantly became Satan, Jesus said, "I saw Satan as lightning fall from the heights" (Luke 10:18). This suggests the brevity of time, between when Lucifer was dwelling in the presence of God as an angel, and then corruption occurred in him and instantly he became Satan, and the brief time it took for Satan to come to Earth to deceive Eve. Once Adam and Eve forfeited their title deed to rule over all the earth to Satan, then Satan probably tempted one third of the angels to follow him with the notion that he, Satan, would give them rule of the earth for following him. The very same temptation he gave to Jesus.

Review: God declared that all things were very good. This is evidence against Satan and his demons falling before the creation account in Genesis chapter 1 and 2. The timing of the curse for Lucifer in Gen. 3:15, indicates that he had just fallen to Earth as lightning and tempted Eve. If Lucifer fell in Gen. 1:1, then his curse would be located closer to that event. But since his curse is mentioned in the midst of the curses upon Adam, Eve, the serpent, the land, and all the animals, then Lucifer fell along with the others involved in the same event.

When Lucifer was still a glorified angel walking about in Eden (Ezekiel 28:13).[235] Lucifer could not have sinned and become Satan and taken a third of the angels with him because God would not have looked out over all that He had made and said, *it was very good*. But according to the gap theorists, Satan and his demons were already existing and in full force on the first day of creation. God, even though He sees Satan and his demons and all the dead fossils, said *all things are very good*? No chance.

Furthermore, since gap theorists believe that angels were already existing billions of years before the first day of creation, they are unclear as to what was created on the first day of creation. Some gap theorists have speculated that Jesus was created on the first day as the light. But that cannot be correct because Jesus is the I AM, which means eternal God, and Jesus was co-creator with His Father and Holy Spirit. Therefore, Jesus is doing the creating (John 1:1). The creator of everything cannot be created. Otherwise, the statements in John 1 and Colossians 1:16 that clarify Jesus created all things couldn't be said if Jesus was created. So that theory is wrong. Some gap theorists think that the light that was created on the first day was the sun, but that cannot be correct because the sun, moon, and stars were finished forming on the fourth day of creation, so gap theorists are left with thinking that this light that was created on the first day was some unknown light. It seems unsatisfactory to leave the first day of creation as a big question mark to ensure that angels were created before Gen. 1:2.

A clue exist in the curse placed on Eve because of sin, that helps us understand when Lucifer fell and became Satan. This is found in Gen. 3:16 "To the woman He said, 'I will greatly multiply your pain in childbirth, in pain you will bring forth children.'" If she had not had any children, or menstrual cycle, she would be thinking and probably would ask God, "What is childbirth? and Lord, You will greatly multiply my pain from what? I have no reference point to understand the magnitude of the curse like Adam does for his curse." In other words, Adam, all creatures, the serpent, and even Satan had knowledge of the difference between the pre-curse and post-curse, why would not Eve? All the animals lost the ability to communicate to every living thing and some became carnivores, snakes lost the ability to walk, Lucifer lost being a highly ranked angel, and Adam lost access to easy food. Only Eve was unaware of how the curse changed her life? That is not in harmony with all others knowing the pre-curse conditions and the post-curse conditions. Could it be that the birth of Cain recorded in Gen. 4 occurred prior to the fall of Adam and Eve, and Moses used the same literary technique that he used in several places of creation, by giving a general statement and then going back to give more details with the birth of Cain. If Eve had given birth prior to the fall, then she would of had knowledge of the magnitude of the curse, then she would have understood what God was talking about, as far as birth,

---

235 Ezekiel 28:13: "You were in Eden, the garden of God."

and greatly multiplying her labor pain. Then she would have fully understood the change to her, as all the others understood their change.

Additionally, Eve lived in the presence of the LORD, in the Garden of Eden. This was a holy place, where nothing unclean could dwell. Considering that when a woman is in her menstrual cycle, she is considered unclean to enter the holy place, and everything she touches, lies on, or sits on is considered unclean (Lev. 15:19), this is evidence that Eve never experienced a menstrual cycle while dwelling in the holy place called the Garden of Eden. How did Eve not have her monthly cycle? When she was fashioned on the sixth day, she was at the peak of fertility, then she conceived with the first relation between her and Adam at the end of the sixth day. Therefore, she went at least 11 months (9 for birthing process, 2 for menstrual build up after pregnancy) without a cycle. If Eve got pregnant again after giving birth, then she would not of had a menstrual cycle. Therefore, if Eve kept getting pregnant, it is medically proven, that Eve could have gone many years without having a menstrual cycle, at least up until the curse. Because every woman will tell you that her menstrual cycle is a curse.

After God creates Adam (mid-point of the day) and Eve (toward the end of the day) on the sixth day, they are both at optimal physical condition, peak hormone production for fertilization, and naked. No one should think they disobeyed God's command to "multiply" (Gen. 1) till chapter four. In Gen. 4:1 it mentions Adam having *relations* with Eve, but that does not mean that was the first time, especially since relations is plural. With God's blessing, and command to multiply on the sixth day (Gen. 1:28), and *God brought her to the man* as a bride (Gen. 2:22), they would have consummated their marriage on the sixth day as the sun was setting. Immediately after, Adam declares, *This is now bone of my bones, and flesh of my flesh; She shall be called Woman, because she was taken out of man* (Gen. 2:23). Now immediately following this, God eloquently declares that *man shall leave his father and his mother, and be joined to his wife; and they shall become one flesh. And the man and his wife were both naked and were not ashamed* (Gen. 2:24–25). This is God's graceful way of explaining they knew each other in a honeymoon situation as husband and wife. The Father that gave His daughter, and the minister that declared them to be husband and wife, was God. All this occurred before the sun set on the sixth day of creation. Therefore, it is plausible that Eve became pregnant from the first honeymoon night and gave birth 9 months later—many decades before the fall. With this hypothesis, she would have understood the difference from pre-curse and post-curse, as did all the other creatures on Earth, and she would have understood what God was talking about during the curse. Considering the names of their offspring, Cain and Abel, may provide some help. The name Cain is derived from a couple of root words that mean to strike fast (like a lance), to strike a musical note, mourn, create, and so on (Strong's Conc., #7014, 7013, 6969, and 7069). This seems to indicate a quick birth. Now Abel's name has a definition that includes "something transitory and unsatisfactory" (Strong's Conc., #1893 and 1892). Could this be the passing of a more difficult labor from the curse? It is possible. We know many children born to Adam and Eve that are not mentioned in the Bible. For example, when their son Cain receives a mark from God as judgment for murdering his brother Abel, so that no one would kill him, then Cain flees to Nod, east of Eden, and there he takes a wife and has children (Gen. 4:16–17). This indicates that other brothers of Cain would want to kill him because he killed their brother Abel. Although, the genealogy of Adam in Gen. 5 records that Adam at 130 years became the father of Seth, does not negate that Adam had prior children. For example, Cain and Abel are mentioned as being born prior to the birth of Seth, and both Cain and Abel were old enough to offer sacrifices to God prior to Seth's birth—a practice associated with priesthood that commenced at age 30 (Numbers 4:23). Before the birth of Seth, Cain heads east of Eden to another dwelling, and there he marries his wife (either a daughter or granddaughter to Adam and Eve) and has children. Thus, it is easy to conclude that Adam and Eve had many children that are not mentioned in the Bible.

Therefore, this suggests that potentially the fall of Adam and Eve occurred at least a year after creation, potentially after the birth of Cain. Considering that Satan does not have patients because it is from God, then immediately upon Satan's fall, he left heaven and descended to Earth as *lightning* from the *heights* (Luke 10:18), and possessed the snake (serpent), and tempted Eve on the same day.

Therefore, the fall of Lucifer potentially occurred after Eve gave birth to Cain, and Lucifer tempted Adam and Eve on the same day that he fell from heaven. This may give some insight as to when Lucifer sinned and how much time occurred between Lucifer's sin and the temptation of Eve in the Garden of Eden. Tying this information with the gap theory, is that Lucifer did not fall in Gen. 1:1, but fell after creation was all said and done.

Review: With Eve giving birth to Cain in the Garden of Eden before the fall, and considering that Satan would have tempted Eve on the same day that he fell from heaven as lightning, then Lucifer potentially fell many decades after creation.

Lucifer was in Eden with Adam and Eve before the fall. Ezekiel 28:12–17: *You were in Eden, the garden of God.* Gap theorists want to make this a different Eden than the Eden that Adam and Eve were in in Gen. 2:8–3:24: *The LORD god planted a garden* [on the third day] *toward the east, in Eden and there He placed the man whom He had formed* [on the sixth day]. Later on the sixth day, God created Eve (verses 21–23). God rested from all His work on the seventh day. Then we pick up the narrative of Gen. 3. The location is still the Garden of Eden. At some unknown time after God rested on the seventh day, Lucifer had fallen and possessed a serpent to deceive Eve. And the rest is history. But the problem for gap theorists is that they interpret the Eden of Ezekiel 28 to be a different Eden than the one in Gen. 2:8–3:24—even though they are the same Hebrew word and Satan is referenced in both Scriptures. If they were different Edens, then God would have declared the Ezekiel Eden as the first Eden, and God would have declared the second Eden as a New Eden or a second Eden. After all, that is exactly what God does for the New Heaven and New Earth and New Jerusalem in Revelation 21. The conclusion is they are the same Eden, the same garden that God planted.

Chapter Summary: The Gap theory is an attempt to fit the Bible to mankind's views, rather than fitting man's views to the Bible. Upon deeper inspection, the gap theory does not harmonize with the Bible. The hypothesis does not add to the credibility of the Bible by trying to fit the Bible to evolutionary timelines. In fact, the gap theory undermines the credibility of the Bible and causes its believers to be called least in the Kingdom of Heaven for annulling portions of Scripture. The gap theory does not fit, and God warns against teaching false doctrine and leading others astray.

"Once you eliminate the impossible, whatever remains, however improbable, must be the truth."[236]

If you have comments or questions to the author, email them to: Lawrence@creationministry.org.
If you wish to donate to this ministry, which is tax deductible, go to: www.creationministry.org.

---

236 Sir Arthur Conan Doyle, 1890, Sherlock Holmes, *The Sign of the Four*, Ch, 6, (Doubleday p.111).

Statement of Faith

I, Dr. Troy Lawrence, accept, believe, and teach the following Statement of Faith regarding the principles of theology:

The Holy Scriptures

The Bible was written by God through the pen of men as they were moved under the inspiration of the Holy Spirit (2 Timothy 3:16). Therefore, every jot and tittle of the original manuscripts are one hundred percent perfect, inerrant, and infallible (Matthew 5:17–18). We teach the literal, grammatical-historical interpretation of Scripture, which affirms a literal six-day creation, where everything was created in six rotations of the earth (Exodus 20:11) about six thousand years ago (Gen 5, 11), and which supports the global flood (Genesis 7–9).

As God wrote His Word through the pen of humans, He used their individual personalities and styles of writing. Those human writers composed the sixty-six books of the Bible given to us by and through the Holy Spirit that represent the absolute and complete Word of God (1 Corinthians 2:7–14).

Although there may be several applications of a certain verse, only one interpretation is true. The proper meaning is to be understood and known, as one is enlightened by the Holy Spirit as they diligently apply the literal, grammatical-historical method of interpretation (1 Corinthians 2:7–16). Although the opinions of scientists may be against Scripture, the proper interpretation will always be supported with science, as much as science is able to comprehend the majesty of holy Scripture.

God

The one and only living and true God (Deuteronomy 6:4) is infinite, perfect in all attributes, one in essence, and eternally exists in three Persons—the Father, Son, and Holy Spirit (Matthew 28:19)—each deserving equal worship and obedience.

God The Father

God the Father is the first person of the Trinity; He is Co-Creator of all things and is an omnipotent Spirit (John 4:24). He has never been seen by man (John 1:18) because He is invisible (Colossians 1:15).

God The Son

We affirm that Jesus the Christ, the second person of the Trinity, is Co-Creator of all things (Colossians 1:16) and co-eternal with the Father and Holy Spirit (John 10:30, John 8:56-58). All appearances of God throughout the Bible were exclusively God the Son—Jesus (Colossians 1:15, 1 John 4:12). Therefore, one may find many records of Jesus frequently appearing to humans in the Old Testament (Genesis 3:8, 18:1-8, 32:24–30). Jesus shed His immortal flesh and divine prerogatives of deity to be born of the virgin Mary (Matt 1:23, 25), and He was one hundred percent mortal human and still one hundred percent God in divine essence (John 1:1–14).
We accept that Jesus the Christ will return to receive the church, judge the ungodly, and set up His millennial kingdom on earth (Revelation).

God The Holy Spirit

We accept that the Holy Spirit is a divine person, eternal, possessing all the attributes of personality and deity, including intellect (1 Cor 2:10–13), emotions (Eph 4:30), will (1 Cor 12:11), omnipresence (Psalm 139:7–10), omniscience (Is 40:13,14), omnipotence (Rom 15:13), and truthfulness (John 16:13).

We accept that the Holy Spirit is the sovereign agent in regeneration, baptizing all believers in the body of Christ (1 Cor 12:13). The Holy Spirit also indwells, sanctifies, instructs, empowers us for service, and seals us unto the day of redemption (Rom 8:9–11, 2 Cor 3:6, Eph 1:13).

Holy Angels
We teach that angels are created beings (Colossians 1:16, Ezekiel 28:13,15) in the image of God (Gen 6:2, Job 38:7). Although they currently have a higher order than man, they are not to be worshiped. They are fellow servants and worshipers of God (Rev 19:10, Col 2:18, Heb 2:6,7).

Fallen Angels (Demons)
We teach that Lucifer was once a high-ranking angel (Ezekiel 28:13-15), but he sinned and became Satan (Isaiah 14:12–17) and is the author of sin, a murderer, and the father of lies (John 8:44). He stole the kingdom of this earth from Adam and Eve by deceiving Eve with his lies as he possessed the snake in the Garden of Eden (Gen 3:1–5) he became the ruler of this world (2 Cor 4:4, John 12:31) and deceived one third of all angels to follow him (Rev 12:4).

Mankind
Adam and Eve were made in the image and likeness of God on the sixth day of creation (Gen 1:26,27). They were created fully mature, complete, free of sin, perfect, intelligent, and with free will (Gen 2:7-25).With their free will, they believed the deceit of Satan and were tempted, carried away, and enticed by their own lust (James 1:14), and they sinned. Since the wage of sin is death (Romans 6:23), they needed an innocent life to atone for their sin because the law has always been a life for a life (Deut 19:21). Since they murdered their own spirits, their lives were required. But God is loving and merciful, and He sacrificed an animal (Gen 3:21) as a foreshadow of the cross ~four thousand years later (Col 2:16,17). We teach that through one man, sin entered into the world, and death occurred because of sin, and death spread to all men because all sinned (Romans 5:12, Romans 3:23).

Physical curses can be passed down from sinful fathers to the third and fourth generation (Exodus 20:5). But those physical curses can be undone by living Godly (Exodus 20:6). As a result of Adam, all will physically die whether they are saved or not (1 Corinthians 15:22). However, no one inherits any spiritual consequence from Adam or from any parent because each person will be judged according to their own deeds (Ezekiel 18:20, 30). We reject the church tradition of original sin and sin nature, and believe each person is born spiritually alive, not saved, and will spiritually die when they sin after reaching the age of accountability. Then, as a result of their own sins, they take on a new nature and become a child of wrath (Ephesians 2:1–5). Then they need to be born again like they once were at their birth (John 3).

Salvation
Salvation is wholly of God by grace on the basis of the redemption of Jesus the Christ, the merit of His atoning shed blood, and not on the basis of human works, no matter how meritorious those works appear in our fallen eyes (Ephesians 1:4–11). As the Father draws us to Him (John 6:44) and we confess with our mouth Jesus as Lord and believe in our heart that God raised Him from the dead, we will be saved (Romans 10:9) by grace alone, faith alone, and not of our works (Ephesians 2:8). We believe that this does not give us license to sin so that grace may abound—certainly not (Romans 6:1)—but our works authenticate our faith and convert heart, for faith without works is dead (James 2:14–26).

The election for salvation is the act of God, established before the foundation of the world, He chose in Christ those whom He graciously imputes righteousness, saves, and sanctifies (Romans 8:28–30, Ephesians 1:4). Sovereign election does not conflict with our free will or negate our responsibility to repent and trust Jesus as Lord and Savior (Jeremiah 18:5–10).

Made in the USA
Columbia, SC
23 December 2019